ROBERT B. FISCHER, Ph.D.

Professor of Chemistry, Indiana University

A Basic Course in
The Theory and Practice of

QUANTITATIVE
CHEMICAL ANALYSIS

Second Edition

W. B. SAUNDERS COMPANY

Philadelphia and London

Preface

ANALYTICAL CHEMISTRY is one of the most active areas of chemical research. Furthermore, workers in other areas of chemistry, in other physical and biological sciences and in several types of engineering are decidedly dependent upon the results of chemical analyses. These reasons are sufficient to justify a prominent place in the chemistry curriculum for the course in quantitative analysis. Nevertheless, the most important reason for the study of quantitative analysis is an even more fundamental one—quantitative chemical analysis is a means for teaching and emphasizing the truly quantitative thinking which underlies all of chemistry.

This book is written for students who are already familiar with the subject matter of the average course in general chemistry. The author has attempted to present the material in the way which his experience and judgment have deemed best, both in regard to organization and in regard to content. At the same time, he recognizes that circumstances vary widely from one school to another; therefore, he has tried to make the organization flexible enough to permit adaptation to varying circumstances.

Introductory material and topics of concern in all areas of quantitative analysis are presented in Part I. The unit operation approach is used in describing the laboratory operations and in outlining the various schemes of analysis. The chapter on the analytical balance gives due consideration to the substitution type of balance. The chapter on the treatment of data is self-complete, so it can be postponed until later in the course if the instructor so desires.

Gravimetric methods of analysis are described in Part II and volumetric in Part III. The author prefers to take up gravimetric methods first, but he recognizes that there is also much to be said for the reverse order. Therefore, Parts II and III are such that either one may come directly after Part I without appreciable loss of continuity. Results of recent research work on the formation of precipitates have been incorporated into Chapter 8. The theory of neutralization reactions is based upon modern concepts of acids and bases; aqueous solutions are emphasized but not to the exclusion of other solvent systems. The discussion of complex formation methods is treated on a par with other types of volumetric analysis. The theory of oxidation-reduction methods is presented in a consistent, modern manner.

Parts IV and V include discussions of optical and electrical methods of analysis. This material is primarily descriptive. Students who are not chemistry majors should receive an introduction to these methods in their first (and often only) course in quantitative analysis but generally do not require a theoretical treatment. The descriptive approach should also serve as a valid introduction to these topics for students who will subsequently take a full course in optical and/or electrical methods.

There is more than enough laboratory work in this book for a one semester course. Although there are enough experiments for a two semester course, it is suggested that, when two semesters are available, the instructor make some assignments to check and to use procedures directly from the current literature. It is also suggested that the instructor have his students deliberately depart from the conventional procedures in some experiments to ascertain quantitatively the importance of experimental variables, such as ignition temperature and time, and choice of indicator in titrations. A few specific suggestions of this type are appended to some experiments; the instructor and student may devise other variations. It is really not necessary to have an unknown in every experiment. Some of the experiments in electrical methods of analysis include directions for constructing inexpensive instruments by means of which the necessary measurements may be made.

Systematic methods of making stoichiometric and equilibrium calculations are presented and used throughout all chapters. Numerous sample problems are worked out completely. There are more than enough problems at the ends of the chapters for assignment in the average course. Answers are listed in an Appendix.

The author is indebted to many students and teachers for valuable discussions and communications on the subject matter of quantitative chemical analysis as well as to contributors to the published literature. Any merit which this book may possess is due in large part to these persons. The author must, of course, accept full responsibility for all shortcomings and errors which may appear. Comments and suggestions from students and from teachers are cordially invited.

ROBERT B. FISCHER

Bloomington, Indiana

Contents

Part Four. Optical Methods

Part Five. Electrical Methods

Part Six. Appendices

Laboratory
Experiments

Part One

INTRODUCTION

Chapter I

Review of
Fundamental Principles

ANALYTICAL chemistry is composed of two major branches, qualitative analysis and quantitative analysis. In qualitative analysis the chemist is concerned with the detection and identification of the constituents of the sample being analyzed. In quantitative analysis, the relative or absolute amount of one or more of the constituents of that sample is determined. The result of a qualitative analysis is expressed in words, names or symbols of elements, ions or molecules, while the result of a quantitative determination is expressed in numbers. A complete analysis of any sample must include both qualitative and quantitative determinations. The qualitative analysis must precede the quantitative, since the former serves as a necessary guide in selecting methods and procedures for the latter.

Modern analytical chemistry is based on the fundamental laws and principles which it has helped to establish. In beginning the study of quantitative analysis it is well for the student to review some of these fundamental principles.

THE ATOMIC THEORY AND LAWS OF CHEMICAL COMBINATION

The atomic theory is probably the most important of all chemical theories. It was proposed by Dalton (1766–1844) to provide an explanation of previously observed relationships among the weights of substances taking part in chemical combinations. As further experiments were undertaken to verify and to elaborate it, the existence of atoms came to be accepted as definite fact. The atomic theory may now be summarized in the following statements:

1. The elements consist of numbers of exceedingly minute particles, called atoms, which are indestructible in any chemical reaction.
2. The naturally occurring atoms of an element are always alike and, in particular, have the same average weight.
3. Atoms of different elements have weights which are different and characteristic.

4. Molecules of compounds are formed by combinations of relatively
   small numbers of the same or different atoms in ratios which are fixed and
   which are characteristic of the compound.

These fundamental concepts explain the observed regularities of behavior
expressed in the several laws of chemical combination.

Law of Definite Proportions. The law of definite proportions
states that the proportions by weight of the various components of a compound are immutably fixed, regardless of when or how the compound is
secured or prepared.

Law of Multiple Proportions. This law may be stated as follows:
When two elements combine to form more than one compound, the weights
of one element combining with a fixed weight of the other element to form the
different compounds must be in the ratio of small whole numbers.

Law of Reciprocal Proportions. This law may also be deduced
from the postulates of the atomic theory. If a grams of element or compound
A combine with or react with b grams of element or compound B, and if a
grams of A combine with or react with c grams of element or compound C,
and if B and C will combine with or react with each other, then the weights
of B and C combining or reacting together are in the ratio of $b:c$ or a simple
multiple thereof.

These three laws of chemical combination are all based upon large
amounts of analytical data; yet all three are readily explained on the basis
of the atomic theory. They are of great significance in quantitative analysis.

Law of Conservation of Matter. This law underlies quantitative
relationships during chemical changes. It may be stated as: There is no
increase nor decrease in the quantity of matter during a chemical change. It
has been well established, both in theory and in experiment, that matter and
energy are interrelated and even interchangeable and that one may be
converted in part into the other during certain nuclear reactions. However,
there is no change in the quantity of matter in any ordinary chemical reactions, and chemical reactions are encountered in most areas of quantitative
analysis. This fact is of fundamental importance because the composition of
a sample of matter can seldom be determined quantitatively without causing
part or all of it to undergo one or more chemical changes prior to the final
measurements.

ATOMIC WEIGHTS

The numerical values of the atomic weights are not a matter of uncertainty today. The atomic weights of the elements are known with a high
degree of accuracy, largely through the efforts of T. W. Richards and his
collaborators, notably Baxter and Hönigschmid. Further refinement of these
values does not appear to be worth the great labor that would be involved.
Moreover, it is now possible to determine atomic weights quite accurately by
physical means, using the mass spectrograph. Nevertheless, atomic weight

determinations as such are worthy of consideration at this point, both because of their fundamental importance and because they undoubtedly represent the most precise chemical analyses ever performed.

Oxygen is the primary standard for all atomic weight designations, but the metallic oxides are often of rather indefinite composition due to impurities inevitably present. Therefore, most of the atomic weights of metallic elements have been determined with reference to silver rather than to oxygen. The atomic weight of silver must be determined especially accurately. Only an approximate value of the atomic weight of silver can be determined by reference to the combining weights in silver oxide, because this compound

Table 1. Determination of Ratio of $Ag:NO_3$

Grams of silver	Grams of silver nitrate	Grams of $AgNO_3$ per 1.00000 g. Ag
6.14837	9.68249	1.57481
4.60825	7.25706	1.57480
4.97925	7.84131	1.57480
9.07101	14.28503	1.57480
9.12702	14.38903	1.57481
9.01782	14.20123	1.57480
	Average	1.57480

cannot be prepared in a state of sufficient purity. Consequently, the atomic weight of silver must be determined by an indirect procedure, usually one involving knowledge of the atomic weight of nitrogen. The latter must, in turn, be determined by some other method as, for example, by calculation from gas density measurements. The key step in finding the atomic weight of silver then becomes the determination of the weight ratio $Ag:NO_3$ in the compound $AgNO_3$. In principle this is a simple undertaking—a weighed quantity of silver is converted into silver nitrate by treatment with nitric acid, the excess acid is driven off by evaporation, and the remaining silver nitrate is weighed. In practice, however, the determination is tedious and difficult since it necessitates a convincing demonstration that the silver nitrate weighed is actually pure and free of nitrite, mother liquid, and so forth. Data secured in this experiment are shown in Table 1. These figures represent the probable ultimate accuracy to which chemical analyses can be carried.

From the formula, $AgNO_3$, it is apparent that each atom of silver gives one molecule of silver nitrate, and the experimental results show that a molecule of silver nitrate is 1.57480 times as heavy as a silver atom. That is,

$$\frac{\text{atomic weight of silver}}{\text{molecular weight of silver nitrate}} = \frac{1.00000}{1.57480}$$

If we take the figure 14.0080 as the correct value for the atomic weight of nitrogen and the defined value of 16.0000 for the atomic weight of oxygen, we then obtain the equation

$$\frac{\text{atomic weight of Ag}}{\text{atomic weight of Ag} + 14.0080 + 3 \times 16.0000} = \frac{1.00000}{1.57480}$$

from which the atomic weight of silver is found to be 107.880. By this means it is possible to determine the atomic weight of silver with a probable accuracy of 1 part in 100,000, or 0.001 per cent.

By reference to this accurate value for the atomic weight of silver as a secondary standard, it is possible to determine the atomic weights of most of the metals and some of the nonmetals by analyses of their halogen compounds. In a typical case the metallic halide is prepared in the purest form possible, using several samples from different sources and purified by different methods. In a final operation the halide is fused in a stream of the vapor of the appropriate halogen, or hydrogen halide, to free it entirely of volatile foreign matter that might be trapped in the crystals. The metallic halide is then weighed, dissolved and treated with a slight excess of silver nitrate solution. The insoluble silver halide thus obtained is carefully washed, collected, dried and weighed. From the weight of the silver halide and a knowledge of the formulas of the compounds involved, the atomic weight of the metal may be computed.

Consider experimental data for the determination of the atomic weight of lead to illustrate this process. It was found that 1.00000 gram of lead bromide, $PbBr_2$, yields 1.02330 gram of silver bromide, AgBr. The atomic weight of silver had already been found to be 107.880, as described in the preceding paragraphs, and that of bromine to be 79.916 by direct comparison with silver. The formulas $PbBr_2$ and AgBr indicate that two molecules of silver bromide are obtained from every one molecule of lead bromide. The weight data suggest, therefore, that two molecules of silver bromide weigh 1.02330 times as much as does one molecule of lead bromide. Expressed mathematically, this relationship becomes

$$\frac{\text{molecular weight of PbBr}_2}{2 \times \text{molecular weight of AgBr}} = \frac{1.00000}{1.02330}$$

$$\frac{\text{atomic weight of Pb} + 2 \times \text{atomic weight of Br}}{2 \times (\text{atomic weight of Ag} + \text{atomic weight of Br})} = \frac{1.00000}{1.02330}$$

$$\frac{\text{atomic weight of Pb} + 2 \times 79.916}{2 \times (107.880 + 79.916)} = \frac{1.00000}{1.02330}$$

from which the atomic weight of lead is found to be 207.21.

These examples indicate that it is possible to determine unknown atomic weights if the necessary data on combining weights (or percentage composition) and the formulas are available. The three factors, atomic weights, formulas and composition, may be considered as the pivotal points of a triangle so constituted that any one factor may be computed when the other two are known. Since today all the important atomic weights are known with high accuracy, the chief uses of this triangular relationship are in calculation of the formula of a compound when its weight composition is known, and in calculation of its weight composition when its formula is known. These calculations are greatly facilitated by another concept, that of the gram-atomic weight and the gram-molecular weight.

GRAM-ATOMIC WEIGHT AND GRAM-MOLECULAR WEIGHT (MOLE)

The term gram-atomic weight is defined as the weight in grams numerically equal to the atomic weight. A gram-atomic weight of any element always contains the same number of atoms as a gram-atomic weight of any other element. Since this unit does refer to the same number of atoms, any relationships that can be discerned among the numbers of atoms involved in a reaction can be readily converted to a weight basis. That is, any relationship in terms of the numbers of atoms involved is also true for the numbers of gram-atomic weights involved. Thus, when carbon is burned to carbon monoxide, one atom of oxygen is required by each atom of carbon, or one gram-atomic weight of carbon requires one gram-atomic weight of oxygen for its conversion to carbon monoxide. Therefore, 12 grams of carbon (one gram-atomic weight) require 16 grams of oxygen (one gram-atomic weight) for change to carbon monoxide. If only 1 gram of carbon is present, this represents 1/12 of a gram-atomic weight of carbon, so just 1/12 of a gram-atomic weight of oxygen will be required; that is, 1/12 of 16, or 1.333 grams of oxygen.

The parallel concept for compounds is that of the gram-molecular weight, or *mole*, in which a mole of a compound represents a weight in grams of the compound numerically equal to its molecular weight. Since the molecular weight of a compound can be defined in the same terms as the atomic weight of an element, it is plain that a gram-molecular weight, or mole, of a compound must contain the same number of molecules as there are atoms of oxygen in 16 grams of oxygen, or as there are atoms of any element in a gram-atomic weight of that element. Thus, a mole of any compound must always contain the same number of molecules as a mole of any other compound, and this number of molecules is numerically equal to the number of atoms in a gram-atomic weight of any element. *Therefore, any relationship between the numbers of atoms and molecules in a reaction must also be true for the numbers of gram-atomic weights and moles in that reaction.*

For example, in the reaction represented by the chemical equation

$$2\,CO + O_2 \longrightarrow 2\,CO_2$$

two molecules of carbon monoxide yield two molecules of carbon dioxide, or one molecule of carbon monoxide yields one molecule of carbon dioxide. Therefore, one mole of carbon monoxide must yield one mole of carbon dioxide, so 28 grams (one mole) of carbon monoxide will yield 44 grams (one mole) of carbon dioxide. If only 2 grams of carbon monoxide are available, only 2/28, or 1/14 of a mole is present, so only 1/14 of a mole of carbon dioxide will be obtained. Since a mole of carbon dioxide contains 44 grams, 1/14 of a mole represents $1/14 \times 44$, or 3.143 grams.

This chemical equation also suggests that one mole of oxygen is consumed for every two moles of carbon monoxide, or that 1/2 mole of oxygen is consumed for every mole of carbon monoxide burned. Therefore, 28 grams (one mole) of carbon monoxide consume 16 grams (1/2 mole) of oxygen. If only 1 gram of carbon monoxide is burned, only $1/28 \times 1/2$ mole of oxygen will be required; that is, $1/28 \times 1/2 \times 32$, or 0.5714 grams of oxygen.

SOLUTIONS OF ELECTROLYTES

Electrolytes are substances which, in solution, conduct electricity. On the basis of certain anomalies of solutions of electrolytes in comparison to other solutions, Arrhenius, in the late nineteenth century, suggested the then radical idea that all ionizable materials are dissociated as soon as they are dissolved in water, whether or not they are subjected to an applied electrical potential. This theory suggests that electrolyte materials exist in solution not in molecular form, but rather as charged particles called ions. These ions migrate under the influence of a difference of potential, so that the solution is capable of conducting an electric current; but the ions are there at all times whether or not the current is flowing. Furthermore, it has since been found that ionic materials like sodium chloride do not exist in molecular form even in the solid state, which actually consists of a highly organized array of sodium ions and chloride ions. The Arrhenius theory indicates that all chemical materials can be classified according to the degree of their dissociation in aqueous solution. This classification is set up as follows: (1) non-electrolytes, which are substances which do not ionize in solution; (2) weak electrolytes, which are substances which are only partially ionized in solution; (3) strong electrolytes, substances which are substantially completely ionized in solution.

Certain aspects of the behavior of concentrated solutions of strong electrolytes suggested to Arrhenius that even these materials might be incompletely ionized. However, this part of the Arrhenius theory has now been displaced by the Debye-Hückel theory, which states the complete ionization of strong electrolytes and postulates a combination of the ions with solvent molecules and a "clustering" of the positive and negative ions to form loose aggregates. Under these conditions, ionization must be viewed as complete, although the clustering may produce some effects which resemble those that would result from incomplete ionization. The Debye-Hückel theory is of enormous theoretical importance, although the practicing analyst performs most of his work with relatively dilute solutions in which there is relatively little "clustering" of ions.

One of the most important aspects to the analyst of these theories of electrolytes is the suggestion that the properties of solutions of strong electrolytes are additive functions of the properties of the ions present. Thus a solution of sodium chloride possesses properties associated with the sodium ion and properties associated with the chloride ion. Similarly, a calcium chloride solution has properties representing both calcium ions and chloride ions. Both of these solutions show some properties in common, and these are those properties which are associated with the chloride ion. Advantage may be taken of these specific properties of chloride ion in framing a method of analysis for chloride ion, ignoring to a considerable extent the nature of the other ions in the solution. Thus, an analysis for chloride based upon precipitation, collection and weighing of silver chloride should be successful regardless of the nature of the chloride salt present in the solution, provided that it is one which ionizes completely.

This generalization is, of course, subject to certain restrictions. One limitation has already been indicated—the chloride material must all be present in an ionizable form. A correct result may not be obtained if, for example, the chloride is linked to cobalt in certain complex compounds. Fortunately, most of the common inorganic chlorides are strong electrolytes so that the analyst need not expect much difficulty from this source. However, he should exercise a reasonable amount of caution in performing chloride determinations, as, for example, in the presence of dissolved mercury or cadmium, since these materials form chloride compounds that are not completely ionized.

A second limitation of significance arises in that few quantitative tests are completely specific. The precipitation of an insoluble silver salt in dilute acid medium is not an entirely specific property of chloride ion since bromide and iodide ions will give precipitates under the same conditions.

Within these limitations, the general principle suggested by the Arrhenius theory is valid—a test for an ion in solution may be performed without taking account of the other materials present in the solution, provided that nothing is present which forms weakly ionized compounds with the ion (or the reagent) in question and provided that there is nothing present which can interfere with the specificity of the test. This principle is generally assumed in most noninstrumental methods of quantitative analysis, but its limitations must be clearly recognized and its basis in the Arrhenius theory must be acknowledged.

CHEMICAL EQUATIONS

A chemical equation consists of chemical symbols, numbers, + signs, — signs and = signs or arrows, and is used as a "chemical shorthand" to represent a chemical reaction. A complete chemical equation must indicate the reacting substances, the products and the relative numbers of each.

It is important that each substance be written in such a way that its true form is indicated. Many of the reactions encountered in quantitative analysis take place in solution, and solutions of electrolytes are ionized. Therefore, when a reaction occurs between ions, the reacting substances should be written as ions and not as molecules.

For example, the reaction occurring when solutions of sodium chloride and of silver nitrate are brought together is occasionally and carelessly written in the form

$$NaCl + AgNO_3 \longrightarrow AgCl + NaNO_3$$

This equation can hardly be a true representation of the reaction, however, because three of the four compounds included are strong electrolytes, which are completely ionized in solution. A much more valid representation of this reaction is indicated by the equation

$$Cl^- + Ag^+ \longrightarrow AgCl$$

Note that the sodium ions from the sodium chloride solution and the nitrate ions from the silver nitrate solution are omitted entirely. This omission is proper because these ions remain unchanged throughout the reaction. Since the equation represents a reaction, it should include nothing which does not enter into that reaction. While it is not always desirable to simplify an equation to this extent, such a formulation is useful in making plain the fundamental nature of the reaction.

In writing chemical equations, not all substances should be represented ionically. Substances which exist as molecules should be represented in equations as molecules. Thus, each chemical substance should be listed in the form in which it predominantly exists, whether that be ionically or molecularly. Substances which are not represented in ionic form may be grouped under four headings:

1. Insoluble precipitates, such as silver chloride in the preceding example, which do not contribute many ions to the solution but tend rather to remove their component ions from the solution. Many solid substances are crystalline and are actually ionized even in the solid state; these ions are not able to react independently of one another so their formulas are still written molecularly.

2. Gases which are evolved from the solution and, therefore, cannot remain in ionized form.

3. Weak electrolytes, such as water and some acids, which are only slightly ionized in solution. These substances may react as ions, but the dominant form in solution is not that of ionized material.

4. Complex ions which are predominantly undissociated into their constituent parts.

All the reactions encountered in this course may be classified under two headings, oxidation-reduction reactions and reactions not involving oxidation and reduction. Changes in oxidation state occur in the former type of reaction, while each element retains the same oxidation state throughout the latter type.

The writing of a chemical equation consists basically of two steps: (1) indication of the reactants and the products, and (2) balancing by listing the relative numbers of each. The former is based solely on experiment—the equation represents a reaction; therefore, there can be no equation until or unless there is a reaction to be represented. The balancing may be accomplished from experimental data also, but it is usually accomplished by inspection for nonoxidation-reduction reactions. The balancing of oxidation-reduction equations is often more complex and requires special procedures to be discussed in Chapter 14.

CHEMICAL EQUILIBRIA

The theory of dynamic equilibrium is another fundamental concept in analytical chemistry. The concept of a dynamic state of equilibrium indicates the relationship between the experimental conditions and the concentrations of all reacting substances when they are in equilibrium with each other. In considering the principles of chemical equilibria, we must first consider the law of mass action.

Law of Mass Action. The law of mass action is concerned with the rates at which reactions proceed. Fundamentally, the rate of a reaction must depend on only two factors: the number of collisions between the atoms or molecules or ions of the reactants; the fraction of those collisions which is fruitful in accomplishing reaction. The fraction which is fruitful is dependent upon the temperature and the presence of catalysts, but when such conditions are held constant, a reaction rate is simply a function of the number of collisions of the reacting bodies. If the number of these collisions is doubled, the reaction rate must also be doubled.

A relationship between the concentrations of the reacting materials and the number of collisions between them must now be devised. As an example, a type reaction may be considered:

$$A + B \longrightarrow Z + Y$$

If the concentration of A is suddenly doubled (that is, if the number of A particles in a fixed volume is doubled), it is reasonable to expect that the number of collisions between A and B will momentarily be doubled and that the rate of reaction will accordingly be doubled. Similarly, if the concentration of A is held constant and the concentration of B is doubled, the rate of reaction will be doubled. Now, if the concentrations of both A and B are doubled, the number of collisions between A and B particles is quadrupled, so the rate of reaction is quadrupled. These considerations suggest that the rate of the reaction may be expressed by the equation

$$\text{rate} = k\,[A]\,[B]$$

in which k is a proportionality constant and [A] and [B] represent the concentrations of A and B, respectively.

It is now necessary to broaden the type reaction being used as an example. A more generalized type reaction may be represented by the equation

$$aA + bB \longrightarrow zZ + yY$$

in which a, b, z and y represent the numbers of particles of A, B, Z and Y respectively, which are involved in the completed, balanced equation. Reasoning similar to that of the preceding paragraph suggests the conclusion that the rate of the reaction may be expressed by the equation

$$\text{rate} = k\,[A]^a\,[B]^b$$

in which all symbols are analogous to those already defined. This equation is a mathematical expression of the very important and widely applicable Law of Mass Action, "The velocity or rate of a chemical reaction is proportional to the product of the concentrations of the reacting substances, each concentration raised to the power equal to the number of molecules (or ions or such) of the reactant which appear in the balanced equation for the reaction."

State of Equilibrium.   Most reactions of analytical significance are reversible—at least to a slight extent. Consequently, in the reaction

$$aA + bB \rightleftharpoons zZ + yY$$

the reverse reaction between Z and Y has a real significance. The law of mass action may be applied to this reverse reaction as well as to the forward reaction. The rates of the two reactions may be expressed by the equations

$$\text{rate}_r = k_r\,[A]^a\,[B]^b$$
$$\text{rate}_l = k_l\,[Z]^z\,[Y]^y$$

in which the subscripts r refer to the reaction to the right and subscripts l to the reverse reaction to the left. When A and B are first mixed with no Z or Y present, the reaction will begin to go to the right at a finite rate. As this forward reaction continues, the concentrations of A and B are diminished, so the rate_r diminishes. Initially, the rate of the reverse reaction, rate_l, is zero because no Z or Y is present. However, as the forward reaction proceeds, the concentrations of Z and Y increase, so the rate_l becomes finite and increases. Thus, the rate_r starts at its maximum value and diminishes therefrom while during the same time the rate_l starts at zero and increases thereafter. Sooner or later the two rates become equal and the system is said to be in a state of equilibrium. The concentrations of A, B, Z and Y remain constant thereafter. It must be emphasized that the forward and reverse reactions do not stop but rather continue at equal rates; this means that the system is in a dynamic state of equilibrium, not a static one. The equilibrium state may be represented mathematically as follows:

$$\text{rate}_r = \text{rate}_l$$

$$k_r [A]^a [B]^b = k_l [Z]^z [Y]^y$$

The factors k_r and k_l are difficult to evaluate accurately, and it is customary to combine them by rearranging the equation

$$\frac{k_r}{k_l} = \frac{[Z]^z [Y]^y}{[A]^a [B]^b}$$

$$K = \frac{[Z]^z [Y]^y}{[A]^a [B]^b}$$

The constant K is simply a lumped constant, k_r/k_l, and is designated the *equilibrium constant* for the state of equilibrium. Since K is a function of the several concentration factors, all of which may be measured experimentally upon a system at equilibrium, the numerical values of K can be determined for particular reactions.

The equilibrium constant concept may be applied to an even more generalized type reaction

$$aA + bB + cC + \ldots \rightleftharpoons zZ + yY + xX + \ldots \ldots$$

$$K = \frac{[Z]^z [Y]^y [X]^x \ldots \ldots}{[A]^a [B]^b [C]^c \ldots \ldots}$$

Equilibrium Constant. Since the equilibrium constant, K, is used extensively throughout analytical chemistry, a close study of it even at this introductory time should be rewarding. Attention should be called to the convention—purely a matter of convenience and chosen quite arbitrarily— that the value of K refers to a ratio in which the concentrations of the products of the reaction (right-hand side of the chemical equation as written) appear in the numerator, and the concentrations of the primary reactants (substances on the left-hand side of the chemical equation as written), in the denominator. With this convention it is possible to tell by a glance at the numerical value of K whether a reaction tends to go far toward completion to the right or whether it goes only slightly to the right before reaching equilibrium. Thus, in a reaction in which K is numerically large, the concentration function of the products is large with respect to the concentration function of the reactants, so that equilibrium is reached only when the reaction has proceeded far to the right. Conversely, when K is small, equilibrium is reached before the reaction has proceeded very far toward the right. It must be emphasized that this rule deals with concentrations at equilibrium and tells us absolutely nothing about the rate of approach to that equilibrium. For example, the equilibrium constant for the all-gas reaction

$$2\,H_2 + O_2 \rightleftharpoons 2\,H_2O$$

is very large at room temperature, indicating that practically all of the hydrogen and oxygen are converted to water when equilibrium is reached. Nevertheless, mixtures of hydrogen and oxygen can remain apparently unchanged at room temperature for years. This fact does not signify any failure of the equilibrium concept; it merely means that the rate of reaction of hydrogen and oxygen at room temperature is so slow that the rate of approach to equilibrium is immeasurably slow. If this reaction rate is increased by, for example, the introduction of a palladium catalyst, then equilibrium is quickly achieved; in this equilibrium, mixture will be relatively much water and only very small quantities of hydrogen and oxygen as would be predicted from the large value of the equilibrium constant.

Effects of Conditions upon the Equilibrium Constant. The variation of the numerical value of K with the conditions and nature of the reaction must be considered.

Nature of the reaction. The position of the state of equilibrium depends on the nature of the materials involved. The unique character of each reaction is adequately reflected in the unique value of the equilibrium constant which goes with it. The numerical values of equilibrium constants are tabulated for many reactions in several tables in this book as well as in standard reference books.

Concentrations. Concentrations may be altered by changing the pressure or volume in gaseous equilibria, by diluting or concentrating a liquid reaction mixture, by adding or withdrawing some of one or more of the substances involved in the state of equilibrium, and so on. These alterations in concentration produce changes in the number of collisions and, hence, in the reaction rates. However, the equilibrium constant expression was derived with just such changes in mind, and the value of K remains constant whatever the absolute values of the concentrations may be. In approaching equilibrium the concentrations adjust themselves so as to meet the conditions of the equilibrium expression.

It is apparent that the units selected for expressing the concentrations influence the numerical value of the constant for any particular reaction. Therefore, it has become necessary in tabulating and using the constants to employ some standard units of concentration. For substances in solution, such as ions and un-ionized molecules, concentrations are expressed in moles per liter. For gases, concentrations are expressed in units of atmospheres of partial pressure. For water molecules in aqueous media and for solid substances in contact with, but not dissolved in, water, the concentration may be taken uniformly as unity; this real simplification will be justified subsequently in this chapter. These units are arbitrary to some extent; yet their usage has become almost completely standardized throughout the world.

Catalysis. The presence of a catalyst may hasten the approach to a state of equilibrium as already stated, but catalysis always affects both the forward and reverse reaction rates precisely to the same extent. Therefore, although catalysis may diminish the time required to establish a state of equilibrium (that is, until the system is in a condition such that the equilibrium constant takes effect), it never, under any circumstances, alters the value of K in the final equilibrium mixture.

Temperature. Unlike changes in concentration and catalysis, temperature variations produce real changes in the numerical values of equilibrium constants. This fact was indicated in the discussion of reaction rates earlier in this chapter. By the methods of thermodynamics, a branch of physical chemistry, it is possible to estimate the numerical change in the equilibrium constant for a given reaction for any stated temperature change. However, in analytical chemistry it is usually sufficient to refer to tabulated values for common reactions at one or more typical temperatures and to know qualitatively whether a K value increases or decreases as the temperature is raised or lowered. This qualitative estimation may be made with the aid of the principle of Le Chatelier.

Principle of Le Chatelier. The principle of Le Chatelier enables the chemist to make qualitative predictions of the effects of specific variations upon a system at equilibrium, whereas the equilibrium constant serves as the basis of quantitative considerations. This principle may be stated in the general form "When a stress is applied to a system in equilibrium, the point of equilibrium tends to shift in such a direction as to diminish that stress."

A change in temperature is one of the several types of stress concerning which application of the principle of Le Chatelier reveals useful information. Increasing the temperature of a system at equilibrium, in effect, supplies heat energy. The Le Chatelier principle then predicts that the point of equilibrium will shift in such a way as to consume at least part of this excess heat energy; that is, when the temperature is raised, an endothermic reaction (one which absorbs heat) is favored over an exothermic reaction (one in which heat is liberated). Therefore, if a reaction going from left to right in the equation is an exothermic one, a rise in temperature favors the reverse reaction and makes the numerical value of the equilibrium constant smaller. Conversely, a drop in temperature favors the forward reaction and increases the value of K. Similarly, if the forward reaction is an endothermic one, the value of the equilibrium constant increases with a rise of temperature and decreases if the temperature drops. These qualitative indications are usually sufficient for the analytical chemist.

Le Chatelier's principle also provides an important qualitative guide to the way in which an equilibrium is shifted by changes in the concentrations of the reacting substances. The stress in this case is the change in concentration, so it may be predicted that the point of equilibrium will shift in such a way as to minimize this change. Thus, if one of the components in an equilibrium mixture is diminished in concentration (for example, by removing part of it from the reacting system), the system will reach a new position of equilibrium by moving in such a direction as to restore in part the concentration of the component which was withdrawn. Similarly, when an additional quantity of one of the components is introduced to a system in equilibrium, the system shifts toward a new point of equilibrium in such a direction as to consume part of the added material. The principle of Le Chatelier provides only a qualitative indication of the effect of a change in reactant concentration. Quantitative data on the effects are provided through calculations based on the equilibrium constants, as will be shown in subsequent chapters.

Completeness of Reaction.   Any equilibrium constant expression assumes that the reaction is reversible. Most common reactions encountered in analysis are, in principle, reversible, so equilibrium calculations are applicable. It is important, however, that reactions used as the bases of analytical determinations go substantially to completion. For example, when chloride is determined by precipitation and weighing of silver chloride, essentially all of the chloride present in the unknown sample must be converted to silver chloride:

$$Cl^- + Ag^+ \rightleftharpoons AgCl$$

The precipitation of an indeterminate fraction of the chloride as silver chloride would clearly be inadequate. In this example the precipitation reaction may be considered as quantitatively complete when the amount of material not precipitated is a negligible fraction of the total weight of silver chloride. Thus, if the precipitate is to be weighed on a balance with a sensitivity limit of 0.0001 gram, any amount of material left in solution which weighs less than this is of no consequence.

It is now important to consider under what conditions reversible reactions will go to practical completion. Le Chatelier's principle suggests that an equilibrium reaction will be driven to the right if one or more of the right-side products of the reaction is continuously removed. Under such conditions the equilibrium reaction proceeds far to the right in an attempt to reform the component as fast as it is withdrawn. Even a reversible reaction goes to practical completion if this withdrawal is continuous and effective. Three important ways in which a reaction product may be effectively removed from a reaction mixture are: (1) by allowing a gaseous product to escape; (2) by precipitating the product in a relatively insoluble form; (3) by binding one of the products in a complex ion in solution. If one or more of these conditions is present, the reaction proceeds substantially to completion, the degree of completeness depending upon the thoroughness with which the reaction product is removed. The question of the completeness of a reaction arises repeatedly in quantitative chemical analysis. Le Chatelier's principle is useful in indicating the qualitative trends, and the more precise data which are often required are obtained with the aid of the equilibrium constant equation.

Note that the area factor has cancelled out. The final constant for this type of system is designated the solubility product constant and given the symbol, K_{sp}.

Consider next the slightly soluble compound, silver chromate. A state of equilibrium between dissolved and undissolved silver chromate may be represented by chemical and mathematical equations as

$$Ag_2CrO_4 \rightleftharpoons 2\ Ag^+ + CrO_4^=$$

$$K_{sp} = [Ag^+]^2\ [CrO_4^=]$$

This forward reaction does not occur stepwise, as in the case of acids of the H_2A type, so there are no corresponding stepwise ionization constants for this type of system.

A more generalized chemical equation for the state of equilibrium between dissolved and undissolved substances may be stated as

$$A_aB_bC_c \rightleftharpoons aA + bB + cC$$

The corresponding solubility product constant equation is

$$K_{sp} = [A]^a\ [B]^b\ [C]^c$$

The solubility product constants are listed for a number of common, slightly soluble substances in Appendix 1. A very small number for the constant signifies a lower solubility than does a larger number.

COMPLEX ION DISSOCIATION CONSTANTS

Another one of the means listed for driving a reaction to practical completion was formation of a complex ion in solution. Every type of complex ion is dissociated to some extent. The states of equilibria existing between complex ions and their component parts form another important application of equilibrium constants.

Consider the dissociation of a ferric thiocyanate complex:

$$FeSCN^{++} \rightleftharpoons Fe^{+++} + SCN^-$$

species are in solution, so the equilibrium constant may be formulated

$$K_d = \frac{[Fe^{+++}]\ [SCN^-]}{[FeSCN^{++}]}$$

This type of equilibrium constant is designated a dissociation constant for a complex. The reciprocal of a dissociation constant is also encountered under the designation of a stability constant. For uniformity and consistency, however, these systems are represented in this textbook as dissociation constants in which the concentration of the complex is in the denominator and the concentrations of its dissociated forms are in the numerator. Thus, a

IONIZATION CONSTANTS OF ACIDS AND BASES

Solutes in aqueous solutions have already been classified into the following three categories: (1) nonelectrolytes, those which are not ionized at all; (2) weak electrolytes, those which are only partially ionized; (3) strong electrolytes, those which are completely ionized. Some weak electrolytes are so slightly ionized in aqueous solution that for practical purposes they may be considered to be totally un-ionized; yet the distinction between nonelectrolytes and weak electrolytes is a real one. The equilibrium concept can be applied to the state of equilibrium established between ionized solute and un-ionized solute in a solution of a weak electrolyte, and herein lies one of the major areas of applicability of the concept in analytical chemistry. The equilibrium concept is especially useful in dealing with solutions of weak acids and weak bases; that is, in dealing with acid and base solutions, respectively, in which the acid and the base are only partially ionized.

Consider the general type weak acid, HA, for which the state of equilibrium between ionized and un-ionized acid may be represented by the chemical and mathematical equations

$$HA \rightleftharpoons H^+ + A^-$$

$$K_a = \frac{[H^+]\ [A^-]}{[HA]}$$

The numerical values of the equilibrium constants for a number of common weak acids of this type are listed in Appendix 2. The chemical equation could be written also in the reverse form,

$$H^+ + A^- \rightleftharpoons HA$$

inasmuch as the reactions are reversible and, at equilibrium, proceed in both directions at equal rates. It is clear that the equilibrium constant based upon this chemical equation would be the reciprocal of that for the reverse chemical equation since we conventionally place the concentration expressions for the right-side substances in the numerator. Therefore, in preparing and using the data of Appendix 2, we must further stipulate that the values listed are for constants based upon chemical equations written with the un-ionized solute on the left. This custom is quite arbitrary, but some self-consistent rule is necessary. Accordingly, a small number for K signifies an acid which is weaker, less ionized, than one with a larger value of K.

Consider next the general type weak acid H_2A in which each molecule of un-ionized acid yields two hydrogen ions upon complete ionization. It has been found experimentally that such acids ionize stepwise, as indicated by the chemical equations

$$H_2A \rightleftharpoons H^+ + HA^-$$

$$HA^- \rightleftharpoons H^+ + A^=$$

for which we can write two equilibrium constant equations

$$K_1 = \frac{[H^+][HA^-]}{[H_2A]}$$

$$K_2 = \frac{[H^+][A^=]}{[HA^-]}$$

It is possible to add the two chemical equations to give an over-all one

$$H_2A \rightleftharpoons 2H^+ + A^=$$

for which the combined ionization constant, $K_{1,2}$, would be

$$K_{1,2} = \frac{[H^+]^2[A^=]}{[H_2A]}$$

It will be noted that $K_{1,2}$ is numerically equal to the product of K_1 and K_2. Since the ionization of such acids does proceed stepwise, it is usually necessary to use the individual chemical equations and equilibrium constants, so the combined ones are of limited usefulness. A weak acid which contains three ionizable hydrogen ions per molecule is characterized by three ionization constants. As indicated in the data of Appendix 2, the first ionization constant is always numerically larger than the second, and the second greater than the third if there are three.

The equilibrium concepts may be applied to solutions of weak bases in a manner entirely analogous to that of weak acids. For example, a generalized ionization equilibrium of a weak base, BOH, may be represented by chemical and mathematical equations as follows:

$$BOH \rightleftharpoons B^+ + OH^-$$

$$K_b = \frac{[B^+][OH^-]}{[BOH]}$$

Numerical values of ionization constants of common weak acids are also listed in Appendix 2.

Water molecules ionize partially to form both hydrogen and hydroxyl ions:

$$H_2O \rightleftharpoons H^+ + OH^-$$

The equilibrium constant for this state of equilibrium might be formulated first as

$$K = \frac{[H^+][OH^-]}{[H_2O]}$$

This point of equilibrium normally lies far to the left, that is, with most of the water molecules un-ionized. For every liter of water, we have very nearly one liter of undissociated water molecules. The concentration of water molecules is essentially fixed in water and in all dilute aqueous solutions. Therefore,

the denominator of the preceding equilibrium constant equation which may be combined with K to form a new constant, K_w, the constant of water:

$$K_w = [H^+][OH^-]$$

The hydrogen ion concentration may vary so tremendou solution to another that it is often convenient to express it in a form. The pH of a solution is defined as the negative logarithm hydrogen ion concentration:

$$[H^+] = 10^{-pH}$$

Similar units may be used to express other concentrations, suc

$$[OH^-] = 10^{-pOH} \quad \text{and} \quad [Cl^-] = 10^{-pCl}$$

and also to express equilibrium constants, as

$$[K] = 10^{-pK}$$

SOLUBILITY PRODUCT CONSTANT

One of the means listed for driving a reaction to pract was precipitation of a relatively insoluble substance. None analytical precipitates is totally insoluble. The states of eq between dissolved and undissolved materials present and application of equilibrium constants in quantitative chemic

Consider the state of equilibrium between dissolved silver chloride:

$$AgCl \rightleftharpoons Ag^+ + Cl^-$$

This system differs from those considered thus far in this ch distinct phases are present. Silver chloride is present as a so ions appearing on the right side of the equation are preser solution phase. No reaction can take place in either direc the two phases are in physical contact, so the magnitude of the solid substance influences the rates of reaction. Thu reaction to the right and the rate of reaction to the left are

$$rate_r = k_r \times area$$

$$rate_l = k_l \times area \times [Ag^+][Cl^-]$$

At equilibrium, the two rates are equal to each other:

$$rate_r = rate_l$$

$$k_r \times area = k_l \times area \times [Ag^+][Cl^-]$$

$$\frac{k_r \times area}{k_l \times area} = [Ag^+][Cl^-]$$

$$K_{sp} = [Ag^+][Cl^-]$$

very small number for the constant signifies a more stable complex than does a larger number. Dissociation constants for several complex ions of interest in quantitative analysis are listed in Appendix 3.

It frequently happens that two types of ion can unite to form a series of two or more different complexes. For example, ferric and thiocyanate ions can form not only the one-to-one complex, $FeSCN^{++}$, but also complexes with more than one thiocyanate ion for each ferric ion. The formation is stepwise within the series, and each step may be represented by an equilibrium constant just as is done with the stepwise ionization of acids which contain more than one ionizable hydrogen ion.

SIMULTANEOUS EQUILIBRIA

Systems encountered in quantitative analysis are most frequently those in which several equilibria are simultaneously in existence. For example, a saturated solution of a slightly soluble hydroxide must, if in equilibrium, satisfy a solubility product constant and one or more acid or base ionization constants. A complex ion may contain as one of its dissociated components an ion which forms a weak acid or a weak base. Of course, for any aqueous solution of a weak acid or base, the ionization constant of water may be as significant as, or may even be more significant than, the ionization constant of the solute.

It is frequently possible to neglect one or more of the equilibrium constants involved in a system of simultaneous equilibria when making numerical calculations. This is never done blindly or simply for convenience; it is done only when there is a valid basis for knowing that the magnitudes of the quantities of interest are not significantly affected by doing so. In all cases it is possible to write and to use all of the equilibrium constants involved in a particular system, to combine them mathematically as desired, and to solve for the desired information if sufficient information concerning the system is available. Each student of quantitative chemical analysis should endeavor to become familiar with the general, over-all approach to solving numerical problems involving systems in equilibrium, and he should also strive to become proficient at making all appropriate approximations to fit each situation which he encounters. Examples will be described in subsequent chapters.

REVIEW QUESTIONS

1. Why were the experimental chemists of a few hundred years ago essentially analytical chemists?
2. State the laws of definite proportions, multiple proportions and reciprocal proportions.
3. Explain the validity of the law of definite proportions and the law of reciprocal proportions on the basis of the atomic theory.

4. Why do the atomic weight determinations represent in a real sense the ultimate in quantitative techniques?
5. What is the Arrhenius theory of ionization? Wherein does it hold, and wherein does it fail?
6. Distinguish between electrolytes and nonelectrolytes.
7. Distinguish between strong electrolytes and weak electrolytes.
8. State and illustrate the Le Chatelier principle.
9. Derive a general equation for an equilibrium constant from the law of mass action.
10. What is the effect of a change in temperature upon (a) the rate of a reaction, and (b) an equilibrium constant?
11. What is the effect of a catalyst upon (a) the rate of a reaction, and (b) an equilibrium constant?
12. Formulate solubility product expressions for CaF_2, $Fe(OH)_3$, $Ca_3(PO_4)_2$ and $MgNH_4PO_4$.
13. Write chemical equations for the equilibria existing between each of the following complex ions and its dissociation products: $Cu(CN)_4^=$; $Ag(S_2O_3)_2^=$; $Ag(NH_3)_2^+$.
14. Formulate dissociation constant expressions for each of the complex ions of question 13.
15. Distinguish clearly between the dissociation constant and the stability constant for a complex ion.

SUGGESTIONS FOR ADDITIONAL READING

For further review of any of the topics considered in this chapter, consult any of the standard textbooks of general chemistry.

Types of
Quantitative Analysis

FUNDAMENTALLY, every quantitative analytical determination rests on the measurement of a property which is related, directly or indirectly, to the amount of the desired constituent present. An ideal method of measurement is one in which no constituent other than the desired one contributes to the quantity being measured. Adequate selectivity is seldom encountered in practical situations unless the desired constituent is first separated from some or all of the other components of the sample undergoing analysis. So the two major operations in a quantitative determination are separation and measurement.

The methods of quantitative analysis may conveniently be classified on the basis of the chemical or physical property which is measured. On this basis, quantitative procedures are classified as (1) gravimetric, (2) volumetric, (3) optical and (4) electrical. In some instances, two or more of these types are combined into a single measurement, and some measured quantities do not readily fall into any of these categories. However, this classification is very useful and is employed throughout this book.

Quantitative methods of analysis may alternatively be classified on the basis of the type of sample encountered. Thus, there are organic and inorganic methods, also macro methods, micro methods and related categories indicative of the amount of sample which is used.

GRAVIMETRIC ANALYSIS

The simple and obvious fact that the weight of a substance is indicative of its amount is the basis for gravimetric methods of analysis. Each determination involves the separation of the desired constituent into a form which is of known percentage composition and which can be weighed accurately. From this information, along with the weight of the original sample, the percentage by weight of the desired constituent is readily computed. Further classification of the methods of gravimetric analysis may be made on the basis of how the desired constituent is separated into a weighable form.

Precipitation Methods. This is the most important subgroup of the methods of gravimetric analysis. The sample to be analyzed is put into solution, and then the desired constituent is isolated through the addition of a suitable reagent with which the desired constituent can form an insoluble precipitate. For example, the chloride content of a sample may be determined by addition of excess silver nitrate to an aqueous solution of the sample, whereby silver chloride is precipitated. This precipitate is filtered, washed to remove contaminants, dried to remove residual washing liquid and, finally, weighed. From the weight of the silver chloride thus obtained and the weight of the original sample, the percentage of chloride in the original sample may be calculated. The accuracy of the answer obtained with a procedure of this type is primarily dependent upon the purity of the substance which is weighed. Many specific, accurate precipitation methods of analysis are available to the analytical chemist today. Some of these, as well as a detailed discussion of the principles, advantages and disadvantages of these methods, are described in Chapters 6, 7 and 8.

Electrodeposition Methods. A second subgroup of gravimetric methods includes the methods in which the desired constituent is separated from a solution of the unknown sample by deposition on an electrode. This separation is based upon the oxidizability or reducibility of the desired constituent at the electrode. For example, copper is frequently determined by applying a voltage of sufficient magnitude to cause electrical current to flow between two platinum electrodes immersed in a moderately acidic solution of the sample. In due time essentially all of the copper ions will be deposited upon the negative electrode as metallic copper, and the difference between the initial and final weights of this electrode indicates directly the copper content of the sample. Electrodeposition methods may be likened to precipitation methods in that the electric current passing through the solution serves as the precipitating reagent. Electrodeposition methods are discussed in Chapter 19.

Volatilization Methods. In this subgroup are included those methods in which the desired constituent is separated from the sample by virtue of its volatility with heat or with certain reagents. Two examples may be cited. The water of hydration of barium chloride crystals may be determined simply by drying a weighed portion of the sample at $150°$ C until no more loss of weight occurs; the difference between the initial and final weights of the sample indicates directly the water content of the initial sample. With a suitable experimental layout, the evolved water might also be collected by absorption on an appropriate reagent; the increase in weight of the absorber would indicate the weight of water which was evolved by the sample.

A second example of a volatilization procedure is that of the determination of the combined carbon dioxide content of a carbonate sample, such as calcium carbonate or a limestone. The sample is treated in a suitable apparatus with acid to liberate the combined carbon dioxide as free carbon dioxide gas. This gas is absorbed in a vessel containing an appropriate absorbent.

The gain in weight of this vessel during the experiment represents the combined carbon dioxide content of the sample. Volatilization procedures are perhaps the simplest of all gravimetric ones, and some are discussed in further detail in Chapter 7.

VOLUMETRIC ANALYSIS

Gravimetric methods of analysis are frequently quite time-consuming. This drawback is obviated to an appreciable extent in the second major category of quantitative methods, volumetric methods of analysis. In this group, the steps of isolation, purification and weighing of the precipitate are replaced by measurements of volume. A substantial amount of time can be saved, particularly if many similar determinations are to be made. For a particular constituent, volumetric methods may even be more accurate than gravimetric methods. Volumetric methods may be subdivided into groups, depending on the mode of carrying out the determination or on the chemical principle underlying the method.

Titrimetric Methods. With the possible exception of colorimetric procedures, this is probably the most important subgroup of all quantitative analytical methods. In titrimetric methods the desired constituent is put into solution and allowed to react with a reagent solution. The reagent solution must be a standard solution, which means it must be of known concentration. The standard solution is gradually added from a buret, which is a device for delivering and measuring the volume of a solution, until just enough has been added to react with all of the desired constituent. This point is called the end point and must somehow be rendered recognizable to the analyst who is conducting the determination. The volume of standard solution required is then read from the graduation marks on the buret and, assuming the concentration of the standard solution and the amount of the sample to be known, the amount of desired constituent may be calculated.

Titrimetric methods may be further classified on the basis of the nature of the chemical reaction between the desired constituent and the standard solution. On this basis there are four major categories of titrimetric methods.

1. Neutralization methods. In this method hydrogen or hydroxyl ions react either with each other or with some other acidic or basic constituent. A typical example is the determination of the carbonate content of soda ash by reaction with a standard solution of hydrochloric acid.

2. Precipitation methods. In this type the desired constituent and the standard solution react to form an insoluble precipitate. In contrast to gravimetric precipitation methods, the precipitate is allowed to remain in suspension, and the necessary experimental operations are completed when the end point has been reached. The chloride content of an unknown solution may be determined volumetrically with a standard silver nitrate solution.

3. Oxidation-reduction methods. The primary reaction involved in a method of this type is the transfer of electrons from the substance undergoing oxidation to the substance undergoing reduction. Either the desired constituent or the solute of the standard solution may be the substance to be oxidized, and the other one must be the substance to be reduced. A common and very important oxidation-reduction method of analysis is the determination of iron by reaction of ferrous ion with a standard solution of ceric sulfate.

4. Complex formation methods. In this type the desired constituent and the standard solution react to form a soluble complex ion. A very important example is the determination of small amounts of calcium ion by its reaction with a standard solution of a sodium salt of the organic acid, ethylene diamine tetraacetic acid, to form a complex ion.

Titrimetric methods are discussed in detail in Part III, Chapters 9 through 16.

Gasometric Methods. The analysis of gaseous mixtures is often performed by measuring the volume of the sample at known temperature and pressure, selectively absorbing the components one at a time, and measuring the volume again after removal of each component. This procedure provides a direct measure of the volume of each component at known temperature and pressure. The results may, of course, be readily translated to weight units. Gasometric methods require special types of apparatus and are of less importance than a number of other types of analytical methods, from both the pedagogical and the practical viewpoints. Therefore, gasometric methods will not be discussed further in this book.

OPTICAL METHODS

The third and fourth major categories of quantitative analytical methods, optical and electrical methods, are based on the measurement of certain physicochemical properties, generally with the aid of instruments. Optical methods are considered in Chapters 17 and 18. Classification of optical methods into subgroups may be based upon what optical property is used in making the measurement, how the sample interacts with light energy or the type of instrumentation used to measure that property. A detailed classification of these methods will not be made in this introductory chapter; rather, an example will be cited to indicate the relationships which these methods have to gravimetric and volumetric methods.

One very common optical method of analysis is that of absorption colorimetry. The basis of this method is the fact that the concentration of a colored substance in solution is proportional to the amount of light energy of a restricted wavelength that is absorbed by that colored substance. For example, the permanganate ion absorbs green light to a considerable extent. Very low concentrations of permanganate in solution can be determined with a simple instrument called a colorimeter. The instrument includes a source of a light beam of suitable color, a cell for holding the test solution in the path of the light beam, and some means of measuring the intensity of the light which passes through the cell. A photocell and an indicating meter generally suffice as the measuring device. The colorimeter must be standardized, or calibrated, by noting the instrument readings for one or more solutions of permanganate of known concentration. A large number of unknown samples can be analyzed rapidly after the calibration is complete.

This example illustrates the fact that optical methods of analysis depend upon some property of the desired constituent other than its chemical reactivity. Chemical reactions may precede the final measuring step, such as getting all of the manganese in the sample into the permanganate form or removing other components of similar color, but the measuring step itself does not include a chemical reaction.

A wide variety of laboratory equipment has been developed for use in optical methods of analysis. It ranges all the way from simple test tubes, sufficient for some procedures in which the human eye serves as the detector, to complex and delicate instruments costing many thousands of dollars, designed for automatic or semiautomatic operation with light to which the human eye is not sensitive.

Many of the procedures are characterized by speed, good selectivity and high sensitivity. Selectivity is the ability to determine the desired constituent in the presence of other substances. Sensitivity is the ability to determine very low concentrations of the desired constituent. Hence these methods are absolutely essential in fulfilling the demands made upon the modern analytical chemist.

ELECTRICAL METHODS

The category of electrical methods of analysis includes all those methods in which the primary measurement is one of a basic electrical quantity, such as voltage, resistance, rate of current flow or quantity of current flow. The category does not include those methods in which electrical equipment is used for other purposes, such as electrical devices for measuring optical properties. Electrodeposition methods, which have already been mentioned under gravimetric methods, may also be included under the category of electrical methods. Electrical methods of analysis are described in Chapters 19 and 20.

A few examples may be cited to illustrate the role of electrical methods relative to other methods. The concentration of hydrogen ions in an aqueous solution can be measured simply by dipping two properly selected electrodes into the solution, connecting wires from the electrodes to a voltmeter and reading the voltage. No chemical change is made in the solution whatever, and the answer to the determination may be obtained almost instantaneously.

The same measurement may be used as a means of locating the end point in a neutralization titration. In this case the determination is a volumetric one, with an electrical measurement serving as the indicator.

As another example, consider the determination of iron by measuring the quantity of electricity required to reduce all the iron from the ferric to the ferrous form. From the quantity of electricity used, the total number of electrons may be calculated, so the number and the weight of iron atoms may be determined. This determination is, in a sense, a titrimetric one in which the unknown is titrated directly by electrons.

Electrical methods are ideally suited to development for automatic or semiautomatic analytical processes. Whenever a quantity, such as a concentration or other analytical unit, can be converted into an electrical quantity, various types of automatic recording and control are possible.

It must be emphasized that optical and electrical and other methods of analysis using instruments have by no means antiquated gravimetric and volumetric methods. Indeed, many of the instrumental methods are gravimetric and volumetric methods. Furthermore, even the more classical types of gravimetric and volumetric procedures are among the most widely used methods of analysis today. Modern research in analytical chemistry, in pointing the way to future progress, is greatly emphasizing gravimetric and volumetric methods along with optical, electrical and other methods.

METHODS OF SEPARATION

The methods of separating the desired constituent from substances which would otherwise interfere in the final measurement are just as important in quantitative chemical analysis as are the final measurements. Precipitation, electrodeposition and volatilization have already been mentioned as methods of separation which are useful in gravimetric analysis. All three are valuable in nongravimetric methods as well.

Other methods of separation which are employed in all categories of quantitative determinations include chromatography, ion exchange and solvent extraction. Chromatographic separations are based upon differences in the tightness with which the several components are adsorbed upon a suitable medium; these procedures are especially useful in qualitative analysis but find important application in quantitative work as well. In ion exchange separations, one type of ion is "traded" for another. For example, aluminum ion interferes in the gravimetric determination of sulfate, but it may be replaced by noninterfering hydrogen ions by the ion-exchange technique. Separations by solvent extraction are based upon differences in relative solubilities of two or more components in two or more solvents. For example, lead ion may be separated from a number of ions which would interfere in the colorimetric measurement of lead ion by extracting the lead from aqueous solution into chloroform.

Adequate separation of interfering constituents does not necessarily

IONIZATION CONSTANTS OF ACIDS AND BASES

Solutes in aqueous solutions have already been classified into the following three categories: (1) nonelectrolytes, those which are not ionized at all; (2) weak electrolytes, those which are only partially ionized; (3) strong electrolytes, those which are completely ionized. Some weak electrolytes are so slightly ionized in aqueous solution that for practical purposes they may be considered to be totally un-ionized; yet the distinction between nonelectrolytes and weak electrolytes is a real one. The equilibrium concept can be applied to the state of equilibrium established between ionized solute and un-ionized solute in a solution of a weak electrolyte, and herein lies one of the major areas of applicability of the concept in analytical chemistry. The equilibrium concept is especially useful in dealing with solutions of weak acids and weak bases; that is, in dealing with acid and base solutions, respectively, in which the acid and the base are only partially ionized.

Consider the general type weak acid, HA, for which the state of equilibrium between ionized and un-ionized acid may be represented by the chemical and mathematical equations

$$HA \rightleftharpoons H^+ + A^-$$
$$K_a = \frac{[H^+]\,[A^-]}{[HA]}$$

The numerical values of the equilibrium constants for a number of common weak acids of this type are listed in Appendix 2. The chemical equation could be written also in the reverse form,

$$H^+ + A^- \rightleftharpoons HA$$

inasmuch as the reactions are reversible and, at equilibrium, proceed in both directions at equal rates. It is clear that the equilibrium constant based upon this chemical equation would be the reciprocal of that for the reverse chemical equation since we conventionally place the concentration expressions for the right-side substances in the numerator. Therefore, in preparing and using the data of Appendix 2, we must further stipulate that the values listed are for constants based upon chemical equations written with the un-ionized solute on the left. This custom is quite arbitrary, but some self-consistent rule is necessary. Accordingly, a small number for K signifies an acid which is weaker, less ionized, than one with a larger value of K.

Consider next the general type weak acid H_2A in which each molecule of un-ionized acid yields two hydrogen ions upon complete ionization. It has been found experimentally that such acids ionize stepwise, as indicated by the chemical equations

$$H_2A \rightleftharpoons H^+ + HA^-$$
$$HA^- \rightleftharpoons H^+ + A^=$$

for which we can write two equilibrium constant equations

$$K_1 = \frac{[H^+][HA^-]}{[H_2A]}$$

$$K_2 = \frac{[H^+][A^=]}{[HA^-]}$$

It is possible to add the two chemical equations to give an over-all one

$$H_2A \rightleftharpoons 2 H^+ + A^=$$

for which the combined ionization constant, $K_{1,2}$, would be

$$K_{1,2} = \frac{[H^+]^2 [A^=]}{[H_2A]}$$

It will be noted that $K_{1,2}$ is numerically equal to the product of K_1 and K_2. Since the ionization of such acids does proceed stepwise, it is usually necessary to use the individual chemical equations and equilibrium constants, so the combined ones are of limited usefulness. A weak acid which contains three ionizable hydrogen ions per molecule is characterized by three ionization constants. As indicated in the data of Appendix 2, the first ionization constant is always numerically larger than the second, and the second greater than the third if there are three.

The equilibrium concepts may be applied to solutions of weak bases in a manner entirely analogous to that of weak acids. For example, a generalized ionization equilibrium of a weak base, BOH, may be represented by chemical and mathematical equations as follows:

$$BOH \rightleftharpoons B^+ + OH^-$$

$$K_b = \frac{[B^+][OH^-]}{[BOH]}$$

Numerical values of ionization constants of common weak acids are also listed in Appendix 2.

Water molecules ionize partially to form both hydrogen and hydroxyl ions:

$$H_2O \rightleftharpoons H^+ + OH^-$$

The equilibrium constant for this state of equilibrium might be formulated first as

$$K = \frac{[H^+][OH^-]}{[H_2O]}$$

This point of equilibrium normally lies far to the left, that is, with most of the water molecules un-ionized. For every liter of water, we have very nearly one liter of undissociated water molecules. The concentration of water molecules is essentially fixed in water and in all dilute aqueous solutions. Therefore, the denominator of the preceding equilibrium constant equation is a constant which may be combined with K to form a new constant, K_w, the ionization constant of water:

$$K_w = [H^+] [OH^-]$$

The hydrogen ion concentration may vary so tremendously from one solution to another that it is often convenient to express it in an exponential form. The pH of a solution is defined as the negative logarithm of the molar hydrogen ion concentration:

$$[H^+] = 10^{-pH}$$

Similar units may be used to express other concentrations, such as

$$[OH^-] = 10^{-pOH} \quad \text{and} \quad [Cl^-] = 10^{-pCl}$$

and also to express equilibrium constants, as

$$[K] = 10^{-pK}$$

SOLUBILITY PRODUCT CONSTANTS

One of the means listed for driving a reaction to practical completion was precipitation of a relatively insoluble substance. None of the common analytical precipitates is totally insoluble. The states of equilibria existing between dissolved and undissolved materials present another important application of equilibrium constants in quantitative chemical analysis.

Consider the state of equilibrium between dissolved and undissolved silver chloride:

$$AgCl \rightleftharpoons Ag^+ + Cl^-$$

This system differs from those considered thus far in this chapter in that two distinct phases are present. Silver chloride is present as a solid phase and the ions appearing on the right side of the equation are present throughout the solution phase. No reaction can take place in either direction except where the two phases are in physical contact, so the magnitude of the surface area of the solid substance influences the rates of reaction. Thus, the rate of the reaction to the right and the rate of reaction to the left are, in order:

$$\text{rate}_r = k_r \times \text{area}$$

$$\text{rate}_l = k_l \times \text{area} \times [Ag^+] [Cl^-]$$

At equilibrium, the two rates are equal to each other:

$$\text{rate}_r = \text{rate}_l$$

$$k_r \times \text{area} = k_l \times \text{area} \times [Ag^+] [Cl^-]$$

$$\frac{k_r \times \text{area}}{k_l \times \text{area}} = [Ag^+] [Cl^-]$$

$$K_{sp} = [Ag^+] [Cl^-]$$

Note that the area factor has cancelled out. The final constant for this type of system is designated the solubility product constant and given the symbol, K_{sp}.

Consider next the slightly soluble compound, silver chromate. A state of equilibrium between dissolved and undissolved silver chromate may be represented by chemical and mathematical equations as

$$Ag_2CrO_4 \rightleftharpoons 2\,Ag^+ + CrO_4^=$$

$$K_{sp} = [Ag^+]^2\,[CrO_4^=]$$

This forward reaction does not occur stepwise, as in the case of acids of the H_2A type, so there are no corresponding stepwise ionization constants for this type of system.

A more generalized chemical equation for the state of equilibrium between dissolved and undissolved substances may be stated as

$$A_aB_bC_c \rightleftharpoons aA + bB + cC$$

The corresponding solubility product constant equation is

$$K_{sp} = [A]^a\,[B]^b\,[C]^c$$

The solubility product constants are listed for a number of common, slightly soluble substances in Appendix 1. A very small number for the constant signifies a lower solubility than does a larger number.

COMPLEX ION DISSOCIATION CONSTANTS

Another one of the means listed for driving a reaction to practical completion was formation of a complex ion in solution. Every type of complex ion is dissociated to some extent. The states of equilibria existing between complex ions and their component parts form another important application of equilibrium constants.

Consider the dissociation of a ferric thiocyanate complex:

$$FeSCN^{++} \rightleftharpoons Fe^{+++} + SCN^-$$

All species are in solution, so the equilibrium constant may be formulated as

$$K_d = \frac{[Fe^{+++}]\,[SCN^-]}{[FeSCN^{++}]}$$

This type of equilibrium constant is designated a dissociation constant for a complex. The reciprocal of a dissociation constant is also encountered under the designation of a stability constant. For uniformity and consistency, however, these systems are represented in this textbook as dissociation constants in which the concentration of the complex is in the denominator and the concentrations of its dissociated forms are in the numerator. Thus, a very small number for the constant signifies a more stable complex than does a larger number. Dissociation constants for several complex ions of interest in quantitative analysis are listed in Appendix 3.

It frequently happens that two types of ion can unite to form a series of two or more different complexes. For example, ferric and thiocyanate ions can form not only the one-to-one complex, $FeSCN^{++}$, but also complexes with more than one thiocyanate ion for each ferric ion. The formation is stepwise within the series, and each step may be represented by an equilibrium constant just as is done with the stepwise ionization of acids which contain more than one ionizable hydrogen ion.

SIMULTANEOUS EQUILIBRIA

Systems encountered in quantitative analysis are most frequently those in which several equilibria are simultaneously in existence. For example, a saturated solution of a slightly soluble hydroxide must, if in equilibrium, satisfy a solubility product constant and one or more acid or base ionization constants. A complex ion may contain as one of its dissociated components an ion which forms a weak acid or a weak base. Of course, for any aqueous solution of a weak acid or base, the ionization constant of water may be as significant as, or may even be more significant than, the ionization constant of the solute.

It is frequently possible to neglect one or more of the equilibrium constants involved in a system of simultaneous equilibria when making numerical calculations. This is never done blindly or simply for convenience; it is done only when there is a valid basis for knowing that the magnitudes of the quantities of interest are not significantly affected by doing so. In all cases it is possible to write and to use all of the equilibrium constants involved in a particular system, to combine them mathematically as desired, and to solve for the desired information if sufficient information concerning the system is available. Each student of quantitative chemical analysis should endeavor to become familiar with the general, over-all approach to solving numerical problems involving systems in equilibrium, and he should also strive to become proficient at making all appropriate approximations to fit each situation which he encounters. Examples will be described in subsequent chapters.

REVIEW QUESTIONS

1. Why were the experimental chemists of a few hundred years ago essentially analytical chemists?
2. State the laws of definite proportions, multiple proportions and reciprocal proportions.
3. Explain the validity of the law of definite proportions and the law of reciprocal proportions on the basis of the atomic theory.

4. Why do the atomic weight determinations represent in a real sense the ultimate in quantitative techniques?

5. What is the Arrhenius theory of ionization? Wherein does it hold, and wherein does it fail?

6. Distinguish between electrolytes and nonelectrolytes.

7. Distinguish between strong electrolytes and weak electrolytes.

8. State and illustrate the Le Chatelier principle.

9. Derive a general equation for an equilibrium constant from the law of mass action.

10. What is the effect of a change in temperature upon (a) the rate of a reaction, and (b) an equilibrium constant?

11. What is the effect of a catalyst upon (a) the rate of a reaction, and (b) an equilibrium constant?

12. Formulate solubility product expressions for CaF_2, $Fe(OH)_3$, $Ca_3(PO_4)_2$ and $MgNH_4PO_4$.

13. Write chemical equations for the equilibria existing between each of the following complex ions and its dissociation products: $Cu(CN)_4^=$; $Ag(S_2O_3)_2^=$; $Ag(NH_3)_2^+$.

14. Formulate dissociation constant expressions for each of the complex ions of question 13.

15. Distinguish clearly between the dissociation constant and the stability constant for a complex ion.

SUGGESTIONS FOR ADDITIONAL READING

For further review of any of the topics considered in this chapter, consult any of the standard textbooks of general chemistry.

Types of
Quantitative Analysis

FUNDAMENTALLY, every quantitative analytical determination rests on the measurement of a property which is related, directly or indirectly, to the amount of the desired constituent present. An ideal method of measurement is one in which no constituent other than the desired one contributes to the quantity being measured. Adequate selectivity is seldom encountered in practical situations unless the desired constituent is first separated from some or all of the other components of the sample undergoing analysis. So the two major operations in a quantitative determination are separation and measurement.

The methods of quantitative analysis may conveniently be classified on the basis of the chemical or physical property which is measured. On this basis, quantitative procedures are classified as (1) gravimetric, (2) volumetric, (3) optical and (4) electrical. In some instances, two or more of these types are combined into a single measurement, and some measured quantities do not readily fall into any of these categories. However, this classification is very useful and is employed throughout this book.

Quantitative methods of analysis may alternatively be classified on the basis of the type of sample encountered. Thus, there are organic and inorganic methods, also macro methods, micro methods and related categories indicative of the amount of sample which is used.

GRAVIMETRIC ANALYSIS

The simple and obvious fact that the weight of a substance is indicative of its amount is the basis for gravimetric methods of analysis. Each determination involves the separation of the desired constituent into a form which is of known percentage composition and which can be weighed accurately. From this information, along with the weight of the original sample, the percentage by weight of the desired constituent is readily computed. Further classification of the methods of gravimetric analysis may be made on the basis of how the desired constituent is separated into a weighable form.

Precipitation Methods. This is the most important subgroup of the methods of gravimetric analysis. The sample to be analyzed is put into solution, and then the desired constituent is isolated through the addition of a suitable reagent with which the desired constituent can form an insoluble precipitate. For example, the chloride content of a sample may be determined by addition of excess silver nitrate to an aqueous solution of the sample, whereby silver chloride is precipitated. This precipitate is filtered, washed to remove contaminants, dried to remove residual washing liquid and, finally, weighed. From the weight of the silver chloride thus obtained and the weight of the original sample, the percentage of chloride in the original sample may be calculated. The accuracy of the answer obtained with a procedure of this type is primarily dependent upon the purity of the substance which is weighed. Many specific, accurate precipitation methods of analysis are available to the analytical chemist today. Some of these, as well as a detailed discussion of the principles, advantages and disadvantages of these methods, are described in Chapters 6, 7 and 8.

Electrodeposition Methods. A second subgroup of gravimetric methods includes the methods in which the desired constituent is separated from a solution of the unknown sample by deposition on an electrode. This separation is based upon the oxidizability or reducibility of the desired constituent at the electrode. For example, copper is frequently determined by applying a voltage of sufficient magnitude to cause electrical current to flow between two platinum electrodes immersed in a moderately acidic solution of the sample. In due time essentially all of the copper ions will be deposited upon the negative electrode as metallic copper, and the difference between the initial and final weights of this electrode indicates directly the copper content of the sample. Electrodeposition methods may be likened to precipitation methods in that the electric current passing through the solution serves as the precipitating reagent. Electrodeposition methods are discussed in Chapter 19.

Volatilization Methods. In this subgroup are included those methods in which the desired constituent is separated from the sample by virtue of its volatility with heat or with certain reagents. Two examples may be cited. The water of hydration of barium chloride crystals may be determined simply by drying a weighed portion of the sample at $150°$ C until no more loss of weight occurs; the difference between the initial and final weights of the sample indicates directly the water content of the initial sample. With a suitable experimental layout, the evolved water might also be collected by absorption on an appropriate reagent; the increase in weight of the absorber would indicate the weight of water which was evolved by the sample.

A second example of a volatilization procedure is that of the determination of the combined carbon dioxide content of a carbonate sample, such as calcium carbonate or a limestone. The sample is treated in a suitable apparatus with acid to liberate the combined carbon dioxide as free carbon dioxide gas. This gas is absorbed in a vessel containing an appropriate absorbent.

The gain in weight of this vessel during the experiment represents the combined carbon dioxide content of the sample. Volatilization procedures are perhaps the simplest of all gravimetric ones, and some are discussed in further detail in Chapter 7.

VOLUMETRIC ANALYSIS

Gravimetric methods of analysis are frequently quite time-consuming. This drawback is obviated to an appreciable extent in the second major category of quantitative methods, volumetric methods of analysis. In this group, the steps of isolation, purification and weighing of the precipitate are replaced by measurements of volume. A substantial amount of time can be saved, particularly if many similar determinations are to be made. For a particular constituent, volumetric methods may even be more accurate than gravimetric methods. Volumetric methods may be subdivided into groups, depending on the mode of carrying out the determination or on the chemical principle underlying the method.

Titrimetric Methods. With the possible exception of colorimetric procedures, this is probably the most important subgroup of all quantitative analytical methods. In titrimetric methods the desired constituent is put into solution and allowed to react with a reagent solution. The reagent solution must be a standard solution, which means it must be of known concentration. The standard solution is gradually added from a buret, which is a device for delivering and measuring the volume of a solution, until just enough has been added to react with all of the desired constituent. This point is called the end point and must somehow be rendered recognizable to the analyst who is conducting the determination. The volume of standard solution required is then read from the graduation marks on the buret and, assuming the concentration of the standard solution and the amount of the sample to be known, the amount of desired constituent may be calculated.

Titrimetric methods may be further classified on the basis of the nature of the chemical reaction between the desired constituent and the standard solution. On this basis there are four major categories of titrimetric methods.

1. Neutralization methods. In this method hydrogen or hydroxyl ions react either with each other or with some other acidic or basic constituent. A typical example is the determination of the carbonate content of soda ash by reaction with a standard solution of hydrochloric acid.

2. Precipitation methods. In this type the desired constituent and the standard solution react to form an insoluble precipitate. In contrast to gravimetric precipitation methods, the precipitate is allowed to remain in suspension, and the necessary experimental operations are completed when the end point has been reached. The chloride content of an unknown solution may be determined volumetrically with a standard silver nitrate solution.

3. Oxidation-reduction methods. The primary reaction involved in a method of this type is the transfer of electrons from the substance undergoing oxidation to the substance undergoing reduction. Either the desired constituent or the solute of the standard solution may be the substance to be oxidized, and the other one must be the substance to be reduced. A common and very important oxidation-reduction method of analysis is the determination of iron by reaction of ferrous ion with a standard solution of ceric sulfate.

4. Complex formation methods. In this type the desired constituent and the standard solution react to form a soluble complex ion. A very important example is the determination of small amounts of calcium ion by its reaction with a standard solution of a sodium salt of the organic acid, ethylene diamine tetraacetic acid, to form a complex ion.

Titrimetric methods are discussed in detail in Part III, Chapters 9 through 16.

Gasometric Methods. The analysis of gaseous mixtures is often performed by measuring the volume of the sample at known temperature and pressure, selectively absorbing the components one at a time, and measuring the volume again after removal of each component. This procedure provides a direct measure of the volume of each component at known temperature and pressure. The results may, of course, be readily translated to weight units. Gasometric methods require special types of apparatus and are of less importance than a number of other types of analytical methods, from both the pedagogical and the practical viewpoints. Therefore, gasometric methods will not be discussed further in this book.

OPTICAL METHODS

The third and fourth major categories of quantitative analytical methods, optical and electrical methods, are based on the measurement of certain physicochemical properties, generally with the aid of instruments. Optical methods are considered in Chapters 17 and 18. Classification of optical methods into subgroups may be based upon what optical property is used in making the measurement, how the sample interacts with light energy or the type of instrumentation used to measure that property. A detailed classification of these methods will not be made in this introductory chapter; rather, an example will be cited to indicate the relationships which these methods have to gravimetric and volumetric methods.

One very common optical method of analysis is that of absorption colorimetry. The basis of this method is the fact that the concentration of a colored substance in solution is proportional to the amount of light energy of a restricted wavelength that is absorbed by that colored substance. For example, the permanganate ion absorbs green light to a considerable extent. Very low concentrations of permanganate in solution can be determined with

require complete physical separation. Some substances which would otherwise interfere may be rendered nonobjectionable chemically simply by adjusting the pH by dilution or by adding a complexing agent.

ORGANIC AND INORGANIC ANALYSIS

Thus far in this chapter quantitative analytical methods have been classified according to the mode of carrying out the primary measurements. These methods can also be classified according to some aspect of the nature of the unknown sample for which they are most useful. For example, methods well suited for the analysis of organic species may be distinguished from those intended primarily for application to inorganic substances. Analytical methods for organic compounds may be classified as gravimetric or volumetric, but they differ from those suited for inorganic compounds by virtue of the chemical reactions utilized or the goals of the analysis. For instance, it may be of interest to determine the total quantity of $-OH$ groups or $-COOH$ groups in a particular organic substance, such methods being designated "functional group analyses"; whereas the methods suited for inorganic compounds generally confine themselves to determinations of the elements which are present, often regardless of their initial state of oxidation or combination. In general, the methods described in this text are intended primarily for the analysis of inorganic substances.

MACRO, SEMIMICRO, MICRO AND ULTRAMICRO METHODS AND TRACE METHODS

Another classification of quantitative methods may be made on the basis of the quantity of material taken for the analysis. This classification is again a rather arbitrary one. In general, the designation *macroanalysis* is applied to determinations involving 0.1 gram or more of the sample. When the sample to be analyzed falls within the approximate range of 0.01 gram to 0.1 gram, the method is called *semimicro*. *Microanalysis* denotes sample weights of 0.001 to 0.01 gram. In recent years there has been a great increase in the scope and importance of analyses of samples weighing less than 0.001 gram, even as little as 0.000 001 gram, and such methods are designated *ultramicroanalysis*. The dividing lines are obviously not sharp and do shade into one another. Also, the experimental methods used in one category may be useful in another. Many standard microanalysis methods are merely conventional macroanalytical methods refined and modified for use with the smaller amounts of material, while other micromethods are useful primarily only within that domain.

While any such generalizations are subject to numerous exceptions, it appears that gravimetric methods are most useful for macro and semimicro determinations. Volumetric procedures are commonly applied to macro, semimicro and micro determinations. Most, but not all, determinations on an ultramicro scale are made by instrumental methods, but instrumental methods are by no means limited to the ultramicro range.

The immediately preceding classification of quantitative methods is based on the amount of the sample taken for analysis. The individual components being determined are the major constituents of the sample, that is, present to the extent of about 1% or more. Methods used to determine lesser constituents of the sample are termed *trace* methods. Note that the designations macro, semimicro, micro and ultramicro signify something of the quantity of sample taken for analysis, while the term trace analysis signifies that the lesser constituents are being determined regardless of how much sample is available to the analyst. Trace methods are usually of the instrumental type, although not always so. There are reliable trace methods in common use whereby as little as one-tenth of a part per million ($0.000\,01\%$) of a particular constituent can be determined readily.

REVIEW QUESTIONS

1. Explain how a qualitative analysis is a useful adjunct to a quantitative analysis.
2. What is the distinguishing feature which makes one determination gravimetric and another volumetric?
3. Compare gravimetric, volumetric, optical and electrical methods of analysis with one another on any three significant points.
4. Distinguish between microanalysis and trace analysis.

SUGGESTIONS FOR ADDITIONAL READING

Item 11, Appendix 7.

Chapter 3

The Analytical Balance

THERE are a number of general tools which are useful in all branches of quantitative laboratory work. The analytical balance is essential not only in gravimetric analysis but in much of volumetric analysis as well. The construction and operation of the balance and the methods of making weighings are considered in some detail in this chapter. Other tools and operations which are of general usefulness in quantitative analysis are described in the next chapter.

PRINCIPLES OF THE ANALYTICAL BALANCE

The analytical balance is basically a first-class lever. The lever is called the beam and is represented in Figure 1 as the line AB. The beam is supported on a knife edge as its fulcrum at point O. Weights or other objects may be suspended from both ends of the beam. Distances L and R are the two lever arms, equaling the distances AO and BO, respectively. A pointer, OP, is attached rigidly at right angles to the beam at its fulcrum.

A weight, W_L, applied at A results in a force, $W_L \times L$, tending to cause a counterclockwise rotation of the beam. Similarly, a weight, W_R, applied at B results in a force, $W_R \times R$, tending to cause a clockwise rotation of the beam. The beam is in a stationary horizontal position, or at least is oscillating back and forth about such a position, when the forces causing clockwise and counterclockwise rotation equal each other. This condition may be represented mathematically as

$$W_L \times L = W_R \times R$$

The weight of the beam is of some significance, as will be described subsequently, but for the present discussion will be considered as centered at point O so that it contributes neither to clockwise nor counterclockwise rotation. If the beam is initially in a stable position, as represented by this equation, and if an object of weight W_O is added to W_L, for example, the tendency toward counterclockwise rotation is increased, and the beam departs from its initial position. This fact leads us to a consideration of the three main methods of making weighings on analytical balances: by direct comparison, by substitution, by sensitivity.

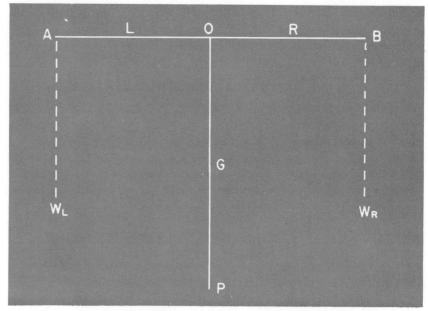

FIGURE 1.   Diagram to illustrate the principle of the analytical balance (see text).

Weighing by Direct Comparison.   The increased tendency toward counterclockwise rotation caused by adding the object, the weight of which is W_O, to the left side of the beam can be offset by adding a corresponding amount of weight to the right side so that the initially stable or equilibrium condition of the beam is restored. Letting W_w represent the amount of weight on the right which is found to correspond to W_O on the left, the initial and final states of the beam may be represented mathematically:

$$\text{initial} \qquad W_L \times L = W_R \times R$$
$$\text{final} \quad (W_L + W_O) \times L = (W_R + W_w) \times R$$

The two equations may be combined to yield the equation

$$W_O \times L = W_w \times R$$

If L and R are equal to each other, as is quite accurately the case with analytical balances designed to be used for weighings by the direct comparison method,

$$W_O = W_w$$

Objects of known weight are used to comprise W_w, making it possible by this method to determine the weights of unknown objects.

Weighing by Substitution.   In weighing by substitution, the increased tendency toward counterclockwise rotation caused by adding the object to the left side of the beam is offset by removing a corresponding portion of W_L so that the initially stable or equilibrium condition of the beam is restored. No change is made on the right side of the beam, so the initial and final weights at A must equal each other. The weight of the object is equal to that portion of W_L which had to be removed to restore the initial condition of the beam.

Some analytical balances are constructed specifically for weighing by substitution and others are designed primarily for weighing by direct comparison. Both methods are widely used in quantitative work. The methods will be compared and evaluated later in this chapter.

Weighing by Sensitivity. A third method of weighing is based upon the magnitude of the deflection of the pointer rather than upon restoring the beam to its initial condition. This method is generally used in conjunction with either the direct comparison or the substitution method rather than independently of them. Consider again the addition of a small weight, w, to the left end of the beam in Figure 1. The increased tendency toward counterclockwise rotation, with no change in the tendency toward clockwise rotation, would permit the beam to find an equilibrium position only when vertical with A at the bottom. Such a condition would be useless in determining the magnitude of w. However, if the beam and its attachments are constructed so that some of the mass is below the plane of the line AOB, but still symmetrically distributed to the left and right of point O, the effective center of gravity of the beam will be at some point on OP rather than at point O. The weight of the beam, W_b, is of no consequence when the beam is horizontal because its lever arm length is zero. However, when the beam is deflected in a counterclockwise direction (A'B', Fig. 2), W_b exhibits a clockwise tendency equal to $W_b \times \overline{G'D}$. Point G' is the effective center of gravity of the entire beam assembly. A new position of equilibrium is established when the beam reaches a position such that the added clockwise and counterclockwise forces equal each other:

$$w \times \overline{CO} = W_b \times \overline{G'D}$$

or

$$w = \frac{W_b \times \overline{G'D}}{\overline{CO}}$$

For any one balance, W_b is a constant, and there is one specific value of $\overline{CO}$ for every possible value of $\overline{G'D}$. Thus, the deflection distance G'D provides a direct indication of the magnitude of w. This deflection distance is generally read at the lower end of the pointer, behind which is placed a stationary graduated scale. In some balances, however, the deflection distance is read by an optical method in which a beam of light is reflected off one end of the beam or off the pointer onto a viewing screen, with a graduated scale on the beam or the pointer or on the viewing screen.

It may be noted from Figure 2 that the lever arm distances through which the initial forces W_L and W_R operate are AO and BO, respectively, for the initial beam condition (AB), and only CO and EO, respectively, for the final beam condition (A'B'). However, both arm lengths are reduced by the same relative amount, so the counterclockwise and clockwise forces caused by W_L and W_R equal each other under either condition. It should also be

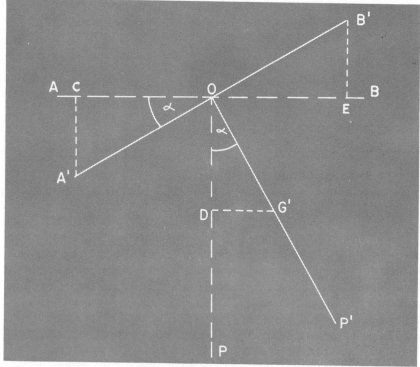

FIGURE 2.   Diagram to illustrate the discussion of the sensitivity of an analytical
balance (see text).

noted that the angles of deflection are generally so low that CO and EO are,
on a relative basis, not much different than AO and BO, respectively.

The term sensitivity is used to express quantitatively the magnitude of
deflection produced by one unit of weight. The units are, typically, scale
divisions (or millimeters) per milligram.

A further derivation from Figure 2 can serve to describe several factors
of significance in regard to balance design.

$$\text{angle } AOA' = \text{angle } POP' = \alpha \qquad \text{(the two angles have sides}$$
$$\text{mutually perpendicular)}$$

$$\cos \alpha = \frac{\overline{CO}}{\overline{A'O}}$$

$$\sin \alpha = \frac{\overline{G'D}}{\overline{OG'}}$$

$$w \times \overline{CO} = W_b \times \overline{G'D} \qquad \text{(as shown above)}$$

$$w \times \overline{A'O} \times \cos \alpha = W_b \times \overline{OG'} \times \sin \alpha \qquad \text{(combining three}$$
$$\text{preceding equations)}$$

$$\frac{\sin \alpha}{\cos \alpha} = \frac{w \times \overline{A'O}}{W_b \times \overline{OG'}} \qquad \text{(rearranging)}$$

or
$$\tan \alpha = \frac{w \times \overline{A'O}}{W_b \times \overline{OG'}}$$

Now, α is a measure of the sensitivity of a balance; for a given w, a large α signifies a greater sensitivity than does a small α. Therefore, the last preceding equation reveals several factors of importance in designing a balance of high sensitivity: (1) make the balance arm length, $\overline{A'O}$ or L, long; (2) make the weight of the beam, W_b, small; (3) make the distance from the fulcrum to the center of gravity of the beam assembly, $\overline{OG'}$, small. All three of these factors are somewhat competitive. For example, long arm length and light weight are contradictory, and the combination of long arm length and light weight is competitive to the requirements of mechanical strength and rigidity.

CONSTRUCTION OF THE ANALYTICAL BALANCE

The basic principles of operation are generally the same for all types of analytical balances with the exception of a few specialized types. Nevertheless, there is much variation in the actual construction of balances. Stability and sturdiness are obvious requirements, and a sufficiently high degree of sensitivity is also very important. Typically, objects weighing up to 100 grams must be weighed with an accuracy of 0.1 milligram (0.0001 gram).

Beam. The beam, as already described, must possess maximum rigidity for minimum weight. The beam can last almost indefinitely in ordinary use, but it may become seriously warped if the balance is overloaded. As illustrated in Figure 3, the upper edge of the beam in many common types of analytical balance is graduated precisely, and a small weight called the rider may be placed on it at any desired point. The rider mechanism is actuated from outside the balance case. The rider may be used to make the final small weight adjustments; its effective weight is determined by its distance from the center knife edge in accordance with the physical laws governing lever action. For example, if the rider is placed halfway between the center and right-hand knife edge, it exerts only half the force it would exert if placed immediately above the right-side knife edge. The number of graduations on the beam varies with the design of the balance and the weight of the rider. In a typical analytical balance the major divisions correspond to one milligram each with subdivisions for fifths or tenths of milligrams.

Knife Edges. The most critical parts of an analytical balance are the knife edges on which the moving parts pivot, one as the fulcrum at the center of the beam and one where each of the pans for the object and/or weights is suspended near the ends of the beam. Like the jewels of a good watch, these pivots must be nearly frictionless, tough enough to withstand ordinary day-by-day wear and tear, and hard enough to resist long-term wear. Each pivot

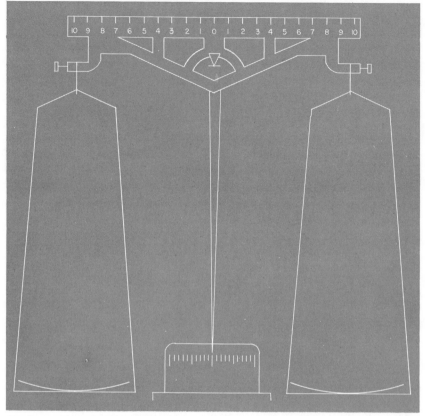

FIGURE 3.   Drawing of an analytical balance, showing the beam, the central knife
edge, two pans, the pointer and the scale.

consists of a wedge-shaped agate piece in contact with a flat agate plate.
Agate is very hard but is also quite brittle. Therefore, these components will
withstand years of normal usage but may be irretrievably damaged if
subjected to sudden or violent stress. The construction and operation of the
balance are planned with an eye to sparing the knife edges all unnecessary
strain. Synthetic sapphire is occasionally substituted for agate, but agate is
somewhat less susceptible to cracking and chipping and stands up at least
as well over long periods of use.

The central pivot, which serves as the fulcrum for the beam, consists of
a flat plate built into the top of the central supporting column and a wedge-
shaped piece of agate rigidly attached to the beam (Figure 3). Pans to hold
the object and the known weights are suspended by stirrups which rest on
agate knife edges close to the ends of the beam. Balances designed for
weighing by the direct comparison method have one pan mounted in this
way at each end of the beam, while some balances designed for the substitution
method have a pan at one end only (further described on page 40). The

system must be very low in friction at the knife edges in order for the balance to be sufficiently sensitive for quantitative analytical work, and this causes the moving system to tend to oscillate back and forth about its equilibrium or rest position instead of coming quickly to that position. Mechanisms to check these oscillations and to support the beam and the pans away from the knife edges when not in use are actuated by knobs at the base of the balance case. One of these governs the position of the pan arrests. These are thin strips of metal, tipped with felt, which check the motion of the pans when raised to touch the pans from underneath. The other arrest mechanism works through the central column to raise supports for the upper parts of all of the agate pivots so they may be kept out of contact with the bearing surfaces. In this state the agate surfaces bear no loads and, therefore, cannot be injured by sudden shocks when, for example, large weights are added to or removed from the balance pans.

Pointer. The oscillations of the beam over the equilibrium point are indicated by the movements of the pointer in front of a stationary graduated scale (Figure 3). Adjustment of this central point under no-load conditions is made by means of the screw at one end of the beam. This adjustment should be made only by the instructor or other experienced analyst.

Center of Gravity Adjustment. As already discussed, the position of the center of gravity of the oscillating system influences the sensitivity of the balance. Slight adjustment is possible by moving a small weight on the pointer rod up or down. This is a critical and delicate adjustment and should be made only by persons thoroughly familiar with balance design and construction.

Case. The entire moving mechanism of the balance is enclosed within a wooden or metal case fitted with a movable glass front door counterpoised with sash weights. The base of the case rests on leveling screws. Upon initial installation the balance should be accurately leveled by adjusting the legs on which it rests until the spirit-levels inside the case are horizontal. For all observations of a weighing operation, except preliminary ones, the balance door should be kept shut to avoid the disturbing effects of air currents set up by the ventilation system, the respiration of the operator, and so on. The balance door should also be left shut when the balance is not in use to provide maximum protection against dust and corrosive fumes.

Satisfactory performance of analytical balances requires that they be properly placed. Balances should be located in well-lighted, draft-free rooms of fairly uniform temperature. They should be placed on solidly constructed tables. If the tables are subject to vibration, felt or rubber pads or small shock absorbers should be placed under the legs of the balance. Enough table top space should be available around the balances for placement of boxes of weights and laboratory notebooks.

Damping Devices. Any method of determining the rest point of an oscillating beam assembly is bound to take appreciable time, particularly if a large number of weighings is to be made. Several devices have been developed to dampen these oscillations so the pointer can quickly come to its stationary

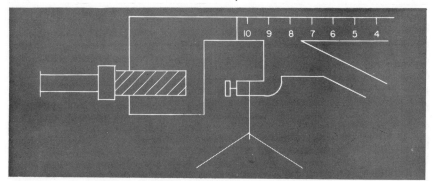

FIGURE 4.   Drawing of a magnetic damping device mounted around one end of the
beam of an analytical balance.

rest point. A magnetic damping device is shown in Figure 4. The oscillations
are damped by eddy currents induced in thin sheet aluminum extensions of
the beam by strong permanent magnets fastened to the case. In other
balances light pistons are attached to the moving system in such a way that
they move within rather closely fitted stationary cylinders with closed ends.
This system is called air damping.

In either magnetic or air damping the effect is to reduce the oscillations
to a single, rather slow swing in which the pointer travels directly to its rest
position. There is no significant loss of sensitivity, because the resistance to
the movement of the moving system of the balance drops to zero as it comes
to rest.

Chainomatic Device.   In some balances, a fine-linked chain replaces
the smaller weights. As illustrated in Figure 5, one end of the chain is
attached to the right arm of the beam and the other to a scale with graduations
and vernier, usually reading from 0.1 to 100.0 milligrams. The scale may be
vertical as shown, or it may be round; in either case, the chain may be
manipulated by a wheel outside the balance case. At the zero reading, a fixed
fraction (typically one-half) of the chain weight is supported by the beam.
As the control is rotated, the effective chain weight supported by the beam is
increased and may be read directly from the scale, with the aid of the vernier,
to the nearest tenth of a milligram in a typical analytical balance. The
accuracy is comparable to that of an ordinary rider balance; there is considerable saving of time because the chain can be adjusted to a suitable
position while the beam is free to oscillate. With a balance equipped with both
chainomatic and damping devices, an object can be weighed to the nearest
tenth of a milligram in three minutes or less.

Some chainomatic balances have beam graduations similar to the ordinary
rider scale, but more deeply indented. One or more heavy riders can be
moved to make changes of weight in 0.1 gram units up to one gram. The
chain mechanism covers the range from 0.0001 to 0.1 gram, so no individual
weights less than 1 gram are required.

Projection Reading Device. In one type of projection reading device, light from a lamp outside of the balance case is focused through a transparent micro scale attached to the pointer. A magnified image of this scale is projected onto a matt glass screen which has a sharply defined vertical line in the center, the position of which is adjustable to coincide with the zero on the micro scale under the true rest point conditions. When the beam is set in motion, the magnified image of the scale passes across the screen. Magnetic or air damping quickly arrests the oscillation of the beam. A glance at the screen gives a direct indication of how far the present rest point is displaced from the true rest point. The scale is usually calibrated directly in weight units. In effect, the principle is that of weighing by sensitivity with the added feature of direct reading in weight units rather than in empirical units which would have to be converted into weight units. The projection reading device is usually designed to give direct reading of the weight within 0 to 100 milligrams of the center line. Thus, the analyst must use other means, either by

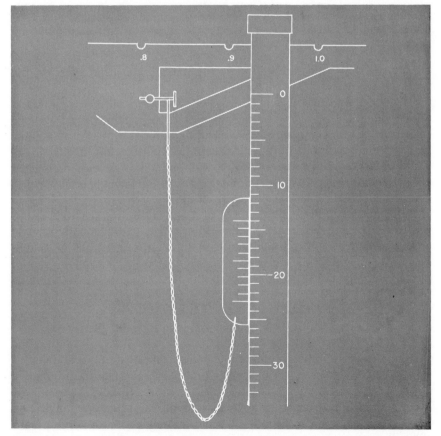

FIGURE 5.   Drawing of a chain device attached to the beam of an analytical balance.

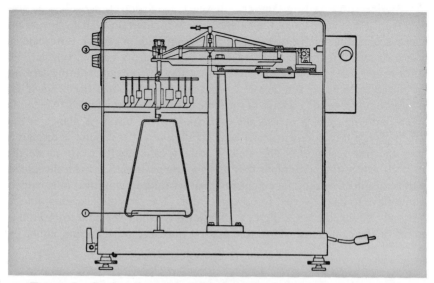

FIGURE 6. Section through a single-pan substitution type balance. When a load is placed on pan (*1*), weights (*2*) are removed until the load on the sapphire plane of the beam (*3*) is restored to its initial value.

the direct comparison method or by the substitution method, to get the weight to the nearest 100 milligrams.

In some projection reading devices, the transparent micro scale attached to the pointer is replaced by a reflecting micro scale attached directly to one end of the beam. The principle of measuring, directly in weight units, how far a rest point is displaced from the true rest point is the same in either case.

Single-Pan Substitution Type Balance. The balance diagramed in Figure 6 is designed for semiautomatic, rapid weighing by the substitution method. The beam is mounted from front-to-back (left-to-right in Figure 6) in the case. There is only one pan, and it is suspended from the front end of the beam. There is a constant weight, typically of 200 grams, mounted directly upon the rear end of the beam, and the equivalent of the same in smaller weights is supported from the front end along with the pan. With no load on the pan, all of the 200 grams is required on the front end of the beam to balance the fixed weight on the rear. When the object is placed on the pan, weights equaling that of the object must be removed to restore the initial condition of the beam. In the balance represented in Figure 6, these weights are removed by turning dials, and the values may be read directly from the dials or from a read-out device mechanically linked to the dials. Four knobs read (1) hundreds of grams, either 0 or 100, (2) tens of grams from 0 through 90, (3) grams from 0 through 9, and (4) tenths of grams from 0.0 through 0.9. The next three significant figures are read from the scale of a projection reading device. Air damping is employed. A complete weighing to the closest tenth of a milligram can be made in much less than a minute. Balances of this type are commercially available for weighings of various magnitudes of load and of sensitivity.

Microbalances. The common analytical balance can handle loads up to 200 grams without appreciable danger of damage, and weighings can be made to the closest tenth of a milligram. Microbalances are designed for smaller loads and for weighings to the closest microgram (0.000 001 gram or 0.001 milligram). A microbalance differs from a standard analytical balance in degree more than in kind. A conventional type of rider system is usually employed, but the sensitivity is such that a weight difference of 0.01 milligram or so changes the rest point by one scale division. A magnifying eyepiece is used to view the scale and pointer so that readings to the nearest tenth of a scale division are obtained. In order to achieve a sensitivity as great as this, the beam must be very light, as described on page 35, and this necessarily limits severely the maximum load which is permissible without danger of bending or other physical damage. Large maximum load and maximum sensitivity must be considered as conflicting quantities, and each balance must be designed as a compromise between the two.

For weighings of extremely minute samples, a milligram or less, quartz fiber torsion balances have been developed. The principle of the first class lever is not employed. In making a weighing with this instrument, the twist imparted to the quartz fiber by the torque of the object in the pan is neutralized by twisting the fiber to restore the system to a neutral point. The amount of twist is read with the aid of a vernier and is then converted into weight units with the aid of a calibration chart. These instruments were little more than laboratory curiosities until World War II, during which they made it possible to perform gravimetric precipitation analyses upon the first small fraction of a milligram of plutonium that was isolated. More recently, the principle of the quartz fiber torsion balance has been used in the development of semi-automatic balances which are quite rugged in spite of their extreme sensitivity.

ANALYTICAL WEIGHTS

Construction. Weights of 1 gram and over are usually made of bronze, brass or stainless steel and may be protected from atmospheric corrosion by a thin coating of lacquer. The weights of less than 1 gram are usually made of heavy aluminum foil or thin platinum foil and in no case should require any further protection from atmospheric corrosion. The weights should be handled only with ivory-tipped pincers, and these pincers should be used for no other purpose. The individual weights should never be handled with the fingers, since the film of grease, salt and moisture inevitably left on the surface would change their values in an indeterminate fashion.

There are several quality classifications of analytical weights. Class M weights are of the highest precision scientific standards and are used almost entirely as reference standards and even then only in the most exacting work. Class S weights are also used for reference and calibration purposes and, occasionally, for precision analytical weighings. Class S-1 weights are used for some calibration work and also for many of the more accurate analytical weighings on a routine basis. Class P weights (formerly designated class S-2 weights) are used for much routine analytical laboratory work and are also used in much student work in quantitative analysis. There are additional classifications of weights for less precise general laboratory work, for technical weighings and for commercial uses.

There are constructional differences among the various classes of weights. Each class M weight is of a one-piece construction. During manufacture the actual weight is brought up to the desired value by plating or fusing a thin layer of platinum, rhodium or gold onto the surface of the weight. This layer provides additional protection from the atmosphere, although the base material of construction should not require any further protection. Class S, S-1 and P weights of 1 gram and larger contain a small inner cavity to which access is made by unscrewing the small knob on top. The weight is made slightly lighter than its face value, and then tiny pieces of brass, aluminum or other similarly stable materials are inserted into the cavity to adjust its weight within the prescribed tolerances. Class M weights are never coated with lacquer, but class S, S-1 and P weights may be.

Calibration. The absolute accuracy which can be expected for the indicated value of any given weight depends somewhat upon the denomination of that weight and upon the classification of the weights. The National Bureau of Standards has established some recommended tolerances which have been accepted by manufacturers of weights and by analysts as standard tolerances. These prescribed tolerances are of two types: (1) acceptance tolerances, which are for new or newly adjusted weights; (2) maintenance tolerances, which are for weights which have been in use. This distinction is made in recognition of the fact that weights of certain denominations and classes can and should be adjusted very closely so that they will remain within useful tolerances for a reasonable period of time. Within each type of tolerance, there are individual tolerances for individual weights and group tolerances for specified groups of weights taken collectively. The acceptance tolerances, both individual and group, are listed in Table 2 for the classes of weights which are of most significance in analytical chemistry.

The maintenance tolerances differ from the acceptance tolerances listed in Table 2 as follows:

Class M—from 500 mg. to 100 mg., 0.0105 individual and 0.020 group; all others same as acceptance tolerances.

Class S—100 mg. and up, twice acceptance tolerances, both individual and group; others same as acceptance tolerances.

Class S-1—same as acceptance tolerances.

Class P—twice acceptance tolerances.

Although there are no detailed group tolerances for class S-1 and P weights, there is the additional requirement for class S-1 weights that not more than one-third of the weights of a new or newly adjusted set of weights may be in error by more than one-half the prescribed tolerances.

Weights which have been in use for some time and weights for which a higher degree of accuracy is desired must be calibrated directly. There are several possible means of calibration, any one of which can be usefully employed. The rider must, of course, be included in the calibration procedures. First, if another, accurately calibrated set of weights is available

Table 2. Acceptance Tolerances for Analytical Weights

Denomination	Class M		Class S		Class S-I	Class P
	Individual	Group	Individual	Group	Individual	Individual
100 g	0.50 mg		0.25 mg		1.0 mg	2.0 mg
50	0.25		0.12		0.60	1.2
30	0.15		0.074		0.45	0.90
20	0.10		0.074	0.154	0.35	0.70
10	0.050		0.074		0.25	0.50
5	0.034		0.054		0.18	0.36
3	0.034		0.054		0.15	0.30
2	0.034	0.065	0.054	0.105	0.13	0.26
1	0.034		0.054		0.10	0.20
500 mg	0.0054		0.025		0.080	0.16
300	0.0054		0.025		0.070	0.14
200	0.0054	0.0105	0.025	0.055	0.060	0.12
100	0.0054		0.025		0.050	0.10
50	0.0054		0.014		0.042	0.085
30	0.0054		0.014		0.038	0.075
20	0.0054	0.0105	0.014	0.034	0.035	0.070
10	0.0054		0.014		0.030	0.060
5	0.0054		0.014		0.028	0.055
3	0.0054		0.014		0.026	0.052
2	0.0054	0.0105	0.014	0.034	0.025	0.050
1	0.0054		0.014		0.025	0.050

for comparison, each weight in the set to be calibrated may be weighed against the weight of corresponding denomination in the standard set. Thus, an additive or subtractive correction is found directly for each weight, and the corrected value should subsequently be used in place of the labeled value for that weight. Second, one weight may be assumed to be correct and all others calibrated relative to it. For example, a 1 gram weight may be assumed to be correct and the others weighed relative to it. Any absolute error in the one picked as the standard is, of course, reflected proportionally in the others, but this does not necessarily lead to any final inaccuracy in analytical determinations. This situation exists because the results of many analytical determinations are expressed in terms of weight per cent so that any error in weighing the desired constituent is offset by a proportional error in weighing the over-all sample. Third, the relative calibration of the method just mentioned may be rendered absolute by use of a single, absolutely known weight as the standard for the set. This is the essence of the Richards' method of calibration, which fundamentally is the standard method for weighings of the highest absolute accuracy since it was developed in conjunction with Richards' atomic weight determinations.

The primary standard unit of mass is the *international kilogram*, a platinum-iridium cylinder, preserved in the International Bureau of Weights and Measures at Sèvres, France. A very accurate copy of this original cylinder is kept in the National Bureau of Standards in our own country. Of necessity, all scientific weighings are ultimately comparisons to the standard kilogram. Other units are based on tenfold multiples or submultiples of the standard. Thus, practical units of weight include the gram, which is one-thousandth of the kilogram; the milligram, which is one-thousandth of a gram; and the microgram, which is one-millionth of a gram. Most weight units in this book are expressed in grams, abbreviated *g.*, and in milligrams, abbreviated *mg.*

A few general rules in the use of weights help to keep errors to a minimum. Each weight should always be returned to the same position in the box. When there is a choice of two or more weights of the same denomination, one should always be used in preference to the others. Two smaller weights of the same denomination may be distinguished by the number of turned-up corners; a second brass weight of the same denomination is usually stamped with an asterisk or other distinguishing mark and is called a primed weight. In some sets of weights the denominations are selected so that there need be no duplicate weights within a set.

DETERMINATION OF THE REST POINT

The essential steps in the operation of weighing include the determination of the rest point of the unloaded two-pan balance (or fully loaded single-pan substitution type balance), placing the object on the appropriate pan, placing weights systematically on the other pan (or removing weights systematically from a single-pan substitution type balance), comparing the rest point after each trial addition (or subtraction) of weight with the initial rest point, and summation of the weights when the initial rest point has been reinstated. These steps are really of only two types, determination of rest point and systematic use of weights.

The rest point is the point on the graduated scale at which the pointer comes to rest after its oscillations cease. According to this definition, this point could be determined by permitting the beam assembly to continue oscillating until the pointer actually does come to rest. In practice this is an excessively time-consuming process unless a damping device is used. With a damping device the pan and beam supports are simply released, in that order, and the scale reading noted as soon as the pointer reaches a stable position. Excessive damping should be avoided, however. If the pointer is not allowed to make one or two oscillations before stabilizing, a false rest point may result from frictional effects which are not uniform throughout, as caused, for example, by inevitable dust particles on the knife edges.

Even without a damping device, however, it is possible to determine the rest point quickly, without waiting for the pointer to come to rest, by the method of long swings.

Method of Long Swings. In an ideal balance, with frictionless bearings and no air resistance to the swings, the true rest point would be at the midpoint between successive extreme points reached by the pointer when it swings to the left and then to the right. This condition does not exist with an ordinary balance unless the amplitude of the swings is kept very small. Ordinarily the swing is progressively damped by frictional effects and the amplitude decreases appreciably. Some means must be employed to find the true rest point independent of frictional damping. The method of long swings makes this possible.

In this method, the movable system is set into oscillation so that the total pointer amplitude amounts to somewhere between three and seven scale divisions. This is started by lowering the pan supports and then the beam support. If the beam does not begin to swing adequately, a gentle waft of air from waving the hand near one pan will usually start it. No readings are recorded for the first complete swing. Then on consecutive swings the extreme positions reached by the pointer are recorded. If the graduations on the scale are not numbered, they are customarily identified by denoting the divisions to the left and right as negative and positive, respectively, starting at the central mark as zero. This scale zero should not be confused with the rest point; they may or may not happen to coincide. The pointer readings should be estimated to the nearest tenth of a scale division. The operator must sit squarely in front of the balance and hold his head still rather than moving it to follow the swings; otherwise parallactic errors in reading the scale would be introduced.

Consider, for example, successive readings to be -3.2, $+2.8$, -3.0, $+2.5$, and -2.7. Unequal numbers of swings to the left and to the right must be taken. After noting these data, the beam support and the pan arrests should be re-engaged when the pointer is close to the center of the scale. These readings are tabulated and each set (right and left) averaged.

$$
\begin{array}{cc}
-3.2 & +2.8 \\
-3.0 & +2.5 \\
-2.7 & \\
\hline
\text{Average is } -3.0 & \text{Average is } +2.6
\end{array}
$$

The midpoint between these average extremes is, in this example, -0.2, and this is the rest point.

That this procedure does avoid errors due to frictional damping can be readily demonstrated. Suppose that the idealized readings, assuming no frictional damping, are $-a$, $+b$, $-c$, $+d$ and $-e$, and assume that there is actually a small but uniform damping for each left-to-right and each right-to-left swing, this damping effect being designated x. The actual readings will, therefore, be

$$
\begin{array}{ll}
-a & +(b - x) \\
-(c - 2x) & +(d - 3x) \\
-(e - 4x) &
\end{array}
$$

The left average is $\dfrac{-a - c - e + 6x}{3}$ or $\dfrac{-a - c - e}{3} + 2x$, and the right average is $\dfrac{b + d - 4x}{2}$ or $\dfrac{b + d}{2} - 2x$. We get the midpoint between these averages by adding them algebraically and dividing by 2

$$
\dfrac{\dfrac{-a - c - e}{3} + 2x + \dfrac{b + d}{2} - 2x}{2}
$$

The x quantities drop out. Thus, this method does yield a rest point which is not affected by frictional effects.

It is suggested that these rest point determinations be recorded in the back pages of the laboratory notebook and that only the finally established weights be recorded with the main body of the experimental data. The rest point for an unloaded balance should remain quite constant for days and even for weeks. However, it is preferable to check the unloaded rest point at the beginning of each weighing session when two or more relatively inexperienced persons are assigned to the same balance, as is commonly the case in a student laboratory.

Method of Short Swings. The frictional effects with a good balance are insignificant relative to the accuracy of reading the scale if the total amplitude of the swings is limited to, for example, only one scale division. Under such conditions the rest point may be taken as the midpoint between the two extreme positions of the pointer on a single swing. This, the method of short swings, is fairly rapid and can be reasonably accurate. However, it is more susceptible to error from minute dust specks and chips on the knife edges than is the method of long swings.

Single Deflection Method. In the single deflection method, the exact rest point is never determined. Instead, a point related to it is determined and used. The single deflection point is the extreme point to which the pointer swings when first released. Clearly, the procedure whereby the movable system is released from its supports is very critical, and many variations of this procedure have been proposed. In some cases, it is recommended that the pan arrests be lowered first and then the beam support, on the theory that the beam support can be released more reproducibly than can the pan arrests. In other cases, it appears that the pan arrests can be released more reproducibly; then this should be the final step in initiating the deflection. Special types of pan arrests have been proposed for releasing the pans more reproducibly. In any event, the essence of the single deflection method is that the moving parts of the balance must be released in precisely the same way in successive determinations. The method is simple and extremely rapid and, in experienced hands, yields excellent results.

It is recommended that the student use the method of long swings until he is firmly established in quantitative laboratory work. Then he may profitably experiment with the method of short swings and the single deflection method and decide for himself which of the methods to use in subsequent work to fit his particular situation and the available apparatus.

SYSTEMATIC USE OF WEIGHTS

(This section refers specifically to weighing by the method of direct comparison. Similar principles apply to weighing by the substitution method with a one-pan balance, but the specific application of these principles varies somewhat.)

The operation of weighing by the method of direct comparison consists of the determination of what weight or combination of weights, when placed on one pan with the object on the other pan, will restore the balance to the same rest point (or single deflection point) as that obtained under unloaded conditions. This procedure, of necessity, requires several trial and error operations until the correct combination of weights is found. It is not necessary to make complete rest point determinations until very close to the correct summation of weights in use, as a quick glance at the direction of dominant pointer deflection will reveal whether the weights in use are much too heavy or much too light. A systematic procedure in making the trials must be followed if accurate weighings are to be accomplished with reasonable rapidity. The fundamental method of rest point equality will be described in detail, and then the definition and use of balance sensitivity will be discussed as a shortened version of the fundamental method of making analytical weighings.

Weighing by Rest Point Equality.   The rest point under conditions of no load must be determined as already described. This will be designated simply as the true rest point from now on. The object is placed in the middle of the left-hand pan; it should be handled with pincers, a bit of paper or a piece of lint-free cloth, never with the fingers. Under no condition is anything placed on, or removed from, either balance pan unless the pan arrests and beam supports are in position. A weight that is expected to be too heavy is selected from the weight box and placed on the right-hand pan. The beam is set free to swing as already described. If the weight on the right-hand pan is too heavy, as expected, the pointer will deflect to the left of the true rest point. Even a partial release of the beam support suffices to verify this fact. Then the next smaller weight is placed on the right-hand pan in place of the first one, assuming that the first one was found to be too heavy. If the weight causes pointer deflection to the left of the true rest point, it is removed and the next smaller weight tried. If the weight results in pointer deflection to the right of the true rest point, it is left on the right-hand pan and the next smaller one placed on also. This process is continued systematically, starting with a weight almost certain to be too heavy and progressing through the weight box, with the weights being used in order of decreasing denomination. Whenever the pointer deflects to the left of the true rest point, indicating too much weight on the right-hand side, the most recently added weight is removed. Whenever the pointer deflects to the right of the true rest point, indicating insufficient weight on the right-hand side, the most recently added weight is left on the pan. This systematic procedure involves a continual framing of the desired weight within narrower and narrower limits. If the analyst were to start out with smaller weights, that is, if he were to proceed on the basis only of lower limits rather than both upper and lower limits, he would not only waste time but would frequently encounter the necessity of removing several smaller weights in favor of a larger one in order to have sufficient weights available to complete the weighing.

It is not necessary to determine the trial rest point until close to the final adjustment of weights on the right-hand side. Near the true rest point, however, it becomes necessary to determine the trial rest point carefully. The procedure is continued until the observed trial rest point coincides with the true rest point. With most balances weights from the weight box are used until the correct weight is framed within upper and lower limits separated by either 10 or 5 milligrams. Then the remaining adjustments are made by means of the rider, so that final weighings are made to the nearest tenth of a milligram. The balance door must be shut for final rest point determinations.

The adding up of the weights used is a frequent source of error, strange as it may seem. A double check on this step in the weighing process is decidedly advantageous. First, the weights corresponding to empty spaces in the weight box should be added. Second, the weights should be added as they are returned, one at a time, from the balance pan to the box. The weight indicated by the final position of the rider should be included in each summation. Particular attention is required to keep the units straight as some weights may be marked in grams, others in milligrams and, occasionally, others in centigrams.

Weighing by Sensitivity. In the method just described, the intent was to adjust the weights so that the rest point of the loaded assembly would match that of the unloaded balance. Much of the time required in that method is in the final, small adjustments of weight, each of which requires a rest point determination. In the sensitivity weighing method, an exact match need not be obtained, and only one rest point need be determined for the loaded balance, provided that the one rest point be within several scale divisions of the true rest point. The final summation of weights, correct to the nearest tenth of a milligram, is then calculated from the difference between the rest point of the loaded balance and the true rest point.

In making this computation, the sensitivity of the balance must be known. As defined on page 34, the sensitivity of a balance is the magnitude of the pointer deflection produced by one unit of weight. Typical units of sensitivity are scale divisions per milligram. The sensitivity-reciprocal, which is in units of milligrams per scale division, is often more convenient to use. The terms sensitivity and sensitivity-reciprocal are occasionally used interchangeably, but misunderstanding as to which is meant can be prevented by

Table 3. Typical Sensitivity Data

Load	Sensitivity (Change of rest point for 1.0 mg. weight increment)	Sensitivity-Reciprocal (mg./division)
0	2.5	0.40
5	2.5	0.40
10	2.3	0.43
20	2.1	0.48
50	1.8	0.56

designating the units involved. The sensitivity of a balance can be determined experimentally by direct application of the definition, i.e., observe the no-load rest point, add a weight of one milligram to one side of the beam and observe the rest point again.

The sensitivity varies somewhat with the load on the pans, so it should be determined under a variety of load conditions. Each determination under load is similar to that of the no-load determination except that equal or nearly equal weights of the appropriate values are first placed on both pans. Two rest points must be observed for each determination of the sensitivity, one before and one after adding one milligram to one side. Typical data are indicated in Table 3. For weighings which happen to fall intermediate between two loadings for which sensitivity values have been determined, the analyst may use the nearer one or interpolate between the known sensitivities or, for the most refined work, he may redetermine the sensitivity with the load of interest.

It may be noted that the sensitivity (divisions per milligram) generally decreases as the load increases. This is to be expected because the increased load results in increased friction at the knife edges and also because of an effective increase in distance from the central knife edge to the center of gravity of the system.

In weighing by sensitivity, the observed trial rest point is recorded along with the summation of weights then in use, and the true rest point and the sensitivity are already known. The simple calculation is best illustrated by an example. Consider a weighing with −0.2 as the true rest point, sensitivity values as listed in Table 3, and an observed rest point of +2.6 with weights totalling 12.2150 grams in place on the right-hand pan. Our trial rest point is 2.8 divisions too far to the right, the closest listed sensitivity-reciprocal value is 0.43 mg per division at 10 grams load, so that an additional 0.43 × 2.8 or 1.2 milligrams are needed. The correct weight is, then, 12.2150 g. + 1.2 mg. or 12.2162 grams. Special care must be exercised in deciding whether to add or subtract the final value. If the trial rest point is to the right of the true rest point, more weight is needed on the right-hand side, while less is needed if the trial rest point is to the left of the true rest point on the scale.

Weighing by sensitivity is an excellent modification of the standard method of weighing by rest point equality since it eliminates all but one of the full rest point determinations once the true rest point is approached. It can be recommended highly even to beginners. Even if the sensitivity is not used as such, a rough idea of the sensitivity of the balance will aid the analyst in finding the weight of final and true rest point equality by minimizing the number of trials needed. Even an approximate idea of the sensitivity of a balance is a great timesaver.

Laboratory Experiment I

INTRODUCTION TO THE ANALYTICAL BALANCE

No step-by-step procedure will be given for this experiment, because each student must become familiar in the laboratory with all of the design and operating factors discussed in this chapter. The laboratory work should include the following:

1. Inspect the balance, identifying the parts described on pages 35 to 40.

2. Determine the no-load rest point by the method of long swings.

3. Determine the no-load rest point by the method of short swings.

4. Determine the sensitivity for the no-load condition and for several different loads, using the method of long swings.

5. Weigh a crucible by use of long swings and the sensitivity; check the sensitivity calculation by adding (or subtracting) the weight correction calculated from the sensitivity and determining the rest point.

6. Weigh a crucible cover by use of long swings and the sensitivity.

7. Weigh the crucible and cover together by use of long swings and the sensitivity; compare this weight with the sum of the separate weights for the crucible and cover.

Notes: If the student balances have damping devices, the rest points in steps 2 through 7 may be determined directly rather than by the methods of swings. If the balances have removable damping devices, it is suggested that several rest points be determined both with and without the damping devices. If one-pan substitution type balances are used, steps 1, 2, 5, 6 and 7 should be performed with appropriate modifications in the methods of observing rest points and of adding weights.

ERRORS IN WEIGHING

We have thus far considered the apparatus and the techniques of analytical weighings and will now consider some of the possible sources of error to which these measurements are subject. (Inaccuracy of the weights has already been discussed.)

Balance Arm Inequality. In the method of weighing by direct comparison, it is tacitly assumed that the weight of the object on the left-hand pan equals the summation of weights required on the right-hand pan to restore the moving system to the true rest point. This is true only if the lengths of the two sides of the beam from the central knife edge are equal. As shown on page 31, the condition in which the true rest point is restored may be represented by the equation

$$W_o \times L = W_w \times R$$

Thus, the weight of the object, W_o, equals the summation of the analytical weights, W_w, only if the two arm lengths, L and R, equal each other. The arms of a common analytical balance are typically each 10 centimeters long and are equal within about 0.0001 centimeter. Thus, error due to balance arm inequality amounts to about 1 part in 100 000 (0.0001 cm. in 10 cm.), which is significant only in the most refined work.

It is of interest to note that even the residual error due to balance arm inequality often corrects for itself in analytical work. Rearrangement of the preceding mathematical equation yields

$$W_o = W_w \times \frac{R}{L}$$

If the weight of one object is to be divided by the weight of another, measured on the same balance (as is done in most gravimetric determinations), the ratio $\frac{R}{L}$ cancels out, so no error whatever results from balance arm inequality.

When a single object or sample is to be weighed on the balance and the value of its weight is not to be related by division to another weight, no such self-compensation arises. Two general methods are available to correct for balance arm inequality in weighings of single objects; the method of substitution, and the method of double weighing.

Correction by substitution.   In the method of weighing by substitution, described on pages 32 to 33, no error whatever results from balance arm inequality. This is, in fact, one of the advantages of the substitution method compared to the method of direct comparison. Some balances designed specifically for substitution weighing have one arm much longer than the other, with no error resulting from this inequality.

The substitution method may be used in a modified form with a conventional two-pan balance. The object is first placed on the right-hand pan and some substance placed on the left to restore the true rest point. The substance on the left may be parts of a set of weights, copper shot, sand— anything which may be placed on the pan in suitably adjustable quantity. The contents of the left-hand pan are left intact and the object on the right replaced by calibrated weights to restore the true rest point again. The summation of right-hand weights required in the second step equals the weight of the object, corrected for any balance arm inequality. To prove this, let W_o, W_w, W_1 equal the weights of the object, the calibrated weights in the second step, and the left-hand substance, respectively, and L and R be the balance arm lengths as before. In the two steps

$$LW_1 = RW_o$$
$$LW_1 = RW_w$$
so
$$RW_o = RW_w$$
or
$$W_o = W_w$$

The right and left sides could be reversed throughout, of course.

Correction by double weighing.   In the double weighing method with a conventional two-pan balance, the object is first weighed conventionally with the object on the left and the analytical weights on the right. A second weighing is made with the object on the right and the weights on the left. Using L, R and W_o as defined previously and W_1 and W_2 as the two observed weighing values,

$$LW_o = RW_1 \qquad \text{or} \qquad \frac{W_o}{W_1} = \frac{R}{L}$$

$$LW_2 = RW_o \qquad \text{or} \qquad \frac{W_2}{W_o} = \frac{R}{L}$$

so
$$\frac{W_o}{W_1} = \frac{W_2}{W_o}$$

or
$$W_o = \sqrt{W_1 W_2}$$

The weight of the object can be calculated directly from the two observed weighings. Unless the balance arms are far from equal, the last equation may be approximated by a simpler one,

$$W_o = \frac{W_1 + W_2}{2}$$

Air Buoyancy. By Archimedes' classical principle, the apparent weight of an object immersed in a fluid is less than its true weight in a vacuum by a quantity equal in magnitude to the weight of the fluid displaced by the object. In analytical weighings, the object on one pan is buoyed up by the weight of air which it displaces, and the weights on the other pan are buoyed up by the weight of air which they displace. The two buoyancies cancel each other only if the object and the weights are of the same density so that they displace equal quantities of air. (The situation is analogous with a one-pan balance for substitution weighings.) Accordingly, any error resulting from buoyancy effects is made more significant the greater the difference in density between the object and the weights. Brass weights typically have a density of about 8.4, so the error would be greater, for example, in weighing a solution of density about 1.0 than in weighing a solid precipitate of density closer to that of the brass weights.

Calculation for correction. A mathematical equation has been developed whereby an observed weight can be corrected to the corresponding weight in a vacuum, in which case there would be no buoyancy effects. One form of this equation is

$$W_v = W_a + \left(\frac{W_a}{d_o} - \frac{W_a}{d_w}\right)d_a$$

in which W_v and W_a are the weights of the object in a vacuum and in air, respectively, and d_o, d_w and d_a are, in order, the densities of the object, of the weights and of the air. It may be noted that $\frac{W_a}{d_o} \times d_a$ equals the weight of air displaced by the object and $\frac{W_a}{d_w} \times d_a$ is the weight of air displaced by the weights; thus the equation is valid. The d_a value may be taken as 0.0012 gram per ml. The correction of weights to vacuum is necessary only in the most refined weighings and in semi-refined weighings of water and dilute solutions, the densities of which are much less than that of the weights.

Because this equation does include the density of air and because the density of air is somewhat dependent upon the barometric pressure, fluctuation in barometric pressure will produce variations in apparent weight of an object. The over-all buoyancy error is often insignificant, however, so that any error due to barometric pressure variations would be even less significant.

Temperature Effects. Changes in temperature can cause error in weighing, and this source of error can be any one of several types. The density of air and, to a much lesser extent, the densities of objects and weights vary with temperature fluctuation, so the temperature also influences the magnitude of the buoyancy error. Again, however, this factor is very seldom significant, and it is taken care of by proper buoyancy corrections.

A more common and more serious temperature effect is encountered whenever the object to be weighed is not at the same temperature as the balance and its surroundings. Without this temperature equilibrium between the object and the balance, air convection currents are induced which lead either to false weights or to such erratic balance behavior that no rest point can be observed. Objects that are too hot produce rising currents and give weight results which are too low; cold objects appear to weigh too much. These errors can be of appreciable magnitude in analytical work of the accuracy commonly expected in industrial laboratories and student laboratories as well.

Other Atmospheric Effects. Another way in which the atmosphere may cause error in weighing is by adsorption on the object of moisture from the surrounding air. Adsorption of water by the materials being weighed can usually be prevented by weighing them in a closed container but the possibility of adsorption on the outer surface of the container remains. The extent of this error depends both upon the nature and area of the exposed surfaces and the humidity of the air. A large glass object would likely appear to weigh more on a humid day than on a dry day. In laboratories in which microbalances are used, air conditioning is a necessity. In the more common analytical work, a suitable routine for the drying of specimens and containers must be established.

Other possible interactions between the object and the atmosphere include actual chemical reactions involving atmospheric carbon dioxide or oxygen. The use of tightly closed weighing vessels is valuable in minimizing this type of error. It must be recognized that interaction of the object with atmospheric moisture, carbon dioxide or oxygen does not signify any shortcomings of the weighing apparatus but rather means that the material being weighed is not entirely the material desired to be weighed.

Electrification of Containers. Another possibility of serious error arises from electrification of the containers used in weighing. Glass containers tend to acquire a static charge when wiped with dry cloth or chamois. This charge is partially transferred from the object to the balance, causing the latter to swing erratically. Furthermore, the charged pan on which the object rests is attracted to the uncharged floor of the balance so that the apparent weight is too great. The error is more pronounced when the surrounding humidity is low. Some analysts attempt to drain off any such static charges by placing a small amount of radioactive substance in the balance case; presumably enough of the air molecules are ionized to drain off any static charges which may otherwise remain. It is also possible to prevent the formation of the charge in the first place. If the object must be wiped, it should be wiped with a very slightly dampened cloth or chamois. In this way no static charge should be developed, and any resulting film of water on the glass surface will be removed by evaporation if the object is allowed to stand in the balance room for a half hour before weighing.

Further Comparison between Balances Designed for Direct Comparison and for Substitution Weighing. The principles of weighing by the substitution method, as employed, for example, in the one-pan types of balance, have been known for many years, but this type of balance has only recently come into widespread use. Some points of comparison between the two types of weighing have already been mentioned in this chapter, but a few additional comments are in order.

One end of the beam in a balance of this type carries a fixed load, typically 200 grams, which can be rigidly attached to the beam. Thus, only two instead of three knife edges are required.

The substitution balance makes all weighings under constant load, which is both advantageous and disadvantageous. The advantage arises from constant sensitivity, which has already been shown to exist only under constant load conditions. This constant sensitivity is necessary for any system in which the scale deflections are calibrated directly in weight units. Unfortunately, however, the constant load which is employed is the maximum load, which means that the sensitivity of the balance is at a minimum and that the physical wear upon the knife edges is at a maximum in all weighings. Even though common analytical balances can accept loads up to 200 grams, weighing loads are seldom much over 30 grams in most analytical work. A 30-gram load results in less friction and wear upon the critical parts of the balance than does a 200-gram load, even though the latter may not be prohibitive.

The use of a two-pan balance with weighing by direct comparison makes it possible to provide some self-compensation for the influence of humidity upon weighings of bulky glass objects. By using as a counterweight a similar piece of glassware, the same process of moisture adsorption occurs on both object and counterweight, thus minimizing error from the adsorbed film of moisture. This method cannot be used on a one-pan substitution type of balance.

In summary, it must be concluded that each type of balance has some advantage over the other and that excellent analytical work is possible with both.

Summary of Precautions. It has generally proved advantageous to avoid errors, if at all possible, rather than to attempt to correct for them once they have occurred. As an aid in avoiding them, the following tabulation of precautions in using the balance is of value:

1. The balance room should be kept as clean and neat as possible. Every movement within the room should be made only after due consideration of the dangers involved in jarring the balances when they are in operation.

2. The moving elements of the balance should never be touched with the fingers. The weights should be handled with ivory-tipped pincers which are used for no other purpose. The objects weighed should be handled with pincers of suitable design, lint-free cloth or glazed paper—never with the fingers.

3. An accumulation of dust on the balance pans or on the weights (an unlikely occurrence if the balance and the weight box are kept shut when not in use) may be removed by gently brushing with a small camel's hair brush.

4. Only glass or metal objects should be weighed directly on the pans. Powdery materials of any sort, wet objects and chemicals should never rest directly on the pans but should be weighed in suitable containers.

5. Care should be taken that objects placed on the pan carry no detachable material. The bottoms of crucibles should be inspected for soot and, particularly important, for sulfuric acid if this material is used as a desiccant. Any indication of foreign material on the pans should be called to the instructor's attention at once.

6. The zero point of the balance should be checked frequently, for highest accuracy before and after each weighing. If the zero point moves to a position more than one scale division from the center of the pointer scale the instructor should be asked to adjust it.

7. The ordinary student balance is supposed to bear a load of 200 grams without danger of damage, but probably 100 grams is a better limit if the balance is being used by beginners. The beam arrest must be up when placing the object on the pan.

8. The object is usually placed on the left pan and the weights on the right. This is merely a matter of convention, but once an analysis has been begun in this way, the subsequent weighings of the same run should be carried out in the same way so that any error due to balance arm inequality will cancel out. Every analysis should be completed on the same pan of the same balance and with the same set of weights with which it was begun.

9. If large objects of low density (glass vessels) must be weighed, all weighings should be completed within as short a time as possible. All objects weighed must be in complete temperature equilibrium with the balance, and vessels with tightly fitting stoppers should be opened momentarily ust before the weighing.

10. The use of the beam and pan arrests is critical in the careful operation of the balance. The pan arrests should be lowered before the beam support except in the single deflection method, in which the reverse order is followed. The beam support and then the pan arrests should always be raised, if possible, near the middle of a swing when the pointer is near the center of its scale. The beam support must be manipulated gently and smoothly to avoid chipping either the knife edge or the flat plate in contact with it. Both the beam and the pans should be supported by their arrests when making any changes on the pans. The chain, if any, may be adjusted, however, while the pan arrests are off and the beam is free to swing.

11. Both the object and the weights should be centered on the pans so that the latter hang vertically. In adding weights a systematic procedure should be followed, always working down from weights which have been shown to be too large. In determining the final rest point, the door of the balance case must always be tightly shut.

12. When leaving the balance, no weights or objects should be left on the pans. Both beam and pan arrests must be in place. The rider should be set on the zero mark or, if this is not possible, it should be suspended on its hook above the center of the scale. The case should be shut as a protection against fumes.

REVIEW QUESTIONS

1. Define or characterize "rest point" and "sensitivity."
2. State briefly and specifically what an analytical balance is.
3. State concisely the principle of making a weighing on an analytical balance by the methods of direct comparison and of substitution.
4. Distinguish between class M, class S, class S-1 and class P weights on the bases of construction and accuracy.
5. Express each of the following in grams: 26 milligrams; 23 kilograms; 112 micrograms.
6. Compare the methods of long swings, of short swings and of single deflection on the bases of speed and accuracy.
7. Explain clearly how a damping device restricts the movement of the beam and yet does not affect the location of the rest point.
8. Is it feasible for a projection reading device to be used on an undamped balance? Explain.
9. Explain how the one-pan type of balance makes possible all weighings under constant load conditions.
10. Compare the one-pan and two-pan types of balances with respect to construction, convenience and accuracy.
11. Indicate the order of magnitude of the error introduced in the use of a common analytical balance by each of the following sources of error: balance arm inequality; air bouyancy; normal temperature fluctuations.

PROBLEMS

1. The following readings were obtained for the swings of a balance with equal 10 gram loads on each pan: +7.6; −6.4, +7.0, −5.8, +6.8. Calculate the rest point.
2. When a 1.0 mg. weight was added to the right hand pan of Problem 1, the readings were: +2.0, −8.2, +1.4, −7.6, +0.7. Calculate the sensitivity of the balance at this load.
3. With the same balance as in Problems 1 and 2, with a crucible on the left pan and weights totaling 10.12 grams on the right pan, and with the rider set at 6.0 mg. on the right side of the beam, the readings were: +4.6, −3.7, +4.0, −3.4, +3.4. Calculate the weight of the crucible.
4. From the following data obtained on a common analytical balance, calculate the weight of the object:
   Weights on pan: 16.41 grams
   Swings when rider is at 1.0 mg.: −6.4, +7.8, −6.3, +7.6, −6.1
   Swings when rider is at 2.0 mg.: −7.3, +4.0, −7.1, +3.8, −6.8
   Swings on unloaded balance: −5.2, +2.6, −5.1, +2.5, −5.0
5. A student using a balance equipped with a chain device and magnetic damping adjusted his balance so the true rest point was 0.0 on the scale. He then placed

his object on the left pan, left the rider on the beam at 0 and placed 12.0 grams of weights from his weight box on the right pan. With the chain at 46.0 mg., the rest point was −2.1 divisions. With the chain at 45.0 mg. and all else remaining the same, the rest point was −0.5 divisions. What was the weight of his object?

6. Consider the same balance as in Problem 5, but with a different object on the left pan. With 11.0 grams of weights from the box on the right pan, the rider set in a notch labeled 0.3 gram and the chain at 27.2 mg., the rest point was +1.3 division. What was the weight of the object?

7. A certain object was placed on the right pan of a balance, and the sum of the weights required to counterbalance it was 19.2624 grams. The same object was then placed on the left pan, and its apparent weight was 19.2660 grams. Calculate (a) the balance-arm ratio and (b) the corrected weight of the object.

8. A bottle made of glass (d = 2.4) weighs 16.1487 grams in air when weighed with weights of brass (d = 8.4). Calculate the weight of the bottle in vacuo.

9. A platinum (d = 21.4) object weighs 16.1487 grams in air when weighed with weights of brass (d = 8.4). Calculate the weight of the object in vacuo.

10. The volume occupied by 1.0000 gram of water, weighed in air with brass (d = 8.4) weights at 20° C. is 1.0028 ml. Calculate the weight in vacuo of 1.0000 ml. of water at the same temperature.

11. Calculate the apparent weight, measured in air with brass (d = 8.4) weights, of 1.0000 ml. of mercury if it weighs 13.546 grams in vacuo.

12. If the left arm of a balance is 10.000 cm. in length and the right arm is 10.010 cm., what is the apparent weight of a 1.0000 gram object weighed with the object on the left pan?

SUGGESTION FOR ADDITIONAL READING

Item 15, Appendix 7.

Chapter 4

The General Unit

Operations and Tools

of Quantitative Analysis

I⊤ is the purpose of this chapter to provide an introduction to the laboratory work of quantitative analysis and to the general operations which are common to most analytical methods. The complete procedure for an analysis consists of several unit operations. The first four of these general laboratory operations are common to both gravimetric and volumetric methods and may be listed as follows:

1. Sampling.
2. Drying the sample.
3. Weighing the sample.
4. Dissolving the sample.

Subsequent unit operations differ for gravimetric and volumetric methods and will be discussed in Chapters 6 and 9, respectively.

INTRODUCTION TO LABORATORY WORK

The student of quantitative analysis must keep several points in mind in order to achieve success in his laboratory work. The average student can acceptably master the manual techniques necessary in analytical work, but considerable careful practice is necessary. The student who does not consistently develop and practice habits of cleanliness, neatness and order right from the start of his laboratory work cannot achieve the level of manual dexterity required to analyze samples successfully.

The development of speed and accuracy in laboratory work will also be facilitated by a thorough understanding of the experiment or determination before entering the laboratory and by careful advance planning of the laboratory work. The student should understand the basic principles of the method involved and prepare an outline of the procedure in his laboratory notebook before starting the actual laboratory work. Without this advance preparation, the student is likely to make careless mistakes and to be forced into time-consuming and otherwise unnecessary repetition of the work.

Cleaning of Equipment and Handling of Reagents. Most analytical glassware may be cleaned by scrubbing with a dilute detergent solution, rinsing thoroughly with tap water and finally rinsing once or twice with small volumes of distilled water. Several detergents are marketed specifically for this purpose, although common household detergents are fairly satisfactory. When glassware is contaminated with solids of known composition, appropriate solvents should be used prior to regular washing and rinsing. It is much easier to clean a piece of glassware immediately after use than after the residual portions of its contents have dried in or on it.

The desk top requires regular, daily washing. Spilled liquids must be wiped up immediately with copious amounts of water, lest they contaminate apparatus, reagents and solutions. Also, some of the plastic materials used for lab bench tops are easily stained by, for example, silver nitrate solutions. The cupboards and drawers in which apparatus is stored must also be kept clean and neat at all times.

No chemical, when once removed from a stock bottle, should be returned to it. In most cases a solid chemical should be poured directly from its bottle onto a watch glass or weighing paper which is on a platform or trip balance and only the necessary amount should be taken. If an excess is inadvertently taken from the stock bottle, it should be discarded. When it is necessary to break up a caked solid, this should be done with a clean spatula or stirring rod. Liquid reagents should be removed from stock bottles by pouring into a beaker or other suitable receptacle, not by insertion of a pipet into the reagent bottle. The design and proper use of pipets and other items of volumetric glassware are discussed in Chapter 9.

Nonvolatile liquids may be disposed of by flushing down the drain with water; the flow of water should be continued long enough to flush the sink and traps. Solid wastes should never be placed directly in the sink. Soluble ones should be dissolved and then flushed down the drain. Insoluble solids, other than particularly hazardous ones, should be placed in special disposal receptacles provided for them. Certain substances such as metallic sodium and cyanide solutions require special disposal procedures. Consult the instructor whenever in doubt.

Each student should become thoroughly familiar with the laboratory safety rules. The location and proper use of fire extinguishers should be noted before beginning work in any laboratory area. The procedures for obtaining first aid treatment should be noted; no cut or injury of any kind should be neglected, no matter how minor it may appear. Special precautions in the handling of the chemicals for each experiment should be considered. Some type of eye protection, at least for protection from flying objects from the front, should be worn in all laboratory work, with the exception of work in the balance room and in similarly safe and isolated locations. The instructor will post or discuss rules for laboratory safety, and all prescribed regulations and policies must be adhered to rigidly.

Laboratory Notebook. The most carefully designed experiment cannot yield the desired result if any part of the data essential for the calculations is mislaid or is not recorded. A well-planned laboratory notebook minimizes the probability of such an occurrence, so the notebook may justifiably be considered an important item of laboratory equipment.

A permanently bound notebook with numbered pages should be used. A book measuring about 5" × 7" is best. A book of larger size is not convenient for use around the analytical balance, and smaller pages are not adequate.

The first few pages of the notebook should be reserved for the table of contents and should be filled in as the work of the course progresses. The first page for each determination should be used for an outline of the procedure and a mathematical statement of the method of calculation. The procedure should not be copied from the textbook into the laboratory notebook but rather should be written in the student's own words to suit his particular situation. A reference to the appropriate pages in the textbook should be included.

The numerical data of the experiment should be entered on the next page or pages as needed. A form for summarizing these data can be prepared, even before beginning the laboratory work, with blanks for the insertion of all necessary items. With the form for his data before him, the analyst is constantly reminded of the data required and is not likely to use a crucible before weighing it or to neglect to measure and record some other equally important quantity.

The laboratory worker should always be alert to notice all significant and potentially significant factors during the experiment. Any unusual appearances of precipitates, apparent variations from one filter to another, exceptionally high humidity in the laboratory on a working day, and so forth, can conceivably be of significance. All these factors should be recorded in the notebook. To aid in subsequent checking of calculations, it is recommended that both the general formula on which calculations are based and the complete numerical calculations be shown in the notebook.

The date of every observation should be noted. This practice is of extreme importance in industrial laboratories because patent decisions have hinged on data in dated laboratory notebooks. While it is improbable that your course notebook will be the subject of a patent dispute, there are other more immediate advantages to dating observations that make it a generally desirable practice. For example, an anomalous result may be traced to a weighing made on a day of excessively high humidity or to the use of a standard solution on a date too long after it was prepared.

The laboratory notebook is the permanent record of the experiments; consequently, all notations must be made in ink as neatly as feasible. All data must be recorded directly into the notebook. Recording data first on scratch paper is a nonscientific procedure and may easily lead to loss or error in transcribing essential data. Should it become necessary to alter a figure, the incorrect entry should be crossed out with a single line (if erased or otherwise obliterated, the incorrect item is no longer available) and the corrected value entered above it. When a figure is crossed out, an accompanying explanation is generally desirable. Erasures and missing pages are not to be tolerated under any circumstances.

Reagents. Chemical reagents are among the essential tools of quantitative analysis. Many reagents come in various grades of purity. It is difficult to generalize as to the meaning of certain purity designations.

Table 4. Concentrations of Stock Solutions of Some Common Reagents

Stock ammonium hydroxide	not less than 27% by weight NH_3	(about 14.2 molar)
Stock acetic acid	about 99.5% by weight $HC_2H_3O_2$	(about 17.4 molar)
Stock hydrochloric acid	not less than 36.5% by weight HCl	(about 12 molar)
Stock nitric acid	not less than 68% by weight HNO_3	(about 15 molar)
Stock perchloric acid	about 70% by weight $HClO_4$	(about 11.6 molar)
Stock phosphoric acid	not less than 85% by weight H_3PO_4	(about 14.7 molar)
Stock sulfuric acid	not less than 95% by weight H_2SO_4	(about 17.5 molar)

Maximum tolerances of various impurities are often listed by the manufacturers, and it is becoming common also to indicate actual analyses of the lots from which the individual containers are filled by the manufacturer. The less specific designations such as "C.P." (chemically pure) and "reagent grade" generally denote quite pure substances, sometimes with specified tolerances, but the analyst is more interested in the actual data of purity whenever provided. Fairly high purity is required for most reagents in quantitative determinations, although the specific requirements vary from one case to another.

Reagents obtained in a highly purified state from the manufacturer are often contaminated by accident or carelessness in the laboratory. Special care must be taken to insure that no contaminant gets into a bottle while reagent is being withdrawn, that covers are kept on tightly when not in direct use, and so forth. It is really more economical in the long run to buy analytical reagents in small (for example, 1 lb.) containers rather than in larger ones, as the danger of contamination increases with the number of times the container is opened.

Until relatively recent times, the lack of reliably pure reagents was a major source of difficulty in quantitative analysis. The development of large scale manufacturing methods for the production and bottling of them has been a major achievement. The analytical chemist must continue to be a very cautious person, even to the extent of checking the purity of his reagents in critical work. However, the situation now is far less discouraging than it was in years gone by when manufacturers failed to designate purity quantitatively and when such purity designations as were given were not always reliable.

Ammonium hydroxide and several of the common acids are commercially available in the form of concentrated solutions. Since these reagents are used in so many analytical procedures, it is desirable for the student to become familiar with the approximate concentrations of these stock solutions. Common specifications include those of Table 4. The molar method of expressing concentrations of solutions will be described in some detail in Chapter 9. Throughout the procedures in this book, required concentrations of these reagents will be expressed in terms of volume dilutions of these stock solutions. Thus, "1 to 1 dilution" signifies one part of stock solution diluted with 1 part of water, and so forth. Acids should be diluted by adding acid to water, not vice versa.

Miscellaneous Items of Glassware, Polyethylene and Platinum.
Stirring rods are frequently used in every analytical laboratory. They may be cut from glass rod and firepolished to make the ends smooth. A stirring rod, one end of which is covered by a short gum rubber sleeve, is useful in transferring moist precipitates from one container to another; this item is called a rubber policeman.

The wash bottle is an essential tool in both gravimetric and volumetric methods of analysis. In the standard glass types the liquid is ejected by blowing. Now available is a "squeeze-type" wash bottle of polyethylene. The neck of the glass water bottle may be wrapped with heavy twine for handling hot liquids.

Numerous items made of polyethylene are in widespread use. A full assortment of polyethylene ware is now available, including beakers, bottles, graduates, funnels, and so forth. In comparison with glass, polyethylene is less reactive with substances such as hydrofluoric acid and is less fragile. On the other hand, glass items are inexpensive and their greater rigidity makes them more suitable for containers of calibrated volume.

Platinum vessels are very useful in analytical chemistry but are very expensive and can be ruined easily if not used correctly. Platinum is very useful, for example, in the form of crucibles for some high temperature ignitions and in the form of electrodes for electrochemical work. However, platinum is attacked by reducing gases such as those found in the reducing zone of a gas flame and by some other gases as well. Some solids also cause difficulty. Detailed information should be obtained before using platinum ware in any other than rigidly specified applications.

SAMPLING

In a course in quantitative analysis the student receives each sample ready for drying and weighing or in a solution ready for subsequent steps. Therefore, he need not be concerned in his laboratory work with the unit operation of sampling. In practical situations, however, obtaining a sample suitable for analysis is often a source of major difficulty and frequently limits the validity of the final result. The analytical chemist must be very much interested in the origin of his samples and, insofar as is possible, should exercise some control over how those samples are obtained.

Two types of situation are encountered: (1) the determination of the composition of a pure substance; (2) the determination of the average composition of a mass of material. The former is encountered, for example, in the analytical branch of a laboratory engaged in synthesizing hitherto unknown compounds. The crude samples must be subjected to distillation, crystallization and other means of purification in preparing final samples suitable for analysis.

If it is desired to obtain an analysis of a larger body of material, it is essential that the sample taken be truly representative. The importance of this rather obvious statement can hardly be overemphasized. Relatively little difficulty is encountered when the larger bulk of material is so thoroughly homogeneous that any portion of it which is of sufficient mass for analysis exhibits the same composition as any other portion. Such is the case with properly mixed gases and thoroughly agitated liquids and true solutions, but considerable difficulty is frequently encountered with less homogeneous materials.

Sampling errors may be classified into two groups, systematic and random. Systematic errors are those which result from repeated preference for one component of the body of material. Examples are the taking of each sample of a quiescent body of liquid from near the surface when, in fact, concentration gradients may exist at various levels, or the favoring of large pieces of a mixture of solid particles when, in fact, the large and small pieces may differ considerably in composition. Coal ash, for example, generally predominates more in fine particles of coal than in larger chunks.

Random errors are those which exhibit just as much tendency to make results high as to make them low. This type of error is less dangerous than is a systematic error for two reasons: the results of the analyses of a series of replicate samples can reveal directly something about the magnitude of random errors but give no indication whatever of the presence of systematic errors; random errors in sampling can be minimized by taking more samples or larger samples, but this procedure would not necessarily minimize a systematic error.

A statistical basis for the unit operation of sampling has been devised, based in large part upon the statistical concepts to be introduced in Chapter 5.

The full theoretical treatment is not presented in this book, but three general conclusions are of particular significance:

1. For absolute accuracy of sampling, the sample must consist of the entire body of material. However, absolute accuracy is seldom desired and is, in fact, never attainable in other parts of the analysis anyway.
2. The size of sample which should be taken is determined by (1) the maximum error or uncertainty which can be tolerated which is, in turn, set by (a) the accuracies of other operations of the complete analysis and/or (b) the use to which the results are to be put, and by (2) the extent of heterogeneity of the material.
3. The statistical approach is largely void if a systematic error exists, although statistical concepts are of value in devising totally independent methods of sampling so as to check the possibility of a systematic error.

Gases and Liquids. Gases are generally very homogeneous, and samples may be collected in bottles after evacuation or by displacement of the air initially present in the bottle. A one-phase liquid may be assumed to be homogeneous after moderate agitation. Sampling of a quiescent body of liquid is generally to be avoided but, when necessary to do so, portions should be taken from several depths.

Solids. Solid materials which are composed of large numbers of individual pieces often exhibit much variation from piece to piece as well as within a piece. It is usually necessary to take a gross sample larger than that which can be subjected to analysis in the laboratory and then to reduce it systematically both in particle size and in over-all mass to yield the final analytical sample. In order to minimize the danger of an undetected systematic error in sampling, the gross sample should preferably be taken while the larger bulk of material is in motion, as during the unloading of a carload or while the material passes along a conveyor belt. If the material is stationary in one big pile, those portions which have "filtered" down to the base of the pile and become inaccessible may differ in composition from those portions which are left in more accessible positions. The required mass of the gross sample is determined jointly by the expected variation from one particle to another and by the size of the individual pieces. For coal in lumps greater than one inch in average dimension, the gross sample should be as large as one thousand pounds to yield results of typical quantitative accuracy. For materials which are in smaller pieces and of greater homogeneity, smaller gross samples are acceptable.

The subdivision of the gross sample to a sample suitable for analysis in the laboratory includes reduction of particle size along with the reduction of mass. Formal procedures have been developed for various types of material, all designed to minimize the danger of a systematic error at each step and to render random errors as small as possible. A final particle size of about 100 mesh is usually satisfactory.

Various types of crushers, pulverizers, mills and mortars are useful for the grinding operations. The jaw crusher contains two steel plates, one of which moves back and forth against the other one, which is stationary; this crusher is useful in reducing pieces of material down to pea-size. The disk pulverizer contains two plates, one concave and one convex, rotating near each other; the particles encounter diminishing space between the two plates as they proceed so that further reduction in particle size results. In a ball mill, the particles to be pulverized are rotated along with some sort of hard pellets in a revolving crock: the continual striking of the pieces results in a breaking down of the sample into smaller particles. Both porcelain and agate mortars are useful for final grinding operations. The proper motion in a mortar is a circular, grinding one, not one of pounding.

Precautions must be taken to ensure that the sample is not contaminated by the grinding apparatus. The surfaces which come in contact with the specimen must be of harder material than the sample. Some samples undergo chemical change during grinding: for example, ferrous ion may be oxidized to ferric. The water content may also be altered during grinding and crushing operations.

DRYING THE SAMPLE

The role of water in quantitative analysis is particularly significant because of the possible exchange of water between the atmosphere and the sample, which may markedly affect the composition of the latter. Analytical results secured with a perfectly dry sample may be significantly different from the values obtained when the same sample contains a quantity of moisture at the time it is weighed out for the determination. Consequently, the water content must be a known factor if the analytical results are to be meaningful. Then, if a wet sample is used, the results may be converted to a dry basis; or the results secured with a dried sample may be modified to represent the analysis of the original wet substance.

Absolute and Reproducible Dryness. Some analytical samples may be brought to a condition of absolute dryness by prolonged heating. Then the sample in its container is put into a desiccator and cooled in contact only with dried air. The dried sample can then be weighed rapidly on the analytical balance in a state of dryness which is for all practical purposes absolute. However, the severe conditions required for the complete expulsion of tightly bound water are apt to produce secondary effects, like loss of carbon dioxide from carbonates and oxidation of sulfides. A sample which has undergone such indeterminate secondary changes is no longer representative of the original material. Therefore, when dealing with samples which can undergo secondary reactions during intensive drying, the goal of absolute dryness must be relinquished in favor of a goal of reproducible dryness. It is essential to attain at least this condition. Otherwise, the water content will vary with time, place and circumstances such as atmospheric humidity, so that analyses made by different analysts or by the same analyst on different occasions will fail to agree.

Drying by Heating: Ovens, Burners and Furnaces. The commonest method of achieving reproducible dryness is to heat the sample for one or more hours at 105° to 110° C. in a well-ventilated oven. This treatment is often insufficient to expel tightly bound water, but it does remove the loosely bound water. The latter is the water fraction most likely to show variations with atmospheric conditions, so its elimination generally results in producing samples of an adequately reproducible state of dryness. However, this temperature is high enough to cause undesirable secondary reactions with some substances. The drying temperature selected must always be a compromise between requirements for complete drying and prohibition of secondary reactions.

The sample should be placed in the drying oven in such a manner that air can have free access to essentially all of the sample. One good method is shown in Figure 7.

Burners of three types are commonly used in quantitative analysis when higher temperatures are required for drying or for other purposes. The Tirrill burner is of the basic Bunsen type and provides regulation of both gas and air intake. The flame is cone-shaped and consists of three fairly distinct zones. The innermost zone consists of gas emerging from the barrel of the burner. The middle zone consists of gas reacting with oxygen admitted through the burner. The outermost zone is formed by gas which remains from the middle zone and which reacts with oxygen from the surrounding air. The hottest part of the flame is at the junction of the middle and outermost zones and may be of the order of 1 500° C. No crucible or other similar object can be situated entirely within this hottest part of the flame. The maximum temperature attainable in a covered porcelain crucible in a Tirrill

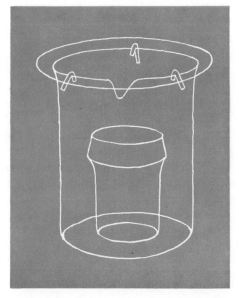

FIGURE 7. A weighing bottle in a beaker covered with a watch glass supported on glass hooks, ready for insertion in the drying oven. The cover of the weighing bottle may be laid alongside the bottle in the beaker.

burner is about 650° C, while the interior of a covered platinum crucible may reach about 1 000° C.

The Fisher-Meker burner has a grating across the orifice at the top of the barrel that splits the single set of cones of the flame into a series of smaller ones. This permits air which is admitted through the burner to get at the gas more adequately than in a Tirrill burner, so relatively little of the gas burns with oxygen from the surrounding air. Higher temperatures are obtainable, about 800° C. and 1 200° C., respectively, in covered porcelain and platinum crucibles.

The blast burner is designed to permit air or tank oxygen to enter from the base of the burner along with the fuel in such a way that more efficient mixing occurs and somewhat higher temperatures are attainable. Fuels other than natural or bottled gas, including hydrogen and acetylene, can also be used for special purposes.

Desiccators.   A desiccator is a vessel used to achieve and maintain an atmosphere of low humidity for the storage of samples, precipitates, crucibles, weighing bottles, and so forth. The common form consists of three parts: a ground glass cover which slides onto the body of the desiccator to form an airtight seal, a perforated plate upon which the articles to be stored are placed, and a lower portion in which a desiccant may be placed.

Glass wall desiccators are most commonly used. However, aluminum desiccators are also commercially available. They possess the advantages of light weight, relative durability and rapid cooling but have the disadvantages that certain desiccants must not be placed directly against the floor and lower walls of the desiccator and that the walls are not transparent. Some desiccators are equipped with side arms, whereby they can be connected to a vacuum pump so that the contents may be kept under a vacuum rather than merely in an atmosphere of dry air. The same connector can also be used to introduce an atmosphere of nitrogen or other special gas to provide the inner atmosphere for special purposes.

Special care is required even in the use of such a simple piece of equipment as a common desiccator. A hot crucible or other hot vessel should be allowed to cool in air for at least sixty seconds prior to insertion. Otherwise, the air within the desiccator will be hot when the desiccator is closed and a partial vacuum will develop as it cools. Upon subsequent opening of the partially evacuated unit, a sudden inrush of air can easily result in spilling of samples within. However, the hot crucible must not be permitted to stand in room air any longer than necessary, or the interaction of crucible and contents with moist air may be excessive.

Weighing bottles and crucibles should not be handled directly with the fingers after drying or ignition. One simple, yet effective method of handling them for insertion into and withdrawal from the desiccator, as well as for any handling necessary in the weighing operation, is shown in Figure 8. Crucible tongs should, of course, be used with hot objects and may be used in any case.

A desiccator should be opened no more often than absolutely necessary as each opening permits the entry of moist room air. The action of the desiccant in removing moisture from the air is a rather slow one, and the desiccator must remain closed for an appreciable period of time before the inner atmosphere is made dry. Without doubt, the usual and overly frequent openings of the desiccator in student laboratories limit the efficiency of the desiccator much more seriously than does the inherent lack of an ideally perfect desiccant.

Desiccants. A desiccant is a chemical substance which has the property of combining with moisture from the surrounding atmosphere. No

Table 5. Relative Effectiveness of Some Desiccants

Desiccant	mg. H_2O in I liter air at equilibrium
P_2O_5	0.00002 or less
BaO	0.0007
$Mg(ClO_4)_2$	0.002
H_2SO_4	0.003
$CaSO_4$	0.004
$CaCl_2$	0.36

desiccant is ideally perfect; that is, no desiccant can make and keep the air within a closed desiccator perfectly dry. Some desiccants are more effective than others, as indicated in Table 5. The smaller the amount of moisture remaining per liter of air, the more effective the desiccant can be. Calcium chloride is commonly used, but it is clearly one of the less effective ones. Sulfuric acid is a good desiccant, but the danger of splashing and spilling presents a practical drawback. Porous barium oxide is satisfactory; however, this material swells as it takes on moisture so that sufficient space must be

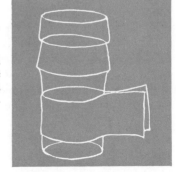

FIGURE 8.   A strip of paper wrapped around a weighing bottle. The ends of the paper may be grasped with the thumb and forefinger, thus permitting handling of the bottle without touching it directly with the fingers.

provided for this expansion. Phosphorus pentoxide may be effective, yet it is not convenient to handle and its effectiveness is limited by an insulating film of phosphoric acid formed early in use. Anhydrous magnesium perchlorate and calcium sulfate are two modern, effective desiccants. Some commercially available desiccants include a colored substance along with the desiccant proper, the hue of the color changing as the water content increases. Thus the analyst can tell at a glance when replacement of the desiccant is needed. Some desiccants are reversible; the spent material can be dried by heating and then used over again. Others are best discarded when once spent.

Drying by Evaporation. When analytical specimens undergo secondary changes even under mild conditions of oven drying, the method of evaporation must be used. In this method the finely ground sample is simply exposed to air at room temperature so that any excess water may evaporate. The surrounding air itself may be dried by a desiccant or may be maintained at a constant level of humidity. Vacuum drying is occasionally employed, but it has little or no advantage over air drying. Sometimes drying by evaporation cannot be avoided, but the so-called "air-dry" material is usually somewhat uncertain in composition, showing substantial variations with changes in the relative atmospheric humidity. Metal samples are usually sufficiently dry after rinsing in acetone or other volatile solvent which is miscible with water and then air drying for a short time.

Drying the Container. The same possibilities of absolute or reproducible dryness are involved in the preparation of containers for weighing. A porcelain crucible may be brought to a condition of absolute dryness, but this condition is difficult to attain with glass vessels which cannot sustain a high temperature ignition. Even if absolute dryness were attainable, it would be practically impossible to weigh glass in this condition because it readily adsorbs moisture from the air. Thus, a condition of reproducible dryness is the goal in preparing glass containers for weighing, the weight of the equilibrium film of adsorbed water being considered as part of the weight of the container. Although dry glass initially does pick up water readily, an equilibrium film of moisture is realized only slowly; thus, it is usually more convenient to approach equilibrium from a condition in which there is too much water on the glass. Therefore, in preparing a glass object for weighing, it is customary to wipe it with a slightly dampened cloth so that the surface is fully saturated. The vessel is then wiped gently with a dry cloth to remove any gross excess of water, and the final approach to an equilibrium film of water is accomplished by allowing the object to stand in the balance room for one-half hour before weighing. This half-hour period is also desirable to bring about temperature equilibrium between the object and the balance and its surroundings. The air-dry condition of glass vessels is more critical in microanalytical work than in ordinary analytical work, since the weighings must be more exact. Air conditioning is virtually essential for the balance room in microanalytical laboratories.

WEIGHING THE SAMPLE

After sampling and drying, the next of the unit operations in a quantitative analysis is weighing the sample. The design and use of the balance were described in Chapter 3.

Replicate samples are almost invariably required in quantitative work. The number of individual portions which should be carried through the analysis depends upon the desired accuracy, the nature of the method and the nature of the sample. Generally, triplicate samples are desirable and quadruplicates may be advisable. The number of weighings is held to a minimum if the several samples are weighed out by difference. That is, the container (often a weighing bottle with the over-all sample) is weighed, one portion is removed and the bottle weighed again. The process is repeated until the desired number of samples have been weighed out. Thus, four weighings suffice for three portions of the sample, and five weighings suffice for four portions.

Solid samples should generally be weighed out in or from standard type weighing bottles. A weighing bottle is a thin-walled glass container of 1 to 100 ml. volume and fitted with a ground glass cover. Powder samples are often weighed in weighing bottles, and liquid samples may also be weighed in such containers. The weighing bottle should be handled with a clean cloth, a strip of paper pinched around it as in Figure 8 or chamois finger tips—never with the bare fingers. The cover should be in place when storing in the desiccator but not during drying in the oven. The cover should be dried along with the bottle, however. Powder samples may be inserted or withdrawn by means of a small spatula or a scoop. A useful spoon may be fashioned easily from a strip of aluminum. Some powders may be transferred by pouring, which is facilitated by a twisting, rotary motion. A powder funnel, which is a conventional funnel with a short and wide stem, is useful but not necessary. A camel's hair brush is often useful in transferring final traces of dry powders from one container to another.

Small flasks with ground glass stoppers are also useful for weighing out liquid samples. Containers for liquids must be kept stoppered to prevent continual evaporation. In certain cases liquid samples are measured by volume rather than by weight.

It is seldom necessary to weigh out any exact, predetermined quantity of sample. It almost always suffices to have portions of individually known weight such that each weighs about the same predetermined value, or such that each comes within well-spaced, approximate, predetermined limits of maximum and minimum weight. In fact, it is often preferable to have the several replicate samples differing somewhat in weight so that certain types of errors (to be discussed later) can be recognized more readily.

When it is necessary to weigh out a sample of an exact, predetermined weight, it is advisable to use a watch glass instead of a covered weighing bottle. The sample is slowly and carefully poured on until a state of balance is indicated with the predetermined weight. It is advisable to pour on the sample slowly until just over the state of balance, then to withdraw small portions with a weighing spoon or spatula until the condition of balance is restored.

DISSOLVING THE SAMPLE

With few exceptions the weighed sample must be put into solution before separation and measurement of the desired constituent. Whenever possible, the sample is dissolved in water. Organic solvents are suitable for many organic materials, although this book is concerned principally with the analyses of inorganic substances which are not soluble in organic solvents. Many different methods are used to modify the solvent properties of water or to change the sample to make it water soluble, and each particular type of sample presents its own requirements. The two most general methods are acid treatment and fusion with a flux. The former is useful for dissolving many metals and salts, while the latter is particularly useful for the dissolution of oxides and ores which are not soluble in acids.

Table 6. Electromotive Series of the Metals

Lithium
Rubidium
Potassium
Barium
Strontium
Calcium
Sodium
Magnesium
Aluminum
Manganese
Zinc
Chromium
Iron
Cadmium
Cobalt
Nickel
Tin
Lead
Hydrogen
Antimony
Bismuth
Arsenic
Copper
Silver
Mercury
Platinum
Gold

Acid Treatment. Acids may be classified as nonoxidizing acids, such as hydrochloric, sulfuric and dilute perchloric, and oxidizing acids, such as nitric and hot, concentrated perchloric. This distinction is quite arbitrary as there are reactions in which sulfuric acid, for example, can serve as an oxidizing agent. The electromotive series of the metals, Table 6, may be used as a guide in predicting the dissolving power of nonoxidizing acids on metals. In general, any metal above hydrogen in the series will displace hydrogen ion from acid solution, although some of the reactions are very slow. Metals below hydrogen in the electromotive series generally require use of an oxidizing acid to accomplish dissolution.

With respect to the dissolving of salts, acids may be classified as strong acids and weak acids. Strong acids are highly or completely ionized in aqueous solution and weak acids only slightly so. Strong acids, such as hydrochloric, can dissolve salts of which the anions form weak acid molecules. For example, calcium carbonate dissolves in hydrochloric acid by means of the chemical reaction

$$CaCO_3 + 2\,H^+ \longrightarrow Ca^{++} + H_2CO_3$$

Most oxides are soluble in hydrochloric acid, although some are not affected by any of the common acids or even by aqua regia. Aqueous solutions of weak acids, such as acetic, are of limited usefulness in the dissolution of inorganic samples.

An acid solution may serve not only as an acid but also as a complexing or a precipitating agent. Chloride ion, for example, can form soluble complexes with some metal ions, thus increasing the solubility of salts of those metal ions. Sulfate ion is a relatively poor complexing agent. A few chlorides and sulfates are insoluble in water, but nearly all nitrates are soluble.

The practical use of the more common acids in dissolving metals and salts may be summarized as follows:

1. Hydrochloric acid dissolves all common metals except antimony, bismuth, arsenic, copper, mercury and silver. The reaction is very slow with lead, cobalt, nickel, cadmium and a few other metals above hydrogen in the electromotive series. Salts of weak acids and most oxides are soluble. Iron oxide ores are generally soluble by digestion with hydrochloric acid. A residue of silicious material may remain after dissolution of the ore sample in the acid. Its presence may not interfere in subsequent steps, but it can be removed by filtration or dissolved by a fusion method if desired.
2. Dilute sulfuric acid dissolves all common metals except lead, antimony, bismuth, arsenic, copper, mercury and silver.
3. Hot, concentrated sulfuric acid dissolves all common metals. An anion of a less volatile acid may be replaced from solution by boiling and evaporation with sulfuric acid.
4. Nitric acid attacks most metals, though the thin oxide films formed on aluminum and chromium surfaces retard further solvent action. Tin dissolves, but immediately forms insoluble metastannic acid. Nitric acid also attacks insoluble salts of oxidizable anions, such as metal sulfides.
5. Hot, concentrated perchloric acid dissolves all common metals, but it should be used with extreme caution since easily oxidizable substances, including some organic substances, react with explosive violence. In case of any doubt whatever, a milder oxidizing agent should be used first, and only approved procedures should be followed in each case. Dilute perchloric acid at room temperature behaves much differently and may be used routinely as a strong acid solution.
6. Aqua regia, composed of hydrochloric and nitric acids, attacks all metals. This combination provides hydrochloric acid in an oxidizing medium. The complexing characteristics of the chloride ion are particularly significant in the dissolution of gold and platinum.

Some other combinations of two acids and of one acid plus a complexing, oxidizing or reducing agent are useful as solvents in specific cases.

The use of strong acids to dissolve samples introduces the possibility of loss by volatilization of one or more components of the sample, particularly if a hot acid medium is employed. Volatile weak acids may be lost, and many other substances which are nominally nonvolatile may be lost to an extent significant in highly accurate work.

If only one constituent of a sample remains undissolved after acid treatment, it may be possible to filter, wash and weigh that residue to provide a determination for that constituent. Thus, the unit operations of dissolving the sample and of separating the desired constituent are accomplished simultaneously. For example, nitric acid dissolves all of the components of brass except tin, which remains as a residue of metastannic acid. Metastannic acid is converted to tin oxide upon high temperature ignition, so the amount of tin in the brass sample can be calculated from the weight of the residue after its ignition.

Fusion.   When acid treatment fails to bring a sample into solution, fusion of the sample with a flux may convert it into a water-soluble form. Fusions are especially useful with silicate and carbonate rocks and ores which are not attacked by hydrochloric acid, but they are also useful with many other samples. The flux is usually alkaline, thus minimizing volatility loss of "acid gases" such as hydrogen sulfide and sulfur dioxide.

One of the most commonly used fluxes is sodium carbonate, which converts acidic oxides, such as silicon dioxide, into soluble sodium salts. The reaction may be illustrated by the equation for the fusion of an aluminum silicate, $Al_2(SiO_3)_3$ or $Al_2O_3 \cdot 3\,SiO_2$, with sodium carbonate:

$$Al_2(SiO_3)_3 + 4\,Na_2CO_3 \longrightarrow 3\,Na_3SiO_3 + 2\,NaAlO_2 + 4\,CO_2$$

Metal ions other than aluminum may end as carbonates or as oxides which are soluble in acid if not in water. A mixture of sodium and potassium carbonates melts at a lower temperature than just sodium carbonate, which fact is desirable with some samples but not with others.

In practice about five grams of sodium carbonate are used for each gram of the sample. The flux is placed in a platinum crucible sufficiently large that it will not be over half full. The weighed sample is inserted and stirred with the flux. The mixture is heated gradually until it becomes molten, at which temperature it is maintained until the original sample appears to be completely destroyed. A half hour is often sufficient. The melt is then allowed to cool and the button which forms is treated with hot water. The resultant solution is strongly alkaline but is ready for subsequent unit operations of separation and measurement.

Potassium pyrosulfate is also commonly used as a flux for the dissolving of difficultly soluble oxides. The pyrosulfate liberates sulfur trioxide upon heating which, in turn, reacts with the oxide to form a soluble sulfate, as illustrated by the equations for the dissolving of ferric oxide:

$$K_2S_2O_7 \longrightarrow K_2SO_4 + SO_3$$

$$Fe_2O_3 + 3\,SO_3 \longrightarrow Fe_2(SO_4)_3$$

If the heating occurs too rapidly, the sulfur trioxide liberated in the first reaction escapes to the surrounding air before entering into the second reaction. Typically, twenty or more grams of the pyrosulfate are used for each gram of the sample, and the temperature is held just above the melting point, about 300° C., and raised to "red heat" only briefly at the end of the reaction time. Platinum or silica crucibles are satisfactory for pyrosulfate fusions.

Other useful fluxes include sodium peroxide and mixtures of either potassium chlorate or potassium nitrate with sodium carbonate. Each of these provides a powerful oxidizing action in an alkaline medium. Iron or nickel crucibles are generally used. Even these materials are attacked by the alkaline melt, but they are relatively inexpensive and the metal introduced into the sample is usually not a serious interference.

A mild oxidation action can be introduced into sodium carbonate fusions by use of magnesium oxide along with the carbonate. The magnesium oxide remains solid throughout the fusion in such a form that it provides porosity with resultant free access to air throughout the reaction medium. This flux is known as Eschka's mixture.

REVIEW QUESTIONS

1. What is the one main requirement of a sampling process?
2. Distinguish critically between absolute dryness and reproducible dryness.
3. In what situations must organic solvents be used in drying samples and precipitates?
4. Compare platinum crucibles and porcelain crucibles with respect to usefulness in quantitative analysis.
5. Explain the errors which might be involved in interpreting the composition of a sample from the percentage of water if the latter is determined by loss of weight.
6. Name three common desiccants and compare them on the bases of effectiveness, ease of use and possibility of regeneration.
7. Sketch the flame of a Tirrill burner and indicate relative temperatures in the various zones within the flame.
8. With the aid of chemical equations, explain the solubility of each of the following: sodium sulfate in water; ferric oxide in hydrochloric acid; calcium phosphate in hydrochloric acid; copper in nitric acid; gold in aqua regia.

SUGGESTIONS FOR ADDITIONAL READING

Items 2, 11 and 26, Appendix 7.

Chapter 5

Treatment
of Analytical Data

THE specific methods of calculating the results of an analytical determination from the experimental data will be presented in Chapters 6 and 9 for gravimetric and volumetric methods of analysis, respectively. Consideration is given in the present chapter to some mathematical concepts encountered in all types of calculations and to statistically valid methods of handling and interpreting data.

SIGNIFICANT FIGURES

Definition. *Significant figures* are the digits necessary to express the results of a measurement to the precision with which it is made. Consider, for example, the weighing of a crucible first on a rough balance to the nearest tenth of a gram and then on an analytical balance to the nearest tenth of a milligram, the results of the two weighings being 11.2 grams and 11.2169 grams respectively. Three digits are used in expressing the result of the first measurement and six for the second. Any fewer digits could not express the results of the measurements to the precision with which they were made, and no more digits could justifiably be used for either value; therefore, the first weight is expressed in three significant figures and the second in six.

Consider next the measurement of an extremely small number such as the number of moles of hydrogen ion in one liter of pure water at room temperature. This quantity can be measured, and the result could be written as 0.000 000 1 moles. Eight digits, including the zeros, have been used. However, the same number could be written as 1×10^{-7} moles, in which case only one digit has been used exclusive of the exponential factor. Thus, the result of the measurement has only one significant figure no matter which way it is written, because only one digit is *necessary* to express the results of the measurement to the precision with which it was made. The zeros to the left of the 1 in 0.000 000 1 and the exponential factor of 1×10^{-7} are used merely to locate the decimal point so do not fit into the definition of significant figures. A similar consideration is encountered in measurements of very large numbers. For example, the number of molecules in a mole of any compound can be written as 6.02×10^{23}, and this number contains three significant figures. The exponential factor again serves only to locate the decimal point.

It is important that each person making measurements express the results of the measurements with the proper number of significant figures. Another person who reads, and in any way uses, the results of those measurements can usually tell at a glance how many significant figures are intended. However, there is a possibility of uncertainty in recognizing the number of significant figures in reading large numbers. For example, a recorded volume of 2 000 ml. might signify one significant figure, meaning that the measured value was closer to 2 000 than 1 000 or 3 000. Or it could signify the measured quantity to be closer to 2 000 than to 2 001 or 1 999, with four significant figures. Likewise, the number 2 000 might intend two or three figures to be significant. This possible uncertainty can be avoided very simply if the one who makes the measurement in the first place writes it in an exponential form—2×10^3, 2.0×10^3, 2.00×10^3 or 2.000×10^3—depending upon whether he intends one, two, three or four figures, respectively, to be significant. It is advisable to express the results of measurements in this exponential form whenever there can possibly be any confusion as to whether zeros to the left of the decimal point are significant or not.

Absolute Uncertainty and Relative Uncertainty. Uncertainty in measured values may be considered from either of two distinct viewpoints. *Absolute uncertainty* is the uncertainty expressed directly in units of the measurement. A weight expressed as 10.2 grams is presumably valid within a tenth of a gram, so the absolute uncertainty is within one-tenth of a gram, and a volume measurement written as 46.26 ml. indicates an absolute uncertainty within one-hundredth of a ml. Absolute uncertainties are expressed in units of the type of quantity being measured—gram, liter, and so forth.

Relative uncertainty is the uncertainty expressed in terms of the magnitude of the quantity being measured. The weight of 10.2 grams is valid within one-tenth of a gram and the entire quantity represents 102 tenths of a gram, so the relative uncertainty is about 1 part in 100 parts. The volume written as 46.26 ml. is valid within one-hundredth of a milliliter in 4 626 hundredths of a milliliter, so the relative uncertainty is 1 part in 4 626 parts, or about 0.2 parts in a thousand. It is customary, but by no means necessary, to express relative uncertainties as parts per hundred (per cent) or as parts per thousand. Relative uncertainties do not have dimensions of mass, volume or such, as a relative uncertainty is simply a ratio between two numbers, both of which are in the same dimensional units.

To illustrate further the distinction between absolute and relative uncertainty, consider the results of weighings of two different objects on an analytical balance to be 0.002 1 gram and 0.543 2 gram. As written, the absolute uncertainty of each number is one ten-thousandth of a gram, yet the relative uncertainties differ widely—1 part in about 20 for one value and one part in about 5 000 for the other value.

Significant Figures in Mathematical Operations. Very seldom is the result of an analytical determination based solely upon one measured value. Even the weighing of a single sample normally requires two weight measurements of the weighing bottle, both before and after removing a portion of the sample; the result of one weighing must be subtracted from that of the other to get the sample weight. Frequently, one measured value must be multiplied or divided by another. The analyst is concerned with significant figures not only in dealing with results of single measurements but also in conjunction with numbers computed mathematically from two or more measured quantities. The arithmetic operations of addition and subtraction may be considered together, as may multiplication and division.

In addition and subtraction. The concept of significant figures in a number obtained by an addition or subtraction operation is illustrated in the following example:

weight of bottle plus sample . . . . . . 11.216 9 g
weight of bottle alone . . . . 10.811 4 g
weight of sample . . . . 0.405 5 g

Each of the quantities measured directly contains six significant figures, while the weight of the sample has only four. (The zero to the left of the decimal point is in good form but is not necessary so is not significant.) Now, assume that one weighing was made less precisely, as

$$11.216\ 9 \text{ g}$$
$$10.81 \qquad \text{g}$$
$$\text{not} \quad 0.406\ 9 \text{ g, but rather } 0.41 \text{ g}$$

With the decimal points aligned vertically, the computed result has significant figures no farther to the right than has the individual number whose last figure is farthest from the right. Note that, with absolute uncertainties of 0.0001 g and 0.01 g for the two numbers to be added, the absolute uncertainty of the sum is 0.01 g. The rule for handling significant figures in addition and subtraction may be stated thus: the computed result has an absolute uncertainty as great as that of the individual number which has the largest absolute uncertainty.

In multiplication and division. The concept of significant figures in multiplying and dividing operations must be based upon relative uncertainties. The product or quotient should be expressed with sufficient significant figures to indicate a relative uncertainty comparable to that of the factor with the greatest relative uncertainty. Consider the example

$$9.678\ 234 \times 0.12 = 1.2$$

Expressing this result as, for example, 1.161 3 would be totally unjustifiable in view of the relative uncertainty of the second factor.

The rule that the relative error of a product or quotient is dependent upon the relative error of the least accurately known factor suggests the important generalization that in measuring quantities which must be multiplied or divided to get a final result, it is advantageous to make all the measurements with approximately the same relative error. It is a waste of time to measure one quantity to one part in a hundred thousand if it must subsequently be multiplied by a number which cannot be measured any better than within one part in a hundred. Similarly, it is advisable to measure quantities which are to be combined by addition or subtraction to about the same absolute uncertainty. It would be foolish to take pains to measure one weight to a tenth of a milligram if it is to be added to a weight which for some reason cannot be measured any closer than to, say, 10 milligrams.

Atomic and molecular weights often appear as multiplication and division factors in calculations of analytical results. The computed result can have no less relative uncertainty than that of the atomic or molecular weights; yet these values are known so accurately that they seldom limit the accuracy of a computed result.

PRECISION AND ACCURACY

The terms precision and accuracy have been used without definition in the preceding discussion. A more definite look at the meaning of these two terms is now appropriate.

Precision refers to the variability among replicate measurements of determinations of the same quantity. Consider three determinations of the percentage of lead in a brass sample by one analyst to be 2.63%, 2.62% and 2.62%, and three results obtained for the same sample by a second analyst to be 2.60%, 2.75% and 2.81%. The results of the first analyst exhibit much less variation among themselves than do those of the second, so the precision of the first set of results is better than that of the second.

Accuracy refers to the difference between a measured value and the true value for a quantity to be measured. Strictly speaking the true values are never known except in counting discrete objects ("there are exactly 12 students in this class") and in defined quantities ("the atomic weight of oxygen is exactly 16.000 0"). All other types of measurement including mass, length, volume, and so forth, are actually comparisons to standards and these comparisons must consist of measurements. So the term accuracy refers to the difference between a measured value and the value which is accepted as the true or correct value for the quantity measured.

The distinction between precision and accuracy may be likened to the results of a series of arrows shot at an archery target—precision refers to how close together the several arrows hit and the accuracy of each one refers to how close to the bull's-eye each lands. It is possible for a replicate series of measurements or determinations to be very precise and yet highly inaccurate. It is, however, quite meaningless to consider the accuracy of a series of values unless their precision is reasonably good. The analyst desires to achieve acceptable precision and accuracy in all of his work and to assess how accurate and precise his work and methods are. The terms accuracy and precision will be treated more quantitatively later in this chapter.

The analytical chemist, in common with other workers in science, is continually interested in the cause and the magnitude of errors in his measurements. He examines the quantitative data he obtains not with the question as to whether or not error is present but rather with the question as to how much error and uncertainty exist. He recognizes that error is always present and that he will not completely eliminate error even though he does continually strive to recognize, to minimize and to evaluate the errors which enter into his measurements.

Errors may be arbitrarily divided into two categories, systematic and random. This classification was mentioned briefly in Chapter 4 with reference to errors in sampling and will now be considered within a more general context.

Systematic Errors. Systematic errors are those one-sided errors which can be traced to a specific source, either in the strategic scheme of the experiment or in the apparatus used in its conduct. Such errors can often be minimized by a modified plan of attack. Even when the errors cannot be completely suppressed in this way, an understanding of their origins often makes it possible to deduce a correction factor to be applied to the final result, or at least to estimate the probable residual error in that result.

Where one or more large errors appear to be present, it is frequently possible to discover their origins by a series of carefully controlled experiments in which the experimental conditions and quantities are varied widely in a systematic way. The resultant error must follow one of three courses: (1) the error may remain relatively constant and independent of the experimental conditions; (2) the magnitude of the error may vary systematically with one or more of the experimental conditions; (3) the error may persist as a random error. If the error in a precipitation process proves to be constant in magnitude, such possibilities as reagent contamination must be considered.

If a systematic variation of the error is evident, the parameter linked to this variation frequently indicates the cause. For example, in a gravimetric determination, a negative deviation which increases with the volume of the wash liquid, and which decreases when the sample size is increased, indicates the possibility of a solubility loss. The loss may be reduced, or even entirely suppressed, by employing a different precipitating form or by altering the conditions of precipitation. If this is not possible, a correction factor deduced from the measured solubility of the precipitate involved may be used with good satisfaction. Similarly, a positive variation linked to the sample size in a gravimetric procedure could indicate that the desired precipitate is retaining some other component and thus is not pure.

When an apparently random error is encountered it may be a systematic error linked to some experimental condition not yet investigated or controlled. For example, an apparently random error could ultimately prove to be associated with variations in atmospheric humidity, perhaps indicating that the sample is adsorbing water during the weighing process.

Systematic errors tend to make the observed or calculated values consistently too high or too low. This means that determinate errors can make results highly inaccurate without affecting the precision of replicate results. Good precision does not necessarily mean good accuracy. The danger of retaining one-sided errors without recognizing their presence can be minimized by varying at least some experimental factors in replicate experiments. When three or four portions of the same sample are to be analyzed, they should vary to a modest but appreciable extent in weight. In critical analyses, duplicate sets of samples should be analyzed by entirely different methods since it is unlikely that the same determinate errors would appear to the same extent in entirely different analytical procedures.

Random Errors.   The cause of a random error may or may not be known. Some personal judgment is required in all measurements, such as in reading balance pointer swings, noting just when a container is filled to a predetermined calibration mark, and so forth, and random inaccuracies are bound to occur. Some random errors arise within the method itself, such as impurity of a supposedly pure precipitate, variations with stirring and with speed of mixing reagents, and so forth. Random variations in room temperature and other environmental factors may introduce random error into analytical results.

The analyst can and should minimize random errors insofar as is feasible by careful work, by choice of schemes of analysis which have been or can be proven to be valid and by keeping environmental factors as constant as can be done reasonably. However, residual random errors remain even when all reasonable efforts are made to insure careful and accurate work.

A mathematical analysis of this type of error provides two criteria for the recognition of random errors: (1) small deviations from the correct value are much more frequent than large ones; (2) positive and negative deviations of equal magnitude occur with about the same frequency. These two criteria are expressed graphically in Figure 9, which shows the normal distribution of the errors in a large number of runs of a determination which is ideally perfect aside from random errors. The characteristic distribution of errors, particularly as expressed in criterion (2), suggests that if a large number of determinations are made of the same quantity and if the measurement is affected only by random errors, the average of all the values should indicate directly the correct value. Even when relatively few measurements are made, the average provides a more reliable estimate of the correct value than does any one of the individual determinations, assuming that only random errors are present. The quantitative treatment of averages and of measures of precision and accuracy will be discussed in the next section of this chapter with further reference to the normal distribution curve of Figure 9.

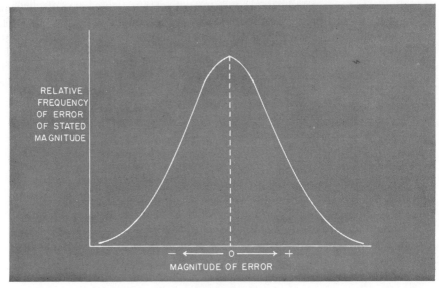

FIGURE 9.   Normal distribution curve.

STATISTICAL TREATMENT OF DATA

Every student of quantitative analysis must develop a working familiarity with a few fundamental statistical concepts. In order to recognize errors and to minimize their effects upon the final result, the analyst must run each determination more than once, usually in triplicate or quadruplicate. Then he must combine the results of these replicate experiments to yield his answer for the determination. Statistical methods are employed in combining and in interpreting these replicate measurements.

Average.   The average is defined as a measure of central tendency. There are several methods of expressing the central tendency. However, one method is the simplest and at the same time about the best from a theoretical standpoint. This is the *arithmetic mean*, commonly called by the more general term *average*, and it is obtained by adding the replicate results and dividing by the number of those results. Consider the following four results of the determination of chloride in a simple salt mixture:

$$
\begin{array}{ll}
\text{a.} & 22.64\,\%\ \text{Cl} \\
\text{b.} & 22.54\,\%\ \text{Cl} \\
\text{c.} & 22.61\,\%\ \text{Cl} \\
\text{d.} & 22.53\,\%\ \text{Cl} \\
\end{array}
$$

$$4\,|\,90.32$$

arithmetic mean is 22.58 % Cl

Deviation. The average, as the measure of central tendency, is very important, but it does not in itself indicate all the information which can be derived from a series of numerical results. The extent of the variations from this average is also of considerable interest. The variation of a single value from the average may be expressed simply as the difference between the two, and this difference is designated the *deviation*. Thus, if X_1, X_2 and X_3 represent the several numerical values and $\overline{X}$ represents the arithmetic mean calculated as described in the preceding paragraph, the several deviations, d_1, d_2, d_3, are

$$d_1 = X_1 - \overline{X}$$
$$d_2 = X_2 - \overline{X}$$
$$d_3 = X_3 - \overline{X}$$

It is conventional to subtract the arithmetic mean from the specific value, as indicated, and not vice versa. Thus the deviation is positive if the one experimental value is greater than the arithmetic mean, and negative if the arithmetic mean is greater. The algebraic sum of all the deviations in a set must equal zero, at least within close limits set by rounding off numbers—a consequence of the definition of the arithmetic mean. The individual deviations may be expressed either in absolute units or in relative units. For example, the deviation of the weight 11 grams from the weight 10 grams is one in absolute units of grams, and it is 1 part in 10 in relative units. The latter may also be expressed as 10 per cent or as 100 parts per thousand.

Average deviation and standard deviation. The analyst is interested not only in averages and in individual deviation values, but he needs a single number whereby he can represent the over-all deviations within a series of replicate results. This over-all deviation is actually the precision. There are several methods of expressing it numerically, but only two will be mentioned here: the average deviation, and the standard deviation.

The *average deviation* of an individual result is the arithmetic mean of the individual deviations, disregarding the + and − signs on each individual deviation. The *standard deviation* of an individual result is the square root of the arithmetic mean of the squares of the individual deviations. These two definitions may be expressed mathematically as

$$\overline{d} = \frac{d_1 + d_2 + d_3 + \text{etc.}}{n}$$

$$s = \sqrt{\frac{d_1^2 + d_2^2 + d_3^2 + \text{etc.}}{n - 1}}$$

in which d_1, d_2, d_3, etc., are the individual deviations, n is the number of individual deviations, $\overline{d}$ is the average deviation and s is the standard deviation.

Consider the following illustrative data:

% Cl	d	d²
22.64	+0.06	0.003 6
22.54	−0.04	0.001 6
22.61	+0.03	0.000 9
22.53	−0.05	0.002 5
90.32	0.18	0.008 6

$$\text{average} = \frac{90.32}{4} \qquad \bar{d} = \frac{0.18}{4} \qquad s = \sqrt{\frac{0.008\ 6}{4-1}}$$

$$\text{average} = 22.58 \qquad \bar{d} = 0.04 \qquad s = 0.05$$

It is clear that it is easier to calculate the average deviation, $\bar{d}$, than to calculate the standard deviation, s. Nevertheless, there are valid theoretical reasons why the standard deviation is a better measure of the over-all deviations, so it is much more widely used.

Confidence Limits. In order for us to recognize more fully the true significance of the arithmetic mean and the standard deviation, we must refer again to the curve of Figure 9. This curve, which may be derived mathematically, represents the normal distribution of the errors or deviations in a large number of runs of a determination which is ideally perfect aside from random errors. It has already been pointed out that small deviations are much more frequent than large ones. This latter statement may be made quantitative with the use of the standard deviation. The mathematical treatment from which the curve is derived reveals, for example, that 68% of the individual deviations are less than the standard deviation, that 95% are less than twice the standard deviation, and that 99% are less than 2.5 times the standard deviation. This means that 68% of the X values fall within the range of $\overline{X} \pm s$; 95%, within the range $\overline{X} \pm 2s$; and 99%, within the range $\overline{X} \pm 2.5s$.

Any data which are based directly on the normal distribution curve or on its mathematical origins are not directly applicable to most analytical situations. There are two reasons for this fact: (1) the derivation specifies random errors only, while many analytical data are influenced by one-sided, systematic errors as well; (2) the derivation specifies a large number of runs (actually an infinite number) while only relatively small numbers of runs are feasible in practical situations. Because of (1), one-sided, systematic errors must be eliminated before the concept of confidence limits (to be described shortly) may become applicable. Because of (2), the analyst can never know with absolute certainty whether his arithmetic mean is the absolutely correct value or not unless he does run an extremely large number of determinations. Even with a few determinations, however, he can specify a range of values centered upon his arithmetic mean and then specify that there is a 50-50 chance, or a 95 out of a 100 chance, or a 99 out of a 100 chance (or any other desired chance) that the true value does lie within that range. That is, he can know and specify the probability that the true answer lies within a given range, and he can indicate that range in terms of the arithmetic mean and standard deviation. That range is designated the *confidence limit*, and the likelihood that the true value lies within that range is designated the *probability*. The probability is conveniently expressed in percentage units.

Statistical data are listed in Table 7 from which the confidence limits may be ascertained for practical analytical situations. The number of replicate determinations is represented by n; f_{50}, f_{95}, f_{99} are the factors by

Table 7. Factors for Calculating Confidence Limits

n	f_{50}	f_{95}	f_{99}
2	0.72	9.0	45.
3	0.47	2.5	5.7
4	0.38	1.6	2.9
5	0.33	1.2	2.1
6	0.30	1.0	1.6
10	0.22	0.72	1.0
20	0.15	0.47	0.64

(with n individual values for calculating the average, $\overline{X}$, the true value may be expected to lie within the range $\overline{X} \pm fs$ with a % probability as indicated by the f subscript)

which the standard deviation of an individual result must be multiplied to yield the confidence limits for 50%, 95% and 99% probability, respectively, in the form $\overline{X} \pm fs$. Thus, the analyst may state that the true value lies within the range $\overline{X} \pm f_{50}s$ and have a 50-50 chance of being correct. Or he may state that the true value lies within the range $\overline{X} \pm f_{95}s$ and be 95% certain of being correct.

The use of Table 7 may be illustrated by continuing the example used earlier in this chapter. Four results of a chloride determination yielded an arithmetic mean ($\overline{X}$) of 22.58% Cl with a standard deviation (s) of 0.05 units. From Table 7, for n = 4, f_{50} is 0.38; so there is a 50-50 likelihood that the true value lies within the range $22.58 \pm 0.38 \times 0.05\%$ Cl, or $22.58 \pm 0.02\%$ Cl. Or there is a 95% probability that the true value lies within the range $22.58 \pm 0.08\%$ Cl, and a 99% probability that it is within $22.58 \pm 0.14\%$ Cl. It is clear from this example, and from the table, that the limits must be widened as the required probability of being correct is increased. It is also clear from the table that the importance of each additional trial beyond three or four diminishes as the total number n increases. These facts are in keeping with common sense; statistical concepts should be considered as a means of making common sense quantitative and not as a substitute for common sense.

The probability value used in expressing the results of an analytical determination is quite arbitrary. In any case, the probability chosen should be stated or otherwise indicated. Probabilities of 95% and 99% are most commonly employed in analytical work, while a 50% probability is also useful in student work. Therefore, 50%, 95% and 99% data are included in Table 7, although other probabilities could be used and occasionally are. In view of these concepts, it is not good form for a student to report his results for a particular determination as, say, 22.58% Cl; it is much better form to report it as, say, "22.58 ± 0.02% Cl with 50% probability level." Consult your professor for instructions as to what probability form is to be used in reporting results from your laboratory work.

Rejection of an Observation. Every student of quantitative analysis is occasionally confronted with a series of results of replicate determinations, one of which appears to be far out of line with the others. Even experienced analytical chemists encounter the same situation. Consider the series of results:

$$22.64\% \text{ Cl}$$
$$22.54\% \text{ Cl}$$
$$22.22\% \text{ Cl}$$
$$22.69\% \text{ Cl}$$

The third value appears to be out of line. If this third determination were subject to a large one-sided error, such as spilling of some precipitate prior to weighing it, it should be rejected prior to computing the arithmetic mean and confidence limits. However, in a small series of data such as this, all four values *could* be valid for ascertaining the arithmetic mean. The beginning student is perhaps too greatly inclined to discard a datum which does not seem to agree with the body of his measurements, so it is apparent that some standard criterion for such rejection is necessary.

First, any value may be rejected if a particular reason for its inaccuracy is known. If it is known that part of a precipitate was spilled or that a volumetric container leaked, that result may be discarded at once. Sometimes such a determination need not even be completed. Other times, the analyst may suspect that a specific error may have entered in one sample in a determination but he may not be certain at the time—he should complete that sample and then discard the result if it appears particularly erroneous in the proper direction. Second, if no experimental reason for rejection is known but a value still appears out of line, some statistical test must be employed in deciding whether to reject an observation. A simple and statistically valid test is based upon the differences between the highest and lowest values as calculated both with and without the suspicious value. Let R_1 be the difference between the highest and lowest values with all values included, and let R_2 be the difference between the highest and lowest values excluding the suspicious one. If the ratio, $R_1 \div R_2$ exceeds the critical value listed for the appropriate n number in Table 8, the suspected observation should be rejected; otherwise, it should be retained. For each n value there are two critical $R_1 \div R_2$ ratios listed in Table 8, one for 95% probability level and one for 99% probability level. When the 95% column is used, the chance of an extreme value being rejected when it should have been retained is 5%, while there is only a 1% chance that a value rejected on the basis of the 99% column should have been retained. Consider again the four values, 22.64% Cl, 22.54% Cl, 22.22% Cl and 22.69% Cl. R_1 is 0.47 (22.69–22.22) and R_2 is 0.15 (22.69–22.54). The ratio $R_1 \div R_2$ is 0.47 ÷ 0.15 or 3.12. The critical values from Table 8 are greater than 3.12, so the value should be retained. Consider

Table 8. Factors for Retention or Rejection of Extreme Values

n	Critical Values of $R_1 \div R_2$	
	At 95% Probability Level	At 99% Probability Level
3	16.9	83.3
4	4.3	9.0
5	2.8	4.6
6	2.3	3.3
8	1.9	2.4
10	1.7	2.1

next the four values, 22.64, 22.69, 22.65 and 22.22. Here R_1 is 0.47, R_2 is 0.05 excluding the 22.22 value; $R_1 \div R_2$ is 9.4, which is even greater than the 99% factor in Table 8, so the 22.22 result can be rejected with less than a 1% chance of making a mistake in doing so.

It is suggested that the 99% probability column of Table 8 be employed in student work in deciding whether or not to reject an observation, unless your professor instructs you differently. In any case, you should recognize, even quantitatively, what the residual chances are that a value being rejected should have been retained.

If more than one value is doubtful, this test can be repeated after the most extreme value has been rejected. This is ordinarily not recommended, however. If two values are doubtful in a series of only four or so, it would be much better to repeat the whole experiment to obtain more values. It should be noted that the effect upon the arithmetic mean of one or even of two discordant values is relatively less significant when they are one or two of many than when they are one or two of only a few.

Comparison of Averages. The student in quantitative analysis is called upon to employ in his laboratory work the statistical concepts described thus far in this chapter. He is not usually called upon to compare averages; yet this operation is of considerable importance in the final interpretation and use of the data which are obtained in the analytical laboratory. Consider the example of some determinations of the density of nitrogen which were performed in the laboratory of Lord Rayleigh in 1894. Batches of nitrogen were prepared by various means from the chemical compounds, NO, N_2O and NH_4NO_2, and also from dry, CO_2-free air by several methods of removing oxygen. Measurements of the mass of nitrogen required to fill a certain flask under specified conditions revealed for ten batches of "chemical nitrogen" an arithmetic mean of 2.299 71, and for nine batches of "atmospheric nitrogen" an arithmetic mean of 2.310 22; the over-all standard deviation within each group can be considered to be about 0.000 30. The question

Table 9. *Critical t Values for Comparison of Averages*

D. F.	Critical t Value at	
	95% Probability Level	99% Probability Level
1	12.7	63.7
2	4.3	9.9
3	3.2	5.8
4	2.8	4.6
5	2.6	4.0
6	2.5	3.7
8	2.3	3.4
10	2.3	3.2
15	2.1	2.9
20	2.1	2.8

(D. F. (degrees of freedom) is n + m − 2)

arose, was there a significant difference between the two averages? That is, was the density of the "chemical nitrogen" the same as that of the "atmospheric nitrogen" or, more basically, was nitrogen from both sources the same?

We can answer this question on the basis of the *t test* for comparing averages. This test will be presented empirically here along with recognition of its statistical validity. The quantity t is defined as

$$ t = \frac{\bar{x} - \bar{y}}{s} \sqrt{\frac{nm}{n + m}} $$

in which $\bar{x}$ and $\bar{y}$ are the two averages, m and n are the number of individual values averaged to obtain $\bar{x}$ and $\bar{y}$, respectively, and s is the over-all standard deviation. In Table 9 are listed critical t values at 95% and 99% probability levels. The D. F. value, degrees of freedom, is a common statistical term which is simply n + m − 2 in this application. If an observed or calculated t exceeds the indicated critical t value, the chances are 95 out of 100 or 99 out of 100 (depending upon which critical t value of Table 9 is used) that the averages are significantly different.

The t value for the nitrogen data may be calculated as follows:

$$t = \frac{\bar{x} - \bar{y}}{s}\sqrt{\frac{nm}{n + m}}$$

$$t = \frac{2.310\ 22 - 2.299\ 71}{0.000\ 30}\sqrt{\frac{10 \times 9}{10 + 9}}$$ (the larger average is conventionally taken as $\bar{x}$, the smaller as $\bar{y}$)

$$t = 76$$

From Table 9, the limiting values of t with D. F. $= 17(n + m - 2)$ is far less than 76, even at 99% probability level. (No critical values are listed for D. F. $= 17$, but they would logically lie between those for D. F. $= 15$ and 20.) So the "chemical nitrogen" and the "atmospheric nitrogen" are almost certainly different. Lord Rayleigh, employing a somewhat different but comparable statistical test, recognized this difference, and this fact led directly to the discovery shortly thereafter of the inert gases in the atmosphere!

A further example should be in order. Consider four gravimetric determinations of chloride in a particular sample yielding the arithmetic mean, 20.44% Cl, and four volumetric determinations of chloride in the same sample yielding the arithmetic mean 20.54% Cl, both with standard deviations of about 0.08. Are the results of the gravimetric and volumetric methods significantly different? The t test provides the answer.

$$t = \frac{\bar{x} - \bar{y}}{s}\sqrt{\frac{nm}{n + m}}$$

$$t = \frac{20.54 - 20.44}{0.08}\sqrt{\frac{4 \times 4}{4 + 4}}$$

$$t = 1.77$$

The critical t values for D. F. $= 6(n + m - 2)$ are 2.5 and 3.7 at the two listed probability levels, so there is no statistical justification for concluding that the two averages are significantly different.

It has been assumed in both examples that the standard deviations are about the same for both averaged sets of data. If the standard deviations differ by more than a factor of two or so, the s value in the equation for t must be a properly weighted combination of the two standard deviations so the t test is more complex. No further consideration will be given to this point in this book. If the t test leads to inconclusive results as, for example, if an observed t value lies between the 95% and 99% critical t values, additional data are required to resolve the question of whether or not the two averages are significantly different. The t test is particularly useful in comparing two different analytical procedures for the same constituent (although here the standard deviations of the two may differ widely), in comparing test results by two different analysts or in two different laboratories or on two different days, and in establishing the identity of two samples.

REVIEW QUESTIONS

Define and illustrate each of the following terms:
1. Significant figures
2. Precision
3. Accuracy
4. Systematic error
5. Random error
6. Average
7. Deviation
8. Standard deviation
9. Confidence limits
10. What is meant by "50% probability"? by "100% probability"?

PROBLEMS

1. What is the correct expression of the weight of a mixture of 21 grams of one substance and 2.0794 grams of another?
2. Calculate the molecular weight of acetic acid, $HC_2H_3O_2$, from these atomic weights: H, 1.0080; C, 12.011; O, 16.00000.
3. Calculate the molecular weight of gadolinium nitrate, $Gd(NO_3)_3$, from these atomic weights: Gd, 156.9; N, 14.008; O, 16.00000.
4. Solve: $\dfrac{24.26 \times 1.9}{94.63 \times 0.002140}$.
5. Solve: $16.4963 + (1.73 \times 0.2)$.
6. The following results were obtained in replicate determinations of % Cl in a chloride sample: 59.83; 60.04; 60.45; 59.88; 60.33; 60.24; 60.28; 59.77. Calculate (a) the arithmetic mean, (b) the standard deviation, and (c) the standard deviation in relative (per cent) units.
7. If the sample of problem 6 was pure sodium chloride, calculate the absolute and relative errors of the mean.
8. The following determinations were made of the atomic weight of carbon: 12.0080; 12.0095; 12.0097; 12.0101; 12.0102; 12.0106; 12.0111; 12.0113; 12.0118; 12.0120. Calculate (a) the arithmetic mean and (b) the standard deviation, and (c) express the atomic weight of carbon on the basis of 99% probability confidence limits.
9. A student obtained 39.17%, 39.99%, 39.21% and 37.72% Fe in a sample. (a) Should any result be rejected on statistical grounds? (b) What is his range for 50% probability confidence limits? If the correct answer is 39.33% Fe, what are his (c) absolute error and his (d) relative error in parts per thousand?
10. A student obtained 0.0971, 0.0968, 0.0976 and 0.0984 in repeated measurements of the molarity of a solution. (a) Should any result be rejected on statistical grounds? (b) What is his range for 50% confidence limits? (c) for 95% confidence limits?

11. An iron determination by a gravimetric procedure yielded an average of 46.20% Fe for six trials, and four trials by a volumetric procedure yielded an average of 46.02% Fe, both standard deviations being 0.08% Fe. Is there a significant difference in the results between the two methods?
12. The mass of an object was found to be 18.2463 grams with a standard deviation of 0.0003 gram when weighed by eleven students in one class, while eight students in another class got an average of 18.2466 grams with the same standard deviation. Is there a significant difference in the results obtained by the two classes?

SUGGESTIONS FOR ADDITIONAL READING

Items 14 and 31, Appendix 7.

Part Two

GRAVIMETRIC METHODS

Chapter 6

The Unit Operations, Tools and Calculations of Gravimetric Analysis

THE THREE major classifications of quantitative analytical methods are gravimetric, volumetric and instrumental. Gravimetric methods are now to be studied in detail in three chapters. The general operations, tools and methods of calculation are discussed in this chapter. Specific gravimetric procedures are presented in Chapter 7, while the precipitation process is studied in more detail in Chapter 8.

UNIT OPERATIONS IN GRAVIMETRIC METHODS

A gravimetric method of analysis may generally be considered as consisting of eleven major operations:

1. Sampling.
2. Drying the sample.
3. Weighing the sample.
4. Dissolving the sample.
5. Adjustment of the conditions of this solution.
6. Precipitation.
7. Digestion.
8. Filtration.
9. Washing.
10. Drying or ignition.
11. Weighing.

The first four are in common with the unit operations for methods other than gravimetric. Number 11 is a repeat of the third one as far as the experimental operation is concerned, and 10 is to a lesser extent a repeat of the second operation. So the laboratory unit operations 5 through 9 are those especially characteristic of gravimetric methods. These operations are centered around the precipitation process—preparation for it, performing it, and handling the precipitate after it is obtained. There are some gravimetric methods in which two or more of these steps may be combined or, occasionally, omitted altogether. Nevertheless, these are the unit operations generally encountered in gravimetric methods of analysis. Emphasis is placed in this chapter on operations 5 through 9 and some aspects of 10 since the others were considered in Chapters 3 and 4.

ADJUSTMENT OF THE CONDITIONS OF THE SAMPLE SOLUTION

Varied treatments are required to bring different samples into solution. Sometimes water is a suitable solvent, often an acid medium is required, and other treatments are often necessary. Unfortunately, the nature of the solution, once the sample is dissolved, is seldom directly suitable for the precipitation step. However, rather simple adjustments of the conditions of this solution are usually sufficient. Factors which must be considered include volume, concentration ranges of the unknown constituent, presence of and concentration range of other components, pH and temperature. These factors are all interrelated.

Volume. The volume of the sample solution is, of course, closely related to the concentration factors. Ideally, the volume should be large enough that the solution can be handled readily with available apparatus without significant losses and yet not so large that it becomes bulky and inconvenient to handle. The apparatus available for use influences the choice of solution volume or, conversely, the solution volume may be determined by other factors so that it, in turn, dictates the choice of apparatus. Solution volumes ranging from ten to a few hundred ml. are convenient to handle in the laboratory. A solution which is too large in volume may usually be concentrated by boiling off the excess solvent; the danger of loss of a desired component through volatility from the hot solution must be recognized and the desired part of the sample must, of course, remain in solution. A solution which is of too small volume can be increased in volume by adding more solvent; the dangers of hydrolysis or other solvolysis reactions must be considered, and the desired constituent must not become too dilute.

Concentration Range of the Unknown Constituent. The unknown constituent must be in a concentration range such that the precipitation step may be carried out successfully. If the constituent which is to be precipitated is excessively concentrated at the time of precipitation, the precipitate will inevitably be impure, particularly if other components are also very concentrated. If, however, that constituent is too dilute, an excessive amount of the precipitated substance may remain in solution. The latter factor ties in directly with the choice of solution volume. Although the solubility per unit volume remains constant, the more dilute the constituent is the larger the fraction of it that remains in solution. This generalization holds true whether the low concentration arises from an extremely small gross amount of the unknown constituent in a moderate volume of solution or from a moderate gross amount of constituent in an excessively large volume of solution.

Even though the exact concentration of the unknown constituent is not known, an approximate composition of a sample is generally known prior to its subjection to a quantitative analysis. This fact arises because qualitative data must precede quantitative data, and qualitative data properly are, or can be made, semiquantitative whether they are obtained by direct laboratory qualitative tests or by a knowledge of the past history and nature of the sample. Therefore, the volume of the solution of the sample in a gravimetric procedure should be so adjusted that the concentration of the desired constituent falls within the range set by the factors of purity and solubility of the precipitate. These factors will be considered in further detail in Chapter 8.

Presence of and Concentration Ranges of Other Constituents. The analytical chemist must be concerned not only with the status of the unknown constituent in the sample solution; he must be equally concerned with the presence of other constituents and their approximate concentrations. A complete qualitative analysis would, of course, have revealed the identity of all other components of the sample, and the reagents used in preparing the sample solution will indicate the presence of still more components. In many cases, however, the quantitative analyst must make qualitative tests for specific substances which are known to interfere in the particular gravimetric procedure. There are virtually no perfectly specific precipitating agents; that is, there are no reagents available which can form a precipitate with one and only one constituent. Therefore, the analyst must be especially cognizant of the presence of other constituents which can react with the precipitating agent which is to be employed. Indeed, the presence of certain other constituents along with the unknown one frequently dictates which of two or more possible precipitating agents is to be used.

Furthermore, any and every substance present in the solution can contribute to impurity of the precipitate whether or not it forms a nominally insoluble substance with the precipitating agent. Every precipitated substance tends to carry down with it some of every component of the solution from which it was precipitated, even some of the solvent itself. The several mechanisms of this process are discussed in Chapter 8. Suffice it to say here that the extent of the impurity caused by any foreign constituent increases as its concentration increases and that some constituents exhibit the effect to a much greater extent than others. Clearly, then, the analyst must be concerned about the presence and concentration ranges of all constituents in the sample solution.

The removal of part or all of any particularly serious interfering substance may take any one of several courses, depending upon the particular situation. Several possibilities may be listed:

1. A separate precipitation and filtration procedure may be useful in removing the interfering substance. Care must be taken to insure that no significant amount of the unknown constituent is lost at the same time. This principle is applied, for example, in the analysis of limestone, described in Chapter 7, in which ferric ion is removed as its hydrous oxide prior to precipitation of calcium as its oxalate. If the ferric ion were not removed first, it would interfere in the calcium determination.

2. The solution may be diluted with more solvent. The unknown constituent, of course, is diluted as well as all others.

3. The pH may be adjusted to make the desired precipitation reaction more selective. For example, chloride is determined gravimetrically as silver chloride in one of the determinations described in Chapter 7. Either phosphate or carbonate will interfere, by precipitation as silver phosphate or silver carbonate, unless the solution is made distinctly acid to complex the interfering ion:

$$H^+ + PO_4^= \longrightarrow HPO_4^= \quad \text{and} \quad H^+ + CO_3^= \longrightarrow HCO_3^-$$

4. The interfering substance may be bound in a soluble but sparingly ionized form even without directly involving hydrogen ions. For example, ammonia complexes silver ion:

$$Ag^+ + 2\,NH_3 \longrightarrow Ag(NH_3)_2^+$$

The same principle could be applied in the volumetric determination of calcium and magnesium in water (Chapter 13) in which interference from cupric ion could be prevented by complexing it with cyanide ion.

5. The constituent to be removed may be extracted into a solvent immiscible with that used in preparing the sample solution. The constituent which is removed may be the one which would subsequently interfere or, conversely, the unknown constituent may be extracted away from others. For example, ferric ion can be extracted from an aqueous hydrochloric acid solution into ether, thus separating it from many other ions. The technique of extraction is employed in the colorimetric determination of nickel as described in Chapter 17.

6. Some potentially interfering substances can be removed by adsorption. For example, many substances can be adsorbed from solution onto fine-mesh silica gel. Some substances are adsorbed more readily than others, so it is often possible to separate one constituent from the others. Adsorption procedures have been developed very extensively under the designation of *chromatography* for separations in conjunction with qualitative analysis and also for quantitative work. In *column chromatography*, the adsorbent of silica gel or other particulate material is placed in a cylindrical tube. A buret can be used, although several special tubes have been developed. The sample solution is applied at the top of the column, and then a solvent is passed through. The several constituents

emerge from the bottom of the tube in inverse order of the tightness by which they are adsorbed in the presence of the particular liquid medium employed. Clear-cut separations are often accomplished, particularly with organic substances. In *gas chromatography*, the adsorbent particles are also packed into a tube, often much longer than a buret. The unknown gaseous mixture is inserted at one end and caused to flow through the tube by passage of a "carrier gas." The several components are again caused to emerge from the other end of the tube in inverse order of their adsorbabilities. This experimental technique has proven to be tremendously versatile and valuable in gas analysis, although the final measurements of the separated components are seldom if ever made gravimetrically. In *paper chromatography* a strip of filter paper can serve as the adsorbent. The test solution, generally just one or two drops, is placed near one end of the strip. That end is then immersed in a solvent, but not deeply enough for the liquid level to touch the spot at which test sample was applied. Capillary action then causes the solvent to flow along the length of the strip, which may be either in an upward, a horizontal or a downward direction, depending upon the physical arrangement. As the solvent flows, it carries along the constituents of the test solution at a characteristic rate for each constituent. The separated components may be collected as the solvent drips off of the other end of the strip or, more frequently, the process is stopped while the components lie in different positions along the paper. The techniques of paper chromatography are seldom encountered in gravimetric analysis, but they are very useful with colorimetric and other types of measurement of the separated constituents. Many valuable modifications of the chromatographic techniques have been developed.

7. Closely allied to chromatographic adsorption procedures are *ion exchange* procedures. The test solution is passed through a cylinder packed with a synthetic resin called the exchanger. There are two types of exchangers, cationic and anionic. The cationic exchangers have organic acid groups, the replaceable hydrogen ions of which are exchanged for other cations in the test solution. This reaction may be represented by the equation

$$E{\cdot}H + Na^+ \longrightarrow E{\cdot}Na + H^+$$

in which E· represents all of the exchanger molecule except for one replaceable hydrogen ion and Na^+ represents the cation which is to be removed from the test solution. The test solution receives hydrogen ions in place of other cations. The anionic exchangers are resins having organic basic groups, such as $-NH_2$. The type may be represented as $E{\cdot}NH_2$, and it hydrolyzes in water

$$E{\cdot}NH_2 + H_2O \longrightarrow E{\cdot}NH_3{\cdot}OH$$

retaining the hydroxyl ion on its surface. The hydroxyl ion can then exchange for another anion from the test solution; for example,

$$E{\cdot}NH_3{\cdot}OH + Cl^- \longrightarrow E{\cdot}NH_3{\cdot}Cl + OH^-$$

The test solution receives hydroxyl ions in place of other anions. A variety of cationic and anionic exchangers have been developed, and their use represents one of the biggest recent strides forward in the continuing development of analytical chemistry. Some specific situations call for the use of a cationic exchanger, others for an anionic exchanger, and both types are occasionally useful for the same test solution.

The ion exchange technique can be used, for example, in the removal of ferric and aluminum ions prior to the gravimetric determination of sulfate by precipitation as barium sulfate. This step could readily be inserted in the sulfate experiment of Chapter 7 if the sample contained sufficient aluminum or iron to warrant it. A somewhat different application of ion exchangers is used in the volumetric determination of total salt content as described in Chapter 10. Essentially all of the cations of the unknown salt solution are replaced by hydrogen ions, and the latter are measured by an acid-base titration procedure.

pH. One of the most significant factors in the adjustment of the condition of the sample solution is the pH. This factor is important for three broad reasons: (1) its influence upon potentially interfering substances; (2) its influence upon the solubility of the desired precipitate; (3) its influence upon the filterability and other handling characteristics of the desired precipitate. The significance of pH in minimizing interference can be illustrated in the precipitation of barium chromate in the presence of strontium ion. Strontium chromate is nominally insoluble, but it is more soluble than barium chromate so, in principle, the separation can be accomplished by keeping the chromate ion concentration just large enough for barium chromate to precipitate but insufficient for strontium chromate to come down. In sufficiently acid medium, the equilibrium

$$2\ CrO_4^= + 2\ H^+ \rightleftharpoons 2\ HCrO_4^- \rightleftharpoons Cr_2O_7^= + H_2O$$

is far enough to the right to keep the chromate ion concentration at an adequately low value. As barium chromate precipitates, more chromate ion forms in accordance with Le Chatelier's principle so that the desired precipitation of barium chromate may be completed fairly well without ever exceeding the chromate ion concentration at which strontium chromate would begin to precipitate also.

The solubility of many desired precipitates is very markedly influenced by pH. For example, calcium oxalate is soluble in acids, but is insoluble in a basic medium

$$CaC_2O_4{\cdot}H_2O + H^+ \rightleftharpoons Ca^{++} + HC_2O_4^- + H_2O$$

At a low pH the equilibrium is driven to the right, thus putting or keeping all of the substance in solution, whereas at a higher pH the equilibrium is dominantly to the left.

The influence of pH upon the filterability and other handling characteristics of a precipitate is frequently very important. For example, silver chloride precipitated from a neutral medium is very finely divided and may remain in suspension in its mother liquid for extended periods of time. Yet the same precipitate, if formed at a low pH, consists of larger particles and aggregates of particles which settle out much more readily for easy washing and filtration. This phenomenon will be encountered in further detail in Chapters 7 and 8.

Temperature. The dissolving of most salts is an endothermic reaction, so salt solubilities are generally greater at higher temperatures than at lower ones. The situation is reversed for a few substances, such as calcium sulfate. One goal in the precipitation process in a gravimetric determination is to achieve adequately complete precipitation of the desired substance; therefore, the temperature of the solutions from which it is precipitated is very important. The magnitude of the effect of temperature upon solubility varies widely from one substance to another. For example, silver chloride is more than ten times as soluble at $100°$ C. as at $0°$ C., while barium sulfate is only about twice as soluble in hot water as in cold. Therefore, the extent of the improvement of recovery achieved by lowering the temperature depends on the nature of the precipitate. If the precipitate is one whose solubility is strongly dependent upon temperature and if its solubility at room temperature is excessive, it may still be possible to recover it quantitatively by keeping the mother liquid and the wash liquid cold at the time of filtration. Thus, magnesium ammonium phosphate can be precipitated and recovered quantitatively, but only when the liquids are cooled for filtering and washing.

Even though low temperatures are generally preferable from the standpoint of precipitate solubility, a high temperature may be more beneficial from the equally important standpoint of the efficiency of filtering and washing. For example, barium sulfate can be filtered and washed much more readily if it is precipitated from hot solution than if from cold, even though cold is better from the solubility standpoint. Clearly, a compromise is necessary. In some cases it is feasible to keep the solutions hot during precipitation to get the benefit with respect to physical characteristics, and then to cool the suspension prior to filtration to get the benefit with respect to solubility.

This discussion of the adjustment of the various conditions of the sample solution should not be concluded without emphasizing again that all of these factors are interrelated. Conflicting requirements often arise, and the final conditions selected usually represent a series of compromises.

PRECIPITATION

The unit operation of precipitation is at the heart of every gravimetric procedure except volatilization procedures. The precipitating agent may be in the form of a solution of a chemical substance or it may be an electric current. The latter is described in Chapter 19, so the emphasis here and in the following two chapters will be on the use of chemical precipitating agents. The preceding unit operations are designed to prepare the sample so that the unknown constituent or some other constituent quantitatively related to it is ready for the precipitation step, and subsequent unit operations are for the handling and measuring of this precipitate once it has been obtained. The whole determination is based upon the precipitation reaction.

Fundamental Requirements. The precipitation process must fulfill three fundamental requirements in order to serve as a satisfactory basis of a gravimetric procedure:

1. *The unknown constituent must be precipitated quantitatively.* This means that the fraction of that constituent which is left in solution must be a negligible portion of the total amount of that constituent.
2. *The precipitate must be pure or, at least, it must by the time of final measurement be of known purity.* The precipitate must not include at the time of formation appreciable quantities of any other substance except or unless those other substances are readily removable in the washing and drying operations.
3. *The precipitate must be in a physical form suitable for subsequent handling.* It is not enough that the precipitate be of the correct chemical composition —it must also, for example, consist of particles large enough to be filtered. These three requirements, which will be described in detail in Chapter 8, are closely interrelated one with another. To illustrate, the particle size may influence the purity of a precipitate to a considerable extent. The entire precipitation process is designed to meet these three requirements.

Choice of Precipitating Agent. The chemist who is planning a determination may have two or more available chemical reagents, each of which can form a nominally insoluble precipitate with the unknown constituent. He must choose the one which will cause the precipitation process best to fulfill the three requirements. Consider an unknown salt mixture of which the weight percentage of sulfate is to be determined. Among the cations which form insoluble sulfates are barium, lead and calcium. However, barium sulfate is much less soluble in water than is either lead sulfate or calcium sulfate, so requirement 1 is best fulfilled with a barium salt solution as the precipitating agent. Of the two typical barium salts, barium chloride and barium nitrate, requirement 2 is fulfilled much better by the former because barium sulfate is badly contaminated by barium nitrate if precipitated in the presence of appreciable concentration of nitrate ion; barium chloride is chosen as the precipitating agent for sulfate ion. Hydrogen sulfide can precipitate quite a few substances quantitatively so that it often can fulfill requirement 1 exceptionally well, but precipitations with hydrogen sulfide seldom fulfill requirement 3. So sulfide precipitates are seldom used in quantitative analysis, although they are very useful in qualitative work. The use of thioacetamide as a regent for the homogeneous generation of hydrogen sulfide results in somewhat better fulfillment of requirement 3, and some quantitative procedures of this type have been developed.

Other factors being equal, the cheaper of two possible reagents should be chosen. This factor is important, but in an industrial analytical laboratory the cost of reagents is almost invariably far overhadowed by the cost of the analyst's time.

Precipitation Techniques. The precipitation operation must be conducted in a manner designed to enable the process to fulfill the three listed requirements. Surprisingly enough, the degree to which each of the three is fulfilled is influenced by the way in which the precipitation step is performed. Such factors as concentration and temperature of reagent solution, how rapidly it is added to the sample solution, how great an excess is added, the extent of stirring during mixing of the solutions, whether the inner walls of the precipitation vessel are scratched or not, and so forth, are all of importance. Explanations of these and other factors will be encountered in Chapter 8; we are more concerned now with the experimental procedures for carrying out the precipitations.

Precipitations are generally performed in lipped beakers. Each beaker should be large enough so that it need be no more than about two-thirds full at the end of the precipitation. Each should be equipped with a stirring rod with fire-polished ends, or a mechanical stirrer should be employed. There are three main types of mechanical stirrers. In one, a motor merely replaces the operator in manipulating the stirring rod; the lower end of the stirring rod may be flattened or bent to provide optimum agitation. In another, air pressure operates the stirrer. The third type is a magnetic stirrer; a glass enclosed piece of magnetic metal is inserted into the precipitation vessel and caused to rotate when the beaker is placed over the motor. This type is advantageous in that the space over the beaker is not cluttered up with the stirring assembly. In any of the types, only glass need come in contact with the solution. Even though mechanical stirrers are very useful, simple hand mixing with a stirring rod is usually sufficient unless the stirring must be continued for an extended period of time.

The solution of the precipitating agent should usually be quite dilute, but there are exceptions to this generalization. Most of the factors discussed in conjunction with the optimum range of concentration of the unknown constituent are equally applicable here. In many procedures the precipitating agent should be added slowly, although once again there are numerous exceptions. Burets and pipets (described in Chapter 9) and medicine droppers are useful for the slow addition of one solution to another.

The amount of reagent solution needed should be calculated in advance from an approximate knowledge of the sample. This is important in fulfilling all three of the listed requirements and is also important from the economical standpoint—many reagents are expensive and should not be wasted. The amount of reagent used must be at least enough to react with all of the unknown constituent in order to fulfill requirement (1); a 10 to 100% excess is usually desirable. Since the analyst has, at best, semi-quantitative data from which to calculate the necessary amount of reagent, a test for completeness of precipitation is advisable before proceeding to or beyond the filtration operation. This consists of adding a little more of the precipitating agent, either to the clear supernatant liquid after the precipitate has settled or to the first bit of filtrate in that filtration operation—in either case, the appearance of any additional precipitate means that more precipitating agent is required before proceeding further.

Requirement 3 is usually, but not always, fulfilled best by precipitation from hot solution. Accordingly, if solubility and other factors permit, the sample solution and/or the precipitating agent solution should be hot at the time of mixing. It is advisable to keep a hot solution just below, rather than at, its boiling point to prevent possible loss by splattering.

DIGESTION

A precipitate is seldom ready for filtration immediately after formation. In some instances the particles are so small that the filter medium is unable to retain them, and in others an unnecessarily large amount of impurity is retained if filtration is performed at once. To minimize these possible sources of error, the precipitate must be allowed to stand for a period of time in contact with the liquid from which it was precipitated. This process is known as *digestion*. The process is often carried out at elevated temperatures, although room temperature digestion is also useful, particularly when extended periods of time are required.

The particle size of a precipitate may be increased during digestion through one or both of two distinct mechanisms: small particles coagulate to form aggregates; small crystals dissolve and reprecipitate on larger ones so the average individual crystal size increases. The larger, more readily filterable particles which remain at the end of the digestion period may thus consist of tight aggregates of smaller particles, of larger but fewer single crystals or of both.

One prominent mechanism whereby impurities are retained by a precipitate involves adsorption of the impurity upon the surfaces of crystals of the precipitate. For a given mass of precipitate, there is less surface if the individual particles are large than if they are small. The increase in particle size during digestion not only aids the filterability of a precipitate but also may improve its purity.

The required duration of the digestion period varies widely from one situation to another. Generally, nothing is gained by digesting a gelatinous precipitate for any longer than a few minutes. Precipitates which are unstable in water are best not digested at all, but such situations are quite rare. Digestion periods of an hour or so are common, and periods as long as overnight or even a day or two are not rare. Room temperature digestions were continued for several weeks in the extremely accurate work with silver chloride in the historically important atomic weight determinations referred to in Chapter 1.

Whenever the digestion period extends more than a few minutes, the beaker containing the precipitate and mother liquid should be covered with a watch glass to prevent the entrance of dust or other foreign material. Free access to air should, however, be maintained. The lip on the beaker usually provides enough opening for room temperature digestions. For higher temperature digestions, the watch glass should be supported on three glass hooks set over the top edge of the beaker. This type of covering is preferable when a solution is to be evaporated to dryness or to concentrate the solution.

FILTRATION

At the end of the digestion period, the precipitate should contain essentially all of the unknown constituent or of some constituent quantitatively related to it, should be adequately pure and should be in a physical form ready for filtration. There are several types of filter media. The nature of a precipitate and the temperature at which it must subsequently be dried or ignited frequently dictate which filter medium must be used. If more than one type are usable, convenience is the determining factor.

Filter Paper.   Filter paper is very useful in quantitative work, but it is essential that the proper grade of paper be used for a given precipitate. The paper must be removed from the precipitate by burning before the precipitate can be weighed; therefore, the paper used must be of an ashless variety. Filter paper is made ash-free during manufacture by treatment with hydrochloric and hydrofluoric acids; all components of the paper which will not be volatile upon subsequent ignition are effectively removed by this treatment. A small sheet of a good grade of quantitative filter paper will, upon ignition, leave less than 0.1 milligram of residue. The carbon of the paper presents a strongly reducing atmosphere during ignition, so filter paper is useful as the filtering medium only with precipitates which are not readily reducible.

Filter papers are available in a variety of porosities. Once the filtration is underway, the mat of precipitate on the paper generally limits the effective pore size. However, the porosity of the paper itself is very important, particularly in the early stages of the filtering operation.

The following points are important in folding and placing the paper into a 60 degree funnel for filtration. The paper should be folded twice; the second fold should be such that edges do not quite match (Figure. 10, *A*); then a corner of the slightly smaller section should be torn off (Figure 10, *B*). The paper is then opened on the slightly larger section; this provides a cone with three thicknesses (two with the torn edge) halfway around and one thickness the other halfway around and with an apex angle very slightly greater than 60°. The paper may then be inserted into a 60 degree funnel, moistened with a light stream of water from the wash bottle, and firmly pressed down. The paper should fit tightly all around its upper circumference, and the tear prevents an air column from existing between the glass and the paper.

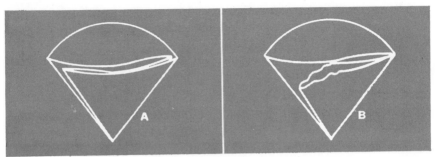

FIGURE 10.   Method of folding filter paper. *A*, original double fold. *B*, tearing off
corner for tighter fit in funnel.

A tightly fitting paper is essential. The filtering operation could be very time-consuming were it not for the aid of a gentle suction as liquid passes through and down the stem; this suction action cannot develop unless the paper fits tightly all the way around its upper circumference.

Some funnels have a constriction in the stem near the apex of the conical portion and others are fluted; this aids in developing the gentle suction action to facilitate the filtration procedure. The stem should remain continuously full of liquid as long as there is liquid in the conical portion if the filter is functioning properly; if spurts of air come along with the liquid the paper is not fitting properly and much time can be wasted. The stem of the funnel should be several inches long so that it can extend a few centimeters down into the receiver beaker, and the tip should touch the side of the beaker. In this way the filtrate is able to run down the side of the beaker without splashing. A completed filter assembly with a paper filter is illustrated in Figure 11.

The filter paper should be large enough so that it is one-fourth to one-half full of precipitate at the end of the filtration. The funnel should, in turn, be large enough for its rim to extend 1 or 2 centimeters above the top circumference of the paper.

Gooch Crucible. A Gooch crucible is made of porcelain with a perforated bottom which is covered by a filtering mat of asbestos fibers. It is useful for filtration of precipitates which must be ignited, particularly those precipitates which would be reduced during ignition in the presence of filter paper. In addition, the Gooch crucible is preferable to papers for filtering solutions, such as potassium permanganate, which attack paper.

The asbestos mat must be freshly prepared for each filtration, and the following procedure is satisfactory: The Gooch crucible is placed in a suction filtering apparatus and, without suction, a well-shaken aqueous suspension of asbestos fibers is poured into it. The proper amount of asbestos to be used must be found by experiment—it should fill the crucible about two-thirds full and should contain enough asbestos to result in a mat about 1 mm. thick. The suspension is allowed to stand for two or three minutes so that the larger fibers may settle to the bottom. Then gentle suction is applied to draw the water through the base of the crucible leaving an even layer of asbestos. The mat must be washed by passing up to 100 ml. of water through it with the aid of suction. The mat is of proper thickness if the perforations in the base are just barely discernible when the crucible is held up to the light. After use, the mat is removed and discarded. Once the asbestos mat is prepared, nothing should be poured through a Gooch crucible unless suction is being applied; otherwise, the mat tends to tear.

Porous Base Filtering Crucibles. There are three types of porous base filtering crucibles: sintered glass, sintered porcelain, Munroe (platinum). A sintered glass crucible is a glass-walled crucible with a porous glass mat as the bottom. This type of filtering crucible is commercially available with several grades of porosity, the nature of the precipitate determining the desired grade. The actual pore sizes are typically from 3 to 15 microns (1 micron = 1×10^{-4} cm.) for "fine" filters, 15 to 40 microns for "medium" filters and 40 to 70 microns for "coarse" filters. The effective pore size may be somewhat less. It is often set, once a filtration has been started, not by the filter medium itself but rather by the tight packing of the particles of precipitate lying on that medium. The sintered glass crucible is very convenient to

FIGURE 11. A filter assembly, with a liquid being decanted into it.

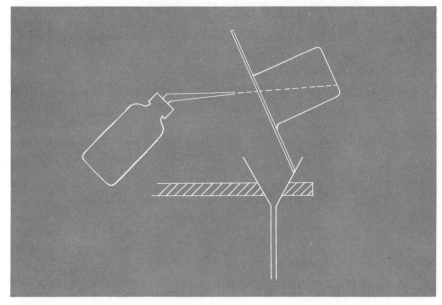

FIGURE 12.   Transferring a precipitate from a beaker to a filter assembly with the
aid of a stream of liquid from a polyethylene wash bottle.

use because no preparation is needed as with the Gooch and no removal of
the filtering medium is required before weighing the precipitate as with filter
paper. It does have to be cleaned after use, however, by shaking out loose
particles of the precipitate and by soaking or rinsing in a suitable solvent. The
glass cannot stand high temperatures, so the sintered glass crucible is used
primarily with precipitates that can be dried effectively at temperatures not
much over 100° C.

The sintered porcelain crucible is similar to the sintered glass except for
the different material of construction. It possesses the advantages of the
glass, with the additional fact that it can withstand higher temperatures of
ignition. A Munroe crucible is made of platinum with the base consisting of
a permanent layer of spongy platinum. It has advantage over glass and
porcelain filtering crucibles in that it can withstand a higher temperature.
However, platinum is quite expensive, and this type of crucible is seldom
used. A general disadvantage of all of the porous base filtering crucibles,
compared to filter paper and the Gooch crucible, is the often difficult task of
cleaning out a precipitate after use.

Transferring the Precipitate to the Filter Assembly.   Special
precautions are necessary in transferring a precipitate to the filter assembly.
This process is tied in with the washing operation, as most of the washing can
be done in the beaker in which the precipitate was formed. All the washings
must, of course, be passed through the filter to insure that no particles of the
precipitate are lost. Liquid should be poured down a glass rod into the filter

assembly to insure that no splashing occurs. The paper cone in the funnel or the filtering crucible should never be over about three-fourths full of liquid plus precipitate.

The bulk of the precipitate is transferred to the filter along with a portion of wash liquid. The remainder of the precipitate is transferred with the aid of a fine stream of water from the wash bottle directed around the edges to push the precipitate out, as illustrated in Figure 12. A rubber policeman, which consists of a small gum rubber tip over the end of a stirring rod, is useful in removing final bits of precipitate from the beaker to the filter assembly. If filter paper is being used, a small piece of the same grade of paper may be used to wipe final traces of the precipitate from the beaker, this paper then being inserted in the filter.

Suction Filtering. The passage of liquid through a filter often proceeds extremely slowly unless suction is applied. Suction filtering could be used with any type of filter media, but it is most necessary with Gooch and sintered base filter crucibles. With paper-in-funnel filtering, a gentle suction action is developed without any outside source as long as the paper is fitted properly. If additional suction is applied in filtration through paper, a hardened filter paper must be used, or a small perforated cone (generally platinum) must be inserted between the paper and the funnel to prevent rupture.

The filtering crucible fits into a rubber ring at the top of a regular suction flask, and the side arm is connected to a water aspirator as the source of suction. Preferably a safety bottle should be inserted between the filter flask and the water aspirator to prevent any backup of water from the aspirator into the filtrate. Once the suction is applied, it should never be stopped until the filter flask assembly is disconnected from the aspirator. A pinch clamp on the tube to the aspirator regulates the flow through the filter. Suction filtration is generally beneficial only with crystalline precipitates.

The filtrate should always be received in a clean vessel as a precautionary measure in case a filter paper rupture necessitates a repeat filtration. Frequently, it must be retained for subsequent determination of another constituent.

WASHING

The precipitate must be washed prior to drying or ignition. In some instances distilled water can serve as the wash liquid. More often it must contain an ion in common with the precipitate to minimize solubility loss and/or an electrolyte to prevent the aggregates of tinier particles from breaking apart and passing through the filter. The electrolyte must, of course, be one which will not leave an appreciable residue when the precipitate, moist with wash liquid, is subsequently dried. Solubility losses are also minimized by using a reasonably small volume of wash liquid, but enough must be used to insure adequate washing. It is much more efficient to use several small portions of wash liquid than to use the same quantity in one larger portion. Most washings require eight or ten portions. Hot liquids generally have lower viscosities than cold ones, and so run through the filter more rapidly; remember, however, that solubility loss may be greater in a hot liquid.

Efficient washing and rapid filtration are facilitated by performing most of the washings in the beaker in which the precipitate was formed rather than in the filter assembly. The supernatant liquid is decanted into the filter, a portion of wash liquid is inserted into the beaker, the beaker and its contents are gently swirled, and the supernatant liquid is again poured off through the filter. This process is repeated several times before the bulk of the precipitate is transferred to the filter in the manner already described. This technique of washing by decantation is distinctly advantageous over the alternate procedure of transferring the precipitate earlier to the filter assembly and washing it there for two reasons: washing is made much more effective by swirling the suspension of precipitate in the beaker with each batch of wash liquid; the wash liquid runs through the filter much more readily before the pores are clogged or covered by particles of the precipitate. The analyst can test whether or not washing is complete by withdrawing a small portion of the filtrate and conducting a qualitative test for some ion known to be present in the original mother liquid.

Gelatinous precipitates are difficult to wash thoroughly because they tend to clog the filtering medium. They can be kept somewhat dispersed by shaking a little filter paper pulp with the suspension prior to filtration. The paper pulp must, of course, be ash-free and must be removed in subsequent ignition. A precipitate should not be allowed to dry until it is completely washed. A dried precipitate tends to cake and to crack so that further washing is difficult or impossible.

DRYING OR IGNITION

The precipitate must be dried to remove moisture left by the last portions of wash liquid. Room temperature is seldom adequate, but many precipitates can be dried successfully when placed in an oven at 110° C. for from half an hour to two hours. However, a higher temperature is often required for one or more of three reasons: some substances retain water up to temperatures much higher than 100° C.; some substances must be transformed to substances of other more definite chemical composition for weighing; removal of filter paper requires heating well above 110° C.

When paper is used for the filtration, it is folded around the precipitate and inserted in a crucible (porcelain, silica or platinum). The ignition must be carried out in two steps: (1) charring or smoking off the paper, and (2) ignition of the precipitate proper at the full desired temperature. If the first step is not completed before the second is begun, the precipitate may be reduced excessively and flames may throw some of the precipitate out of the crucible. The first step is most frequently performed over a burner, even though some other source of heat may be used for the rest of the ignition. The crucible is mounted in a clay, silica, nichrome or platinum triangle held over a burner (Figure 13) If the paper should accidentally burst into flame, the fire should be smothered immediately by replacing the cover completely with crucible tongs. Ideally, the paper should never burst into flame.

After the paper has been removed completely, the temperature of the flame may be increased up to the full desired ignition temperature, or the crucible and contents may be placed in a muffle furnace at the proper temperature. The bottom of the crucible should be in contact with the blue oxidizing flame; tightly adhering soot may be deposited on the crucible if it is in contact with the center cone or the yellow flame. When the ignition period is ended, the crucible is allowed to cool for a few moments in air and is then placed in the desiccator for at least half an hour before weighing. The ignition, cooling and weighing steps should be repeated until successive weighings are in substantial agreement.

A Gooch, Munroe or sintered porcelain crucible should be inserted in another crucible during ignition so that the burner gases will not come in direct contact with the precipitate. Since the weight of the precipitate is to be obtained from the difference in weights of the crucible empty and with the precipitate present, an empty weight must be obtained for the crucible. This should be obtained before the precipitate is inserted, and the empty

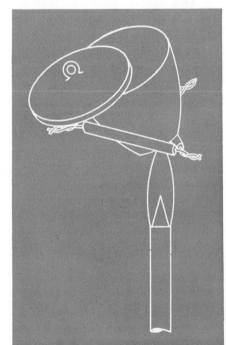

FIGURE 13. Ignition of precipitate with access of air.

crucible must undergo the same ignition procedure, as will subsequently be used when the precipitate is present, before it is weighed. Each crucible should be alternately ignited and weighed until two successive weighings give reasonably constant results, as ± 0.2 mg. Repeat ignitions can be of shorter duration than the first one, both with the empty crucible and with a crucible plus precipitate.

CALCULATIONS IN GRAVIMETRIC ANALYSIS

There are two major types of numerical problems encountered in quantitative analysis. One is the mass law type of problems, including ionization constants for weak acids and bases, solubility product constants for slightly soluble substances, dissociation constants for complex ions and the ionization constant of water. The formulation of these constants into mathematical equations was described in Chapter 1, and some application in gravimetric analysis will be made in Chapter 8. This type of problem is encountered in volumetric as well as in gravimetric analysis. The other type of problem is designated stoichiometric and will be considered in the remainder of this chapter. A stoichiometric problem involves a relationship between the quantities of two substances—"how much of substance A will react with, will produce or is obtained from so much of substance B?" Each stoichiometric problem is based upon some chemical reaction.

The Molar Balance. The solving of stoichiometric problems is greatly facilitated by the use of a special factor, called the gravimetric factor. As a basis for understanding its definition and significance, however, we must first consider the fundamental concept of the molar balance in chemical reactions. A chemical equation indicates the relationship between the number of moles of the various reacting substances. For example, the equation

$$MgCO_3 \longrightarrow MgO + CO_2$$

indicates that the numbers of moles of MgO and of CO_2 which are formed equal each other and each number likewise equals the number of moles of $MgCO_3$ which has reacted. And the equation

$$2\ MgNH_4PO_4 \cdot 6\ H_2O \longrightarrow Mg_2P_2O_7 + 13\ H_2O + 2\ NH_3$$

indicates that the numbers of moles of $MgNH_4PO_4 \cdot 6\ H_2O$ which react, and the numbers of moles of $Mg_2P_2O_7$, of H_2O and of NH_3 which are formed are, in order, in the ratio of $2:1:13:2$. Stoichiometric problems are fundamentally based upon these molar balances, and the molar balances are, in turn, based upon the balanced chemical equations for the underlying reactions. In addition, we must remember that the term percentage refers to a ratio expressed in parts per hundred, and that moles and weight units are related by the equation

$$\text{moles} = \frac{\text{grams}}{\text{molecular weight}}$$

Two sample problems will now be given to illustrate the use of the molar balance in solving stoichiometric problems. In these and subsequent problems, a chemical formula standing by itself in a mathematical equation refers to its formula weight. Thus, CO_2 in a mathematical equation refers to the molecular weight of carbon dioxide, while g CO_2 refers to its weight in grams.

Example 1. How many grams of carbon dioxide can be obtained from 21.00 grams of magnesium carbonate?

$$MgCO_3 \longrightarrow MgO + CO_2$$

Moles of CO_2 obtained = moles of $MgCO_3$ which react

$$\frac{g\ CO_2}{CO_2} = \frac{g\ MgCO_3}{MgCO_3}$$

$$g\ CO_2 = \frac{CO_2 \times g\ MgCO_3}{MgCO_3}$$

$$g\ CO_2 = \frac{44.01 \times 21.00}{84.33}$$

$$g\ CO_2 = 10.96$$

Example 2. How many grams of $MgNH_4PO_4 \cdot 6\ H_2O$ must react (by ignition) to yield 1.000 gram of $Mg_2P_2O_7$?

$$2\ MgNH_4PO_4 \cdot 6\ H_2O \longrightarrow Mg_2P_2O_7 + 13\ H_2O + 2\ NH_3$$

Because 2 moles of $MgNH_4PO_4 \cdot 6\ H_2O$ yield only 1 mole of $Mg_2P_2O_7$,

$$\frac{1}{2} \times \text{moles } MgNH_4PO_4 \cdot 6\ H_2O \text{ which react} = \text{moles } Mg_2P_2O_7 \text{ obtained}$$

$$\frac{1}{2} \times \left(\frac{g\ MgNH_4PO_4 \cdot 6\ H_2O}{MgNH_4PO_4 \cdot 6\ H_2O} \right) = \frac{g\ Mg_2P_2O_7}{Mg_2P_2O_7}$$

$$g\ MgNH_4PO_4 \cdot 6\ H_2O = \frac{2 \times MgNH_4PO_4 \cdot 6\ H_2O \times g\ Mg_2P_2O_7}{Mg_2P_2O_7}$$

$$g\ MgNH_4PO_4 \cdot 6\ H_2O = \frac{2 \times 245.44 \times 1.000}{222.59}$$

$$g\ MgNH_4PO_4 \cdot 6\ H_2O = 2.205$$

The Gravimetric Factor. Close examination of Examples 1 and 2 shows that the third mathematical equation of each is written in the form,

$$\text{wt. of substance sought} = \frac{\text{mol. wt. of substance sought}}{\text{mol. wt. of substance known}} \times \text{wt. of substance known,}$$

with one of the molecular weights multiplied by 2 in the second example.

The *gravimetric factor* is defined as the ratio of the formula weight of the substance sought to the formula weight of the substance known, with the formula weights multiplied by appropriate digits which are the relative numbers of each substance as indicated in the chemical equation relating the two substances. In Examples 1 and 2 the gravimetric factors are, respectively,

$$\frac{CO_2}{MgCO_3} \quad \text{and} \quad \frac{2 \times MgNH_4PO_4 \cdot 6\ H_2O}{Mg_2P_2O_7}$$

The term "formula weight" has been used in the definition in place of the term "molecular weight" to include reacting substances other than molecules. For example, the factor for use in the calculation of the weight of chloride ion required to react with a fixed weight of silver ion according to the equation

$$Ag^+ + Cl^- \longrightarrow AgCl$$

would be $\dfrac{Cl}{Ag}$.

The gravimetric factor can be set up for situations in which any number of chemical reactions intervene between the substance sought and the substance known. For example, calcium in an unknown can be determined by precipitating calcium ion as calcium oxalate and igniting the precipitate to calcium oxide:

$$Ca^{++} + C_2O_4^= + H_2O \longrightarrow CaC_2O_4 \cdot H_2O$$
$$2\ CaC_2O_4 \cdot H_2O + O_2 \longrightarrow 2\ CaO + 2\ H_2O + 4\ CO_2$$

The gravimetric factor relating Ca as the substance sought to CaO as the substance known is simply $\dfrac{Ca}{CaO}$.

It is possible to establish a gravimetric factor with a chemical part of one of the substances used rather than all of it. To illustrate, it may be desired to determine the amount of Na_2SO_4 in a sample, expressing it as SO_3, by precipitating and weighing $BaSO_4$

$$SO_4^= + Ba^{++} \longrightarrow BaSO_4$$

The gravimetric factor is $\dfrac{SO_3}{BaSO_4}$. This situation is analogous to the precipitation reaction preceded by the hypothetical reaction

$$SO_3 + Na_2O \longrightarrow Na_2SO_4$$

so that 1 $BaSO_4$ eventually would result from 1 SO_3.

It is sometimes possible to set up a gravimetric factor without even writing the pertinent chemical equations, although definite chemical reactions must exist to relate the substance sought to the substance known. Consider the series of reactions:

$$FeS_2 \xrightarrow{O_2} SO_2 \xrightarrow{H_2} H_2S \xrightarrow{Cd^{++}} CdS \xrightarrow{O_2} CdSO_4 \xrightarrow{Ba^{++}} BaSO_4$$

with all substances on the arrows being provided in excess so that the S is carried quantitatively throughout all steps. The gravimetric factor relating FeS_2 as the substance sought to $BaSO_4$ as the substance known is

$$\frac{FeS_2}{2 \times BaSO_4}$$

It is noted that S, the substance which was carried through all reactions, appears the same number of times in both numerator and denominator. Consider next the series

$$Na_3AsO_4 \xrightarrow{Ag^+} Ag_3AsO_4 \xrightarrow{Cl^-} AgCl$$

with Na_3AsO_4 as the substance sought and AgCl as the substance known. Here there are no atoms in common between the two substances, but the connecting reactions reveal that the gravimetric factor is

$$\frac{Na_3AsO_4}{3 \times AgCl}$$

Students of quantitative analysis are sometimes confused when writing a gravimetric factor in which the two same types of atom are involved in both substances. For example, MgO is determined by precipitation as $MgNH_4PO_4 \cdot 6\,H_2O$ and ignition to $Mg_2P_2O_7$

$$MgO + 2\,H^+ \longrightarrow Mg^{++} + H_2O$$

$$Mg^{++} + NH_4^+ + PO_4^{\equiv} + 6\,H_2O \longrightarrow MgNH_4PO_4 \cdot 6\,H_2O$$

$$2\,MgNH_4PO_4 \cdot 6\,H_2O \longrightarrow Mg_2P_2O_7 + 13\,H_2O + 2\,NH_3$$

The gravimetric factor is $\dfrac{2 \times MgO}{Mg_2P_2O_7}$. Note that the number of Mg atoms is the same in both numerator and denominator but that the numbers of O atoms differ. As indicated by the chemical equations, the O atoms in the two substances are not even the same O atoms, whereas all the Mg atoms initially in MgO are carried through until they become parts of the $Mg_2P_2O_7$.

Handbooks of chemistry contain lists of gravimetric factors, including their numerical values, for many systems encountered in gravimetric analysis.

Weight and Percentage Calculations. The use of the gravimetric factor is based upon two simple mathematical equations:

1. (wt of substance sought) = (gravimetric factor) × (wt. of substance known)

2a. (% substance sought) $= \dfrac{\text{(wt. of substance sought)} \times 100}{\text{(wt. of sample)}}$

2b. (% substance sought) =

$$\frac{\text{(gravimetric factor)} \times \text{(wt. of substance known)} \times 100}{\text{(wt. of sample)}}$$

Equation 2b is a mathematical combination of 1 and 2a. Any units of weight may be used; but the same units must be used throughout a problem. Equations 1, 2a and 2b and the definition of the gravimetric factor should not be used as blindly memorized formulas for the solving of problems. Rather, each student should check and thoroughly understand their validity on the basis of the fundamental molar balance method of Examples 1 and 2. These two equations, along with the definition of the gravimetric factor, serve as the bases for solving virtually all stoichiometric problems in gravimetric analysis.

Example 3.   How many grams of CO_2 are required to react with CaO to form 10.000 grams of $CaCO_3$?

$$g\ CO_2 = \frac{CO_2}{CaCO_3} \times g\ CaCO_3$$

$$g\ CO_2 = \frac{44.01}{100.09} \times 10.000$$

$$g\ CO_2 = 4.397$$

Example 4.   How many grams of FeO can be obtained from 5.000 grams of $Fe_2(SO_4)_3$?

$$g\ FeO = \frac{2 \times FeO}{Fe_2(SO_4)_3} \times g\ Fe_2(SO_4)_3$$

$$g\ FeO = \frac{2 \times 71.85}{399.90} \times 5.000$$

$$g\ FeO = 1.797$$

Example 5.   How many grams of $BaCl_2 \cdot 2\ H_2O$ are required to precipitate all the sulfate ion present in a 6.670 gram sample of $Fe_2(SO_4)_3$?

$$g\ BaCl_2 \cdot 2\ H_2O = \frac{3 \times BaCl_2 \cdot 2\ H_2O}{Fe_2(SO_4)_3} \times g\ Fe_2(SO_4)_3$$

$$g\ BaCl_2 \cdot 2\ H_2O = \frac{3 \times 244.30}{399.90} \times 6.670$$

$$g\ BaCl_2 \cdot 2\ H_2O = 12.22$$

Example 6.   What is the percentage of CuS in an ore, if conversion of all the S in a 10.000 gram sample to sulfate yielded 3.000 grams of $BaSO_4$?

$$\%\ CuS = \frac{\dfrac{CuS}{BaSO_4} \times g\ BaSO_4 \times 100}{g\ sample}$$

$$\%\ CuS = \frac{\dfrac{95.61}{233.43} \times 3.000 \times 100}{10.000}$$

$$\%\ CuS = 12.29$$

Example 7. 2.0000 grams of a phosphate ore were dissolved and treated so that all the phosphate was precipitated as $(NH_4)_3P(Mo_3O_{10})_4$, of which 1.5000 grams were obtained. Compute the percentage of phosphate $(PO_4^=)$ in the ore.

$$\% \, PO_4 = \frac{\dfrac{PO_4}{(NH_4)_3P(Mo_3O_{10})_4} \times g \, (NH_4)_3P(Mo_3O_{10})_4 \times 100}{g \, \text{sample}}$$

(note the 1 P each in numerator and denominator of factor)

$$\% \, PO_4 = \frac{\dfrac{94.98}{1876.50} \times 1.5000 \times 100}{2.0000}$$

$$\% \, PO_4 = 3.796$$

Example 8. What percentage of Fe_3O_4 is present in an ore, 10.000 grams of which yield 5.000 grams of Fe_2O_3?

$$\% \, Fe_3O_4 = \frac{\dfrac{2 \times Fe_3O_4}{3 \times Fe_2O_3} \times g \, Fe_2O_3 \times 100}{g \, \text{sample}}$$

(note the 6 Fe's each in numerator and denominator of factor)

$$\% \, Fe_3O_4 = \frac{\dfrac{2 \times 231.55}{3 \times 159.70} \times 5.000 \times 100}{10.000}$$

$$\% \, Fe_3O_4 = 48.33$$

Calculation of the Required Volume of Solution of Precipitating Agent. In every gravimetric determination the precipitating agent must be added in excess to precipitate the unknown constituent quantitatively; yet a large excess is often undesirable as stated earlier in this chapter. So the analyst must calculate the approximate required amount of the solution of the precipitating agent. This calculation is based directly upon the first of the two mathematical equations specifying the use of the gravimetric factor. Because this is, at best, a calculation of the approximate volume to use, two (or perhaps only one) significant figures suffice in the answer, depending on how closely the composition of the "unknown" is known prior to its analysis and upon how harmful a moderate excess is in the particular procedure. In many analyses, a 10 to 20% excess is added onto the calculated amount to be sure that there is enough to react quantitatively with the unknown constituent.

Example 9. How many ml. of a solution containing 100.0 grams of $AgNO_3$ per liter are required to precipitate all the chloride present in 1.335 grams of $AlCl_3$?

(1) $\text{g } AgNO_3 = \dfrac{3 \times AgNO_3}{AlCl_3} \times \text{g } AlCl_3$

(2) $\text{g } AgNO_3 = \dfrac{3 \times 169.89}{133.35} \times 1.335$

(3) but g $AgNO_3$ = liters used × g per liter

(4) $\text{g } AgNO_3 \quad = \dfrac{\text{ml. used}}{1\,000} \times 100.0$

$$\dfrac{\text{ml. used}}{1\,000} \times 100.0 = \dfrac{3 \times 169.89}{133.35} \times 1.335 \text{ (combining 2 and 4)}$$

$$\text{ml. used} = 51.02$$

Slightly over 50 ml. are required; 55 to 60 ml. would be a good quantity to use.

Example 10. How many ml. of 98% H_2SO_4 (specific gravity, 1.84) are required to precipitate the barium ion in 10.000 grams of impure $BaCl_2 \cdot 2\,H_2O$?

(1) $\text{g } H_2SO_4 = \dfrac{H_2SO_4}{BaCl_2 \cdot 2\,H_2O} \times \text{g } BaCl_2 \cdot 2\,H_2O$

(2) $\text{g } H_2SO_4 = \dfrac{98.08}{244.30} \times 10.000$

(since 10.000 g is the maximum possible weight of $BaCl_2 \cdot 2\,H_2O$, we will get the maximum possible required amount of H_2SO_4)

(3) but g H_2SO_4 = ml. used × sp. gr. × 0.98
(sp. gr. is defined in g/ml., and 98% of it is H_2SO_4)

(4) g H_2SO_4 = ml. used × 1.84 × 0.98

$$\text{ml. used} \times 1.84 \times 0.98 = \dfrac{98.08}{244.30} \times 10.000 \text{ (combining 2 and 4)}$$

$$\text{ml. used} = 2.226$$

About 2 1/4 ml. may be required as the maximum; experimentally, it would be well to dilute the acid and use a correspondingly larger volume.

Calculation of Proper Weight of Sample. Two types of situation arise in which it is necessary to calculate how large a sample to take for a determination. The first is in deciding how big a sample should be to result in a precipitate that is neither too much nor too little for convenient handling. Weighings on a common analytical balance can be made to the nearest one or two-tenths of a milligram. An accuracy approaching one part in a thousand is often desired, so the precipitate must weigh at least one or two-tenths of a gram. A precipitate usually becomes too bulky for convenient filtering and washing if its weight exceeds about 1 gram. Therefore, a calculation of approximate sample weight to yield a precipitate weight within the limits is needed.

The second type of situation is not encountered in student laboratory work, but it is important in an analytical laboratory in which many samples are to be analyzed by the same procedure. It is possible to make each of the many samples of a certain size so that, for example, each hundredth of a gram of final precipitate shall correspond to 1.00 per cent of the constituent. Then, so long as the correct sample size is used, the result of each determination can be found without going through the usual calculation. A competent analyst can likely make the usual calculation in less time than it takes to portion out a sample of precisely the requisite weight. Nevertheless, if there is special equipment with which to perform the sample weighings, the simplification of the calculations made possible by this method is worthwhile.

Both of these types of situation will now be illustrated by examples.

Example II. About how large a sample of a substance containing roughly one-fourth Ca should be used in the determination of Ca so that the weight of the final precipitate of $CaCO_3$ falls within the range of 0.2 to 0.8 gram?

$$\% \text{ Ca} = \frac{\dfrac{\text{Ca}}{\text{CaCO}_3} \times \text{g CaCO}_3 \times 100}{\text{g sample}}$$

$$\text{or g sample} = \frac{\dfrac{\text{Ca}}{\text{CaCO}_3} \times \text{g CaCO}_3 \times 100}{\% \text{ Ca}}$$

$$\text{g sample} = \frac{\dfrac{40.08}{100.09} \times \text{g CaCO}_3 \times 100}{25}$$

$$\text{g sample} = 1.602 \times \text{g CaCO}_3$$

max. g sample = 1.602 × 0.8   min. g sample = 1.602 × 0.2

max. g sample = 1.3   min. g sample = 0.3

So the sample weight should be within the approximate range, 0.3 to 1.3 gram.

Example 12. What weight of sample should be taken so that each 10.0 mg (0.0100 g) of AgCl obtained in a gravimetric chloride determination shall correspond to 1.00% of chloride in the original sample?

$$\% \, Cl = \frac{\dfrac{Cl}{AgCl} \times g \, AgCl \times 100}{g \, sample}$$

$$or \; g \, sample = \frac{\dfrac{Cl}{AgCl} \times g \, AgCl \times 100}{\% \, Cl}$$

$$g \, sample = \frac{\dfrac{35.46}{143.34} \times 0.0100 \times 100}{1.00}$$

$$g \, sample = 0.2474$$

Indirect Analysis. When determinations for two constituents of a sample are desired, a separate determination is generally performed for each. If a sample contains two constituents that cannot conveniently be separated, however, the percentage of each may be determined by an indirect procedure in which two distinct determinations are made upon the summation of the two constituents. The result of each of the two determinations is expressed in a mathematical equation, and the two equations are combined mathematically. The general principles of the method and the method of calculation may best be shown by means of examples. Note that the calculations are again based upon the gravimetric factor.

Example 13. A sample containing only silver chloride and silver bromide is analyzed by making two determinations: the total weight of the sample is 1.0000 gram; it contains 0.6542 gram of silver. Calculate the percentages of AgCl and of AgBr in the sample.

(1)   g AgCl + g AgBr   = 1.0000 (from the first determination)

(2) g Ag from AgCl + g Ag from AgBr = 0.6542 (from the second determination)

(3) $\dfrac{Ag}{AgCl} \times g \, AgCl + \dfrac{Ag}{AgBr} \times g \, AgBr = 0.6542$ (rewriting 2)

(4)   g AgBr   = 1.0000 − g AgCl (rewriting 1)

(5) $\dfrac{Ag}{AgCl} \times g \, AgCl + \dfrac{Ag}{AgBr} (1.000\text{-}g \, AgCl) \quad = 0.6542$ (substituting 4 into 3)

(6) $\dfrac{107.88}{143.34} \times g \, AgCl + \dfrac{107.88}{187.80} (1.000\text{-}g \, AgCl) \quad = 0.6542$

(7) $0.75262 \times$ g AgCl $+ 0.57443$–$0.57443 \times$ g AgCl $= 0.6542$

(8) $(0.75262$–$0.57443)$ g AgCl $= 0.6542$–0.57443

(9) g AgCl $= \dfrac{0.0798}{0.17819}$

(10) g AgCl $= 0.448$

(11) and g AgBr $= 0.552$ (substituting 10 into 1 or 4)

So the sample contains 44.8% AgCl and 55.2% AgBr. (There are alternate, equally correct methods of proceeding from step (3); the important point is to write the result of each determination as a mathematical equation and then to combine them mathematically to solve for the desired information.)

Example 14. A sample weighing 0.9000 gram, and containing combined Ca and Ba plus other substances which will not interfere in the analysis, is analyzed by converting the Ca and Ba into their oxides, weighing 0.4500 gram, and then changing the oxides into sulfates, weighing 0.7986 gram. Calculate the percentages of Ca and of Ba in the sample.

(1) g BaO + g CaO $= 0.4500$ (from first measurement)

(2) g BaSO$_4$ from BaO + g CaSO$_4$ from CaO $= 0.7986$ (from second measurement)

(3) $\dfrac{BaSO_4}{BaO} \times$ g BaO $+ \dfrac{CaSO_4}{CaO} \times$ g CaO $= 0.7986$ (rewriting 2)

(4) g CaO $= 0.4500 -$ g BaO (rewriting 1)

(5) $\dfrac{BaSO_4}{BaO} \times$ g BaO $+ \dfrac{CaSO_4}{CaO}(0.4500 -$ g BaO$) = 0.7986$ (combining 3 and 4)

(6) $\dfrac{233.43}{153.36} \times$ g BaO $+ \dfrac{136.15}{56.08}(0.4500 -$ g BaO$) = 0.7986$

(7) $1.5221 \times$ g BaO $+ 1.0925$–$2.4278 \times$ g BaO $= 0.7986$

(8) $(1.5221$–$2.4278)$ g BaO $= 0.7986$–1.0925

(9) g BaO $= \dfrac{-0.2939}{-0.9057}$

(10) g BaO $= 0.3245$

(11) g CaO $= 0.1255$ (substituting 10 into 1 or 4)

(12)   % Ba (in original) $= \dfrac{\dfrac{Ba}{BaO} \times g\,BaO \times 100}{g\,sample}$

(usual % calculations, now)

(13)   % Ba $= \dfrac{\dfrac{137.36}{153.36} \times 0.3245 \times 100}{0.9000}$

(14)   % Ba $= 32.29$

(15)   % Ca $= \dfrac{\dfrac{Ca}{CaO} \times g\,CaO \times 100}{g\,sample}$

(16)   % Ca $= \dfrac{\dfrac{40.08}{56.08} \times 0.1255 \times 100}{0.9000}$

(17)   % Ca $= 9.97$

So the sample contained 32.29% Ba and 9.97% Ca. (Again, the mathematical equations representing the two measurements on the summation of the two constituents, Ca and Ba, could have been combined differently, but the answers should come out the same.)

It should be noted that the calculations of indirect analysis involve subtracting numbers from others which may be of comparable magnitude, steps 8 and 9 in Examples 13 and 14. Accordingly, some significant figures may be lost, depending upon how close together each two numbers to be subtracted are. Therefore, the method of indirect analysis is generally not so accurate as would be determinations of each constituent after separating them. But the method is useful in dealing with substances which are chemically similar and which cannot conveniently be separated one from the other. In principle, the method is equally applicable to mixtures of even more than two components—for *n* components, *n* measurements must be made of the summation of components, *n* equations must be written, and they must be combined mathematically to solve for the *n* components in the sample. The accuracy generally drops off even more, however, as more components are included.

REVIEW QUESTIONS

1. List the unit operations in a gravimetric determination.
2. What apparatus is required for each of the following operations: weighing; drying; dissolving; precipitating; digesting; filtering; washing; igniting?
3. What factor tends to make a large solution volume desirable, and what factor tends to make it undesirable?
4. Why is the analyst concerned with the presence of "foreign ions" in his sample solution?

5. Briefly explain the ion exchange technique, distinguishing between cation exchangers and anion exchangers.
6. List the three requirements which a precipitation process must fulfill to make it a suitable basis for a gravimetric determination.
7. What should be done to correct the situation if frequent air bubbles run through a funnel stem along with a filtrate?
8. Compare sintered glass crucibles, filter paper and Gooch crucibles as filtering media on any three significant points.
9. Devise and carry through a calculation to show why washing a precipitate with ten portions of 10 ml. each of wash liquid is more effective than washing it once with a 100 ml. portion.
10. Explain why a hot object should be cooled somewhat in room air before placing it in a desiccator, and explain what error may be enhanced at the same time.

PROBLEMS

GRAVIMETRIC FACTOR PROBLEMS

1. Set up gravimetric factors for each of the following, using chemical formulas for formula weights.

Substance known	Substance sought
$AlPO_4$	Al_2O_3
$Mg_2As_2O_7$	As_2O_3
B_2O_3	B_4O_7
$Fe(NH_4)_2(SO_4)_2 \cdot 6\ H_2O$	Fe
$Mg_2P_2O_7$	P_2O_5
K_2SO_4	KCl
$PbCrO_4$	Cr_2O_3
As_2S_5	As_2O_3
$BaSiF_6$	BaO
BiOCl	Bi_2O_3
B_2O_3	$Na_2B_4O_7 \cdot 10\ H_2O$
Cr_2O_3	CrO_3
Fe_2O_3	Fe
$KClO_4$	KCl
Sb_2S_3	Sb_2O_4
$Zn_2P_2O_7$	$ZnSO_4$
$(NH_4)_2PtCl_6$	N

2. Calculate the numerical values for each of the following gravimetric factors. (It is suggested that the student use logarithms in making these calculations; some of these factors can be used in calculating the results of laboratory work.)

Substance known	Substance sought
AgCl	Cl
$BaSO_4$	SO_3
$BaSO_4$	S
Fe_2O_3	Fe
$CaCO_3$	CaO
$Mg_2P_2O_7$	MgO
Al_2O_3.	Al

3. How much sulfate radical, $SO_4^=$, is there in 1.0000 gram of $MgSO_4 \cdot 7\ H_2O$?

4. How many grams of calcium oxide can be obtained by driving the carbon dioxide off from 2.469 grams of calcium carbonate?
5. How many tons of nitrogen are required to react with 10.50 tons of hydrogen, according to the reaction, $N_2 + 3\ H_2 \rightarrow 2\ NH_3$?
6. How many pounds of molten sodium chloride must be electrolyzed to yield 2.500 pounds of chlorine, $2\ NaCl \rightarrow 2\ Na + Cl_2$?
7. How many grams of Fe_2O_3 can be obtained by oxidation of 2.496 grams of Fe_3O_4?

CALCULATION OF AMOUNT OF PRECIPITATING AGENT

8. A hydrobromic acid solution contains 49.8% HBr, and has a density of 1.515; how many grams of silver nitrate are required to precipitate the bromide from 250.0 ml. of this solution?
9. What volume of a solution containing 8.16% HCl and of density 1.040 is required to precipitate the silver from 1.500 grams Ag_2SO_4?
10. What volume of an aqueous ammonia solution containing 9.90% NH_3 and of density 0.96 is required to precipitate the iron as $Fe(OH)_3$ from 1.000 gram of ferrous ammonium sulfate, $FeSO_4 \cdot (NH_4)_2SO_4 \cdot 6\ H_2O$?
11. A limestone sample contains about 40% CaO; what weight of ammonium oxalate, $(NH_4)_2C_2O_4$, is needed to precipitate the Ca from a 1.0082 gram sample?
12. A solution was bought on the supposition it contained 450 grams HCl per liter; to test it, 10.00 ml. were diluted to 1.0000 liter and 10.00 ml. of that solution formed 0.1785 gram AgCl; by how many mg. per ml. was the original solution off its specifications?
13. What volume of silver nitrate solution containing 10.00 grams of the solid per liter is required to precipitate the chloride from 0.5000 gram of NaCl?
14. What volume of silver nitrate solution containing 0.1000 mole of the solid per liter is required to precipitate the bromide from 0.7700 gram of $BaBr_2$?
15. What volume of silver nitrate solution containing 0.1500 mole of the solid per liter is required to precipitate the arsenate from 0.8943 gram of Na_3AsO_4?
16. What volume of a solution containing 24.82 grams $(NH_4)_2C_2O_4$ per liter is required to precipitate the calcium as the oxalate from a 1.000 gram sample of pure $CaCO_3$?
17. What volume of barium chloride solution (25.00 grams $BaCl_2 \cdot 2\ H_2O$ per liter) is required to precipitate the sulfate from 1.0740 gram pure ferrous ammonium sulfate, $FeSO_4 \cdot (NH_4)_2SO_4 \cdot 6\ H_2O$?

GRAVIMETRIC PERCENTAGE CALCULATIONS

18. 1.5000 gram samples of (a) a silver ore, (b) a salt mixture containing chloride, (c) a salt mixture containing sulfate, (d) an iron ore and (e) a limestone were each dissolved in an appropriate solvent. An excess of (a) hydrochloric acid, (b) silver nitrate, (c) barium chloride, (d) ammonium hydroxide and (e) ammonium oxalate was added, respectively, to form a precipitate which, when ignited and weighed, was (a) AgCl, (b) AgCl, (c) $BaSO_4$, (d) Fe_2O_3, (e) CaO, and which weighed 0.4000 gram. Calculate the percentage (a) Ag, (b) Cl, (c) S, (d) Fe, (e) $CaCO_3$ in each original sample.
19. Calculate the % K in a baking powder sample, 1.0460 gram of which yielded 0.0928 gram of $KClO_4$.
20. Calculate the % Zn in an ore, 1.0762 grams of which yielded 0.7540 gram of $Zn_2P_2O_7$.
21. A commercial iron sample weighed 2.0019 grams. From this sample were obtained 0.1123 gram SiO_2 and 0.0141 gram $BaSO_4$. Calculate the percentages S and Si in the sample.

22. From a 0.3744 gram sample of impure sodium chloride, a precipitate of 0.7642 gram of AgCl was obtained; calculate the percentage NaCl in the sample.
23. A portion of a silver coin weighed 0.3764 gram and gave a precipitate of silver chloride which weighed 0.4502 gram. Calculate the % Ag in the coin and the weight of silver bromide which could have been obtained from it.
24. A 1.0000 gram sample of limestone, after precipitation of the calcium as calcium oxalate, gave a residue of 0.5040 gram of calcium oxide. Calculate the percentage $CaCO_3$ in the sample.
25. If a sample of commercial iron weighing 5.644 grams gave 0.0737 gram $Mg_2P_2O_7$, what is the percentage phosphorus in the sample?
26. The percentage of copper in a sample of iron ore was found to be 33.73 and the moisture content 7.64 per cent. If the sample were completely dry, what would be the percentage of copper?
27. A sample of lime contained 91.64% CaO, 3.94% MgO and 0.37% H_2O. Calculate the percentages CaO and MgO in a dry sample.
28. A 0.9464 gram sample of a brass yielded 0.0837 gram SnO_2 and 0.8064 gram metallic copper. What are the percentages Sn and Cu in this brass?
29. What is the weight percentage KI in a solution whose density is 1.0025 and 25.00 ml. of which yielded 0.3266 gram AgI?
30. A compound is known to be $C_3H_5Cl_3$, $C_3H_6Cl_2$ or C_3H_7Cl. A 0.1582 gram sample was decomposed and the chloride, precipitated as silver chloride, weighed 0.4016 gram. What is the percentage chloride, and which compound is it?

SAMPLE WEIGHT PROBLEMS

31. A sample consists of sodium sulfate with or without impurities. What size sample should be used so the precipitated barium sulfate will weigh not more than 0.6 gram?
32. A brass sample contains from 20 to 40% copper. What size sample should be taken so the precipitate of cuprous thiocyanate, CuSCN, will weigh not less than 0.1 gram nor more than 0.5 gram?
33. What weight sample should be taken in the gravimetric chloride procedure so each mg. of precipitate will correspond to 0.05% Cl?
34. What weight lead ore should be taken for analysis so that each mg. of lead sulfate, $PbSO_4$, will correspond to 0.20% Pb?
35. What weight of limestone sample should be taken so each mg. of CaO will correspond to 0.10% CaO? so that each mg. $CaSO_4$ will correspond to 0.10% CaO?
36. What weight of sample should be taken for analysis so that each centigram of $BaSO_4$ will be equal to the percentage SO_4 in the sample?
37. What weight of ore should be taken for analysis so that each milligram of $Mg_2P_2O_7$ obtained will be equal to 0.03% of P in the ore?
38. What size sample should be taken so each mg. of Mn_3O_4 corresponds to 0.05% Mn in the sample?

(Additional problems of these types and problems of indirect analysis will be found after Chapter 7.)

SUGGESTIONS FOR ADDITIONAL READING

Items 8, 20, 21, 26 and 28, Appendix 7.

Chapter 7

Selected

Gravimetric Methods

THE GENERAL unit operations, tools and calculations of gravimetric analysis were discussed in Chapter 6. Several specific determinations, in which these general factors are applied, are presented in this chapter. The determinations included in this chapter have been selected to include a variety of types of precipitate, procedures and principles. Each is a practical laboratory method for the determination of the stated constituent. Considerable emphasis is placed on sources of error for both pedagogical and practical reasons. The errors will be considered in terms of the three requirements which must be fulfilled by any precipitation process to make it a suitable basis for a method of gravimetric analysis:

1. The unknown constituent must be precipitated quantitatively.
2. The precipitate must be pure, or at least of known purity, at the time of final measurement.
3. The precipitate must be in a physical form suitable for subsequent handling. These three requirements will be modified for the determination by a volatilization method.

DETERMINATION OF WATER IN BARIUM CHLORIDE DIHYDRATE BY VOLATILIZATION

Principle. In a volatilization determination the unknown component or group of components is separated from the rest of the sample by volatilizing it either through application of heat alone or by adding an appropriate reagent. The quantity of volatilized components is measured directly by absorption and weighing of the volatile fraction or indirectly from the loss of weight of the sample. Perhaps the most frequent application of a volatilization procedure is the determination of loosely bound water present in compounds which are not themselves volatile. A simple example of this type is the determination of water of hydration in barium chloride dihydrate, which decomposes upon heating in air at a moderate temperature:

$$BaCl_2 \cdot 2\,H_2O \longrightarrow BaCl_2 + 2\,H_2O$$

The weight loss of the sample upon heating is due only to the loss of water. Therefore, the procedure consists essentially of only three steps: weigh the sample; heat it; weigh it again.

The purity of a sample of barium chloride dihydrate may be determined by this process. In fact, the results can be calculated in terms of percentage $BaCl_2·2 H_2O$, assuming that only water is lost upon heating and that all water comes from the hydrated salt. The procedure which follows is intended to determine the amount of water in a sample of barium chloride dihydrate which may or may not contain some sodium chloride or other nonvolatile components.

Evaluation of the Method. The stated requirements that a precipitation process must be complete and that a precipitate must be pure may be modified for this volatilization procedure to state that the evolution of the water of hydration must be complete and that no other component be evolved. The third requirement, concerning the physical form of a precipitate, is applicable to the final residue which must be weighed, but no practical difficulty arises in this regard.

Barium chloride dihydrate loses essentially all of its water of hydration when heated above 113° C., and the anhydrous salt has melting and boiling points of 962° C. and 1 560° C., respectively. So any temperature over 113° C. should be adequate for dehydration of the hydrated salt, and a temperature far in excess should even be permissible as far as the thermal stability of the anhydrous form is concerned. A temperature of 150° to 200° C. is very good. The temperature must reach a suitable value throughout the particles of the sample, but use of finely divided material and a heating time of an hour are very adequate. There need be no significant error from incomplete loss of the water of hydration. The anhydrous salt is, however, somewhat hygroscopic in normal room air. It follows that the anhydrous salt should be transferred to the desiccator very soon after completion of the drying operation, and it should be weighed quickly when it is removed to the balance case.

A source of error in this type of determination arises from the possible presence in the initial sample of moisture other than the water of hydration. However, this error need not be serious with barium chloride dihydrate if the sample is finely ground in a mortar and exposed for a time to room air prior to its initial weighing. This substance readily comes to a state of equilibrium with respect to air of such reasonable humidity that the salt exists stoichiometrically as the dihydrate. The possibility of adsorption of moisture on components other than the barium chloride dihydrate must be considered, of course; the following procedure is satisfactory with sodium chloride or other nonvolatile and nonhygroscopic substances as possible additional components in the sample.

This determination is a very accurate one, the major possible sources of error being the taking on of moisture by the anhydrous sample prior to or during weighing and random weighing errors.

Applicability.   In principle the procedure is applicable to any determination in which one component or group of components can be separated from the rest of the sample by volatilization. The volatilization may be accomplished either by heat or by use of a chemical reagent.

Specific applications in which heat alone is used to volatilize a component include determination of carbonate content of rocks by heating to drive off carbon dioxide, as

$$CaCO_3 \longrightarrow CaO + CO_2$$

$$MgCO_3 \longrightarrow MgO + CO_2$$

and general determinations of "loss on ignition" to include both moisture and carbon dioxide as well as any similarly volatile organic components. The carbon dioxide content of natural waters can similarly be determined by heat volatilization, but here the evolved gas must be adsorbed (water on a desiccant and carbon dioxide on ascarite, which is sodium hydroxide in shredded asbestos) and its quantity measured by gain in weight of the adsorber. Mercury in ores can be determined by heat volatilization and collection of the evolved mercury on a weighed piece of silver or gold foil.

Applications in which a component is evolved from the sample by a chemical reagent include the determination of silicon dioxide in rocks by evolving the silicon as SiF_4 upon treatment of the rock sample in hydrofluoric acid and heating

$$SiO_2 + 4\,HF \longrightarrow SiF_4 + 2\,H_2O$$

The measurement is based upon loss of weight of the sample, although special steps are required to reconvert all other components back to their original forms prior to the final weighing. Carbon and hydrogen in organic compounds may be determined by burning the sample in a stream of oxygen gas in a closed system. The hydrogen is converted to water, which may be measured by increase in weight of an adsorbing tube containing a desiccant. The carbon is converted to carbon dioxide, which may be measured by gain in weight of an adsorbing tube containing ascarite. These determinations are extremely important, and special pieces of apparatus have been developed to carry out some of the experimental steps semi-automatically.

It may be noted that the simplest, and least selective, type of volatilization determination consists of volatilizing by heat alone and measuring the evolved materials by loss of weight of the sample. The use of an adsorber to collect a certain constituent and/or the use of a chemical reagent to accomplish the volatilization generally increases the experimental complexity of the method but at the same time increases its possible selectivity.

Laboratory Experiment 2

GRAVIMETRIC DETERMINATION OF WATER IN BARIUM CHLORIDE DIHYDRATE BY VOLATILIZATION

Reagents.   None.

Procedure.   Conduct the determination in triplicate. Grind the sample finely in a porcelain mortar. Spread out on a watch glass. Lay over it a V-shaped piece of glass rod, and cover with another watch glass to keep the sample free from dust but accessible to room air. Let stand for several hours, not in direct sunlight. Transfer individual portions weighing from 0.75 to 1.25 gram each into previously ignited and weighed porcelain crucibles. Weigh each crucible again so the sample weight may be calculated by subtracting the empty crucible weight from the weight of crucible plus sample. Place in a drying oven at 150° to 200° C. for two hours, gradually bringing it up to temperature. Keep the crucibles covered with slight cover displacement to permit evolved moisture to escape. Cool for a minute or two in room air and in the desiccator for thirty minutes. Weigh accurately. Reheat for thirty minutes, cool and weigh again until successive weighings agree within about 0.3 mg. Calculate the percentage H_2O in the sample.

    Suggestions for Supplementary Laboratory Work.   This experiment is readily adaptable to a study of the quantitative importance of certain experimental variables. The principal experimental variables include drying time and drying temperature. For this supplementary (or substitute) experiment, use pure barium chloride dihydrate as the sample, and use duplicate portions with each of the following sets of drying conditions: 80° C. for two hours; 110° C. for 30 minutes; 110° C. for two hours; 150° C. for 30 minutes; 150° C. for two hours. Discuss the significance of the set of results.

DETERMINATION OF CHLORIDE

    Principle.   The chloride content of a sample may be determined by adding an excess of silver nitrate solution to a solution of the unknown and weighing the precipitated silver chloride. The entire determination centers around the one chemical reaction

$$Ag^+ + Cl^- \longrightarrow AgCl$$

This precipitate may be classified as a curdy one. The individual particles

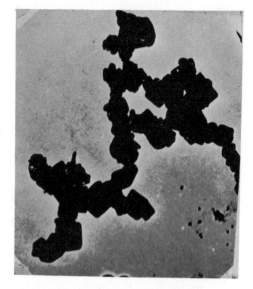

FIGURE 14. Electron photomicrograph of silver chloride, a curdy type of precipitate.

are very small and must coagulate into aggregates before they can be filtered. A highly magnified electron micrograph of a silver chloride precipitate is shown in Figure 14 in which both individual particles and aggregates are clearly seen. The aggregates are often both "chain-like" and "clump-like."

Evaluation of the Method. *I. Completeness of precipitation.* The solubility of silver chloride in pure water is 0.001 4 gram per liter at 20° C. and 0.022 gram per liter at 100° C. To avoid appreciable solubility losses, the precipitate should always be washed and filtered at room temperature or below, even if it is formed at an elevated temperature. Excess silver nitrate is regularly present in the mother liquid and in the first washings, which represses solubility loss by the common ion effect. In washing with as much as 150 ml. of cold, dilute nitric acid, the solubility loss seldom reaches 1 mg. because the wash liquid does not ordinarily become saturated. If this loss should be excessive due to an extremely small amount of precipitate or to a required high accuracy, a washing liquid containing a little silver nitrate may be used. Through the common ion effect, 150 ml. of water containing 0.01 gram of silver nitrate dissolves somewhat less than 0.000 01 gram of silver chloride at room temperature. A very dilute nitric acid medium is desirable to hasten and to maintain flocculation of the tiny particles of the precipitate, but the nitric acid does not markedly alter the solubility of silver chloride. Therefore, the precipitation of silver chloride may readily be made quantitatively complete, and no appreciable error need result from this source.

Chloride ion is an almost omnipresent contaminant, and great care must be exercised to ensure that no undesired chloride is introduced during the determination. In particular, tap water usually contains some chloride ion, which must be removed from all vessels used in the determination by careful rinsing with distilled water.

2. Purity of the precipitate. Silver ion forms a number of sparingly soluble salts. However, the specificity of the precipitating agent is much improved in the presence of a small amount of acid such as nitric acid. Under these conditions, most of the anions of weak acids which form insoluble silver salts will not produce precipitates. For example, silver phosphate precipitates in alkaline medium:

$$PO_4^= + 3\,Ag^+ \longrightarrow Ag_3PO_4$$

But in acid medium another reaction takes precedence:

$$PO_4^= + H^+ \longrightarrow HPO_4^=$$

so that no precipitate forms in the presence of silver nitrate solution. However, even in dilute nitric acid, bromide and iodide ions still yield insoluble precipitates with silver ion, and these ions must be entirely absent or removed before a successful determination of chloride may be undertaken.

Silver chloride precipitates are notable because, when cold-digested, they yield a porous spongy mass that is readily washed free of practically all common impurities by a very dilute nitric acid washing fluid. This characteristic of the precipitate is discernible from Figure 14.

The precipitate must be pure at the time of weighing so any changes in its composition subsequent to precipitation but prior to weighing are significant. The precipitate may be dried quite adequately by heating for an hour at 110° C. A few hundredths of 1 % of water is held very tightly and can be removed only by fusion of the precipitate at about 450° C., but this is not a recommended procedure for inexperienced analysts. Silver chloride may be extensively decomposed upon fusion by traces of organic matter with which it has become contaminated and, furthermore, the material is slightly volatile at temperatures not much above its melting point. Since silver chloride is readily reduced when strongly heated with organic material, the precipitate should not be collected on filter paper because of the resulting necessity of charring off the paper.

Silver halides are decomposed into their constituent elements on exposure to light. The danger of this type of decomposition is particularly grave during the early stages of the precipitation when the milky suspension presents an enormous surface for photochemical reaction. Therefore, the precipitation should be conducted, and the precipitate should be kept, out of bright light insofar as reasonably possible—kept out of sunlight, set inside desk during digestion, worked on in shade-darkened room, and so forth. Silver chloride is almost pure white, but the precipitate is likely to acquire a purplish hue by the time it is weighed. This is due to tiny grains of metallic silver on the surface of the white silver chloride. Even a small amount of light-decomposition results in an appreciable purplish coloration; therefore, the student should not be alarmed at the coloration if he has exercised reasonable caution to prevent excessive decomposition. This light-decomposition may cause either high or low results. The initial decomposition yields free silver and free chlorine:

$$AgCl \xrightarrow{\text{light}} Ag + Cl$$

If excess silver ions are present, as is the case prior to final washings, the liberated chlorine reacts with silver ion to form more silver chloride, such as

$$5\,Ag^+ + 6\,Cl\;(\text{or } 3\,Cl_2) + 3\,H_2O \longrightarrow 5\,AgCl + ClO_3^- + 6\,H^+$$

Stoichiometrically, then, six molecules of silver chloride which decompose result in the presence in the final precipitate of six atoms of free silver plus five molecules of silver chloride. The six silver atoms plus the five silver chloride molecules weigh more than the six silver chloride molecules which should have been present, so the precipitate is too heavy and the result of the determination is too high. If no excess silver ions are present, as is the case after washing, the chlorine atoms liberated through light-decomposition of the precipitate are evolved as chlorine molecules into the atmosphere, so the result of the determination is too low.

3. Physical form of the precipitate. As already noted, the silver chloride is a curdy precipitate and the filtered material consists of porous aggregates of tiny particles. The flocculated precipitate is almost ideal for filtration and washing. A coarse filter is adequate, so filtration is quite rapid and there is no tendency for the pores of the filtering membrane to become clogged. The wash liquid can readily come in contact with virtually all of the initially tiny particles because the larger aggregates are quite porous. However, a serious difficulty arises in that the aggregates can conceivably disperse during washing back into the separate, tinier particles which pass right through the filter membrane. To suppress this phenomenon, known as *peptization*, the precipitate must be washed with a liquid containing some electrolyte. The reason will be discussed in Chapter 8. This electrolyte must be volatile upon subsequent drying of the precipitate. Nitric acid serves very well, not only in preventing peptization but in preventing hydrolysis of any other substances which were initially kept in solution by the acid medium at the time of precipitation.

Applicability. Bromide ion may be determined by the same general procedure and with the same order of accuracy. Iodide determinations are also possible, but the procedure is less satisfactory for three reasons: silver iodide tends to peptize more readily than silver chloride; silver iodide adsorbs certain impurities quite tenaciously; silver iodide is extremely photosensitive. Thiocyanate and cyanide ions are also determinable in this fashion.

Several different weak acid anions can be determined by precipitating their silver salts from a nearly neutral medium. For a successful determination, the sample solution must contain only one kind of anion which can form an insoluble silver salt. For example, phosphate ion may be determined by precipitation and weighing of silver phosphate. In most instances, however, the weak acid anions are more conveniently determined by other procedures.

Several cations may be determined by a reversal of the procedure. Thus, silver may be determined quite accurately by precipitation and weighing of silver chloride or silver bromide. Mercurous mercury and lead ion may also be precipitated as their chlorides, but solubility losses are considerable with lead chloride. Thallous ion may likewise be determined by precipitation and weighing of thallous chloride.

Laboratory Experiment 3

GRAVIMETRIC DETERMINATION OF CHLORIDE IN A SOLUBLE SALT MIXTURE

Reagents

Nitric acid, stock solution

Silver nitrate, solution containing 50 grams $AgNO_3$ per liter of solution

Wash liquid, solution containing 0.5 ml. nitric acid (stock solution) per 200 ml. water

Procedure

Conduct the determination in triplicate. Dry the sample at 110° C. for one hour. Weigh accurately individual portions weighing from 0.4 to 0.7 gram each into 400 ml. beakers. Dissolve in 150 ml. water. Add four or five drops nitric acid (stock solution). Calculate the amount of silver nitrate solution required, assuming the sample to be entirely sodium chloride, unless the instructor advises you differently, and use 10% more than this calculated amount. Heat the unknown solution nearly to boiling, and add the silver nitrate solution in about ten portions, stirring vigorously for one or two minutes after each addition. Set aside for thirty minutes on a steam bath, or overnight at room temperature, until the precipitate settles and the supernatant liquid is clear. Keep the precipitate shielded from bright light insofar as practical at all times. When the supernatant liquid is clear, test for complete precipitation by adding a few more drops of the silver nitrate solution. If further turbidity appears, continue the addition of more silver nitrate solution and digestion until precipitation is complete. Wash by decantation into a previously dried and weighed sintered glass or sintered porcelain filtering crucible with five or six 25 ml. portions of the wash liquid. Then transfer the precipitate quantitatively to the filtering crucible with more of the wash liquid. Dry the crucible and precipitate in an oven at 150° C. for one hour, cool and weigh. (Use the same drying time and temperature for the empty crucible before the filtration.) Repeat the drying and weighing operations until successive weighings agree within about 0.3 mg. The weighed precipitate is AgCl. Calculate the percentage Cl in the sample.

DETERMINATION OF SULFATE

Principle. Sulfur is commonly determined by converting all the sulfur material in a weighed sample to sulfate ion, after which barium sulfate is precipitated, washed, filtered, dried and weighed. The entire determination centers around one chemical reaction

$$Ba^{++} + SO_4^{=} \longrightarrow BaSO_4$$

This precipitate is classified as a crystalline one. The individual crystals are large enough that they can be filtered. Some coagulation is desirable prior to filtration, yet the individual crystals are much larger than they are in a curdy precipitate such as silver chloride. A highly magnified electron photomicrograph of barium sulfate crystals is shown in Figure 15 along with a photomicrograph of nickel dimethylglyoxime, another crystalline precipitate. The individual crystals obtained in the usual precipitation procedures are not perfect geometrical forms, yet there is a generally characteristic structure of barium sulfate crystals. The apparent size and shape of a crystalline precipitate vary with changes in conditions of precipitation, yet the essential difference between a crystalline precipitate and a curdy precipitate is illustrated in a comparison of Figures 14 and 15.

Evaluation of the Method. *1. Completeness of precipitation.* Barium sulfate is soluble in pure water at room temperature only to the extent of about 3 mg. per liter. In practice the solubility is sharply diminished by the presence of excess barium ion in the mother liquid. Barium sulfate is only slightly more soluble at elevated temperatures. This is of particular importance because it permits the use of hot wash water for more effective removal of impurities.

Barium sulfate is markedly more soluble in acid media than in pure water. For example, its solubility in a 1 molar hydrochloric acid solution is about thirtyfold greater than in pure water. This situation arises because sulfuric acid is not completely a strong acid. The first step of ionization,

$$H_2SO_4 \longrightarrow H^+ + HSO_4^-$$

proceeds essentially to completion to the right. However, the second step,

$$HSO_4^- \rightleftharpoons H^+ + SO_4^{=}$$

proceeds only slightly to the right. For example, in 1 molar sulfuric acid solution, only about 1 % of the total sulfate is in the $SO_4^=$ form, about 99 % being in the HSO_4^- form. So when sulfate precipitation is attempted in acidic media, the H^+ ions and the Ba^{++} ions must compete for the sulfate ions. The barium ions are somewhat more successful contenders, but a substantial portion of the sulfate may remain in solution as HSO_4^- ions. For another reason to be encountered shortly, a low pH at the time of precipitation is somewhat desirable even though the solubility losses are enhanced as the acidity of the solution is increased.

2. Purity of the precipitate. Barium ion forms insoluble precipitates with a variety of anions other than sulfate, yet most of them are anions of weak acids so that their barium salts are soluble in acid. In solutions which are rather dilute in acid, only a little of the sulfate is lost as bisulfate ion, but all of the anions of much weaker acids are effectively removed from the scene of action through formation of their undissociated acids. The only anion which remains troublesome under these conditions is fluoride ion. Barium fluoride is quite insoluble in dilute acid solution, and this ion must be removed prior to precipitation of barium sulfate. This removal may be accomplished readily through volatilization of hydrofluoric acid or through complexing with boric acid.

Of the most common cations, other than barium, only lead, calcium and strontium form nominally insoluble sulfates. Interference from lead may be prevented by complexing the lead ion with acetate ion. Calcium and strontium must be removed prior to precipitation of barium sulfate.

Precipitated barium sulfate tends to retain many extraneous materials

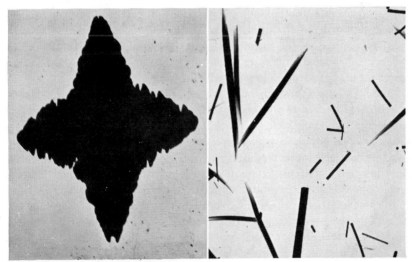

FIGURE 15. Electron photomicrographs of barium sulfate (left) and of nickel dimethylglyoxime (right), both crystalline types of precipitate.

from its mother liquid, and herein lies the chief bar to the highly accurate determination of sulfate ion. The process whereby an otherwise soluble substance is precipitated along with an insoluble substance is termed *coprecipitation*, and many substances can and do coprecipitate with barium sulfate. Discussion of the mechanisms will be included in Chapter 8.

The influence of coprecipitations on the direction of the error in the results is important because it indicates that the errors produced may compensate for themselves even when coprecipitation cannot be entirely suppressed. Consider the coprecipitation of anions, such as chloride and nitrate, in a sulfate determination. The coprecipitated anions must be compensated electrically by positive ions, and barium ions are the most available cations. So this coprecipitation is, in effect, a coprecipitation of $BaCl_2$ or $Ba(NO_3)_2$ along with $BaSO_4$. Note that the coprecipitated substances are soluble by themselves; this means that this is definitely a case of co-precipitation. Insofar as the sulfate is concerned, these coprecipitated substances are merely extra precipitate for weighing. In this case the results tend to be too high when foreign anions coprecipitate with barium sulfate in a gravimetric sulfate determination.

Consider next the coprecipitation of cations, as ferric ion, in a sulfate determination. The cation must be compensated by anions to maintain electrical neutrality and, as the precipitation is normally conducted, this anion is usually the sulfate ion itself. So the precipitate is partially ferric sulfate, $Fe_2(SO_4)_3$ which, upon ignition, is decomposed to ferric oxide, Fe_2O_3. Because each sulfate ion should account for one barium sulfate molecule (molecular weight 233.43) in the final precipitate, and because each sulfate ion involved in a ferric coprecipitation accounts for only one-third of a ferric oxide molecule (molecular weight 159.70, one-third being only 53.23), the precipitate is too light and the result for sulfate comes out too low. Coprecipitation of other cations leads to a similar conclusion whenever the cation replacing a proper barium ion in the precipitate weighs less than the barium ion, as is usually the case. Generally, coprecipitation of foreign cations leads to results that are too low in the determination of sulfate.

One fortunate aspect of the coprecipitation phenomena is now clear—when both foreign cations and foreign anions are coprecipitated, the errors tend to compensate and may yield fairly accurate results. The balancing of the high and low errors is not perfect, of course, unless it be by mere chance. Some ions coprecipitate much more readily than others. The extent of coprecipitation of any ion is a function of its concentration in the mother liquid, and the various conditions of precipitation influence the extent of the coprecipitations.

Barium sulfate must be ignited at a temperature of 500° C. or so to free it of water. The barium sulfate itself is stable even well above this tempera-ture, so that the ignition need not cause any undesired decomposition. However, at high temperature barium sulfate may be reduced by carbon, as from filter paper:

$$BaSO_4 + 4\,C \longrightarrow BaS + 4\,CO$$

This possible source of error is avoided entirely if a sintered porcelain filtering crucible is used. But good results can be obtained even with filter paper if the paper is charred off at the lowest possible temperature, if it does not actually enflame and if the crucible is left entirely uncovered until practically all the paper is gone. A slight decomposition to barium sulfide can be reversed, if necessary, by cooling after ignition, adding a drop of concentrated sulfuric acid, and gently heating to fume off the acid not used up in the reaction

$$BaS + H_2SO_4 \longrightarrow BaSO_4 + H_2S$$

3. Physical form of the precipitate. Barium sulfate is a crystalline

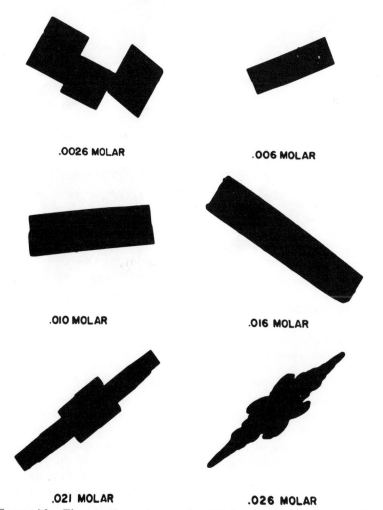

.0026 MOLAR

.006 MOLAR

.010 MOLAR

.016 MOLAR

.021 MOLAR

.026 MOLAR

FIGURE 16.   Electron photomicrographs of barium sulfate showing the effect of the concentration of the sulfate solution upon the size and the degree of perfection of the precipitated particles.

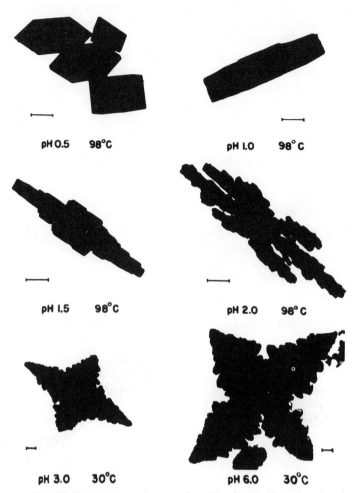

pH 0.5   98°C   pH 1.0   98°C

pH 1.5   98°C   pH 2.0   98°C

pH 3.0   30°C   pH 6.0   30°C

FIGURE 17. Electron photomicrographs of barium sulfate showing the effect
of the acidity of the sulfate solution upon the size and the degree of perfection of
the precipitated crystals.

precipitate so there is little or no danger of losing it by passing through the
filter medium. Barium sulfate often exhibits a tendency to "creep"; that
is, the fine clumps of precipitate, supported on a liquid surface and moving
on it through the action of surface tension, distribute themselves over the
entire wetted surface of the containing vessel, even climbing up and over
the walls if these surfaces are wet. Thus, the particles of the precipitate can
climb up the sides of a wetted filter paper onto the sides of the glass funnel, if
the latter are wet, and may be lost. This possible source of error can be
suppressed by refraining from filling the filter paper any closer than 1.5
cm. from the top or by using a filtering crucible and keeping the upper part
entirely dry.

The crystal size, degree of perfection, rate of coagulation, tendency to creep and other aspects of the physical form of the precipitate are markedly influenced by the conditions of the precipitation. In Figure 16 are shown highly magnified electron photomicrographs of barium sulfate crystals precipitated from solutions of various sulfate ion concentration. It is seen that the particles precipitated from a more dilute solution are more highly perfected crystals than are those precipitated from the more concentrated solutions. There is also a size differential. In the case of some other precipitates, the particle size varies much more markedly with the concentrations of the reacting solutions. In Figure 17 are shown highly magnified electron photomicrographs of barium sulfate crystals precipitated from sulfate media of various hydrogen ion concentrations. At the higher acidity values (lower pH numbers), the crystals are smaller but definitely more highly perfected. In Figure 18 are shown highly magnified electron photomicrographs of barium sulfate crystals precipitated with a fresh solution of barium chloride and with a solution of barium chloride which had been allowed to stand for a time before use. Even such a seemingly insignificant factor as this can very markedly influence the size of the resultant crystals. Some of these phenomena will be encountered in the next chapter, although adequate explanations for some of them are still lacking.

Applicability. Barium may be determined by adding an excess of sulfate ion to a solution of the unknown, just reversing the sulfate procedure. Coprecipitation errors again may be serious. Reasoning similar to that of the preceding section reveals that, in a barium determination, anion coprecipitation leads to low results and cation coprecipitation to high results—just the opposite to the situation in sulfate determinations. Lead may be

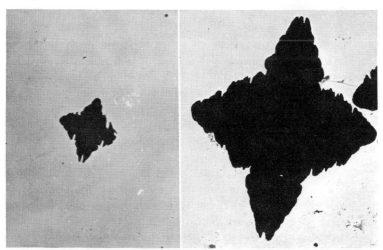

FIGURE 18.   Electron photomicrographs of barium sulfate precipitated with a fresh solution of barium chloride (left) and with a solution of barium chloride which had been allowed to stand for several days prior to use (right).

determined by a similar procedure, but lead sulfate is soluble enough (about 4 mg. per 100 ml. water at room temperature) to make solubility losses somewhat more significant than in barium sulfate precipitations. Strontium and calcium sulfates are nominally insoluble also, but their solubilities (15 mg. per 100 ml. water for $SrSO_4$ and 100 mg per 100 ml. water for $CaSO_4$) are too great for very good quantitative work. These substances are rendered less soluble by using a mixed solvent of alcohol and water, but even then the determinations are not entirely satisfactory.

Laboratory Experiment 4

GRAVIMETRIC DETERMINATION OF SULFATE IN A SOLUBLE SALT MIXTURE

Reagents

Barium chloride, solution containing 5 grams $BaCl_2 \cdot 2\ H_2O$ per liter of solution, and allowed to stand at least 24 hours prior to use

Hydrochloric acid, stock solution

Silver nitrate, solution containing 50 grams $AgNO_3$ per liter of solution

Procedure

Conduct the determination in triplicate. Dry the sample at 110° C. for one hour. Weigh accurately individual portions of 0.3 to 0.6 gram each into 400 ml. beakers. Dissolve in 150 ml. water. Add 1.5 to 2.0 ml. hydrochloric acid (stock solution). Calculate the amount of barium chloride solution needed, including a 10% excess, and put this in a separate beaker. Heat both solutions nearly to boiling. Pour the hot barium chloride solution into the hot sample solution. Stir vigorously for two or three minutes and let stand for 15 minutes or longer. Test for completeness of precipitation by adding a few more drops of the barium chloride solution, adding still more if needed. Then wash with warm water and filter through ashless paper of medium porosity or through a previously ignited and weighed sintered porcelain filtering crucible. Continue washing until a fresh portion of the filtrate yields a negative test for chloride with the silver nitrate solution. If filter paper was used, transfer it with the precipitate to a previously ignited and weighed porcelain crucible and char off the paper over a burner. If a sintered porcelain crucible was used, set it in another porcelain crucible. Ignite in a muffle furnace or over a burner, preferably at 600° C. or somewhat higher, for an hour. Cool and weigh. Repeat the ignition and weighing until successive weighings agree within about 0.3 mg. The weighed precipitate is $BaSO_4$. Calculate the percentage sulfur as SO_3 in the sample.

Suggestions for Supplementary Laboratory Work. The quantitative importance of certain coprecipitation phenomena can be studied profitably by means of variations in this determination. For this supplementary (or substitute) work, run duplicate samples of each of the following, using the procedure of Experiment 4 except as indicated: reagent grade sodium sulfate; reagent grade sodium sulfate with about 5 grams of sodium chloride added to the sample solution prior to precipitation; reagent grade sodium sulfate with about 5 grams of sodium nitrate added to the sample solution prior to precipitation; reagent grade potassium sulfate; reagent grade potassium sulfate with about 5 grams of potassium chloride added to the sample solution prior to precipitation. In each case, compare the percentage sulfur found with the percentage sulfur calculated from the known composition of the sample, and discuss the significance of the results.

(Note: If a sintered porcelain filtering crucible was used, it may be cleaned of barium sulfate after the determination is concluded by scraping out as much as possible with a blunt spatula and then boiling in a highly alkaline solution of ethylene diamine tetraacetic acid.)

DETERMINATION OF IRON

Principle. The iron content of a solution can be determined by precipitating the iron as hydrous ferric oxide:

$$2\,Fe^{+++} + 6\,OH^- + (x - 3)\,H_2O \longrightarrow Fe_2O_3 \cdot x\,H_2O$$

After precipitation, filtration and washing, the precipitate is ignited to an-hydrous ferric oxide, in which form it is weighed. This precipitate is neither curdy, as silver chloride, nor crystalline, as barium sulfate, but rather is classified as being gelatinous. A gelatinous precipitate is one which contains as an intimate part of itself an appreciable but indefinite amount of water. A highly magnified electron micrograph of hydrous ferric oxide is shown in Figure 19, which can be compared with Figures 14 and 15 to show the three categories of precipitates. The gravimetric determination of iron is useful in a first course in quantitative analysis primarily because the procedure illustrates the precipitation and handling of gelatinous materials. Iron is

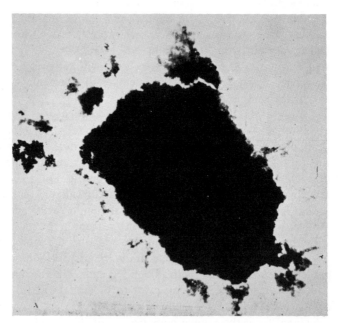

FIGURE 19.   Electron photomicrograph of hydrous ferric oxide, a gelatinous type
of precipitate.

usually determined by volumetric methods rather than by this one. However, iron is frequently separated from other substances by precipitation of hydrous ferric oxide, so the precipitation is useful from a practical standpoint as well as from a pedagogical one.

Evaluation of the Method.   *I.   Completeness of precipitation.* Hydrous ferric oxide is extremely insoluble in water. It is difficult to specify quantitatively just what its solubility is because of its variable composition. Nevertheless, this precipitate is one of the least soluble ones encountered in quantitative analysis. However, ferric ion is complexed by salts of a number of substances, including citric acid, tartaric acid and fluoride, oxalate, cyanide and phosphate ions; therefore, the presence of any one of these substances may partially or entirely prevent the precipitation of ferric ion as the hydrous oxide. This possibility of forming a complex ion is a disadvantage in the iron precipitation, but it may be an advantage in other situations. For example, aluminum or chromium hydroxide may be precipitated selectively as a hydroxide in the presence of complexed ferric ion but not in the presence of uncomplexed ferric ion.

The precipitation of iron as hydrous ferric oxide is incomplete if the iron is not entirely in the ferric form just prior to precipitation. Any ferrous ion which may be present may be oxidized with bromine water or nitric acid just prior to precipitation.

2. *Purity of the precipitate.* Nearly every metallic ion other than the alkali metal ions can form a precipitate of a hydroxide, a hydrous oxide or a basic salt in alkaline solution, so all are possible interferences in the gravimetric iron determination. Careful control of the hydroxyl ion concentration often provides selectivity in precipitation of one hydroxide in the presence of another, and weak bases rather than strong bases are useful in limiting the hydroxyl ion concentration to a predetermined value. The problem is made more complex by excess localized and momentary concentrations of hydroxyl ions where the drops of added reagent enter the solution in the precipitation vessel; this source of difficulty is eliminated in the homogeneous precipitation method to be described later.

Hydrous ferric oxide is a gelatinous precipitate, which means that it retains within the solid phase an appreciable quantity of the mother liquid. Even though the water retained by the precipitate may be volatilized subsequently by ignition, any nonvolatile components present in the mother liquid will remain even through the final weighing operation. Gelatinous precipitates are seldom pure but rather retain as impurities some of any type of foreign ion present to any appreciable extent in the mother liquid. In some cases it is beneficial to redissolve a gelatinous precipitate after filtration and then to precipitate it again—any impurities present in the mother liquid at the time of the first precipitation are present in much less concentration for the reprecipitation.

An additional source of impurity in the precipitate arises from the fact that alkaline solutions attack glass. A residue of silica is formed if the alkaline solution is permitted to stand for an appreciable period of time prior to filtration. Any silica present at the time of precipitation of the hydrous oxide is carried down with the main body of precipitate and remains in the ignited precipitate as silicon dioxide. When it is necessary to determine how much of an ignited precipitate consists of silica, that precipitate may be fused with potassium pyrosulfate. All the oxides except silicon dioxide are converted to soluble sulfates; the insoluble silica which remains can be filtered, washed, ignited and weighed. The weight of silica can then be subtracted from the observed weight of ferric oxide (or aluminum or chromium oxides) to get the true weight of the desired oxide. This refinement in procedure is necessary only in highly accurate work.

An improper ignition operation can prevent the precipitate from being entirely in the desired chemical form at the time of weighing. Ferric oxide is readily reduced during ignition by carbon of the filter paper unless the paper is removed completely at as low a temperature as possible. The reduction most frequently stops at the form Fe_3O_4, although, in extreme cases of reduction, some metallic iron may result. It is also possible to lose part of the iron as volatile ferric chloride if any chloride ion is present at the time of ignition.

3. Physical form of the precipitate. Hydrous ferric oxide is a gelatinous precipitate. The significance of this fact with respect to the purity of the precipitate has already been discussed. Gelatinous precipitates are

quite difficult to filter and wash. Prolonged digestion of the precipitate prior
to filtration does little or no good. The precipitate tends to clog up the pores
of the filter, even to the extent of preventing the passage of liquid through
the filter. A coarse filter paper should be used, and nearly all of the washing
operation should be accomplished in the precipitation vessel by decantation
prior to transfer of the main body of precipitate to the filter. Liquid tends
to form channels through the precipitate on the paper so that it does not
even come in contact with all of the precipitate. The use of filter paper pulp
is recommended. Suction must not be used with gelatinous precipitate
filtrations as it enhances the channeling effect.

Applicability. This general procedure may be used for the determinations of aluminum, chromium, zirconium, titanium and manganese. A
hydroxide or hydrous oxide of each of these may be precipitated with
ammonium hydroxide, and proper ignition of each yields the corresponding
oxide. Hydrous oxide and hydroxide precipitates are seldom pure, particularly when two or more metallic ions are present at the time of precipitation.
Yet these precipitation processes are still widely used in quantitative analysis.

Laboratory Experiment 5

GRAVIMETRIC DETERMINATION OF IRON IN AN ACID-SOLUBLE IRON OXIDE OR SALT

Reagents

> Ammonium hydroxide, 1 volume stock solution diluted with
>   2 volumes water, and filtered just prior to use
> Filter paper pulp
> Hydrochloric acid, stock solution
> Methyl orange indicator, solution containing 0.02 gram methyl
>   orange per 100 ml. water
> Nitric acid, stock solution
> Silver nitrate, solution containing 50 grams $AgNO_3$ per liter of
>   solution
> Wash liquid, solution containing 1 gram NH_4NO_3 per 100 ml. water

Procedure

> Conduct the determination in triplicate. Dry the sample at
> 110° C. for one hour. Weigh accurately individual portions weighing
> 0.8 to 1.0 gram each into 600 ml. beakers. Dissolve in about 30 ml.

water plus 10 ml. hydrochloric acid (stock solution). When the sample is completely dissolved, dilute to 350 ml. with water. Do not carry the experiment beyond this point unless sufficient time (about two hours) is available to complete the washings and filtrations before the end of the laboratory period. Shake one-third of a disk of filter paper pulp in a test tube with water until the disk of pulp is disintegrated, then add it to the sample solution. Add two or three drops of nitric acid (stock solution) to oxidize any ferrous ion which may be present. Heat just to boiling. Add two or three drops of methyl orange. Add the ammonium hydroxide solution until the solution becomes alkaline as indicated by indicator color changing from red to yellow. Allow the precipitate to settle so that the color of the clear liquid layer can be noted with certainty as yellow, adding more indicator if the supernatant liquid should be colorless. Allow the precipitate to coagulate on the macerated filter pulp and to settle for fifteen to thirty minutes (no longer), and then wash and filter it through ashless paper of coarse porosity. Continue the washings until a fresh portion of the filtrate yields no precipitate of silver chloride when acidified with nitric acid and treated with a few drops of the silver nitrate solution. Transfer the paper and precipitate to a previously ignited and weighed porcelain crucible. Char off the paper over a burner, then ignite for one hour in a muffle furnace or over a burner, preferably at 600° C. or somewhat higher. Cool and weigh. Repeat the ignition and weighing until successive weighings agree within about 0.3 mg. The weighed precipitate is Fe_2O_3. Calculate the percentage Fe in the sample.

DETERMINATION OF MAGNESIUM

Principle. Magnesium ion may be precipitated as magnesium ammonium phosphate, $MgNH_4PO_4 \cdot 6\,H_2O$, by slow neutralization with ammonium hydroxide of an acid solution containing magnesium, ammonium and hydrogen phosphate ions. The precipitate is then washed, filtered and ignited to magnesium pyrophosphate, $Mg_2P_2O_7$, for weighing. The precipitation and ignition reactions proceed according to the equations:

$$Mg^{++} + NH_4^+ + HPO_4^= + 5\,H_2O + OH^- \longrightarrow MgNH_4PO_4 \cdot 6\,H_2O$$
$$2\,MgNH_4PO_4 \cdot 6\,H_2O \longrightarrow Mg_2P_2O_7 + 13\,H_2O + 2\,NH_3$$

The hydroxyl ion for the precipitation reaction must be obtained from a weak base such as ammonium hydroxide. A strong base, such as sodium hydroxide, would cause precipitations of additional, undesirable compounds.

Evaluation of the Method. *1. Completeness of precipitation.* Magnesium ammonium phosphate is more soluble than generally desired for quantitative precipitation. The solubility is markedly influenced by the hydrogen ion concentration since the latter, in turn, governs the phosphate ion concentration through the equilibrium

$$H^+ + PO_4^= \rightleftharpoons HPO_4^=$$

The precipitate does not form in acidic solution, but it does in neutral or alkaline solution. The solubility is also influenced by the ammonium ion concentration through the common ion effect, so an excess of ammonium ion should be present for the precipitation process. The solubility is further influenced by the temperature, being appreciably less at temperatures near 0° C. than at room temperature. Therefore, the precipitation of magnesium ammonium phosphate may be made complete only by proper application of the pH effect, the common ion effect and the temperature effect. Magnesium ammonium phosphate enters into supersaturated solution quite readily, so its rate of precipitation is slow. The precipitation vessel must be allowed to stand for an appreciable period of time after precipitation before filtration.

The precipitate of magnesium ammonium phosphate can be lost to an appreciable extent in the wash liquid, through either or both of the following two reactions:

$$MgNH_4PO_4 \cdot 6\,H_2O \rightleftharpoons Mg^{++} + NH_4^+ + PO_4^= + 6\,H_2O$$
$$MgNH_4PO_4 \cdot 6\,H_2O + H_2O \rightleftharpoons Mg^{++} + NH_4OH + HPO_4^= + 6\,H_2O$$

The first reaction represents dissolving through simple ionization and the second through hydrolysis. Both mechanisms of dissolving the precipitate are suppressed by the presence in the wash liquid of a small amount of the weak base, ammonium hydroxide. The wash liquid should also be cooled in an ice bath, and only a reasonably small total volume of wash liquid should be used.

Even with these precautions, the loss of magnesium ion through solubility of magnesium ammonium phosphate represents a major source of error in this procedure.

2. Purity of the precipitate. Since the precipitate of magnesium ammonium phosphate must be formed from slightly alkaline solution, many types of foreign ion can interfere in this determination. Nearly every metallic ion can precipitate as a hydroxide, oxide or basic salt if its solution is made sufficiently alkaline. All cations except the alkalies and ammonium ions must be absent at the time of the precipitation.

Even in the absence of interfering cations, it is possible for the magnesium, ammonium and phosphate ions to combine to form compounds other than the desired one. Some of these contaminating precipitates are listed in Table 10. This table also indicates the form in which each would exist after ignition, whether each improper precipitate would cause the final results in a magnesium determination to be too high or too low, and a general cause for the formation of each improper one. The student should verify each of the stated effects upon the result, recognizing that each magnesium atom or ion of the original sample should appear as magnesium pyrophosphate in the precipitate which is finally weighed. Some contaminants are more serious than others; for example, potassium contamination is much more serious than that due to sodium.

The precipitate may not be converted to pure magnesium pyrophosphate during ignition unless that ignition is carried out correctly. The precipitate is readily decomposed by hot carbon or by a reducing flame, so the filter paper, if used, must be charred off at a temperature no higher than is absolutely necessary, and the ignition vessel must be properly placed in the

**Table 10. Contaminating Forms of the Precipitate
in the Magnesium Determination**

Substance Precipitated	Substance after Ignition	Effect on Results	Cause
$NH_4H_2PO_4$	HPO_3	high	excess H^+ and NH_4^+
$(NH_4)_4Mg(PO_4)_2$	$Mg(PO_3)_2$	high	excess NH_4^+
$MgNaPO_4$	$MgNaPO_4$	high	excess Na^+
$MgKPO_4$	$MgKPO_4$	high	excess K^+
$MgHPO_4$ $Mg(H_2PO_4)_2$	$Mg_2P_2O_7$	low (soluble in wash)	acid
$Mg_3(PO_4)_2$	$Mg_3(PO_4)_2$	low	excess OH^-
$Mg(OH)_2$	MgO	low	excess OH^-

flame of the burner. Some analysts prefer to make the final washings of the magnesium ammonium phosphate with alcohol and then ether and to dry the precipitate at room temperature for weighing as the hexahydrate. The higher temperature ignition to the pyrophosphate is generally more satisfactory, however. A temperature of at least 600° C. is necessary for this ignition.

In view of the large number of interfering cations and the possibility that even the desired ions may combine to form the wrong precipitate, it is necessary that the analyst follow a proven procedure very carefully in order to achieve good results. Some of the possible errors tend to make the results too high and others too low, and it is likely that there is some compensation of errors when good results are obtained. However, reasonably good determinations can be performed if proven directions are followed rigorously throughout the analysis.

3. Physical form of the precipitate. Magnesium ammonium phosphate is formed in a crystalline form which is generally quite easy to handle throughout the washing and filtering operations. There need be no particular difficulty in this determination from the standpoint of the physical form of the precipitate.

Applicability. The procedure for the gravimetric determination of magnesium may be turned around and used for the determination of phosphate. This method is, of course, subject to the same difficulties of obtaining complete precipitation and purity of precipitate. In some instances, such as in the determination of phosphate in a rock, the phosphate is first precipitated as ammonium molybdophosphate, $(NH_4)_3P(Mo_3O_{10})_4$. This precipitation is at least somewhat more selective than that of magnesium ammonium phosphate. This compound is then redissolved and the phosphate again precipitated in the conventional form of magnesium ammonium phosphate.

Arsenate may be determined by an analogous method. The initial precipitate is magnesium ammonium arsenate. Among the cations other than magnesium which can be determined by the same general procedure involving precipitation of an insoluble ammonium phosphate are zinc, manganese, cadmium and cobalt.

Laboratory Experiment 6

GRAVIMETRIC DETERMINATION OF MAGNESIUM IN AN ACID-SOLUBLE MAGNESIUM COMPOUND

Reagents

Ammonium hydroxide, stock solution, filtered just prior to use
Diammonium hydrogen phosphate, solution containing 75 grams $(NH_4)_2HPO_4$ per liter
Hydrochloric acid, stock solution
Methyl orange indicator, solution containing 0.02 gram methyl orange per 100 ml. water
Nitric acid, stock solution
Silver nitrate, solution containing 50 grams $AgNO_3$ per liter of solution
Wash liquid, solution containing 1 volume stock solution NH_4OH diluted with 30 volumes water

Procedure

Conduct the determination in triplicate. Dry the sample at 110° C. for one hour. Accurately weigh individual portions weighing from 0.4 to 0.7 gram each into 400 ml. beakers. Dissolve in about 15 ml. water and 5 ml. hydrochloric acid, adding the latter dropwise while the beaker is mostly covered with a watch glass to avoid loss by splattering. Dilute with water to about 150 ml. Calculate the necessary amount of diammonium hydrogen phosphate, including a 10% excess, and add this to the solution. Add 10 drops methyl orange indicator solution. Cool in an ice bath for at least 15 minutes. Add ammonium hydroxide dropwise until the indicator color changes from red to yellow, then add an excess of 5 ml. more. Allow the suspension to stand overnight. Cool in an ice bath. Filter through ashless paper of medium porosity, and wash with 10 ml. portions of cold wash liquid until a fresh portion of the filtrate, after acidification with nitric acid, gives a negative test for chloride ion with silver nitrate solution. However, do not use more than 10 of the 10 ml. portions of the wash liquid. Transfer the paper and precipitate to a previously ignited and weighed porcelain crucible, and char off the paper over a burner. Ignite for one hour in a muffle furnace or over a Meker burner at 600° C. or somewhat higher. Cool and weigh. Repeat the ignition and weighing until successive weighings agree within about 0.3 mg. The weighed precipitate is $Mg_2P_2O_7$. Calculate the percentage magnesium as MgO in the sample.

DETERMINATION OF COMPOSITION OF LIMESTONE

A typical limestone has the following approximate composition.

	%
CO_2	30–45
CaO	35–45
MgO	10–25
SiO_2	1–20
Fe_2O_3	0– 2
Al_2O_3	0– 5
$Na_2O + K_2O$	0– 3

A complete analysis of a limestone sample includes a determination of each of these constituents along with determinations of all other components which may be present in the particular sample. From a practical standpoint, it is seldom necessary or even advisable to make such a complete analysis. A sample of limestone may in most instances be considered as analyzed adequately when the following five determinations have been made:

1. Loss on ignition.
2. Silica.
3. "R_2O_3" (a group determination including Fe_2O_3, Al_2O_3 and any other similar oxides).
4. Calcium oxide.
5. Magnesium oxide.

An analysis of this type is not complete, yet it is sufficient for most purposes and is designated a *proximate analysis*. A proximate analysis is one in which two or more components are grouped together into one determination and in which some lesser constituents are omitted. The term proximate should not be confused with the term approximate. Proximate refers to the components and groupings of components which are determined and in no wise refers to the accuracy or precision of those determinations.

Loss on Ignition. The first determination in a proximate analysis of limestone is a volatilization procedure, in which the weight percentage of sample which is lost upon ignition at about 1000° C. is determined. The chief reaction occurring during the ignition is the loss of carbon dioxide originally present in the limestone sample as calcium carbonate and magnesium carbonate. In addition, some water may be driven off, ferrous iron and other reduced forms are oxidized, and any organic material present is oxidized and volatilized. Magnesium carbonate loses carbon dioxide readily, but a temperature above 850° C. is required for complete decomposition of calcium carbonate to calcium oxide. So the ignition is best carried out in a platinum crucible, although porcelain is acceptable if a muffle furnace is used rather than a burner.

Determination of Silica. The residue from the ignition is entirely soluble in hydrochloric acid except the silica. The silica forms a colloidal dispersion of silicic acid, which is hydrated silica, $SiO_2 \cdot xH_2O$. The silicic acid forms as a gel which may be dispersed so completely that the solution-suspension may appear clear. Immediate filtration would not remove the silicic acid adequately and, even if it did, the precipitate would be far from pure because of its gelatinous form. Therefore, the initial colloidal dispersion, in hydrochloric acid medium, must be evaporated to dryness. This evaporation serves to dehydrate the silicic acid, thus improving its physical form considerably. The residue is then extracted with hydrochloric acid to redissolve all but the silica. The evaporation and redissolving must be repeated at least once. Instead of the double dehydration with hydrochloric acid, a single evaporation with perchloric acid can suffice—perchloric acid is added to the initial hydrochloric acid solution and the evaporation is stopped shortly before dryness. Perchloric acid can cause violent explosions, and it should not be used by inexperienced analysts except when very carefully following correctly prescribed directions. The residue from the solution following either the double hydrochloric acid evaporation or the single one with perchloric acid is then filtered, ignited to anhydrous silicon dioxide and weighed.

The final precipitate is never pure silicon dioxide. On one hand, some basic oxides such as aluminum oxide and ferric oxide are retained to some extent. On the other hand, somewhat less than all of the silica is removed from the sample by this procedure. Fortunately, one of these errors tends to make the precipitate too heavy and the other not heavy enough, so that the two errors tend to offset each other. Furthermore, the silica left behind will eventually contaminate the R_2O_3 precipitate, tending to make up for the

R_2O_3 components removed prematurely in the silica determination. If very exacting work is required, the purity of the weighed silica may be determined by evaporating it with hydrofluoric and sulfuric acids to volatilize the silica as the tetrafluoride:

$$SiO_2 + 4\,HF \longrightarrow SiF_4 + 2\,H_2O$$

The other cations, left as their sulfates, may be reconverted to oxides by further ignition in air and reweighed. The loss in weight during this process is directly the weight of silica.

Determination of R_2O_3. The solution remaining from the removal of silica is treated with ammonium hydroxide to precipitate the hydroxides and hydrous oxides of iron, aluminum, titanium, and so forth, if present. If manganese is a component of the sample, it should be oxidized with bromine just prior to this precipitation so that manganese will be included in this group. The procedure for the R_2O_3 determination is the same as that already described for the gravimetric determination of iron. The various components are in the forms of their oxides at the time of weighing, and the weight of this residue is taken directly as the R_2O_3 content of the sample.

Any silica not previously removed appears in the R_2O_3 precipitate. For very exacting work, it may be removed by volatilization as the tetrafluoride as already described. The R_2O_3 residue may be analyzed further for each of its several components, if desired, but this refinement is not included in the proximate analysis of limestone.

Determination of Calcium. The filtrate and washings from the R_2O_3 determination are next subjected to separation and measurement of calcium. Calcium is precipitated as calcium oxalate by slow neutralization with ammonium hydroxide of an acid solution containing both calcium ion and oxalic acid. After washing and filtration, the precipitate is ignited to one of several possible weighing forms.

Calcium oxalate is soluble in strongly acid solution because the oxalate ion is the anion of a weak acid. Its solubility is also markedly dependent upon temperature, being less in the cold than in the hot. The precipitation of calcium oxalate is quite complete, even in a slightly acid solution, if the mother liquid and the wash liquid are cool and if excess ammonium oxalate is present for its common ion effect.

Practically all metal ions except those of the alkali metals can interfere in the gravimetric calcium determination. In the proximate analysis of limestone, magnesium is the only one present at the time of the calcium oxalate precipitation. However, if the pH is not raised too high, as it would be if a strong base were used instead of ammonium hydroxide, and if the precipitate were filtered quite soon after formation, relatively little magnesium will appear in this precipitate. It is interesting to note once again that two sources of error tend to offset each other—a slight amount of calcium lost here through solubility of calcium oxalate eventually appears in the magnesium precipitate, and a slight amount of magnesium appears as a contaminant in the calcium oxalate precipitate.

Several different drying or ignition procedures are possible in the calcium determination. Low temperature drying permits the precipitate to be weighed as the oxalate, but it is almost impossible to dry the precipitate quantitatively without decomposing the oxalate to some extent. Ignition at about 500° C. converts the oxalate to calcium carbonate, $CaCO_3$, as a possible weighing form, while ignition at about 850° C. results in a weighing form of calcium oxide, CaO. Ignition to calcium carbonate suffers the disadvantage that the temperature must be kept within a fairly narrow range, about 465° C. to 525° C., to insure that all of the precipitate ends up as the carbonate. Calcium oxide likewise suffers a disadvantage in that it shows some tendency to take on carbon dioxide and water vapor from the air during cooling and weighing. Both the carbonate and the oxide are widely used as weighing forms, as each has some advantage over the other.

Determination of Magnesium. After separation of the calcium, the magnesium remaining is precipitated as magnesium ammonium phosphate, ignited to magnesium pyrophosphate, and weighed. This determination was described in some detail on pages 145 to 149.

The summation of the several determinations in a proximate analysis of limestone should be about 100%. However, they should not be expected to total up exactly. Some constituents, for example sodium and potassium, were not determined, and each of the determinations is subject to some errors, both positive and negative in direction. It should be recognized further that a total near 100% does not necessarily indicate correct results. For example, any silica missed in the silica determination appears in the R_2O_3 result so that the sum of these two could be correct even though each might be in error.

Laboratory Experiment 7

PROXIMATE ANALYSIS OF A LIMESTONE

Reagents

Ammonium chloride, solution containing 1 gram NH_4Cl per 100 ml. solution

Ammonium hydroxide, stock solution

Ammonium hydroxide, 1 volume stock solution diluted with 2 volumes water and filtered just prior to use

Ammonium hydroxide, 1 volume stock solution diluted with 30 volumes water

Ammonium oxalate, solution containing 6 grams $(NH_4)_2C_2O_4$ per 100 ml. solution

Ammonium oxalate, solution containing 0.01 gram $(NH_4)_2C_2O_4$ per 100 ml. solution

Diammonium hydrogen phosphate, solution containing 75 grams $(NH_4)_2HPO_4$ per liter

Bromine water

Hydrochloric acid, stock solution

Hydrochloric acid, 1 volume stock solution diluted with 10 volumes water

Hydrochloric acid, 1 volume stock solution diluted with 30 volumes water

Methyl orange indicator, solution containing 0.02 gram methyl orange per 100 ml. water

Methyl red indicator, solution containing 0.02 gram methyl red in 60 ml. alcohol plus 40 ml. water

Nitric acid, stock solution

Procedure

Conduct the determination in triplicate. Dry the sample at 110° C. for one hour.

Loss on Ignition. Weigh accurately individual portions of about 0.5 gram each into covered crucibles, preferably of platinum, that have previously been ignited and weighed. Ignite at 1000° C. for one hour. Cool and weigh. Do not delay weighing more than thirty minutes after ignition. Repeat the ignition and weighing until successive weighings agree within about 0.3 mg. Calculate the percentage of the sample weight which is lost upon ignition.

Silica. Transfer the residue from the ignition to a small, covered casserole. Rinse the crucible with 5 ml. water containing a drop or two of hydrochloric acid (stock solution), adding the rinsings to the casserole. Add 5 ml. hydrochloric acid (stock solution) to dissolve the residue. (Stirring with a glass rod hastens the solution process.) Evaporate to dryness on a steam bath. Maintain the residue at about 110° C. for an hour. Add 5 ml. hydrochloric acid (stock solution) and let stand for a few minutes. Add 25 ml. water. Place upon the steam bath for five or ten minutes, during which time any soluble material should dissolve. Filter off the residue, which is hydrous silica, on ashless paper of medium porosity. Wash with several small portions of hydrochloric acid (1 : 30 dilution) and then with several portions of water. Collect these filtrates in the original casserole and evaporate to dryness (in two "batches," if necessary). Heat at 110° C., take up in hydrochloric acid and digest as before. Filter and wash the silica from this precipitation as before, reserving these filtrates for subsequent determinations. Place the two silica precipitates in a previously ignited and weighed crucible, char off the paper over a burner, and ignite for one hour in a muffle furnace or over a burner at 500° C. or higher. Cool and weigh. Repeat the ignition and weighing until successive weighings are in substantial agreement. Calculate the percentage SiO_2 in the sample.

R_2O_3. Heat the filtrate and washings from the silica precipitation nearly to boiling. Add a few ml. bromine water. Add ammonium hydroxide (1:2 dilution) dropwise until the solution is alkaline (yellow) to methyl orange. Boil the suspension for a few minutes. After the precipitate has settled, filter on ashless paper of coarse porosity and wash with the hot ammonium chloride solution. Redissolve the precipitate in 20 ml. hydrochloric acid (1:10 dilution) plus a little hot water and repeat the precipitation, using the same filter. Combine the filtrates from both filtrations and washings and reserve for subsequent determinations. Transfer the filter paper and precipitate to a previously ignited and weighed crucible and char off the paper over a burner. Ignite for one hour in a muffle furnace or over a burner, preferably at 600° C. or somewhat higher. Cool and weigh. Repeat the ignition and weighing until successive weighings are in substantial agreement. The weighed precipitate may be considered to be R_2O_3. Calculate the percentage R_2O_3 in the sample.

Calcium. Concentrate the filtrate and washings from the R_2O_3 precipitation to 200 ml., if they exceed that, and make just acid (red) to methyl red with dropwise addition of hydrochloric acid (stock solution). Then add 5 ml. more of the same acid and 50 ml. ammonium oxalate solution (6 grams per 100 ml.). Heat to 70° or 80° C. Add ammonium hydroxide (1:2 dilution) until the solution is just alkaline (yellow) to methyl red. Let stand one hour. Filter on ashless paper of medium porosity and wash with several portions of cold ammonium oxalate solution (0.01 gram per 100 ml.). Redissolve the precipitate from the paper in 150 ml. hot hydrochloric acid (1:10 dilution) and dilute to 200 ml. Reprecipitate, filter and wash as before. Combine the filtrates and washings from both precipitations for subsequent determinations. Transfer the precipitate and paper to a previously ignited and weighed crucible. Char off the paper over a burner and ignite, preferably in a muffle furnace, at 1000° C. Cool and weigh. Repeat the ignition and weighing until subsequent weighings are in substantial agreement. The weighed precipitate should be CaO. Calculate the percentage calcium as CaO in the sample.

Magnesium. Mix the filtrates and washings from the calcium oxalate precipitation with 75 ml. nitric acid (stock solution) and evaporate to dryness on a steam bath. Add 2 ml. hydrochloric acid (stock solution) and 25 ml. water and warm the solution for a few minutes. If a slight silica residue appears, remove it by filtration.

Add 5 ml. more of hydrochloric acid (stock solution) and dilute to 150 ml. Add 25 ml. diammonium hydrogen phosphate solution and ten drops methyl orange indicator solution. Cool in an ice bath for fifteen minutes. Add ammonium hydroxide (stock solution) dropwise until the indicator turns just alkaline (yellow), then add an excess of five ml. more. Allow the suspension to stand overnight. Cool in an ice bath and filter on ashless paper of medium porosity. Wash with not more than five 10 ml. portions of cold ammonium hydroxide (1 : 30 dilution). Redissolve the precipitate in hydrochloric acid (1 : 10 dilution) and dilute to 150 ml. Reprecipitate, let stand, filter and wash as before. Use up to ten 10 ml. portions of wash liquid this time. Transfer the paper and precipitate to a previously ignited and weighed crucible. Char off the paper over a burner and ignite for one hour in a muffle furnace or over a Meker burner at 600° C. or somewhat higher. Cool and weigh. Repeat the ignition and weighing until successive weighings are in substantial agreement. The weighed precipitate is $Mg_2P_2O_7$. Calculate the percentage magnesium as MgO in the sample.

DETERMINATION OF COMPOSITION OF BRASS

The major constituents of brass are copper and zinc, and lesser quantities of tin, lead and iron are generally present. A typical sample of brass has the following approximate composition:

	%
Copper	50–90
Zinc	20–40
Tin	0– 6
Lead	0– 5
Iron	0– 3

The system for the analysis of brass is of considerable practical value, and similar analytical schemes are useful for other alloys as well.

Determination of Tin. All components of brass are soluble upon digestion in hot nitric acid except tin. Tin is converted to the plus four oxidation state and immediately precipitated as hydrous stannic oxide, $SnO_2 \cdot xH_2O$. This precipitate may be filtered, washed and ignited to anhydrous stannic oxide for weighing. Thus the method of dissolving the brass sample serves to separate this one component from all others.

Determination of Lead. After separation of the tin, the lead may be determined by precipitation of lead sulfate and weighed in this form. This determination is similar to the method described on pages 134 to 141 for the gravimetric determination of sulfate as barium sulfate. The coprecipitation errors so significant in the barium sulfate precipitation are generally less severe with lead sulfate, but the solubility of lead sulfate is somewhat greater than that of barium sulfate. In the laboratory directions which follow, lead sulfate is precipitated by homogeneous generation of sulfate ion by slow hydrolysis of sulfamic acid. Alternatively, fairly good results can be obtained with direct addition of sulfuric acid to provide the sulfate ions. Since nitrate ions do coprecipitate with the sulfate precipitates, the nitric acid left from dissolving the sample must be removed in the lead determination.

Determination of Copper. Copper may be precipitated from the filtrate of the lead precipitation, after proper adjustment of the conditions of the solution, as copper thiocyanate, $CuSCN$. The copper must be in the proper oxidation state to insure quantitative precipitation. This precipitate is most conveniently washed and then dried at a temperature of about 120° C. As an alternative procedure for the separation of copper, electrolytic deposition of copper as the metal may be employed. A procedure for the electrolytic separation is included in Chapter 19.

Determination of Iron and Zinc. The laboratory directions which follow do not include determinations of iron and zinc. However, if desired, these determinations can be run on the filtrate and washings remaining after the copper separation. Iron may be determined gravimetrically with precipitation as the hydrous oxide, by the general procedure described earlier in this chapter. Finally zinc may be precipitated as zinc ammonium phosphate and ignited to zinc pyrophosphate, $Zn_2P_2O_7$, for weighing by a procedure similar to that already described for the gravimetric determination of magnesium.

Laboratory Experiment 8

DETERMINATIONS OF TIN, LEAD AND COPPER IN A BRASS

Reagents

Alcohol (20%), 1 volume ethyl alcohol diluted with 4 volumes water
Ammonium thiocyanate, solution containing 10 grams NH_4SCN per 100 ml. solution
Filter paper pulp
Nitric acid, stock solution
Nitric acid, 1 volume stock solution diluted with 25 volumes water
Sodium bisulfite, solution containing 5 grams $NaHSO_3$ per 100 ml. solution
Sodium hydroxide, solution containing 5 grams $NaOH$ per 100 ml. solution
Sulfamic acid

Sulfuric acid, stock solution
Sulfuric acid, 1 volume stock solution diluted with 90 volumes water
(always add acid to water, not vice versa)
Wash liquid, solution containing 1 gram NH_4SCN and 0.1 gram
$NaHSO_4$ per liter of solution

Procedure

Conduct the determination in triplicate.

Tin.   Weigh accurately individual portions weighing about 1
gram each into 150 ml. beakers. Add 10 ml. water, then slowly add
10 ml. nitric acid (stock solution). Cover the beaker with a watch
glass supported on glass hooks. Evaporate to 10 ml. on a steam bath.
Dilute to 50 ml. with water. Keep warm, but not boiling, for a
thirty-minute digestion period. Add one-fourth disk of filter paper
pulp and stir. Filter while still warm through ashless paper. Wash
10 to 20 times with small portions of nitric acid (1:25 dilution).
Combine the filtrate and washings for subsequent determinations.
Transfer the paper and precipitate to a previously ignited and
weighed porcelain crucible, and char off the paper over a burner.
Ignite at the full heat of a Meker burner for thirty minutes. Cool and
weigh. Repeat the ignition and weighing until successive weighings
are in substantial agreement. The weighed precipitate is SnO_2.
Calculate the percentage Sn in the sample.

Lead.   Evaporate the filtrate and washings from the tin
precipitation to a volume of 5 ml. to remove most of the nitric acid.
Add 2 grams sulfamic acid and dilute with water to 50 ml. Cover
the beaker with a watch glass supported on glass hooks and heat on
a hot plate until the solution has evaporated to a volume of 3 to 5 ml.
This requires from one to three hours, depending on the temperature
of the hot plate. Cool the solution, and add 50 ml. water. Filter
through a previously ignited and weighed sintered porcelain crucible
and wash with several portions of sulfuric acid (1:90 dilution).
Combine the filtrate and washings for subsequent determinations.
Ignite the filtering crucible in a larger porcelain crucible at a temperature of 400° C. or above for thirty minutes. Cool and weigh. Repeat
the ignition and weighing until successive weighings are in substantial
agreement. The weighed precipitate is $PbSO_4$. Calculate the percentage Pb in the sample.

Copper.   (See Experiment 40 for an alternate procedure.)
Neutralize the filtrate and washings from the lead sulfate precipitation with sodium hydroxide solution until a precipitate just begins to
form. Add 2 ml. sulfuric acid (stock solution). Dilute to 300 ml.
with water and add 25 ml. sodium bisulfite solution. Heat nearly to

boiling. Add 15 ml. of ammonium thiocyanate solution. Stopper the flask and let stand one or two hours. Filter the precipitate through a previously dried and weighed sintered glass or sintered porcelain crucible. Wash ten times with 10 ml. portions of the wash liquid containing NH_4SCN and $NaHSO_3$, then with six portions of 10 ml. of 20% alcohol. Dry at 110° C. for one hour. Cool and weigh. Repeat the drying and weighing operations until successive weighings are in substantial agreement. The weighed precipitate is CuSCN. Calculate the percentage Cu in the sample.

REVIEW QUESTIONS

1. Water in a sample is often determined by loss of weight upon heating; how can the analyst be sure that no other component is being lost at the same time?
2. Define or characterize and illustrate the following terms: curdy precipitate; crystalline precipitate; gelatinous precipitate.
3. What problems of experimental technique are introduced by the gelatinous type of precipitate?
4. State whether each of the following occurrences would tend to make the results of a determination of water in barium chloride dihydrate by volatilization too high, too low or would be of no effect. Explain each answer.
   a. The dehydration temperature is too low.
   b. The dehydration temperature is too high.
   c. The crucible is placed on the balance pan hot.
   d. The sample is allowed to stand uncovered in open air after heating until weighing.
   e. A bit of plaster unsuspectedly falls from the wall into the crucible before final weighing.
5. Will the results of a determination of chloride by the usual gravimetric procedure be made too high, too low or will there be no effect if each of the following occurs? Explain each answer.
   a. Some carbonate is present in the initial unknown.
   b. The water used in preparing the wash liquid contains some chloride ion.
   c. The precipitate is exposed to bright sunlight while suspended in the mother liquid.
   d. The precipitate is exposed to bright sunlight after washing but prior to weighing.
   e. The precipitate is washed with pure water rather than with water containing an electrolyte.
6. Will the results of a determination of sulfate by the usual gravimetric procedure be made too high, too low or will there be no effect if each of the following occurs? Explain each answer.
   a. An excessive amount of acid is present in the mother liquid.
   b. Fluoride ion is present at the time of precipitation.
   c. Nitrate ion is coprecipitated.
   d. Aluminum ion is coprecipitated.
   e. The ignition temperature becomes too high before the filter paper is completely gone.

7. Will the results of a determination of iron by the usual gravimetric procedure be made too high, too low or will there be no effect if each of the following occurs? Explain each answer.
   a. Part of the iron is in the ferrous form at the time the precipitate is formed.
   b. Fluoride ion is present at the time of precipitation.
   c. The ammonium hydroxide solution is allowed to stand for an extended period of time without filtering prior to use.
   d. The sample is boiled vigorously with hydrochloric acid to get it into solution.
   e. No filter paper pulp is used.
8. In the gravimetric determination of magnesium
   a. Why is the suspension cooled just prior to filtration?
   b. Why is ammonium hydroxide used in the wash liquid?
   c. Why is the phosphate solution added to an acid solution of the unknown rather than to an alkaline one?
9. List two other ions which may be determined by only minor modifications of each of these procedures:
   a. Gravimetric chloride procedure.
   b. Gravimetric sulfate procedure.
   c. Gravimetric iron procedure.
   d. Gravimetric magnesium procedure.
10. Distinguish between the terms "proximate" and "approximate."
11. List in order the gravimetric determinations commonly made in a proximate analysis of limestone, indicating for each the chemical formulas of the substance precipitated and the substance weighed.
12. How can the silica determination of a limestone sample be modified to correct for any R_2O_3 precipitate which comes down with the silica precipitate?
13. List in order the gravimetric determinations commonly made in a brass analysis, indicating for each the chemical formulas of the substance precipitated and the substance weighed.

PROBLEMS

PERCENTAGE PROBLEMS BASED ON THE DETERMINATIONS IN THIS CHAPTER

1. A 0.8046 gram sample of impure barium chloride dihydrate weighed 0.7082 gram after drying at 200° C. for two hours. Calculate the percentage H_2O in the sample.
2. A 0.4926 gram sample of a soluble salt mixture yielded a silver chloride precipitate weighing 0.3221 gram. Calculate the percentage Cl in the sample.
3. A 0.3232 gram sample of a soluble salt mixture yielded a barium sulfate precipitate weighing 0.2982 gram. Calculate the percentage sulfur as SO_3 in the sample.
4. A 0.9291 gram sample of an acid-soluble iron ore yielded a ferric oxide precipitate weighing 0.6216 gram. Calculate the percentage Fe in the sample.
5. From a 0.6980 gram sample of an impure, acid-soluble magnesium compound was obtained a precipitate of magnesium pyrophosphate weighing 0.4961 gram. Calculate the percentage magnesium as MgO in the sample.
6. A 0.5000 gram sample of limestone was found to weigh 0.3428 gram after ignition and to yield precipitates of 0.0925 gram of SiO_2, 0.0210 gram of R_2O_3, 0.1508 gram of CaO, and 0.2161 gram of $Mg_2P_2O_7$. Calculate (a) the percentage loss on ignition, (b) the percentage SiO_2, (c) the percentage R_2O_3, (d) the percentage CaO and (e) the percentage MgO.
7. A 1.0000 gram sample of brass yielded 0.0637 gram of SnO_2, 0.0436 gram of

$PbSO_4$, 1.3420 gram of $CuSCN$, 0.0295 gram of Fe_2O_3 and 0.4623 gram of $Zn_2P_2O_7$. Calculate the percentage composition of the sample.

INDIRECT ANALYSIS (see pp. 120 to 122)

8. A 1.0000 gram sample of a mixture of K_2CO_3 and $KHCO_3$ yielded 0.4000 gram CO_2; what weight of each compound was present in the sample?
9. A 1.1374 gram sample contains only sodium chloride and potassium chloride. Upon dissolving and precipitating the chloride as silver chloride, a precipitate weighing 2.3744 grams was obtained. Calculate the percentage of sodium chloride in the sample.
10. A 1.3310 gram sample of a mixture of sodium chloride and potassium chloride was found to contain 0.7090 gram chloride. What are the weights of K and of Na in the sample?
11. A mixture of potassium iodide and sodium chloride was converted to the sulfates and found to weigh the same as initially. What is the percentage KI in the initial sample?
12. A 0.5000 gram sample of a clay was analyzed for sodium and for potassium by precipitating both as chlorides, which weighed 0.0361 gram, and then precipitating the potassium as K_2PtCl_6, weighing 0.0356 gram. Calculate the percentages of potassium and of sodium as K_2O and Na_2O in the initial sample.
13. A 0.2000 gram sample of an alloy containing only silver and lead was dissolved in nitric acid and precipitated by cold hydrochloric acid to yield 0.2466 gram of mixed chloride. Upon extraction of this precipitate with hot water, 0.2067 gram of silver chloride remained. Calculate the percentage Ag and the weight of $PbCl_2$ not precipitated in the first precipitation.
14. A sample composed of only sodium sulfate and potassium sulfate was found to be 60.66% sulfate, SO_4. What is the percentage Na_2SO_4 in the original sample?
15. A mixture of only calcium carbonate and magnesium carbonate lost 48.00% of its weight when converted to calcium and magnesium oxides. Calculate the percentage of each oxide in the ignited residue.
16. In what proportion should calcium carbonate and barium carbonate be mixed so that the mixture will have the same percentage of carbon dioxide as pure strontium carbonate?
17. A sample contains sodium chloride, sodium bromide, sodium iodide and possibly some inert impurities. A 5.000 gram sample is taken for analysis, dissolved and the solution made up to a volume of 500.0 ml. One 100.0 ml. portion gave a precipitate of palladium iodide, PdI_2, weighing 0.2006 gram. A second 100.0 ml. portion gave a precipitate with silver nitrate of 1.9955 gram. When the latter precipitate was heated in a stream of chlorine to convert the silver halides into silver chloride, the resultant silver chloride weighed 1.6809 gram. Calculate the percentages of each sodium salt in the initial sample.
18. A sample contains 30.00% sodium cyanide, NaCN, and 70.00% potassium cyanide, KCN. What is the percentage CN?
19. A mixture contained only calcium carbonate, strontium carbonate and barium carbonate. The carbon dioxide from a sample weighed 0.2875 gram. The calcium from the same sample was precipitated as calcium oxalate which weighed 0.4357 gram (anhydrous). The barium from the same sample was precipitated as barium chromate which weighed 0.3853 gram. What were the weights of each of the three components in the mixture?

SUGGESTIONS FOR ADDITIONAL READING

Items 1, 6, 7, 10, 17, 18, 28 and 30, Appendix 7.

Chapter 8

Theory of the

Precipitation Process

IN EVERY gravimetric determination except those of the volatilization and electrodeposition types, a precipitate is formed by mixing together two chemical reagents. Both reagents are, with few exceptions, in solution form at the time of mixing. It is the purpose of this chapter to describe in some detail the theory of the precipitation process. In order for a precipitation process to be suitable as the basis of a quantitative determination, it must fulfill the three requirements which have been listed in Chapters 6 and 7: (1) the desired compound must be completely precipitated; that is, the amount left in solution must be negligible; (2) the precipitate must be pure; that is, it must contain at the time of weighing no more than negligible quantities of other substances; (3) the precipitate must be in a physical form suitable for the necessary subsequent operations to be performed upon it. These three requirements are closely interrelated, particularly the latter two.

SOLUBILITY PRODUCT PRINCIPLE

Derivation and Statement. The derivation of the solubility product principle was considered briefly in Chapter 1, along with the proper method of expressing it mathematically for any specific situation. This principle is concerned with the state of equilibrium existing between dissolved and undissolved phases of a slightly soluble substance. A solution in which undissolved solute is in equilibrium with dissolved solute is said to be a *saturated solution*. In gravimetric procedures of analysis, the mother liquid is almost invariably saturated with the precipitate which has been formed, so the solubility product principle is of direct significance.

Calculation of Solubility Product Constants from Solubility Data. The numerical values of the solubility product constants for various substances are listed in the various reference handbooks of chemistry, and some of them are included in Appendix 1 of this book. The analytical chemist is seldom called upon to calculate solubility product constants from any kind of experimental data. Nevertheless, it is desirable for the student of quantitative analysis to know at least one of the ways whereby the numerical values of these constants have been established. One such means is to measure experimentally the solubility of the compound and then to calculate the constant from the solubility data. This type of calculation is of considerable value in leading the student into a working familiarity with the solubility product principle.

Solubility product problems, as well as other types of mass law problems, vary widely from one to another. Nevertheless, all can be solved through a relatively simple, general plan of attack. It is essential for each student to become familiar with the underlying principles, and this general plan of attack is a powerful aid in developing this familiarity. It consists of four steps:

Step 1. Write a chemical equation representing the state of equilibrium involved in the problem. If two or more chemical equilibria are involved simultaneously, write a chemical equation for each.

Step 2. Write a mathematical equation representing each of the chemical equations. The mathematical equation is a solubility product constant equation whenever the chemical equation represents an equilibrium between dissolved and undissolved solute.

Step 3. Write additional mathematical equations from the available data until the number of mathematical equations, including those of Step 2, equals the number of unknowns contained therein.

Step 4. Solve these equations together for the desired unknown.

Special attention must be paid throughout to the units used. Concentrations of species in solution must always be used in units of moles per liter in mass law equations. If data are given or are desired in grams per liter, for example, the necessary conversions must be made. This general pattern will be used throughout this book in solving mass law problems. The four steps will be taken in order. The pattern will now be illustrated with three examples in which solubility product constants are calculated from solubility data.

Example 1. Silver chloride dissolves in water to the extent of 1.25×10^{-5} mole per liter of solution; calculate the solubility product constant of silver chloride.

Chemical Equation:

$$AgCl \rightleftharpoons Ag^+ + Cl^-$$

Mathematical Equations:

(1) $$K_{sp} = [Ag^+][Cl^-]$$

(2) $$[Ag^+] = 1.25 \times 10^{-5}$$

(since 1.25×10^{-5} mole of AgCl dissolve per liter, we get 1.25×10^{-5} mole of each type of ion per liter of solution)

(3) $$[Cl^-] = 1.25 \times 10^{-5}$$

Solving:

$$K_{sp} = (1.25 \times 10^{-5})(1.25 \times 10^{-5})$$

(substituting (2) and (3) into (1))

$$K_{sp} = 1.56 \times 10^{-10}$$

The four steps of the general plan of attack have been followed in order. Equations (1), (2) and (3) contain three unknowns, so we had three equations with three unknowns.

Example 2. The solubility of calcium sulfate is 0.1906 gram per 100 ml.; calculate the solubility product constant of calcium sulfate.

Chemical Equation:

$$CaSO_4 \rightleftharpoons Ca^{++} + SO_4^{=}$$

Mathematical Equations:

(1) $$K_{sp} = [Ca^{++}] [SO_4^{=}]$$

(2) $$[Ca^{++}] = \frac{0.1906}{136.15} \times \frac{1000}{100}$$

(changing the solubility data to moles per liter, and recognizing that the number of moles which dissolves equals the number of moles of each type of ion in solution)

(3) $$[SO_4^{=}] = \frac{0.1906}{136.15} \times \frac{1000}{100}$$

Solving:

$$K_{sp} = \left(\frac{0.1906}{136.15} \times \frac{1000}{100}\right)\left(\frac{0.1906}{136.15} \times \frac{1000}{100}\right)$$

(substituting (2) and (3) into (1))

$$K_{sp} = 1.95 \times 10^{-4}$$

Again equations (2) and (3) make up Step 3 in the four-step plan of attack, and again we have three unknown quantities so need the three mathematical equations (1), (2) and (3).

Example 3. If silver sulfide dissolves in water only to the extent of 8.0×10^{-15} gram in a liter, what is its solubility product constant?

Chemical Equation:

$$Ag_2S \rightleftharpoons 2 Ag^+ + S^{=}$$

Mathematical Equations:

(1) $$K_{sp} = [Ag^+]^2 [S^{=}]$$

(2) $$[Ag^+] = \frac{2 \times 8.0 \times 10^{-15}}{247.83}$$

(changing the solubility data to moles per liter and recognizing we get two moles of Ag^+ ion and one mole of $S^{=}$ ion from one mole of Ag_2S which dissolves)

(3) $$[S^{=}] = \frac{8.0 \times 10^{-15}}{247.83}$$

Solving:

$$K_{sp} = \left(\frac{2 \times 8.0 \times 10^{-15}}{247.83}\right)^2 \left(\frac{8.0 \times 10^{-15}}{247.83}\right)$$

$$K_{sp} = 1.3 \times 10^{-49}$$

Calculation of Solubility Data from Solubility Product Constants. Next let us calculate some solubility data from solubility product constants. This type of problem is more often encountered in analytical work than is the reverse type, because the numerical values of the solubility product constants are well established for many substances. The same four-step plan of attack is useful again, as it is in all mass law problems.

Example 4. The solubility product constant of barium sulfate is 1.08×10^{-10}; calculate its solubility in moles per liter.

Chemical Equation:

$$BaSO_4 \rightleftharpoons Ba^{++} + SO_4^{=}$$

Mathematical Equations:

(1) $$K_{sp} = [Ba^{++}][SO_4^{=}]$$

(2) $$K_{sp} = 1.08 \times 10^{-10}$$

(3) $$[Ba^{++}] = [SO_4^{=}]$$

(the dissolving of $BaSO_4$ is the only source of either type of ion, and the chemical equation indicates that they form in equi-molar quantities)

Solving:

$$1.08 \times 10^{-10} = [Ba^{++}][Ba^{++}]$$

(substituting (2) and (3) into (1))

$$[Ba^{++}] = 1.04 \times 10^{-5}$$

To form 1.04×10^{-5} molar Ba^{++} ion, 1.04×10^{-5} moles of $BaSO_4$ must have dissolved per liter.

Example 5. Calculate number of grams of magnesium ammonium phosphate, $MgNH_4PO_4$, which will dissolve per liter from its solubility product constant, 2.5×10^{-13}.

Chemical Equation:

$$MgNH_4PO_4 \rightleftharpoons Mg^{++} + NH_4^{+} + PO_4^{=}$$

Mathematical Equations:

(1) $$K_{sp} = [Mg^{++}][NH_4^{+}][PO_4^{=}]$$

(2) $$K_{sp} = 2.5 \times 10^{-13}$$

(3) $$[Mg^{++}] = [NH_4^{+}]$$

(the dissolving of $MgNH_4PO_4$ is the only source of any of the three types of ion, and the chemical equation indicates that they form in equi-molar quantities)

(4)
$$[Mg^{++}] = [PO_4^{\equiv}]$$

Solving:

$$2.5 \times 10^{-13} = [Mg^{++}] [Mg^{++}] [Mg^{++}]$$

(substituting (2), (3) and (4) into (1))

$$[Mg^{++}] = 6.30 \times 10^{-5}$$

To form 6.30×10^{-5} mole of Mg^{++} ion, 6.30×10^{-5} mole of $MgNH_4PO_4$ must have dissolved.

$$g\ MgNH_4PO_4\ dissolved/liter = 6.30 \times 10^{-5} \times 137.34$$
$$g\ MgNH_4PO_4\ dissolved/liter = 8.65 \times 10^{-3}$$

Note that four unknowns were involved in the mathematical equations, so four mathematical equations were needed before they could be combined.

Example 6. Calculate the molar solubility of silver chromate from its solubility product constant, 9×10^{-12}.

Chemical Equation:

$$Ag_2CrO_4 \rightleftharpoons 2\ Ag^+ + CrO_4^{\equiv}$$

Mathematical Equations:

(1)
$$K_{sp} = [Ag^+]^2 [CrO_4^{\equiv}]$$

(2)
$$K_{sp} = 9 \times 10^{-12}$$

(3)
$$[Ag^+] = 2 [CrO_4^{\equiv}]$$

(dissolving of Ag_2CrO_4 is the only source of either type of ion, and the chemical equation says 2 Ag^+ ions form for 1 $CrO_4^{\equiv}$ ion)

Solving:

$$9 \times 10^{-12} = (2 [CrO_4^{\equiv}])^2 [CrO_4^{\equiv}]$$

(substituting (2) and (3) into (1))

$$[CrO_4^{\equiv}] = 1.3 \times 10^{-4}$$

To form 1.3×10^{-4} molar $CrO_4^{\equiv}$ ion, 1.3×10^{-4} must be the molar solubility of Ag_2CrO_4.

The two types of problem considered thus far in Examples 1 through 6 should serve to provide familiarity with the solubility product principle and the general method of attacking all mass law problems. Further types of problem arise in the following sections, but the same general plan of attack may be used. From now on it will be assumed in all problems that the solubility product constant data of Appendix 1 are available for use as desired except in those cases in which the constant is the unknown quantity as in Examples 1, 2 and 3.

FACTORS INFLUENCING THE SOLUBILITY OF A PRECIPITATE

Common Ion Effect. In Examples 4, 5 and 6 calculations were made of the solubilities of substances under conditions whereby the only source of ions in solution was the dissolving of the solid substance. The situation is somewhat different in gravimetric separations, for the requisite ions are brought together to form the precipitate rather than being formed from the dissolving of the solid substance. Furthermore, the two or more necessary types of ion come from different sources. For example, one is initially in the sample solution and the other in the reagent solution, so there is not necessarily a 1:1 or 1:2 or any other integral relationship between the amounts of those types of ion. In order to insure that enough of the reagent is available to react with the unknown, an excess of the reagent must be used. So the analytical chemist is interested in the solubility of a precipitate in the presence of an excess of one of its component ions.

The influence of an excess of one of the component ions upon the solubility of a precipitate is called the *common ion effect.* Application of the Le Chatelier principle to the chemical equation representing the state of equilibrium between dissolved and undissolved solute reveals that the excess of a common ion represses the solubility of the substance. Solubility product considerations permit quantitative calculation of the common ion effect.

Example 7. Calculate the molar concentration of sulfate ion remaining in solution in equilibrium with mother liquid which is 1.0×10^{-3} molar in barium ion.

$$BaSO_4 \rightleftharpoons Ba^{++} + SO_4^{=}$$

(1)
$$K_{sp} = [Ba^{++}] [SO_4^{=}]$$

(2)
$$K_{sp} = 1.08 \times 10^{-10}$$

(3)
$$[Ba^{++}] = 1.0 \times 10^{-3}$$

$$1.08 \times 10^{-10} = 1.0 \times 10^{-3} [SO_4^{=}]$$

(substituting (2) and (3) into (1))

$$[SO_4^{=}] = 1.08 \times 10^{-7}$$

Note that this sulfate ion concentration is about one hundredfold less than that of Example 4. The presence of the excess amount of barium ion has repressed the solubility of barium sulfate a hundredfold.

Example 8. Calculate the weight in grams of chloride ion left in solution in the gravimetric separation of chloride as silver chloride, if the total volume is about 200 ml. and if the mother liquid contains 0.01 gram of silver ion.

$$AgCl \rightleftharpoons Ag^+ + Cl^-$$

(1) $$K_{sp} = [Ag^+][Cl^-]$$

(2) $$K_{sp} = 1.56 \times 10^{-10}$$

(3) $$[Ag^+] = \frac{0.01}{107.88} \times \frac{1000}{200}$$

(converting g in 200 ml. to moles per liter)

$$1.56 \times 10^{-10} = \left(\frac{0.01}{107.88} \times \frac{1000}{200} \right)[Cl^-]$$

$$[Cl^-] = 3.4 \times 10^{-7}$$

$$g\ Cl^- = 3.4 \times 10^{-7} \times 35.46 \times \frac{200}{1000}$$

(converting to the desired units)

$$g\ Cl^- = 2.4 \times 10^{-6}$$

Example 9. Repeat Example 8, but with 0.10 gram of excess silver ion. Chemical equation and mathematical equations (1) and (2) same as in Example 8.

(3) $$[Ag^+] = \frac{0.10}{107.88} \times \frac{1000}{200}$$

$$1.56 \times 10^{-10} = \left(\frac{0.10}{107.88} \times \frac{1000}{200} \right)[Cl^-]$$

$$[Cl^-] = 3.4 \times 10^{-8}$$

$$g\ Cl^- = 3.4 \times 10^{-8} \times 35.46 \times \frac{200}{1000}$$

(converting to the desired units)

$$g\ Cl^- = 2.4 \times 10^{-7}$$

A calculation similar to that of Examples 4, 5 and 6 reveals that a solution of 200 ml. volume which is saturated with silver chloride with no excess of silver ion contains 8.9×10^{-5} gram of chloride ion. So the weights of chloride unprecipitated are 8.9×10^{-5} gram, 2.4×10^{-6} gram and 2.4×10^{-7} gram, in the presence of no excess silver ion, 0.01 gram excess silver ion, and 0.10 gram excess silver ion, respectively. The significance of the common ion in reducing the solubility of a precipitate is clearly quite pronounced. In every gravimetric precipitation process, an excess of the precipitating agent must be employed to insure that enough is available to react with the unknown, and this excess serves also to decrease the solubility of the precipitate.

Another useful and similar type of calculation is the calculation of the concentration of a reagent needed to begin precipitation of a compound. This type of calculation is of interest when it is desired to precipitate a substance selectively in the presence of another substance which can react with the same reagent.

Example 10. A solution is initially 0.10 molar each in ferric ion and in zinc ion; from the two solubility product constants, calculate the hydroxyl ion concentrations needed just to begin precipitation of each hydroxide.

$$Fe(OH)_3 \rightleftharpoons Fe^{+++} + 3\ OH^- \text{ and } Zn(OH)_2 \rightleftharpoons Zn^{++} + 2\ OH^-$$

(1) $\quad\quad K_{sp} = [Fe^{+++}]\,[OH^-]^3 \quad\quad\quad\quad K_{sp} = [Zn^{++}]\,[OH^-]^2$

(2) $\quad\quad K_{sp} = 1.1 \times 10^{-36} \quad\quad\quad\quad\quad K_{sp} = 1.8 \times 10^{-14}$

(3) $\quad [Fe^{+++}] = 10^{-1} \quad\quad\quad\quad\quad\quad [Zn^{++}] = 10^{-1}$

$\quad\quad 1.1 \times 10^{-36} = (10^{-1})\,[OH^-]^3 \quad\quad 1.8 \times 10^{-14} = (10^{-1})\,[OH^-]^2$

$\quad\quad\quad [OH^-] = 2.2 \times 10^{-12} \quad\quad\quad\quad [OH^-] = 4.3 \times 10^{-7}$

So ferric hydroxide begins to precipitate when the hydroxyl ion concentration is only 2.2×10^{-12} molar, while zinc hydroxide does not begin to form until the hydroxyl ion concentration reaches 4.3×10^{-7} molar. (This conclusion must be considered as only approximate; the calculation has assumed, in effect, that supersaturation and coprecipitation phenomena do not upset the straightforward conditions of equilibrium; the latter topics will be described later in this chapter.)

The analytical chemist is interested not only in which cation begins to precipitate first but also in how completely the first one is precipitated before the second one begins.

Example 11. How completely can ferric ion be precipitated as the hydroxide before zinc hydroxide begins to precipitate, assuming the zinc ion concentration to be the same as in Example 10? (This question can be answered by calculating the concentration of ferric ion remaining when the second precipitate begins to form.)

$$Fe(OH)_3 \rightleftharpoons Fe^{+++} + 3\ OH^-$$

(1) $\quad\quad\quad\quad\quad K_{sp} = [Fe^{+++}]\,[OH^-]^3$

(2) $\quad\quad\quad\quad\quad K_{sp} = 1.1 \times 10^{-36}$

(3) $\quad\quad\quad\quad\quad [OH^-] = 4.3 \times 10^{-7}$

(when $Zn(OH)_2$ just begins to form in Example 10)

$$1.1 \times 10^{-36} = [Fe^{+++}]\,(4.3 \times 10^{-7})^3$$

$$[Fe^{+++}] = 1.4 \times 10^{-17}$$

An amount of ferric ion left in solution corresponding to a molar concentration of only 1.4×10^{-17} may certainly be considered negligible in a gravimetric determination. Therefore, quantitative separation of ferric ion from zinc ion should be accomplished by precipitation as the hydroxide if the hydroxyl ion concentration is kept just below 4.3×10^{-7} molar. This conclusion should be verified experimentally before considering it as final for three reasons: the calculations have assumed equilibrium conditions with no supersaturation; the gelatinous nature of the iron precipitate, with its variable water content, renders calculations with the solubility product constant for the simple hydroxide only approximate at best; a substance can precipitate along with another substance even under conditions in which it would not precipitate by itself. The first and third of these reasons will be considered in some detail later in this chapter under the headings "supersaturation" and "coprecipitation."

One further example of this type should be of value.

Example 12. Is it possible, apart from supersaturation and coprecipitation phenomena, to separate barium from calcium as the sulfate precipitate, assuming again that each initial cation concentration is 0.1 molar? (Calculate the sulfate ion concentration needed just to begin precipitation of calcium sulfate, then calculate how much barium ion would remain in solution at that concentration.)

$$CaSO_4 \rightleftharpoons Ca^{++} + SO_4^{=}$$

(1) $$K_{sp} = [Ca^{++}] [SO_4^{=}]$$

(2) $$K_{sp} = 1.95 \times 10^{-4}$$

(3) $$[Ca^{++}] = 10^{-1}$$

$$1.95 \times 10^{-4} = (10^{-1}) [SO_4^{=}]$$

$$[SO_4^{=}] = 1.95 \times 10^{-3}$$

$$BaSO_4 \rightleftharpoons Ba^{++} + SO_4^{=}$$

(1a) $$K_{sp} = [Ba^{++}] [SO_4^{=}]$$

(2a) $$K_{sp} = 1.08 \times 10^{-10}$$

(3a) $$[SO_4^{=}] = 1.95 \times 10^{-3}$$

(when $CaSO_4$ just begins to precipitate)

$$1.08 \times 10^{-10} = [Ba^{++}] 1.95 \times 10^{-3}$$

$$[Ba^{++}] = 5.5 \times 10^{-8}$$

With the initial Ba^{++} ion concentration of 10^{-1} molar reduced to 5.5×10^{-8} molar when $CaSO_4$ just begins to form, the separation can be quantitative. The homogeneous generation of sulfate ion by hydrolysis of sulfamic acid can be used to good advantage in keeping the sulfate ion concentration below the critical value of 1.95×10^{-3} molar.

Temperature. The influence of temperature upon the solubility of a precipitate has been considered descriptively in Chapter 6. This relationship may be considered more quantitatively on the basis of the solubility product principle. A solubility product constant is a type of equilibrium constant and, as shown in Chapter 1, equilibrium constants arise from rates of reactions. The dissolving of any one of most substances is an endothermic reaction. So the rate of solution increases as the temperature is raised, and the solubility product constant likewise increases. The dependence of the K_{sp} upon temperature is illustrated by the following data for silver chloride:

$$at \quad 5°\ C., \quad K_{sp} = 0.21 \times 10^{-10}$$
$$at \quad 10°\ C., \quad K_{sp} = 0.37 \times 10^{-10}$$
$$at \quad 25°\ C., \quad K_{sp} = 1.56 \times 10^{-10}$$
$$at \quad 50°\ C., \quad K_{sp} = 13.2 \times 10^{-10}$$
$$at \quad 100°\ C., \quad K_{sp} = 21.5 \times 10^{-10}$$

The K_{sp} is about a hundredfold greater at $100°$ C. than at $5°$ C. For barium sulfate also, the solubility product constant increases as the temperature is raised, but to a much lesser extent.

Nature of the Solvent. The solubility of a given precipitate differs from one solvent to another, so the solubility product constant for a precipitate in water is not applicable in any other solvent. Most inorganic compounds are ionic, so they are more soluble in a polar solvent, such as water, than in a nonpolar solvent, such as carbon tetrachloride. The nonpolar solvents are, however, much better solvents for nonionic and nonpolar organic substances than is water. Ethyl alcohol is interesting and versatile as a solvent. It possesses both polar and nonpolar structural characteristics so that it is a moderately good solvent for a variety of substances.

In some quantitative procedures, a water solvent is changed to some other solvent, such as a water-alcohol mixture, to decrease the solubility of the desired precipitate. The solubilities of most other components in the solution are also decreased, so the precipitate may be rendered less pure at the same time that it is made less soluble.

Complex Ion Formation. The solubility of a precipitate is markedly influenced by the presence of an ion which can form a complex ion with one of the constituent ions of the precipitate. Consider, for example, the solubility of silver chloride in a solution containing thiosulfate ions. The thiosulfate can react with the silver ion to form the complex ion, $Ag(S_2O_3)_2^{=}$.

Thus, when the solution is in equilibrium with solid silver chloride, two chemical equilibria are in existence:

$$AgCl \rightleftharpoons Ag^+ + Cl^-$$

$$Ag^+ + 2 S_2O_3^= \rightleftharpoons Ag(S_2O_3)_2^=$$

An equilibrium constant can be formulated for the complex-forming reaction, taking the concentration of the complex in the denominator by convention, as follows:

$$K = \frac{[Ag^+] [S_2O_3^=]^2}{[Ag(S_2O_3)_2^=]}$$

Equilibrium constants for reaction of this type are often designated dissociation constants, and numerical values for several are listed in Appendix 3.

It is possible to calculate quantitatively the solubility of a precipitate in the presence of a complex-forming ion. The same four-step plan of attack is useful, as it is in all mass law problems. In this type of calculation, more than one chemical equation must be written in Step 1, since at least two states of equilibrium are simultaneously in existence. In Step 2, a mathematical equation must be written for each of the chemical equations in Step 1. The over-all plan of attack remains the same, however.

Example 13. Calculate the molar solubility of solid silver chloride in water containing at equilibrium 1.0×10^{-2} molar thiosulfate ion. (The chloride ion concentration will equal the solubility of silver chloride, since all the chloride ion comes from dissolving silver chloride and since all the chloride ion remains in solution as such.)

Chemical Equations:

$$AgCl \rightleftharpoons Ag^+ + Cl^-$$

$$Ag^+ + 2 S_2O_3^= \rightleftharpoons Ag(S_2O_3)_2^=$$

Mathematical Equations:

(1) $$K_{sp} = [Ag^+][Cl^-]$$

(2) $$K_d = \frac{[Ag^+][S_2O_3^=]^2}{[Ag(S_2O_3)_2^=]}$$

(3) $$K_{sp} = 1.56 \times 10^{-10}$$

(4) $$K_d = 1 \times 10^{-13}$$

(5) $$[S_2O_3^=] = 1.0 \times 10^{-2}$$

(6) $$[Cl^-] = [Ag(S_2O_3)_2^=]$$

(All chlorides and all silvers come, in equal numbers, from dissolving AgCl, so $[Cl^-] = [Ag^+] + [Ag(S_2O_3)_2{}^=]$; but the complex is so slightly dissociated that $[Ag^+]$ is quite negligible when added to $[Ag(S_2O_3)_2{}^=]$.)

(We now have six mathematical equations including six unknowns.)

Solving:

(7) $$[Ag^+] = \frac{1.56 \times 10^{-10}}{[Cl^-]}$$ (combining (3) with (1) and rearranging)

(8) $$[Ag^+] = \frac{(1 \times 10^{-13})\,[Cl^-]}{(1 \times 10^{-2})^2}$$ (combining (4), (5) and (6) with (2) and rearranging)

$$\frac{1.56 \times 10^{-10}}{[Cl^-]} = \frac{(1 \times 10^{-13})\,[Cl^-]}{(1 \times 10^{-2})^2}$$ (combining (7) with (8))

$$[Cl^-]^2 = \frac{(1.56 \times 10^{-10})\,(1 \times 10^{-2})^2}{1 \times 10^{-13}}$$ (rearranging)

$$[Cl^-] = 0.4$$

So the molar solubility of AgCl is 0.4.

As stated in Example 1, the molar solubility of silver chloride in pure water is 1.25×10^{-5}, and this 10^{-2} molar thiosulfate ion has been shown to increase the molar solubility of silver chloride to 0.4. The complexing ion has thus increased the solubility of silver chloride by more than 30 000 times. Obviously, chloride cannot be precipitated quantitatively in the presence of thiosulfate ion.

A number of different anions are complexed by hydrogen ion to form weak acids. For example, phosphate ion and carbonate ion are complexed to form respectively, $HPO_4{}^=$ (or $H_2PO_4{}^-$ or H_3PO_4) and $HCO_3{}^-$ (or H_2CO_3). So the hydrogen ion concentration influences very markedly the solubility of any compound, the anion of which is the anion of a weak acid.

Diverse Ion Effect. The solvent action of water is attributed to its dipolar structure. Water dissolves ionic solids largely by virtue of the interaction between the charge centers on the dipolar water molecules and the charged ions. This electrical interaction is modified considerably if the aqueous solvent contains dissolved salts which contain no ion in common with the precipitate. Such ions are called *diverse ions*. The presence of these salts profoundly alters the ionic environment within the solution, thus changing the solubilities of precipitates in a way that cannot be predicted from the mass law equations in the simple forms in which they have been used in this chapter.

In the terms of the Debye-Hückel concept (Chapter 1), mass law mathematical equations are more exact if concentrations are written in terms of effective concentrations rather than in terms of molar concentrations. Each effective concentration equals the molar concentration multiplied by a factor called the activity coefficient. In solutions which are dilute in all solutes, each activity coefficient is close to unity, so the simple form of the mass law mathematical equation is valid. However, as the over-all ionic content of the solution increases, the coefficient decreases from unity. As a general rule, then, the solubility of a precipitate tends to increase as the concentration of diverse ions in the solution increases.

SUPERSATURATION

Supersaturation is a condition in which a solution phase retains more of the precipitate than can be in equilibrium with the solid phase. It is generally a transient condition, particularly in the presence of some crystals of the solid phase, although some supersaturated solutions may persist for some time under certain conditions.

Consider a solution which is just saturated with silver chloride. If a small additional amount of silver ion is added, either one of two things must occur: the solution may become supersaturated with respect to silver chloride; or some ions may precipitate as solid silver chloride to restore the solution to its saturated condition. It has been found experimentally that, in the absence of suspended solids, the supersaturated condition may be established and it may remain for a considerable period of time. The condition of supersaturation can be established from a saturated state not only by addition of more solute but also by changing the temperature in a direction to decrease the solubility and, in some instances, by removal of some solvent. The concentration existing in a supersaturated solution may be several-fold greater than that in a saturated solution.

Supersaturation is of concern to the analyst for two distinct reasons. First, if the state of supersaturation persists until the time of filtration, the separation of the desired component is less complete than it would be without supersaturation. With moderately soluble substances such as magnesium ammonium phosphate, appreciable solubility loss would occur through supersaturation if the precipitate were filtered immediately after formation, but this source of error is negligible after a reasonable digestion period. It has already been stated that the presence of some of the solid phase tends to relieve supersaturation. Stirring and even the presence of fine scratches on the inner walls of the container also tend to relieve supersaturation. So supersaturation seldom persists until the time of filtration in analytical procedures.

Second, if the state of supersaturation is intense, even though transient, the precipitate tends to form in many tiny particles rather than in relatively few particles of larger size. Extremely finely divided particles are not only difficult to retain on filter media but are also particularly subject to contamination by impurities, as will be described later in this chapter.

NUCLEATION AND CRYSTAL GROWTH

The precipitation of a solid from a liquid phase generally consists of two processes, nucleation and crystal growth. Nucleation consists of the formation within a supersaturated solution of the smallest particles of a precipitate capable of spontaneous growth. Crystal growth consists of the deposition of ions from the solution onto the solid particles which have already been started. The number of particles and, therefore, the particle size for a given mass of precipitate are determined by the number of nuclei formed in the first process.

The number of nuclei which form is apparently determined by the interaction between two factors: the extent of supersaturation in the immediate environment where nucleation occurs; the number and effectiveness of sites upon which nuclei may form.

Significance of Supersaturation in Nucleation. The significance of the extent of supersaturation upon the rate of precipitation may be expressed mathematically by the equation

$$\text{rate} = \frac{Q - S}{S}$$

in which Q is the actual concentration of solute and S is the concentration in a saturated solution. This equation was first stated for the over-all precipitation process by von Weimarn. The number of nuclei which form is directly proportional to the rate of nucleation, so the number of nuclei is directly proportional to the extent of supersaturation, $\dfrac{Q - S}{S}$.

Consider the precipitation of barium sulfate by mixing 100 ml. of 1×10^{-2} M barium chloride solution and 1 ml. of 1 M sodium sulfate solution. If the two solutions are completely mixed before any precipitation occurs, the concentrations of barium ion and of sulfate ion would each be very close to 1×10^{-2} M; thus Q, the concentration of dissolved barium sulfate, would be 1×10^{-2} M. The solubility S, is 1×10^{-5} M, so the $\dfrac{Q - S}{S}$ ratio would be 1 000. However, at the place where the 1 ml. of the sodium sulfate solution first comes in contact with the barium chloride solution, the momentary concentration of sulfate ion would be much higher, even close to 1 M, so the momentary Q (calculated as $\sqrt{[Ba^{++}][SO_4^{--}]}$ would approach 1×10^{-1} and the corresponding $\dfrac{Q - S}{S}$ ratio would be 10 000.

Even though each reactant solution would be quickly diluted by the other by mixing, the transient condition of supersaturation may be considerably more intense than the condition existing soon after mixing. The momentary condition is also relieved by precipitation, as well as by mixing. Nevertheless, the particle size of the final precipitate is markedly influenced by this transient condition. For this reason, it is generally desirable to have the solutions quite dilute at the time of mixing, particularly if the precipitate is an extremely insoluble one. It is furthermore desirable to form a precipitate under conditions whereby it is not so extremely soluble, insofar as feasible. For example, the solubility of barium sulfate is greater in acid medium than in neutral medium, so the momentary $\dfrac{Q - S}{S}$ value is lower if precipitation occurs from the acid medium; the mother liquid can, if necessary, be partially neutralized prior to filtration to minimize solubility loss.

Spontaneous and Induced Nucleation. It is possible, in theory, for a sufficiently large cluster of ions to join together in a supersaturated solution to form a nucleus. In practical situations, however, it is highly probable that purely spontaneous nucleation is far less frequent than is induced nucleation, in which the initial clustering of ions is aided by the presence in the solution of some sites which can attract and hold ions. Introduction of particles of a precipitate into a solution supersaturated with respect to it can initiate further precipitation. Other solid particles or surfaces can also serve as nucleation sites. The surfaces of the container in which the reaction occurs provide many sites, as is indicated by the fact that the particle size of a precipitate may be influenced by the type of container, how scratch-free it is and how it was cleaned prior to use. Insoluble impurities in the reagents and in the water or other solvent also provide nucleation sites. Even common chemicals of reagent grade purity typically contain from 0.005 to 0.010% insoluble components which, when dispersed throughout a solution as tiny particles, could provide extremely large numbers of sites for nucleation. The presence of any colloidal particles in the solution can exert a considerable influence upon the number of nuclei which form and persist as discrete particles throughout a precipitation reaction.

The forces of attraction whereby ions are held on these nucleating sites may be largely electrical in nature, and the more specific forces of adsorption to be discussed later in this chapter are likely of significance. Consider a solution slightly supersaturated with respect to barium sulfate and containing barium, chloride, sodium and sulfate ions. Any negatively charged surface in contact with this solution would attract positive ions. The double charge on the barium ion would tend to give it preference over the sodium ion, although their relative concentrations would also be of importance. A group of adsorbed positive ions would, in turn, attract a group of negative ions, with the double charge favoring sulfate over chloride. But another factor of specificity appears—barium ion has a very specific and very pronounced attraction for sulfate ions so, insofar as the first group consisted of barium ions, the second group would be predominantly of sulfate ions. The resultant cluster of barium and sulfate comprises a nucleus for a crystal of barium sulfate. The situation is analogous if the initial site is positively charged. It is apparent from this illustration that the effectiveness of any particular site in initiating a nucleus is determined by the specificity of its attraction for one of the ions to be precipitated and that this specificity is influenced by the entire ionic composition of the solution.

Some supersaturation is necessary for any precipitation to occur. It seems reasonable that a relatively effective site would require less super-saturation than would a less effective one. The most effective site would be on the surface of a crystal of the substance to be precipitated; in effect, the process of nucleation would be bypassed. A site of no effectiveness at all would be one which could not attract any ions from the solution. It is doubtful that any solid surface could be completely devoid of effectiveness, as virtually all surfaces, including glass, which are in contact with an ionic solution exhibit some electrical effects.

The number of nuclei which form in a precipitation process is a complex function of two factors. First is the number and the distribution with respect to effectiveness of the sites which are available to induce nucleation. This factor is influenced by the type and surface features of the container, the area of contact between container and solution, the purity of all reagents, how long a reagent solution or the water used as its solvent has been exposed to the atmosphere and how fresh the solutions are at the time of use. All of these conditions and others equally diverse have been found to influence the number of particles obtained in precipitation processes. Second is the extent of supersaturation existing at the time of initiation of precipitation because, for a given supersaturation, only certain ones of the sites are able to function.

Changes in Number of Particles During Growth.   The number of nuclei which are initially formed is indicative of the final number of particles, but these two numbers are not necessarily identical for several reasons. First, the solubility of small particles is generally greater than that of large particles, (greater than about 10^{-4} cm. in typical cases). During growth and, particularly, during subsequent digestion, smaller particles tend to dissolve at the expense of larger ones, thus decreasing the total number. Second, two or more individual crystals may coagulate to form a tight cluster which behaves through subsequent unit operations as a single particle, thus decreasing the effective number of particles. The mechanism of coagulation will be considered later in this chapter. Third, a crystal which grows irregularly may break apart into two or more particles, particularly upon vigorous stirring, thus increasing the number of particles. Fourth, a nucleation site may become separated from a growing crystal and serve to nucleate another one, thus increasing the number of particles. These several factors are all closely interrelated with one another.

Processes of Crystal Growth.   Crystal growth, once a nucleus has been formed, consists of two steps: diffusion of necessary ions to the surface of the growing crystal; deposition of these ions at the surface. Either one can be the rate-limiting factor. The diffusion rate is influenced by what the ions are, their concentrations, the stirring rate and the temperature. The surface reaction rate is affected by concentrations, by impurities on the surface and by growth characteristics of the particular crystal. Crystals of over-all perfect geometrical shape are seldom formed in analytical precipitation processes because crystal growth generally does not occur uniformly on all faces. Preferential growth on certain faces may result, for example, in flat plates or in sticks, whereas preferential growth on corners may result in irregular, branched crystals called dendrites. The presence of foreign ions can markedly influence the shape of precipitated particles, possibly by adsorption to prevent or to encourage growth on certain faces.

The subjects of nucleation and crystal growth have been studied in many laboratories for many years. Although much knowledge has been obtained, these processes are so complex that much additional basic research is required for complete comprehension of the mechanisms which are involved.

COLLOIDAL STATE

Definition and Significance. The term *colloidal state* refers to a dispersion of one type of particles in another in which the dispersed particles are in the approximate size range of 1×10^{-7} to 2×10^{-5} centimeters. The dispersed phase may be a solid, a liquid or a gas, and the other phase may likewise be solid, liquid or gas. However, the colloids of most interest in gravimetric analysis are dispersions of solid in liquid, usually of a precipitated substance in its mother liquid.

A colloidal dispersion is not a true solution. In a true solution the dispersed particles are of ionic or molecular size, while they are larger in a colloidal dispersion. A colloidal dispersion is a mixture and a suspension, yet the properties of colloids differ so markedly from mixtures and suspensions in which the dispersed particles are larger that it is meaningful to consider colloidal dispersions apart from simple mixtures and suspensions.

It is distinctly not desirable for a quantitative precipitate to be in the colloidal state at the time of filtration. The most direct reason is that colloidal particles, although they constitute a distinct phase, are so fine that they pass directly through ordinary filtering membranes. In addition, however, two structural features of colloids are closely related to the purity of the precipitate: the localized electrical character of their surfaces; their tremendously large surface area per unit mass. These two features will now be discussed in turn.

Electrical Charges on Surfaces. Most inorganic substances are ionized in the solid state. Solid silver chloride consists of silver ions and chloride ions; barium sulfate, of barium ions and sulfate ions; and so forth. In crystalline solids these ions are regularly arranged in space. A crystal of silver chloride is represented by the model in Figure 20, in which the dark balls represent silver ions and the light balls chloride ions. The regular arrangement is called a *crystal lattice*. This model is intended to permit observation of ions both on the surface and on the interior; a more perfect but less instructive model would show the two types of ion to be of

FIGURE 20.   Model of crystal lattice of
silver chloride.

different sizes and the distances between ions would not be large relative to
ionic radii. Each chloride ion in the interior of the crystal is surrounded by
six silver ions which are its closest neighbors, and each silver ion is similarly
surrounded by six chloride ions. Therefore, each interior ion is fixed quite
rigidly in its position. However, each chloride ion on the surface is associated
with but five silver ions, and each silver ion with but five chloride ions. Under
such circumstances, the chloride and silver ions on the surface should be
expected to show some residual charges, negative and positive, respectively.
An ion on an edge is surrounded by only four oppositely charged neighbors
and a corner ion has only three such neighbors. So the residual charge centers
are even more pronounced at the positions of ions on the edges and at the
corners. Thus, the surface of a crystal is literally covered with localized
centers of positive and negative charge. The over-all surface may be neutral,
with equal numbers of positive and negative centers, but the localized charges
are real.

   Ratio of Surface to Mass.   Perhaps the most unique characteristic of
the colloidal state of matter is the enormous ratio of surface to mass which it
signifies. For example, a 1 centimeter cube of a substance has a total surface
area of 6 square centimeters. If the same mass of the same material is
subdivided into 1×10^{-6} centimeter cubes, there are about a million million
million (10^{18}) cubes, and they expose a total surface area of about 6 000 000
square centimeters. In the 1 centimeter cube, less than one in 10 000 000 of
the ions is on the surface, while in the 1×10^{-6} centimeter cube, about one in
every 12 ions is a surface ion (assuming 2×10^{-8} cm per ionic diameter).
Colloidal particles are characterized by very large surface to mass ratios, so
surface effects are very important in colloid chemistry. Any surface factors,
such as the localized positive and negative charge centers, are very pronounced
when the particles are in the colloidal state. Colloid chemistry is often
defined as surface chemistry because the distinctive characteristics of colloidal
particles generally are surface characteristics.

   Stability of Colloids.   Colloidal dispersions can be very stable, even
though the gravitational force should tend to make them settle out. Some

colloids of gold particles in water prepared by Michael Faraday are still stable a hundred years later. One reason for the stability of colloids is the fact that the particles are in a state of constant motion. The particles continually hit and rebound from each other and from the walls of the container. The colloidal particles are doubtless being hit continually by the smaller molecules of the suspending medium and by any ions contained therein. The continual motion of colloidal particles is called *Brownian movement* and tends to overcome the settling influence of gravity.

A second reason for the stability of colloids is even more significant in analytical chemistry than is the Brownian movement. Ions from the mother liquid are adsorbed at the localized negative or positive charge centers on the surface of colloidal particles to impart an electrical charge to those surfaces. If either cations or anions are adsorbed dominantly, all of the surfaces will take on the same over-all charge, and the particles will tend to repel each other.

The drawing of Figure 21 represents one surface of a silver chloride particle with its localized charge centers. The negative centers will tend to attract and adsorb cations from the mother liquid; and the positive centers, to attract and adsorb anions. This adsorption is highly selective in that a given precipitate will attract certain kinds of ions more readily than others. Generally, there will be one type of ion in the mother liquid which will be attracted more readily than any others, so this type of ion will be adsorbed to cover the surfaces and to impart its charge, either positive or negative, to all of the surfaces. The ions which are adsorbed are held from one direction only, are not so tightly bound as are ions within the interior of the crystal and are generally hydrated at least to some extent. If the ion adsorbed most readily is a cation, there is not enough room left for any anions to be adsorbed directly onto the crystal surface. If some type of cation is most readily adsorbed, all of the colloidal particles become positively charged; and all the surfaces of the particles become negatively charged if some type of anion is most readily adsorbed. In either case, the adsorbed ion layer imparts

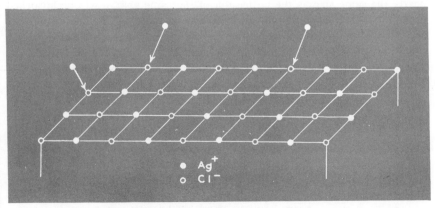

Figure 21. Surface adsorption of silver ions.

stability to the colloidal dispersion. This adsorbed ion layer is called the
primary adsorbed ion layer; it forms directly on the surface of the solid
particles.

Selectivity of Ion Adsorption. The adsorption of ions on the
surface of solid particles in contact with the mother liquid is based upon an
electrical attraction. However, it is not entirely that, or the adsorption would
not be so selective. The tendency of a colloid to adsorb one type of ion in
preference to another rests upon a combination of four factors.

1. Paneth-Fajans-Hahn law. When two or more types of ion are
available for adsorption and when other factors are considered equal, that
ion which forms a compound with the lowest solubility with one of the lattice
ions will be adsorbed preferentially. For example, silver chloride adsorbs
silver ion in preference to sodium ion, because silver chloride is less soluble
than is sodium chloride. Silver chloride also adsorbs silver ion, a cation, in
preference to nitrate ion, an anion, because silver ion forms a less soluble
compound with one of the lattice ions than nitrate does with the other
lattice ion. As a practical outworking of this law, if either lattice ion is
present in excess in the mother liquid, it will be adsorbed preferentially.
The law is also applicable when neither lattice ion is available for adsorption.
To illustrate, silver iodide adsorbs acetate ion in preference to nitrate ion,
because silver acetate is less soluble than is silver nitrate, even though both
are quite soluble.

2. Concentration effect. Other factors being equal, the ion which is
available in greater concentration will be adsorbed preferentially. Furthermore, the tendency of any one type of ion to be adsorbed varies directly with
its concentration.

3. Ionic charge effect. Other factors being equal, a multicharged ion
will be adsorbed more readily than a singly charged ion. This factor is
entirely reasonable because the adsorption is based in part upon electrostatic
attraction between the ion and the oppositely charged centers on the surface.

4. Size of ion. Other factors being equal, the ion which is more
nearly the same size as the lattice ion of the same charge will be adsorbed
preferentially. Consider again the difference in the environments of interior
and surface ions—an ion in the interior in Figure 20 has six equally spaced,
oppositely charged neighbors, while a surface ion is missing one of the six.
The adsorbed ion may be considered to take the place of that missing one.
Therefore, if an ion in the mother liquid is of the same size as the one whose
place it is to take, it should be adsorbed quite readily. For example, radium
ion is adsorbed tightly onto barium sulfate but not onto calcium sulfate;
radium ion is quite close to the same size as is barium ion but not as calcium
ion.

These four factors are in simultaneous operation in each particular
situation. The first one is very often the dominant one, but any of the four
may dominate under certain conditions.

Coagulation and Peptization. *Coagulation* is the process whereby colloidal particles agglomerate together to form larger particles which can settle out to the bottom of the container. In order for the colloidal particles to coagulate, the electrical charge imparted to their surfaces by the primary adsorbed ion layer must be either removed or neutralized. Its removal is not very likely because the forces of attraction between the surface and the primary adsorbed ion layer are quite intense. But the over-all charge on the particles can be modified by an adsorbed layer of water and by a second layer of adsorbed ions.

The lower portion of Figure 22 shows a row of alternating silver and chloride ions on the surface of a particle of silver chloride. Assuming that silver ions are available in the mother liquid, the primary adsorption layer consists of silver ions as shown and the surface is given an over-all positive charge. Water molecules are polar, so water molecules are adsorbed onto the primary layer on the particle surface, and there is also a tendency for the adsorption of a second layer of ions. The secondary adsorbed ion layer is called the *counter ion* layer and in Figure 22 is illustrated as consisting of nitrate ions.

The tightness with which the counter ions are held in and with the water layer, or the completeness with which they cover the primary adsorbed ion layer, determines in large part the stability of the colloidal dispersion. If this secondary layer is sufficient to neutralize the charge due to the primary adsorbed ion layer, the particles coagulate rather than repel each other.

We must now consider what factors influence the tightness and completeness of the counter ion layer. The adsorption of the counter ion layer is much less selective than is adsorption of the primary layer. The Paneth-Fajans-Hahn factor and the ionic size factor are of much less significance because the counter ion is more remote from the body of the lattice and because of the presence of the adsorbed water molecules. The concentration factor is generally the most significant factor in determining both the selectivity and the over-all extent of counter ion adsorption—the greater the ionic content of the mother liquid the more completely will the secondary layer neutralize the charge imparted to the surface of the particles by the primary layer. It must further be recognized that each counter ion is attracted and held in a much less rigid position than is a primary adsorbed ion. For these reasons the counter ions are not to be expected to provide so tight nor so complete a coverage as do the primary ions. However, the counter ion layer

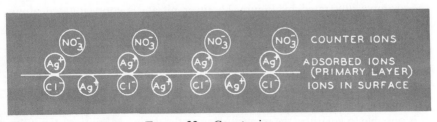

FIGURE 22. Counter ions.

can be sufficient to neutralize the charge imparted to the colloidal surfaces by the primary layer and cause the particles to coagulate. The tendency toward this condition is a function of the concentration of ions in the mother liquid.

The coagulation of colloidal particles through counter ion adsorption is a reversible process. The process whereby coagulated particles pass back into the colloidal state is designated *peptization.* Special precaution must be taken during the washing of a coagulated precipitate to prevent the agglomerates from peptizing and passing back through the filter. When coagulation is accomplished through charge neutralization, as it is in the silver chloride precipitation, peptization would occur if the precipitate were washed with pure water. Instead the wash liquid must contain an electrolyte. This electrolyte must be one which will be volatile upon subsequent drying or ignition of the precipitate, lest it contribute to lack of purity of the precipitate at the time of weighing.

COPRECIPITATION

Coprecipitation is the precipitation of an otherwise soluble substance along with an insoluble precipitate. The two substances may precipitate simultaneously or one following the other. On the basis of solubility considerations alone, it is frequently possible to precipitate one component under such conditions that all other components would be expected to remain completely in solution. However, coprecipitation always occurs to some extent. The coprecipitation of impurities may be insignificant, even in highly accurate work, as with a properly prepared precipitate of silver chloride, or it may be of considerable significance, as with hydrous ferric oxide.

There are several mechanisms whereby coprecipitation can occur. The classification of these mechanisms which is used here is a generally useful one and divides coprecipitation phenomena into four types: surface adsorption; occlusion; post-precipitation; isomorphous replacement.

Surface Adsorption. As already described, ions are adsorbed from the mother liquid onto the surfaces of precipitated particles. This adsorption involves a primary adsorbed ion layer, which is held very tightly, and a counter ion layer, which is held more or less loosely. These ions are carried down with the precipitate, so they cause the precipitate to be impure. In the example illustrated by Figure 22, silver nitrate is coprecipitated along with silver chloride. Coprecipitation by surface adsorption is especially significant when the particles are of colloidal dimensions because of the tremendous surface area which even a small mass of colloidal material can present to the mother liquid.

Impurities coprecipitated by surface adsorption contribute to error in a gravimetric determination only if they are present during the final weighing. It is possible to volatilize the impurity during the drying or ignition step if the impurity is a volatile one. It is sometimes possible, during washing, to replace the initially adsorbed ions with ions which will be subsequently volatile. Yet the wash liquid cannot always get at all of the surfaces, particularly if the agglomerates are tightly packed and nonporous. Steps should be taken at the time of precipitation to minimize surface adsorption, except insofar as it is needed to cause the precipitate to coagulate. Steps which may be taken to minimize surface adsorption include the following:

1. Ensure that the solution from which precipitation is made is dilute in all foreign ions.
2. Form the precipitate in such a manner that large crystals are obtained. Aids in accomplishing this often include slow precipitation, stirring during mixing of reagent solutions and use of dilute solutions.
3. Precipitate from hot solution. This generally increases the solubility of all components, thus decreasing the tendency toward momentary supersaturation and formation of colloidal particles and also decreasing the selective attractive forces upon which the Paneth-Fajans-Hahn Law is based.
4. Replace foreign ions which form relatively insoluble compounds with the ions of the precipitate with other ions forming more readily soluble compounds prior to precipitation; this consideration is based directly on the Paneth-Fajans-Hahn concept.
5. Remove from the solution, or convert to forms of lower charge, highly charged ions of substances which show tendency to coprecipitate.
6. Choose a precipitate of the desired ion such that no other ions in the solution are of the same size as any lattice ion.

It is, of course, necessary to combine two or more of these steps with each other and with other steps to minimize other forms of coprecipitation, so an appreciable amount of coprecipitation by surface adsorption is apt to occur even though reasonable precautions are taken to minimize it. Digestion serves to minimize surface adsorption if the individual crystals undergo recrystallization to form larger, and fewer, crystals with correspondingly less surface area. However, digestion serves to prevent subsequent removal of adsorbed ions if it causes the individual particles to coagulate to form tightly packed, nonporous aggregates of the tinier particles.

Occlusion. Occlusion is the simple physical enclosure of a small portion of the mother liquid within small hollows or flaws which form during the rapid growth of the crystals and their rapid coalescence. These pockets remain filled with the mother liquid after the precipitate has grown to such an extent that they are completely enclosed. In a typical case, one- or two-tenths of 1 % of a precipitate formed from solution consists of the mother liquid from which it was separated.

Ordinary washing is of no effect in removing any material present in completely enclosed regions. When a precipitate is ignited at high temperature, the internal pressure in the pockets may rupture the particles with resultant release of the trapped solvent. Any nonvolatile solutes present in the trapped mother liquid remain as impurity in the precipitate.

The measures which can be taken to minimize occlusion are sufficient and effective so that in most instances occlusion need not be a major source of error. These measures include the following:

1. Keep the solution dilute in all components so the mother liquid which is trapped will not contain much solute.
2. Perform the precipitation under conditions that promote slow growth of crystals, thus minimizing the formation of flaws and voids within the crystals and crystal aggregates.
3. Precipitate under conditions in which the precipitate has appreciable solubility, such as by keeping the hydroxyl ion concentration just barely great enough to precipitate calcium oxalate. This leads to an effective recrystallization of the precipitate, during which smaller particles dissolve and reprecipitate on larger ones.

Post-precipitation. Post-precipitation is another type of precipitate contamination closely associated with surface adsorption. Perhaps it may best be described by an example in which it occurs, in the separation of calcium from magnesium by oxalate precipitation. Calcium oxalate is a moderately insoluble compound which may be precipitated quantitatively. Since it exhibits a tendency to precipitate slowly, it is permitted to remain in contact with the mother liquid for some time prior to filtration. Magnesium oxalate is too soluble to precipitate under ordinary conditions. However, if calcium oxalate is precipitated from a solution containing magnesium ion and if the precipitate is allowed to remain in contact with the mother liquid for a time, magnesium oxalate coprecipitates. Three experimental facts may be noted: no magnesium oxalate separates in the absence of calcium oxalate; very little magnesium oxalate separates simultaneously with calcium oxalate; magnesium oxalate does separate as the calcium oxalate precipitate stands in contact with the mother liquid. These three facts suggest that the surface of the calcium oxalate must be a major factor in the phenomenon, probably in the following manner: Oxalate ion is present in excess in the solution and, therefore, comprises the primary adsorption layer. This effectively produces a relatively high concentration of oxalate ion localized on the calcium oxalate surface, even to the extent of providing a local state of supersaturation with respect to magnesium oxalate, so that a precipitation of some magnesium oxalate ensues.

Figure 23 is an electron photomicrograph illustrating the post-precipitation of silver chloride on silver thiocyanate. This crystal was obtained by slow addition of silver nitrate solution to a solution containing chloride and thiocyanate ions. Silver thiocyanate crystals are of a stick-like structure with straight, smooth edges. The surface bumps in this picture show a precipitation of silver chloride upon the surface of the silver thiocyanate crystal. Since silver thiocyanate is less soluble than silver chloride, the silver thiocyanate was first to precipitate, and the general shape except for the surface is that of the silver thiocyanate. This is not an ideal example of post-precipitation since silver chloride is nominally insoluble, but it is more soluble than the primary precipitate of silver thiocyanate.

The phenomenon of post-precipitation is not an uncommon one, yet it seldom imparts significant errors to the final results of a determination. It may be minimized by bringing the desired precipitate to a filterable condition as soon as possible after first formation. In a few cases an oily organic liquid may be added, as soon as the primary precipitation is complete, to coat the precipitate particles in such a way that their surfaces are no longer in direct contact with the mother liquid. The organic material must, of course, be volatile upon subsequent ignition of the precipitate.

Isomorphous Replacement. The role of the size of an atom as influencing the selectivity of surface adsorption has already been considered. It is also possible for one ion within a crystal to be replaced right in the crystal lattice by another ion of similar size and shape. This phenomenon is designated *isomorphous replacement*. Through this mechanism the impurity actually becomes a part of the crystal lattice, and it cannot be removed by washing. The only real way to eliminate this type of coprecipitation error is to remove the offending ion prior to precipitation of the desired compound.

FIGURE 23.   Electron photomicrograph of silver chloride post-precipitated on silver thiocyanate.

Coprecipitation by isomorphous replacement may be illustrated by the extent of coprecipitation of ions of the alkali metals sodium and potassium with barium sulfate. Ionic radii are 0.95×10^{-8} cm. for sodium ion, 1.33×10^{-8} cm. for potassium ion and 1.35×10^{-8} cm. for barium ion. Experimentally it is found that potassium ion coprecipitates markedly with barium sulfate, whereas sodium ion does not. This is clearly a case of isomorphous replacement of barium ion by potassium ion. It is of further interest to note that replacement of one barium ion by one potassium ion must be accompanied by some other modification to preserve electrical neutrality. Space considerations would certainly not permit two potassium ions to go into the lattice in place of one barium ion. However, a bisulfate ion is similar spatially to a sulfate ion, so electrical neutrality is retained if a bisulfate replaces a sulfate every time a potassium ion replaces a barium ion. That this must occur is indicated by the fact that the coprecipitation of potassium ion is almost negligible at a pH of 5, where there are very few bisulfate ions, while potassium ion coprecipitation is appreciable at a pH of 1, where most of the sulfate exists as bisulfate ion.

Fortunately, coprecipitation by isomorphous replacement is not encountered in very many of the common analytical precipitates. However, it is very significant in those cases in which ionic size factors make it applicable.

PRECIPITATION FROM HOMOGENEOUS SOLUTION

It has already been shown that the extent of supersaturation at the time and place of nucleation plays a major role in determining the particle size of a precipitate. The supersaturation should be held to a minimum in order to obtain a precipitate in the analytically desirable form of relatively large individual crystals. The method of precipitation from homogeneous solution has been developed to assist in accomplishing this goal. In this method the precipitating agent is not added directly but rather is generated slowly by a homogeneous chemical reaction within the solution at a rate comparable to the rate of crystal growth. Thus, the extent of supersaturation does not reach so high a value as would exist if the two reagent solutions were mixed directly.

The homogeneous precipitation procedure is applicable to any precipitation process in which the necessary reagent can be generated slowly by hydrolysis right in the solution of the unknown. But there are relatively few precipitating agents which have been generated this way, so the applications can conveniently be grouped around the reagent.

Homogeneous Precipitation by Means of Urea. Urea is an especially useful agent for homogeneous precipitation. It hydrolyzes very slowly in aqueous solution upon heating:

$$(NH_2)_2CO + 3 H_2O \longrightarrow CO_2 + 2 NH_4OH$$

The hydrolysis product, ammonium hydroxide, is an effective precipitating agent for such ions as ferric and aluminum. These precipitates generally consist of a basic salt rather than merely a hydrous oxide. For example, succinic acid is introduced to a solution of aluminum ion prior to the precipitation, and the resultant precipitate is a hydrous basic aluminum succinate which, upon subsequent ignition, is converted to aluminum oxide, Al_2O_3.

The slow generation of ammonia by the hydrolysis of urea within an initially acidic solution serves to raise the pH gradually, and pH is an important factor influencing the solubility of many substances. For example, calcium may be precipitated quantitatively from ammoniacal solution as the oxalate. This precipitate is soluble in acid, so it can be precipitated by first mixing the oxalate and calcium ion in acidic solution and then raising the pH. The latter step can be accomplished by adding a solution of ammonium hydroxide. However, the separation of calcium from magnesium, for example, is much more complete if the urea hydrolysis method is used.

Homogeneous Generation of Sulfate and Phosphate Ions. Sulfate ion can be generated homogeneously by heating a solution containing sulfuric acid, and also by slow hydrolysis of ethyl or methyl sulfate:

$$HSO_3NH_2 + H_2O \longrightarrow H^+ + SO_4^= + NH_4^+$$

$$(C_2H_5)_2SO_4 + 2 H_2O \longrightarrow 2 H^+ + SO_4^= + 2 C_2H_5OH$$

$$(CH_3)_2SO_4 + 2 H_2O \longrightarrow 2 H^+ + SO_4^= + 2 CH_3OH$$

Barium ion, or any other cation which forms an insoluble sulfate, can be precipitated homogeneously through hydrolysis of sulfamic acid or of either of the two sulfates. By use of certain mixtures of alcohol and water as the solvent, it is possible to effect sharper separations within the alkaline earth elements, barium, strontium and calcium, than is possible by direct addition of a solution containing sulfate ion. A procedure for the determination of lead from a brass sample by precipitation of lead sulfate from homogeneous solution is included in Chapter 7.

Phosphate ion can be generated homogeneously in solution by hydrolysis of either triethyl phosphate or trimethyl phosphate. This reaction is useful in the separation and determination of zirconium and a few other elements.

Homogeneous Precipitation of Sulfides. Many metal ions form insoluble sulfides, the solubilities of which are very much influenced by the pH because hydrogen sulfide is an extremely weak acid. Metal sulfides can be precipitated homogeneously by the slow hydrolysis of thioacetamide:

$$CH_3CSNH_2 + H_2O \longrightarrow CH_3CONH_2 + H_2S$$

Application of this method of generating hydrogen sulfide to analytical procedures is complicated by the fact that some metal ions can apparently

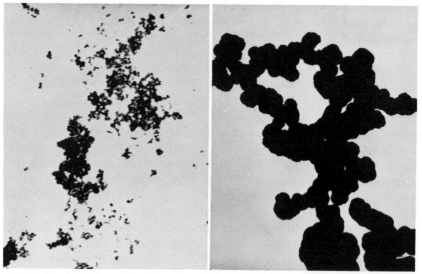

FIGURE 24. Electron photomicrographs of cadmium sulfide. The precipitate on the left was formed by direct use of hydrogen sulfide and that on the right by the homogeneous generation of hydrogen sulfide by the hydrolysis of thioacetamide.

react directly with thioacetamide to form metal sulfides. However, thioacetamide is widely used in the qualitative identification of cations, and several quantitative procedures have been developed. In Figure 24 are shown electron photomicrographs of particles of cadmium sulfide precipitated both by direct addition of hydrogen sulfide and by the homogeneous method.

Several other reagents have been developed for precipitation from homogeneous solution. Further developments are expected in the future.

Nucleation in Homogeneous Precipitation Reactions. Ideally, a precipitate formed from homogeneous solution should consist of large crystals which can be handled easily in subsequent necessary operations and which possess relatively little surface area for the adsorption of impurities. This often is the case to a considerable extent. However, the particle size sometimes falls short of that which is desired. A possible explanation may be deduced from calculations based upon the hydrolysis rate of the reagent which is to be generated homogeneously. These calculations will not be made in this book, but some conclusions may be stated.

Consider the use of a 0.1 M solution of thioacetamide at a pH of 2.0 which is to hydrolyze to precipitate cadmium sulfide from a solution 0.01 M in cadmium ion. Calculations from the hydrolysis rate of thioacetamide at room temperature, from the dissociation constants of hydrogen sulfide and from the solubility product of cadmium sulfide reveal that hydrolysis for 0.17 seconds provides sufficient sulfide ion to equal the solubility product. It is not possible to use a solution of thioacetamide anywhere near so fresh as that, so the conclusion seems inevitable that the nucleation step must occur by direct mixing of the thioacetamide solution (containing some sulfide ion) with the cadmium solution and not by any subsequent homogeneous hydrolysis reaction.

Consider also the precipitation of barium sulfate by the hydrolysis of sulfamic acid. The barium solution is typically 0.01 M. The solubility product of barium sulfate is 1.08×10^{-10}, so a sulfate ion concentration of 1.08×10^{-8} would be sufficient to saturate the solution. The hydrolysis rate of sulfamic acid at room temperature is not known accurately, but the approximate data reveal that only about one second of hydrolysis of a 1% solution would yield sufficient sulfate ion to start precipitation. Of even more significance is the fact that reagent grade sulfamic acid may contain up to 0.050% sulfate ion, which means that the sulfate ion concentration in a 1% solution is 5×10^{-5} M, or 5 000 times greater than that required to equal the solubility product without any hydrolysis whatsoever. Again it appears that the initial stage of precipitation, during which all nucleation occurs, is not one of homogeneous precipitation at all but rather is one of direct mixing of the barium solution with a solution of sulfamic acid containing sulfate ion. Only the subsequent stages of crystal growth proceed by homogeneous reaction.

The use of reagents other than thioacetamide and sulfamic acid presents different situations, but the conclusions are probably the same for most so-called homogeneous precipitation processes. It must be emphasized that, in spite of these considerations, the concentration of the precipitant at the time of starting precipitation is much less in the homogeneous type of procedure than in the usual direct mixing procedures. Thus, the use of the homogeneous method may result in less supersaturation at the time of nucleation, and thereby in improved particle size, even though the ideal of a completely homogeneous precipitation process is not attained.

Detailed directions for numerous laboratory experiments involving precipitation from homogeneous solution are included in reference 7, Appendix 7.

REVIEW QUESTIONS

1. List the properties desirable in a precipitate for a good gravimetric determination.
2. Solubility product equations in which concentrations are expressed in molar units are not completely applicable with solutions which contain high concentrations of foreign ions. Explain why, and suggest how the equations can be made more applicable in such situations.
3. By means of chemical equations and the Le Chatelier principle, predict and explain the effect of
   a. The magnesium ion concentration upon the solubility of magnesium ammonium phosphate.
   b. The hydrogen ion concentration upon the solubility of calcium carbonate.
   c. The thiosulfate ion concentration upon the solubility of silver chromate.

4. Explain why most inorganic substances are more soluble in water than in benzene.

5. Explain why silver chloride is made more soluble by an excess of potassium nitrate and less soluble by an excess of potassium chloride.

6. Why is an indefinitely large excess of a common ion not advisable in a precipitation?

7. Formulate solubility product expressions for the following: $BaSO_4$; Ag_2CrO_4; $Ca_3(PO_4)_2$.

8. Under what conditions may a solubility product be exceeded without formation of a precipitate?

9. Suggest one way in which a solubility product constant may be determined experimentally.

10. The K_{sp} of barium chromate, $BaCrO_4$, is 2.4×10^{-10} and that of lead chromate, $PbCrO_4$, is 1.77×10^{-14}. On a molar basis, which compound is more soluble in water?

11. The K_{sp} of $Mn(OH)_2$ is 4.5×10^{-14} and of $Cu(OH)_2$ is 1.5×10^{-29}. Which compound precipitates at the lower pH, assuming the same cation concentration for each?

12. Two compounds of the types $A(OH)_2$ and $B(OH)_3$ have K_{sp}'s of the same numerical value. On a molar basis, which compound is more soluble in 0.1 M sodium hydroxide?

13. Distinguish clearly between nucleation and crystal growth, and explain why their mechanisms are not identical to each other.

14. Distinguish between induced and spontaneous nucleation, and state the relation between each and the extent of supersaturation.

15. Define or characterize the following terms:
    a. Colloid
    b. Supersaturation
    c. Coagulation
    d. Peptization
    e. Isomorphism
    f. Counter ions
    g. Coprecipitation
    h. Occlusion

16. Compare colloids with true solutions and with simple mixtures.

17. To illustrate surface area in colloids, calculate the surface area of
    a. A cube 1 cm. on a side
    b. The same cube of (a) cut into eight cubes by slicing in half in three directions at right angles.
    c. The same cubes of (b) each sliced further into eight cubes in the same way.

18. Name ten colloids familiar in everyday life.

19. Explain the role of the counter ion layer in determining the stability of a colloidal dispersion.

20. Why are the forces holding the counter ions less selective than those holding the primary adsorbed ions?

21. State and illustrate the Paneth-Fajans-Hahn law.

22. Distinguish between occlusion, surface adsorption, post-precipitation and isomorphous replacement.

23. In terms of the von Weimarn concept of precipitation, discuss the principles of precipitation from homogeneous solution.

PROBLEMS

1-4. Given the following solubility data, calculate the K_{sp} for each compound:
   1. TlCl, 0.32 gram per 100 ml.
   2. $Pb(IO_3)_2$, 3.98×10^{-5} moles per liter.
   3. AgI, 1.40×10^{-6} gram per 500 ml.
   4. $Mg(OH)_2$, 0.0085 gram per liter.
5-7. From the K_{sp} values in Appendix 1, calculate the solubility of each compound in moles per liter:
   5. NiS
   6. SrF_2
   7. $Al(OH)_3$
8-10. From the K_{sp} values in Appendix 1, calculate the solubility of each compound in grams per 500 ml.:
   8. CdS
   9. BaF_2
   10. $Cu(IO_3)_2$
11. What is the maximum concentration of calcium ions that can be present in a liter of solution containing 3.0 moles of F^- ion?
12. Calculate the weight in grams of cuprous ion left in 200 ml. of solution in the precipitation of cuprous thiocyanate, CuSCN, if the solution contains an excess of (a) 1.0 mg. of excess thiocyanate ion, (b) 0.10 gram of excess thiocyanate ion.
13. Calculate the molar concentration of lead ion remaining in solution in the precipitation of lead iodate, $Pb(IO_3)_2$, in the presence of (a) 10^{-4} molar iodate ion, (b) 10^{-2} molar iodate ion.
14. To 150 ml. of a solution containing 0.50 gram Na_2SO_4 is added a 50 ml. portion containing 0.50 gram $BaCl_2$. Calculate the weight in mg. of sulfate as Na_2SO_4 left unprecipitated.
15. To 150 ml. of a solution containing 0.50 gram Na_2SO_4 is added 50 ml. of a solution containing 1.00 gram $BaCl_2$. Calculate the weight in mg. of sulfate ion ($SO_4^=$) left unprecipitated.
16. Calculate the maximum weight in grams of sulfate ion which can be lost through solubility of barium sulfate in 100 ml. of wash water containing no excess of either lattice ion.
17. What hydroxyl ion concentration is needed just to begin precipitation of magnesium hydroxide from a 0.01 molar solution of magnesium sulfate?
18. What weight of ferric ion must be present in a liter of solution just to begin precipitation of ferric hydroxide if the hydroxyl ion concentration is 1.0×10^{-5} molar?
19. If 25 mg. magnesium chloride are added to a solution formed by diluting 10.0 ml. of 0.10 molar sodium hydroxide solution to 1.0 liter, will a precipitate be formed?
20. Show by calculation which anion will be precipitated first when silver nitrate solution is added gradually to a solution 0.10 molar in chloride ion and 0.10 molar in chromate ion.
21. Which solution contains more silver ion per liter, a solution saturated in silver iodate or a solution saturated in silver dichromate?
22. How much lead ion is left in solution when strontium sulfate just begins to precipitate from a solution 1.0×10^{-2} molar in strontium ion?
23. Calculate the molar concentration of ferric ion left in solution when aluminum hydroxide just begins to precipitate from a solution initially 1.0×10^{-2} molar

in both ferric ion and aluminum ion (neglect any dilution during the precipitation process).

24. What is the maximum sulfide ion concentration which may exist in order to precipitate cupric sulfide without precipitating cadmium sulfide, assuming the cadmium ion concentration to be 1.0×10^{-1} molar?
25. Calculate the molar solubility of silver iodide in a solution containing at equilibrium 0.01 molar cyanide ion.
26. Calculate the molar solubility of silver iodide in a solution containing at equilibrium 0.01 molar ammonia, NH_3, concentration.

SUGGESTIONS FOR ADDITIONAL READING

Items 2, 7, 10, 11, 14, 25, 27 and 30, Appendix 7.

Part Three

VOLUMETRIC METHODS

Chapter 9

The Unit Operations, Tools and Calculations of Volumetric Analysis

THE GENERAL unit operations in a volumetric method of analysis may be listed as follows:

1. Sampling.
2. Drying.
3. Weighing the sample.
4. Dissolving the sample.
5. Adjustment of conditions of the sample solution.
6. Preparation of standard solution.
7. Titration of sample solution with standard solution.

The first four are in common with gravimetric methods of analysis and have been described in Chapter 4 so only a brief additional consideration is presented in this chapter. The conditions of the sample solution which must be adjusted frequently include volume, concentration range of unknown constituent, presence and concentration ranges of other constituents, acidity and temperature. These were listed for the fifth unit operation in gravimetric analysis, Chapter 6, but the determining factors are quite different in volumetric analysis. These factors differ widely from one type of volumetric reaction to another; therefore, this operation will be considered in conjunction with specific volumetric procedures in subsequent chapters. Unit operations 6 and 7 are generally characteristic of volumetric procedures and will be discussed in some detail in this chapter. Methods of volume measurement are also included. In volumetric methods as well as in gravimetric, two or more of the unit operations may be combined or one or more may be omitted altogether in certain determinations.

PREPARATION OF THE SAMPLE SOLUTION

Whenever a solid sample is to be analyzed, it must be weighed out accurately even though the procedure is to be primarily a volumetric one.

Therefore, even volumetric methods of analysis frequently require weight measurements as well as volume measurements.

The analyst need not necessarily weigh out individual samples for replicate determinations. Instead, one large sample may be weighed out accurately and dissolved to form a solution of known volume. Then a known fraction of that solution may be taken for each of the replicate determinations. For example, a sample weighing 1.0000 gram could be dissolved and diluted to 250.00 ml., then 50.00 ml. portions could be withdrawn for each of the determinations. The known fractions of the larger quantity of solution are termed *aliquots*. In this example, five separate samples of 0.2000 gram each are obtained by only one weight measurement along with several volume measurements. Any error in the one weight measurement will, of course, be reflected as an error in each of the five sample weights. Herein lies the major disadvantage of this method of preparing the samples. Both the method of weighing one large sample and analyzing aliquots and the method of weighing out individual samples for replicate determinations are widely used.

MEASUREMENTS OF VOLUMES OF SOLUTIONS

Types of Volumetric Glassware. There are three principal types of volumetric glassware: flasks, pipets, burets. Typical items of each type are shown in Figure 25.

A volumetric flask is made of thin glass, has a flat bottom and is calibrated to contain a definite volume of liquid. Occasionally, a second calibration mark is provided so that the flask will deliver a specified volume of liquid. The latter calibration mark provides for the inclusion of a slightly larger volume than does the former, because a thin film of the liquid adheres to the inner walls upon emptying.

Pipets are used primarily to measure aliquot portions of solutions and are of two types. A transfer pipet consists of a long delivery tube, an enlarged bulb of the desired capacity in the center, and a narrow neck or stem on which is a single calibration mark. The delivery tube is long enough to reach near the bottom of a volumetric flask. A measuring pipet has a straight, uniform bore which is graduated along its length. It is used for the delivery of measured, variable volumes of solution. Measuring pipets are useful primarily for the controlled delivery of volumes of 10 ml. and less. Burets are generally more convenient for larger volumes and may be used for smaller volumes as well. Transfer pipets are most widely used in measuring aliquots of fixed size from 1 to 100 ml.

A buret consists of a cylindrical glass tube with graduations along its lengthwise direction and with provision for withdrawing liquid through a small end-opening. It is usually used in the performance of titrations. The cross-section size of a buret is a compromise between two factors: small enough to provide adequate accuracy in the volume measurements; large enough to minimize error from the drainage effects encountered whenever the drainage surface area per unit volume becomes excessive. Delivery of liquid from the buret is accomplished through the capillary tip. The rate of delivery may be controlled by a glass stopcock or Teflon valve assembly just above the tip, or it may be controlled by pinching a rubber tube inside of which is placed a small glass bead in such a manner as to form an opening along one side of the bead for the liquid to pass. The latter method is used in the Mohr buret and is especially valuable for prolonged use with alkaline solutions which would cement glass stopcocks in place. The burets with glass stopcocks and, recently, those with Teflon valve assemblies are more commonly used.

Any possible error from drainage effects is completely avoided in the weight buret. This type is made much more compact by increasing its cross section and is fitted with a glass-stoppered top. No direct readings of volume

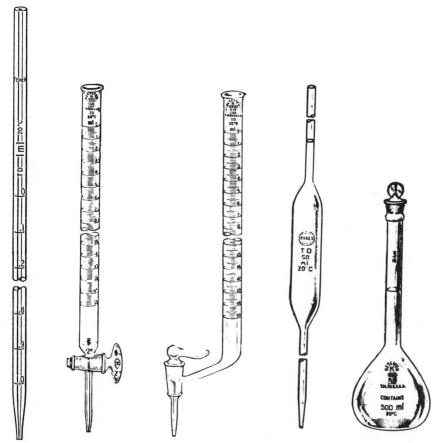

FIGURE 25. Typical volumetric glassware: graduated measuring pipet, burets, transfer pipet and volumetric flask.

are made. Instead, the entire buret is weighed on an analytical balance before and after solution is withdrawn. Not only does this technique eliminate drainage errors, but it also increases the sensitivity of measurement. Weighings may be made to the nearest 0.1 mg. on an ordinary analytical balance, which corresponds to 0.0001 ml. of water. Weight burets have received relatively little use in the past because of the inconvenience and tediousness of weighing, but this situation is changing now that modern semiautomatic balances have come into widespread use. Small polyethylene "wash bottles" have been found to function well as weight burets.

Cleaning of Volumetric Glassware. All items of volumetric glassware must be carefully cleaned prior to use. This is necessary not only to remove possible contaminants but also to assure accurate use. The film of water which adheres to the inner glass walls as a container is emptied of an aqueous solution must be uniform. Even slight traces of grease cause the liquid to adhere in drops rather than as a uniform film. Uneven wetting of the surfaces causes irregularities in the shape of the meniscus, thereby causing further random error in reading the liquid level within the buret, pipet or volumetric flask.

Perhaps the one most important rule to follow in cleaning volumetric glassware is to empty and clean each item immediately after use. Two or three rinsings with tap water, a moderate amount of agitation with a dilute detergent solution, several rinsings with tap water and, finally, two rinsings with small volumes of distilled water are generally sufficient if the glassware is emptied and cleaned immediately after use. If, however, a solution is permitted to evaporate to dryness within a container, the residue may require more severe treatment. Concentrated detergent solutions should be avoided; a 2% solution is generally adequate. No glassware should be permitted to soak in any detergent solution longer than about twenty minutes.

Direct heat from a flame should never be applied to volumetric glassware; drying in an oven at about 105° C. is permissible. However, adequate drying is usually accomplished by permitting the glassware to stand in air at room temperature or by flushing it with clean, dry air.

Prior to lubricating a stopcock, the plug and the barrel should be wiped thoroughly with a clean towel. Any contaminant within the hole through the plug can be pushed out with a piece of wire. A small amount of stopcock grease should be applied near each end of the plug, not directly in line with the hole. The plug is then inserted into the barrel and rotated several times to spread the grease uniformly over the ground-glass surfaces. A properly lubricated stopcock should be seated firmly but should rotate freely. An over-lubricated stopcock tends to slide too easily and may become blocked through the hole. An under-lubricated plug rotates stiffly and unevenly and tends to leak. A stopcock that is properly lubricated can be used for a long period of time without further attention.

Hydrocarbon stopcock greases can be dissolved, when necessary for cleaning, with acetone. Silicone greases do not dissolve readily in any common solvent; recommended procedures are to soak for two hours in "decalin" (decahydronaphthalene) or for thirty minutes in concentrated sulfuric acid.

The use of stopcock grease is not necessary with some types of stopcocks which are now commercially available.

Reading the Meniscus. The bottom of the meniscus should be read unless this is impossible as, for example, with a highly colored solution. A "buret reader" is very useful. It need consist of nothing more than a white index card with a heavy dark line. The card is held behind the container so the observer sees the meniscus against a white background, with the top of the dark band a few millimeters below the meniscus. Light reflected from the surface of the liquid makes the meniscus stand out very clearly. The observer's eye should be at the same height as the meniscus, Figure 26. By noting the appearance of the nearest calibration lines which go all around the container, he can ascertain readily whether or not his eye is at the correct level.

Preparation of Solution in Volumetric Flask. The solute should be weighed out, transferred to the flask directly or through a powder funnel and dissolved in an amount of water considerably less than the capacity of the flask. The solution should then be diluted until the liquid surface lies a few millimeters below the calibration mark. At this time the flask should be swirled gently, with stopper in place, so the entire neck is wetted by the solution. After a two-minute wait for drainage from the walls of the neck, the final dilution is made to the mark.

Alternatively, the desired solute may be weighed and dissolved in a beaker and then poured into the volumetric flask. The beaker must be rinsed several

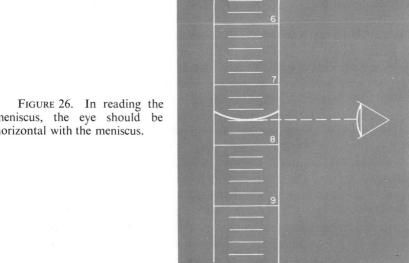

Figure 26. In reading the meniscus, the eye should be horizontal with the meniscus.

times with small volumes of solvent, with the rinsings being used in diluting the solution in the flask. In any case, the solute should be in the flask and completely dissolved before the final dilution is made.

Pipet Techniques.   Suction is used to draw solution up into a pipet, and delivery is controlled by proper admission of air into the neck end of the pipet. Oral suction is satisfactory for nonvolatile solutions which are dilute and are positively known to be safe for handling in this way. Several types of pipetting bulbs are commercially available which fit on top of the pipet and which do not require the use of oral suction. These devices are necessary for handling some solutions and are recommended for general use.

Standardized techniques of filling and emptying pipets are necessary in order to minimize the error which would result from irreproducible drainage effects. It is recommended that, in filling, the pipet be held vertically, that liquid be drawn up about 2 cm. above the mark, that the tip be touched quickly to a piece of clean filter paper, that the pipet be held vertically over a beaker with the tip touching the lip of the beaker and that the liquid be permitted to drain until the meniscus is just at the calibration mark.

In delivering liquid from a transfer pipet, rapid, free delivery should be permitted until the liquid level is in the lower stem of the pipet. Then the tip should be held against the inner wall of the receptacle as in Figure 27 until the flow stops and for an additional count of two. The pipet should be moved horizontally from the wall of the receptacle and finally withdrawn entirely. Some pipets are calibrated for "blow out," in which case the final part of the delivery procedure should be altered to provide for the analyst to blow out the last portion of liquid. This type of pipet, which is relatively uncommon, is marked by the manufacturer with a 1/8 inch opaque band near the top of the pipet. Unless marked in this way, the blow-out technique should not be used in quantitative work.

These procedures for filling and emptying pipets are quite arbitrary, but they are similar to those which have been adopted by the National Bureau of Standards. A slow delivery time followed by a very brief drainage time has been found to be more reproducible in the same over-all period of time than a faster delivery time and a longer drainage period. The National Bureau of Standards recommends, for example, that the tip of a 100 ml. pipet be of such a size that delivery requires sixty seconds or slightly less, in which case very reproducible results are obtained with virtually no additional drainage time.

Buret Techniques.   Delivery of solution from a buret should preferably be made with the stopcock wide open and thus be limited only by its capillary tip until the volume delivered is within 1 or 2 ml. of the needed volume (assuming a 50 ml. buret—use proportional amount for other sizes). The particular circumstances of a titration may make this impossible, but it is usually possible to anticipate approximately what volume will be required even in the titration of an unknown sample. However, the tip should be small enough to make this "free delivery" time quite long. A good 50 ml. buret, for example, typically delivers its full calibrated volume in about seventy-five seconds. Following this delivery the level of the meniscus changes by not more than 0.01 ml. in several minutes, which time is generally sufficient for completing the titration. A faster delivery time, resulting from a larger opening in the tip, would result in much more pronounced drainage from the walls of the buret extending over a much longer period of time. A slower delivery time, from a finer tip, would minimize error from drainage even more, but the longer time would tend to become objectionable.

The proper method of manipulating a buret stopcock while simultaneously swirling the titration vessel is illustrated in Figure 28.

Temperature Effect.   An increase in temperature causes expansion of the glass of which a pipet, buret or volumetric flask is made and also of the solution within it. With regard to the expansion of the glass, a typical flask

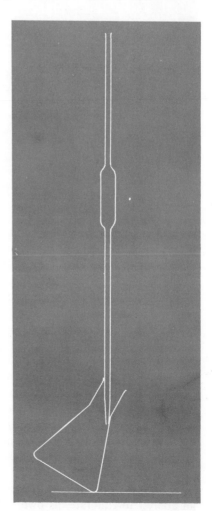

FIGURE 27.   The proper position of a pipet while draining it.

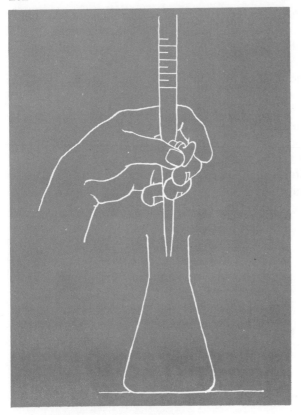

FIGURE 28. In performing a titration, the fingers of the left hand should reach around the barrel of the buret to manipulate the stopcock. The right hand is free for swirling the titration flask.

which holds 1.000 00 liter at 15° C. holds 1.000 25 liter at 25° C. This change is small enough to be insignificant in most quantitative analyses, but it must be recognized in very precise work. Each piece of volumetric glassware is marked by the manufacturer as to the temperature at which its calibration is valid. A temperature of 20° C. has been adopted by the National Bureau of Standards as the base or normal temperature for its calibration of volumetric glassware. Calibrations made at other temperatures may be corrected to 20° C., and vice versa, by the equation

$$V_{20}{}^0 = V[1 + 0.000\ 025(20\text{-}t)]$$

in which $V_{20}{}^0$ and V are the volumes at 20° C. and at t° C., respectively.

The thermal expansion of the solution is generally more significant than is that of the glass. The expansion of water or of any dilute aqueous solution is about 2 ml. in 1 liter for a temperature change of 10° C. Room temperature fluctuations in a non-air-conditioned laboratory often amount to 5° over an extended period of time, which means that the volume change would be of the order of one part per thousand.

Calibration of Volumetric Glassware. It is often necessary for an analyst to calibrate his own volumetric glassware. The calibration may be accomplished simply by weighing the water delivered by, or contained within, the piece of apparatus. One piece of calibrated glassware may, of course, be used for subsequent calibration of others, so a direct weighing is not required for every item. The glassware should be thoroughly clean, and any stopcocks should be properly lubricated prior to calibration.

An item calibrated for use with aqueous solutions must be recalibrated if it is to be used with some other solvent. Otherwise, different drainage characteristics between water and the other liquid could result in appreciable error.

Laboratory Experiment 9

CALIBRATION OF VOLUMETRIC GLASSWARE

Procedure

Buret. Fill the buret with distilled water so that the meniscus is just within the graduated region. Recording the buret readings both before and afterwards, withdraw approximately 10 ml. of water into a previously weighed (nearest mg.) 125 ml. cork-stoppered Erlenmeyer flask. Also record the temperature. Again weigh the flask. Repeat this process with withdrawals of water within the approximate ranges of 0 to 20, 0 to 30, 0 to 40 and 0 to 50 ml. For each set of data, calculate the actual volume of water delivered by multiplying the weight of water by the volume occupied by 1 gram of water at the recorded temperature (Table 11). The volume correction for each range is the difference between the actual volume obtained and the volume as given by the buret readings. Duplicate results within the same volume range should agree within two or three hundredths of a ml., although the corrections for various volume ranges may differ from each other. Plot the data for the different ranges in a calibration curve such as that of Figure 29.

Transfer Pipet. Fill the pipet somewhat over the calibration mark with distilled water at room temperature. Adjust the level so that the meniscus coincides with the calibration mark by careful manipulation of the finger over the upper end of the pipet, discarding the liquid emptied during this adjustment. Allow the pipet to empty into a previously weighed 125 ml. cork-stoppered Erlenmeyer flask. Care should be taken that no droplets of water are present around the outside of the pipet immediately before and during the delivery. Permit the pipet to drain into the flask for a set period of time, such as thirty seconds, and use the same drainage routine subsequently

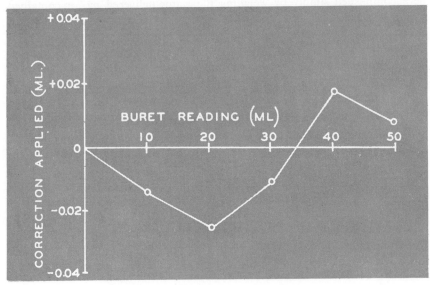

FIGURE 29. Typical buret calibration curve.

with this pipet. Record the temperature. Weigh the flask and its contents. Calculate the actual volume of water delivered by the pipet from the weight of water delivered, its temperature and the volume occupied by 1 gram of water as listed in Table 11.

Volumetric Flask. Calibrate the flask by weighing it empty and again filled to the mark with distilled water.

Table 11. Volume Occupied by One Gram of Water at Various Temperatures

Temperature (° C.)	Volume (ml.)	Temperature (° C.)	Volume (ml.)
11	1.0017	21	1.0030
12	1.0018	22	1.0032
13	1.0019	23	1.0034
14	1.0020	24	1.0036
15	1.0021	25	1.0038
16	1.0022	26	1.0041
17	1.0023	27	1.0043
18	1.0025	28	1.0046
19	1.0026	29	1.0048
20	1.0028	30	1.0051

(These volumes represent those occupied by one gram of water at the stated temperature as weighed in air using brass weights.)

Alternatively, pour into the flask the desired volume of water from some other previously calibrated container and then place a new calibration mark on the flask.

A third alternative method involves calibration of the flask relative to a pipet. For example, fill a 250 ml. volumetric flask with five portions from a 50 ml. pipet, and insert a new calibration on the flask. (This is a useful calibration method even if the pipet has not been calibrated, because the same pipet may be used subsequently for withdrawal of exactly one-fifth aliquots of the contents of the flask.)

STANDARD SOLUTIONS

A standard solution is a solution of known concentration. In a volumetric determination, a portion of a standard solution is used to react with the substance being determined. The standard solution is often the titrating reagent, and the substance being determined is the titrated reagent. For example, a standard solution of silver nitrate may be used in the determination of an unknown quantity of chloride ion by precipitimetry and a standard solution of sodium hydroxide is suitable for the determination of replaceable hydrogen ion in an organic acid mixture by a neutralization process.

Methods of Expressing Concentration of Solutions. The concentration of a standard solution may be expressed in any one of several manners: grams of solute per liter of solution; weight percentage of solute in the solution; molarity; normality; in terms of how much of a certain substance will react with each volume unit of the reagent. The last method is frequently used in industrial analytical laboratories, and normality and molarity are most frequently involved in general analytical usage.

The *molarity* of a solution may be defined as the number of gram-molecular weights (moles) of solute per liter of solution and is designated by the symbol M. For example, the molecular weight of sodium hydroxide is 40.00, so a 0.5000 M solution contains 20.00 grams of sodium hydroxide per liter of solution. The definition of molarity may be stated mathematically as

$$M = \frac{\text{no. of moles of solute}}{\text{liters of solution}}$$

or

$$M = \frac{\text{grams of solute} \div \text{mol. wt. of solute}}{\text{liters of solution}}$$

One reason for the usefulness of molar methods of expressing concentration is the fact that equal volumes of equimolar solutions contain equal numbers of molecules.

The normality, designated N, of a solution is defined as the number of gram equivalent weights of solute per liter of solution.

$$N = \frac{\text{no. of gram equiv. weights of solute}}{\text{liters of solution}}$$

or

$$N = \frac{\text{grams of solute} \div \text{gram equiv. weight of solute}}{\text{liters of solution}}$$

The gram equivalent weight of any substance is defined as the weight in grams of that substance which, in a reaction, is equivalent to or corresponds to 1.008 0 grams of hydrogen. No distinction need be made in this definition between a hydrogen ion and a hydrogen atom because both weigh essentially the same. It is important to note that a chemical reaction is implicit in the concept of equivalent weight. The symbol H in any chemical formula represents 1.008 0 grams of hydrogen, so the relationship between any substance and hydrogen may be derived solely on the basis of chemical formulas without recourse to actual weight units. Therefore,

$$\text{eq. wt. of any substance} = \frac{\text{formula wt. of that substance}}{\text{no. of H's to which that formula corresponds}}$$

In a neutralization reaction, each reactant either provides or combines with hydrogen ions, so in a neutralization reaction

$$\text{eq. wt.} = \frac{\text{formula weight}}{\text{no. of H ions provided by or used by that formula}}$$

For example, the equivalent weights of hydrochloric acid and of sodium hydroxide are the same as their molecular weights. Sodium carbonate in the reaction

$$Na_2CO_3 + HCl \longrightarrow NaHCO_3 + NaCl$$

has an equivalent weight equal to its molecular weight, but its equivalent weight is half of its molecular weight in the reaction

$$Na_2CO_3 + 2\ HCl \longrightarrow H_2CO_3 + 2\ NaCl$$

It is clearly necessary to state or to assume a certain reaction for a substance in specifying its equivalent weight and its normality.

In a precipitation reaction, a hydrogen ion would contribute one valency unit if it were to react. Thus, the equivalent relationship between any substance and hydrogen in a precipitation reaction must be based upon the number of valency units

$$\text{eq. wt.} = \frac{\text{formula weight}}{\text{no. of + or − valency units accounted for by that formula}}$$

Silver nitrate has an equivalent weight equal to its formula weight when used in the precipitation of silver chloride. The equivalent weight of the chromate ion, $CrO_4^=$, is one-half its formula weight when used in the precipitation of silver chromate, Ag_2CrO_4.

The concept of equivalent weight in complex formation reactions is similar to that in precipitation reactions, but complication arises because the total positive and negative valence units involved in the reaction may differ from each other. This fact arises because the complex is not necessarily a neutral species as is an insoluble precipitate. This topic will be considered specifically in Chapter 13.

In oxidation-reduction reactions, hydrogen can react to the extent of one electron per atom, so the equivalent relationship of any substance to hydrogen in a reaction of this type is based upon the number of electrons which that substance gains or loses in the reaction.

$$\text{eq. wt.} = \frac{\text{formula weight}}{\text{no. of electrons gained or lost by that formula}}$$

In the reaction between solutions of ferrous chloride and of potassium dichromate

$$6\,Fe^{++} + Cr_2O_7^= + 14\,H^+ \longrightarrow 6\,Fe^{+++} + 2\,Cr^{+++} + 7\,H_2O$$

each ferrous chloride provides one ferrous ion which, in turn, yields one electron in the reaction, so the equivalent weight of ferrous chloride equals the molecular weight ($FeCl_2/1$). Each potassium dichromate provides one dichromate ion which, in turn, takes on six electrons, so the equivalent weight of potassium dichromate equals one-sixth of its formula weight ($K_2Cr_2O_7/6$).

An *equivalent* is 1 gram equivalent weight, just as a mole is 1 gram-molecular weight. A *milliequivalent*, often abbreviated mEq., is one-thousandth of an equivalent. The normality method, that is, the equivalent method, of expressing the concentration of a solution, is of considerable convenience because the number of equivalents of one reacting substance must equal the number of equivalents of the substance with which it reacts. This one fact is the basis of stoichiometric calculations in volumetric analysis.

Both molar and normal expressions of concentration involve amounts of solute per unit volume of solution, not per unit volume of solvent. The latter method could be employed, although it is of relatively little usefulness in analytical work because of indeterminate volume changes produced upon mixing solvent and solute. The term *molality* designates the number of gram-molecular weights of solute per 1 000 grams of solvent.

Titer refers to the concentration of a solution in terms of the weight of a substance that is equivalent to one unit volume of the solution. For example, a solution of hydrochloric acid could be prepared of such a concentration that 1 ml. would react with 5 mg. of sodium carbonate, so the titer of the acid solution would be five. The titer value refers, of necessity, to one particular reaction, so the specific units should always be stated along with the number.

Primary and Secondary Standards. Standard solutions may be classified as primary and secondary. A *primary standard solution* may be prepared by direct measurement of the weight of solute and the volume to which it is diluted. A *secondary standard solution* is a solution whose concentration cannot be determined directly from the weight of solute and the volume of solution. The concentration of a secondary standard solution must be determined by analysis of a portion of the solution itself.

The term primary standard may be used with reference to the solute substance as well as to the resultant solution. A *primary standard substance* is a substance, a standard solution of which may be prepared by direct measurement of the weight of the substance and the volume to which it is diluted. A primary standard substance must be used, either directly or indirectly, in the preparation of every standard solution. The chief requirements which must be fulfilled by a substance in order for it to be a primary standard substance are the following: it must be obtainable in a pure form; it must be stable both in the pure form and in solution; it must be dryable and nonhygroscopic; it must be soluble in a suitable solvent; it must be capable of entering into stoichiometric reaction with a solution to be standardized or with a substance to be determined. In addition, a primary standard substance should preferably have an adequately high equivalent weight so that a reasonable number of milliequivalents may be weighed out without significant weighing errors.

The preparation of a standard solution involves two processes which may or may not coincide: weighing out the solute, dissolving and diluting to the desired volume; determination of the concentration of the solution. Solutions of secondary standards require standardization against some primary standard, and the process of standardization should, whenever possible, be carried out in the same manner in which the solution is to be used for analyses in order to minimize systematic errors. For example, a solution of silver nitrate, to be used in titration of unknown chloride solutions, should preferably be standardized by titration against primary standard sodium chloride rather than by a gravimetric method.

Preserving Standard Solutions. Special precautions are necessary in storing and preserving standard solutions. The bottle must be kept tightly stoppered to prevent evaporation of solvent which would cause an increase in solute concentration. The bottle should be shaken before withdrawal of a portion of solution to insure uniform composition of both the withdrawn portion and the remainder left in the bottle. Portions of solution, once withdrawn, should never be returned to the bottle. This precaution is necessary to minimize the danger of contamination of the main body of solution, and it means that any unused part of a withdrawn portion should be discarded.

Some standard solutions must be protected from atmospheric gases.

For example, sodium hydroxide solutions are effectively diluted by atmospheric carbon dioxide, which dissolves to form carbonic acid which, in turn, reacts with some of the sodium hydroxide.

Some solutions, for example silver nitrate and potassium permanganate, must be stored in dark glass bottles or otherwise be kept in the dark when not in use to prevent light-catalyzed decomposition. Others, such as sodium thiosulfate, must be protected from possible bacterial-induced decomposition.

TITRATION OF SAMPLE SOLUTION WITH STANDARD SOLUTION

In a volumetric determination, the volume of a solution of known concentration of a suitable reagent which is required to react with a solution of the unknown is measured. The results of the determination are calculated from the amount of that reagent solution required to react with the solution being analyzed. The one main experimental operation in every volumetric determination is the *titration*, which term may be defined as the measured and controlled addition of one solution to another with which it reacts.

End Points and Indicators. Since the result of a volumetric determination is calculated from the amount (concentration and volume) of the reagent which is allowed to react with the substance being determined, an excess of the reagent must not be used. Some means must be provided for ascertaining the point in the titration at which the desired reaction is completed. This point in the titration is designated the end point. The *end point* may be defined as that point in the titration at which equivalent amounts of the main reactants have been brought together; that is, the point at which there is no excess of either reactant.

In order for the analyst to detect the end point, there must be a sharp change in some property of the solution in which the reaction takes place. Some properties that might undergo change and thereby serve as a basis for the detection of the end point are: (1) color of solution (disappearance and/or appearance of one or more colored ions); (2) sharp change in concentration of some ion that can readily be measured; (3) appearance of a precipitate (or appearance of a second precipitate which is highly colored); (4) change in some electrical property of the solution. A substance that gives a discernible indication of any of the changes mentioned is called an *indicator*. It may be one of the reactants or a substance added to the solution.

Quite frequently an indicator end point and a theoretical end point do not coincide perfectly. In other words, the indicator may not be a perfect one. The term end point is usually used to refer to the experimental or indicator end point, while the theoretical end point is designated the *stoichiometric point*. It is a goal in each method of volumetric analysis to make the stoichiometric point and the end point coincide as closely as possible.

Requirements of Reactions. A chemical reaction must fulfill four requirements to make it satisfactory as the basis of a method of volumetric analysis:

1. It must be one definite reaction.
2. The reaction must proceed to completion or nearly so.
3. The reaction must proceed rapidly.
4. An indicator must be available.

The first two requirements arise because it would be impossible to measure how much of one substance is present by measuring how much of another is required to react with it unless the two substances react quantitatively according to one definite reaction. In general, one of the following requirements must be fulfilled by any chemical reaction to permit it to go to completion: an insoluble substance is formed; a slightly ionized substance is formed; a complex ion is formed; the charge of an ion is changed or removed.

The third requirement arises because the analyst must be able to recognize continuously during the titration whether or not the end point has been reached in order that he may know whether to continue or to terminate the titration at each point as he proceeds. It is simply not practical to carry out a titration between substances which do not react quickly. In general, ionic reactions do proceed rapidly, and most useful titrations do involve reactions between ionic solutions. In recent years, however, many useful titrations have been developed employing organic solutions which are nonionic.

The reason for the fourth requirement is obvious; the analyst could never tell when to terminate a titration unless some type of indicator were available. No suitable indicators are available for many chemical reactions. This factor alone eliminates such reactions from usefulness as the bases of methods of volumetric analysis. The development of new indicators, and even of new types of indicators, is one of several fruitful fields of research in modern analytical chemistry.

The various types of volumetric reactions arise directly from the criteria which have been listed for the completion of reactions. Precipitation reactions are those in which an insoluble substance is formed. Neutralization processes are those in which a slightly ionized substance, usually water or a weak acid or base, is formed. Some reactions involving the formation of a complex ion are in general analytical use. Oxidation-reduction processes are those in which the charge on an ion is neutralized or changed.

Performance of Titrations. Titrations with burets may be carried out by the *direct stop end point method* or by the *back titration method.* In the former, the titrating reagent is added from the buret until the precise end point is reached, at which point the delivery of standard solution from the buret must be stopped abruptly. Obviously, the last portions of the reagent must be added very slowly in order to permit accurate observation of the end point. In the back titration method the titrating agent is added rather slowly, but not necessarily dropwise, until the end point is passed. Then another reagent, chemically similar to the substance being titrated in that both react quantitatively with the main titrating reagent, is added dropwise from a second buret until the end point is returned. In this method the volumes and the concentrations of both reagents added from burets enter into the calculations.

Special care must be exercised in manipulating the stopcock on the buret during the titration. As already noted in Figure 28, a right-handed person should mount the buret with the stopcock on the right, and he should manipulate the stopcock with his left hand, reaching his fingers around the buret to the handle of the stopcock. In this way, the analyst naturally exerts a slight inward pressure on the stopcock, preventing the possibility of pulling it out, and his right hand is free for swirling the titration vessel. Titrations are most frequently carried out in Erlenmeyer flasks, although beakers can also be used. The contents of the vessel should be swirled continually during the titration to insure adequate mixing, and the reagent should be added only a drop at a time near the end point. It is even possible to split a drop by permitting a partial drop to form on the tip of the buret, closing the stopcock, and touching an inner wall of the titration vessel to the buret tip to remove the drop. It is necessary to rinse down the inner walls of the vessel with a wash bottle just prior to the final end point to make sure that all of the sample solution is able to react with all the solution which has been delivered by the buret.

STOICHIOMETRIC CALCULATIONS IN VOLUMETRIC ANALYSIS

Calculations in volumetric analysis are essentially of two types, stoichiometric problems and mass law problems. The former type will be discussed in this chapter. Stoichiometric problems are essentially of the type, "How much of substance A reacts with, is equivalent to or is formed by so much of substance B?" All problems involving standardization of solutions and all percentage calculations involving unknowns are of this type. In the following discussion are developed three short, interrelated equations from which any stoichiometric problem may be attacked.

(1) $mEq. = mEq.$ When applied to any single substance, A, this equation is true as a simple identity, $mEq. A = mEq. A$. When applied to two substances, A and B, which react with each other, this equation means that at any true end point the number of milliequivalents of A is numerically equal to the number of milliequivalents of B, $mEq. A = mEq. B$. It will be noted that this equation is merely a mathematical definition of the stoichiometric end point. When two substances, A and B, in the same solution both react quantitatively with a third substance, C, the equation indicates that at the final true end point the number of milliequivalents of C is numerically equal to the total number of milliequivalents of A and B, $mEq. A + mEq. B = mEq. C$

(2) $mEq.\ A = N_A \times ml_A$. In words, this equation states that the number of milliequivalents of any solute equals the normality of the solution multiplied by its volume expressed in milliliters. This expression is simply a mathematical definition of normality, which term has earlier been defined in words as the number of equivalents of solute per liter of solution, which is the same as to say the number of milliequivalents of solute per milliliter of solution.

(3) $mEq.\ A = \dfrac{mg.\ A}{eq.\ wt.}$. This equation may be stated in words, as: the number of milliequivalents of any substance equals the number of milligrams of that substance divided by its equivalent weight. This equation is essentially a definition of the term milliequivalents. The concept of equivalent weight in the various types of volumetric reactions was discussed on pp. 206–7.

Thus, there are three expressions involving milliequivalents. The first is an identity if only one substance is involved or is a mathematical definition of the stoichiometric end point if two or more substances are involved. The second is an expression in volume units, and the third is an expression in weight units. Note that the term *mEq.* refers to *number of milliequivalents*, which varies from one problem to another, while the term *eq. wt.* refers to the equivalent weight, which is determined solely by what the substance is and what reaction it undergoes. These equations readily form a basis for the solution of any stoichiometric problem in volumetric analysis. The examples which follow are taken from neutralization methods of analysis, but the very same methods are used in solving stoichiometric problems in other types of volumetric analysis. Other examples are to be given in subsequent chapters.

Example 1. What is the normality of a solution of hydrochloric acid acid of specific gravity 1.1878 (weight in grams per ml.) and containing about 37% HCl by weight?

$$mEq.\ HCl = mEq.\ HCl \text{ (because only one substance, HCl, is involved)}$$

$$\frac{mg.\ HCl}{eq.\ wt.} = N \times ml.$$

$$\frac{1000 \times 1.1878 \times 0.37}{36.47} = N \times 1.00 \text{ (assuming 1.00 ml. throughout, although any volume would do just as well)}$$

$$N = 12 \text{ (since the 37\% was only approximate, the answer must be considered approximate)}$$

Example 2. What is the normality of a solution of sodium hydroxide of which 25.00 ml. were required to titrate a 0.8300 gram portion of primary standard potassium acid phthalate ($KHC_8H_4O_4$)?

$$\text{mEq. NaOH} = \text{mEq. } KHC_8H_4O_4 \text{ (because NaOH reacts with } KHC_8H_4O_4)$$

$$N \times \text{ml.} = \frac{\text{mg. } KHC_8H_4O_4}{\text{eq. wt.}}$$

$$N \times 25.00 = \frac{830.0}{204.22}$$

$$N = 0.1626$$

Example 3. How many grams of sodium hydroxide should be weighed out to form with 500 ml. of water an approximately 0.5 N solution?

$$\text{mEq. NaOH weighed out} = \text{mEq. NaOH in the solution}$$

$$\frac{\text{mg. NaOH}}{\text{eq. wt.}} = N \times \text{ml.}$$

$$\frac{\text{mg. NaOH}}{40.00} = 0.5 \times 500$$

$$\text{mg. NaOH} = 10\ 000$$

$$\text{or grams NaOH} = 10. \text{ (the 0.5 N was approximate, so the answer is approximate)}$$

Example 4. How many ml. of 0.5000 N hydrochloric acid should be used, plus distilled water, to make a resulting solution of 500.0 ml. of 0.0100 N hydrochloric acid?

$$\text{mEq. HCl taken} = \text{mEq. HCl in final solution}$$

$$N \times \text{ml.} = N \times \text{ml.}$$

$$0.5000 \times \text{ml.} = 0.0100 \times 500.0$$

$$\text{ml.} = 10.00$$

Example 5. 24.00 ml. of 0.4965 N hydrochloric acid were required to react with 42.15 ml. of a sodium hydroxide solution. What is the normality of the latter?

$$\text{mEq. NaOH} = \text{mEq. HCl (because NaOH reacts with HCl)}$$

$$N \times \text{ml.} = N \times \text{ml.}$$

$$N \times 42.15 = 0.4965 \times 24.00$$

$$N = 0.2827$$

Example 6.   What is the percentage purity of a soda ash sample of which a 0.7942 gram portion required 25.26 ml. of 0.5132 N hydrochloric acid for titration?

$$\text{mEq. Na}_2\text{CO}_3 = \text{mEq. HCl (because Na}_2\text{CO}_3 \text{ reacts with HCl)}$$

$$\frac{\text{mg. Na}_2\text{CO}_3}{\text{eq. wt.}} = \text{N} \times \text{ml.}$$

$$\frac{\text{mg. Na}_2\text{CO}_3}{53.00} = 0.5132 \times 25.26 \quad \text{(note that the eq. wt. of Na}_2\text{CO}_3 \text{ is one-half of its molecular weight)}$$

$$\text{mg. Na}_2\text{CO}_3 = 0.5132 \times 25.26 \times 53.00$$

but $$\% \text{ Na}_2\text{CO}_3 = \frac{\text{mg. Na}_2\text{CO}_3}{\text{mg. sample}} \times 100$$

so $$\% \text{ Na}_2\text{CO}_3 = \frac{0.5132 \times 25.26 \times 53.00}{794.2} \times 100$$

$$\% \text{ Na}_2\text{CO}_3 = 86.51$$

Example 7.   What is the percentage of replaceable hydrogen ion in a 0.5069 gram sample of an organic acid to which is added 24.23 ml. of a 0.2965 N sodium hydroxide solution with 0.68 ml. of a 0.2648 N hydrochloric acid solution being required for back titration of the excess alkali?

$$\text{mEq. NaOH} = \text{mEq. H}^+ \text{ in sample} + \text{mEq. HCl (because both acids react with the base solution)}$$

$$\text{N} \times \text{ml.} = \frac{\text{mg. H}^+ \text{ in sample}}{\text{eq. wt.}} + \text{N} \times \text{ml.}$$

$$0.2965 \times 24.23 = \frac{\text{mg. H}^+ \text{ in sample}}{1.008} + 0.2648 \times 0.68$$

$$\text{mg. H}^+ \text{ in sample} = 1.008(0.2965 \times 24.23 - 0.2648 \times 0.68)$$

but $\% \text{ H}^+ \text{ in sample} = \dfrac{\text{mg. H}^+ \text{ in sample}}{\text{mg. sample}} \times 100$

so $\% \text{ H}^+ \text{ in sample} = 1.393$

REVIEW QUESTIONS

1. List the unit operations in a volumetric method of analysis.
2. Define or characterize the following terms:
   a. Titration
   b. Standard solution
   c. Primary standard
   d. Aliquot

    e. Indicator
    f. Molarity
    g. Normality
    h. Equivalent weight
    i. Titer

3. Give an example of the use of a piece of volumetric glassware calibrated to contain a specified volume and an example of the use of a piece calibrated to deliver a specified volume.

4. Contrast a usual buret and a weight buret in regard to construction, ease of use, expected accuracy and significance of drainage effects.

5. Describe and compare three methods of calibrating a volumetric flask.

6. Compare the usefulness of the titer and the normality methods of expressing the concentrations of solutions.

7. List four requirements that must be fulfilled by a substance to make it suitable for use as a primary standard.

8. Distinguish between stoichiometric point and experimental end point.

9. List four requirements which must be fulfilled by a chemical reaction to make it suitable as the basis of a method of volumetric analysis.

10. What apparatus is required for each of the following operations: preparation of a standard solution from a primary standard; calibration of a buret; titration by a back-titration method.

11. Contrast volumetric analysis and gravimetric analysis on several points.

PROBLEMS

1. In the calibration of a 25 ml. pipet, the contents of the pipet when filled to the mark at 25° C. were delivered to a weighing flask and were found to weigh 24.92 grams. What is the corrected volume of the pipet?

2. A buret is calibrated by the weight method at 28° C. If 10.00 ml. as indicated by the buret weighed 10.000 grams, what is the correction factor to be used at this approximate volume?

3. Calculate the weight in grams of solute needed to make 1.0000 liter of 0.1000 N solutions of each of the following: hydrochloric acid; sulfuric acid; sodium carbonate; acetic acid; potassium acid phthalate; potassium hydroxide; barium hydroxide; ammonium hydroxide.

4–7. How many grams of solute are in each of the following solutions?
    4. 1.0000 liter of hydrochloric acid, 0.5000 N
    5. 1.000 liter of sulfuric acid, 0.5000 N
    6. 100.00 ml. of hydrochloric acid, 0.4962 N
    7. 250.00 ml. of potassium acid phthalate, 0.1266 N

8–12. Calculate the normality of each of the following solutions:
    8. Acetic acid, density 1.058, 50.00% $HC_2H_3O_2$
    9. Sulfuric acid, density 1.4051, 51.00% H_2SO_4
    10. Hydrochloric acid, density 1.130, 26.02% HCl
    11. Ammonium hydroxide, density 0.950, 12.72% NH_3
    12. Potassium hydroxide, density 1.239, 25.00% KOH

13. How many ml. of perchloric acid, of density 1.207 and containing 30.00% $HClO_4$, are required for the preparation of 5.000 liters of 0.1000 N acid?

14. How many ml. of 0.0500 N hydrochloric acid are required to react with 40.00 ml. of 0.1500 N sodium hydroxide?

15. How many mg. of sodium hydroxide are required to react with 20.00 ml. of 0.1000 N hydrochloric acid?

16. How many grams of sodium carbonate will be neutralized by 30.00 ml. of 0.1000 N hydrochloric acid?

17. A 25.00 ml. portion of a 0.4962 N solution of hydrochloric acid was found to be equivalent to 36.22 ml. of a sodium hydroxide solution. Calculate the normality of the base solution.

18. A solution of sodium hydroxide is 0.1116 N. How much water should be added to 1.0000 liter of this solution to make the resulting solution 0.1000 N?

19. A sample of dry sodium carbonate weighing 5.0000 grams is dissolved and diluted to 1.0000 liter. In titration against hydrochloric acid, 44.66 ml. of acid are required to neutralize 42.35 ml. of the carbonate. What is the normality of the acid?

20. If 48.20 ml. of a hydrochloric acid solution yield 0.2795 gram of silver chloride, what is the normality of the acid?

21. How large a sample of primary standard sulfamic acid, HNH_2SO_3, should be used for a standardization titration of a sodium hydroxide solution known to be about 0.1 N, assuming that a buret volume of about 30 ml. is desirable?

22. A 0.2222 gram sample of primary standard sodium carbonate required 42.26 ml. of an acid solution for complete neutralization, and 19.62 ml. of the acid solution were equivalent to 22.66 ml. of a base solution. Calculate the normalities of the acid and the base solution.

(More stoichiometric problems involving neutralization reactions are given at the end of Chapter 10, and similar types of problems involving other types of reaction are at the ends of subsequent chapters.)

SUGGESTIONS FOR ADDITIONAL READING

Items 8, 10, 12, 26 and 30, Appendix 7.

Chapter 10

Neutralization Methods

A VOLUMETRIC neutralization method of analysis is one in which the titration is based chemically upon the reaction between an acid and a base. Topics considered in this chapter include the meanings of the terms "acid" and "base," the preparation of standard solutions for laboratory use, and several specific applications to quantitative determinations. In Chapter 11 the underlying theory is considered in more detail, particularly with respect to the equilibria which are involved in acid-base reactions.

DEFINITIONS OF ACID AND BASE

An acid may be defined as a substance which is able to lose a proton to another substance. Conversely, a base is defined as a substance capable of taking on a proton from another substance. The interrelationship may be indicated simply by the chemical equation

$$\text{acid} \rightleftharpoons \text{base} + \text{proton}$$

The acid is the "proton-donor," and the base is the "proton-acceptor."

A proton cannot exist in solution by itself, that is, independently of its surroundings. In any aqueous medium the hydrogen ions exist chiefly as hydronium ions, H_3O^+, rather than as free protons. Similarly, the hydrogen ions in a solution with some other solvent exist as solvated ions, for example as $H(\text{solv})^+$, in which (solv) represents a molecule of the solvent. Therefore, a complete acid-base reaction must include one process in which protons are released and another in which protons are gained, as

$$\text{acid 1} + \text{base 2} \rightleftharpoons \text{acid 2} + \text{base 1}$$

Typical acid-base reactions are represented by the following equations:

	acid 1 + base 2	$\rightleftharpoons$	acid 2 + base 1
(a)	$HCl + H_2O$	$\rightleftharpoons$	$H_3O^+ + Cl^-$
(b)	$H_2O + NH_3$	$\rightleftharpoons$	$NH_4^+ + OH^-$
(c)	$HCl + NH_3$	$\rightleftharpoons$	$NH_4^+ + Cl^-$
(d)	$H_3O^+ + OH^-$	$\rightleftharpoons$	$H_2O + H_2O$
(e)	$H_3O^+ + CO_3^=$	$\rightleftharpoons$	$HCO_3^- + H_2O$

Each of these reactions proceeds quantitatively to the right only if the ease of transferring a proton from acid 1 to base 2 is much greater than is the tendency to transfer a proton from acid 2 to base 1. Consider, for example, the titration of sodium hydroxide by hydrochloric acid, both in aqueous solution, as represented by equation (d). This reaction goes quantitatively to the right because hydroxyl ions (base 2) have a much greater affinity for protons than do water molecules (base 1). Similarly, the reaction of equation (e) goes far to the right because the carbonate ion has a greater attraction for protons than do water molecules. These factors will be considered quantitatively in numerical problems in Chapter 11.

Strengths of Acids and Bases.   A strong acid or base solution is one in which the solute is highly ionized and, conversely, a weak one is only slightly ionized. For example, hydrochloric acid in water is a strong acid because the reaction of equation (a) in the preceding list goes far to the right, and an aqueous solution of ammonia is a weak base because the reaction of equation (b) does not go far to the right.

The role of the solvent is very important in determining the strength of an acid or base. For example, hydrochloric acid is a weaker acid in methyl alcohol than it is in water because methyl alcohol molecules do not take on protons so readily as do water molecules. This means that with methyl alcohol molecules substituted for water molecules in equation (a) the reaction would not proceed so far to the right.

The strength of an acid or base solution must not be confused with its concentration. A concentrated solution is one containing a relatively large amount of solute per unit volume, regardless of whether that solute is highly ionized or not. For example, a 10 M solution is concentrated, whether it be of a strong acid or base or a weak one, while a 0.001 M solution is considered dilute. There is no sharp dividing line between concentrated and dilute. Thus the term "concentration of a solution" refers to how much solute is present per volume, while the term "strength" refers to whether that solute is highly ionized or not.

Electron-Pair Concept of Acids and Bases.   The proton concept of acid-base reactions has been expanded somewhat by Lewis and others to include some reactions in which protons are not involved. The basis of the Lewis concept lies in the grouping of electrons in the outer shells of atoms. An acid is a substance that can accept an electron pair from a base in the formation of a covalent bond, while a base is a substance that can donate a pair of electrons to an acid to form a covalent bond. An acid is thus a substance that has an incomplete outer electron shell so it can accept an electron pair from another substance, called a base, to complete that shell. Acids and bases in the proton concept are acids and bases in the Lewis concept as well. For example, the hydroxyl ion is donating a pair of electrons to a hydronium ion to form a covalent bond when it receives a proton from that hydronium ion. However, there are substances which contain no elemental hydrogen which do fit into the Lewis concept of acids but not into the proton concept.

Most of the acids which are encountered in quantitative inorganic analysis are included in both systems of definition. The more general Lewis concept is particularly useful in dealing with certain organic substances and with nonaqueous media.

The Proton in Chemical Equations. We have seen that the hydrogen ion exists in solution not as a free proton but rather in combination with one or more molecules of the solvent. Nevertheless, it is customary to designate the hydrogen ion simply as H^+ in chemical equations involving aqueous systems. The designation H_3O^+ is descriptively more correct, but even it is not perfectly correct because of the existence of some protons in a more highly hydrated state. Furthermore, other ions in aqueous solution are probably somewhat hydrated also, at least to the extent of being influenced by their environment. No simplified terminology which is usable in the writing of chemical equations can be literally accurate and complete in designating the exact form in which each substance exists. Stoichiometric relationships derived from chemical equations are valid when the hydrogen ion is written as H^+. Mathematical equations representing equilibrium systems are also equally valid when using either H^+ or H_3O^+ for the hydrogen ion as long as the water molecule concentration is taken as unity, as is invariably done in dealing with aqueous solutions.

Throughout this book the solvent is assumed to be water unless otherwise stated, and the hydrogen ion will be written in chemical equations simply as H^+.

INDICATORS FOR NEUTRALIZATION REACTIONS

In the titration of an acid by a base the solution contains unreacted acid prior to the equivalence point and unreacted base after the equivalence point, so the pH of the solution changes at the equivalence point. The indicator must be an agent which reveals to the analyst the point in the titration at which this change takes place. The indicator substance is an organic dye which is itself a weak acid or base. The state of the indicator in solution may be represented by the equation

$$\underset{\text{(color A)}}{In_A} \rightleftharpoons H^+ + \underset{\text{(color B)}}{In_B}$$

in which In_A and In_B represent the acidic and basic forms of the indicator. Each of these forms may be either an ion or an undissociated molecule, but the two are related as shown by the chemical equation. It is essential that color A and color B differ from each other in each case; one may be colorless or both may be of distinct colors. In accordance with a qualitative application of the law of mass action, the point of equilibrium is pushed to the left by excess hydrogen ions and pulled to the right in an alkaline medium (deficiency of hydrogen ions), so the indicator is predominantly of color A in acid solution and of color B in basic solution. The end point in a titration is thus marked by a change from one color to the other.

The indicator color change does not take place instantaneously but rather occurs gradually over a pH range of one or two units. An indicator must be selected for each specific titration such that the range of color change is not too broad and such that the change occurs over the proper portion of the pH scale. These factors are discussed in relation to quantitative mass law and equilibrium considerations in the next chapter.

SELECTIONS OF ACIDS AND BASES FOR STANDARD REAGENTS

Neutralization analyses can involve unknown acids and/or bases, so it is necessary for the general analytical laboratory to have available a standard solution of a base for titration of unknown acids and one of an acid for titration of unknown bases. Not all acids and bases are equally suitable for general usage in this way, so it is necessary to consider which acid and which base would be preferable as the standard reagents.

A weak acid is not suitable as a general purpose standard acid because weak acids do not give good end points in many titrations (discussed in detail in next chapter). Of the more common acids, only hydrochloric acid, nitric acid, perchloric acid and sulfuric acid are highly ionized. Sulfuric acid is chosen occasionally but is not suitable for titrations in solutions containing some cation that forms an insoluble sulfate. Sulfuric acid is also of questionable value here because the second step of its ionization is not complete; that is, sulfuric acid is not completely a strong acid, even though it is much stronger than acetic acid, for example. Nitric acid is seldom used because its solutions tend to be unstable to heat and light, although this objection is not prohibitively serious for dilute solutions. Nitric acid also suffers the disadvantage of entering into oxidation-reduction reactions with some substances in addition to its reactions as an acid. Perchloric acid also enters into some reactions other than those of neutralization. Hydrochloric acid solutions have a tendency toward volatility, yet this factor is of negligible significance with dilute solutions at ordinary room temperatures. Considering all factors, hydrochloric acid is most frequently preferable as the general purpose standard acid reagent.

Standard base solutions for general applicability are usually of sodium hydroxide. Weak bases are generally unsatisfactory, again because sharp end points are not obtained in many titrations. Only very few hydroxides are sufficiently soluble for solutions of adequate concentration to be prepared. From the chemical standpoint, potassium hydroxide is as good as sodium hydroxide. However, the former is more expensive so sodium hydroxide is usually chosen.

PREPARATION OF STANDARD ACID AND BASE SOLUTIONS

Neither hydrochloric acid nor sodium hydroxide, the two substances selected as general purpose standard reagents, is a primary standard. Since pure hydrogen chloride is a gas under ordinary conditions of temperature and pressure, it cannot readily be weighed out. The stock solution of hydrochloric acid which is available in laboratories is about 12 N, but its concentration is not accurately known nor sufficiently constant from one batch to another to permit its use directly as a standard solution. Therefore, a solution of hydrochloric acid must be prepared of approximately the desired concentration and then it must be standardized.

Solid sodium hydroxide is not available in a pure form. Commercially available material is always contaminated by moisture and also by sodium carbonate, at least in trace amounts. Sodium chloride may also be present in small amounts as an impurity. Therefore, a solution of sodium hydroxide must be prepared of approximately the desired concentration and then must be standardized. Furthermore, dissolved carbon dioxide can cause interference in titrations of sodium hydroxide against weak acids since the dissolved carbon dioxide acts as an acid, carbonic acid, to the indicators which must be used in such titrations. For such purposes carbonate must be removed from the solution prior to standardization, and the solution must subsequently be stored away from atmospheric carbon dioxide. The initial removal may be accomplished, for example, by precipitation as barium carbonate. A suitable apparatus for storing and using the solution away from the atmospheric gases is shown in Figure 30. The presence of moderate amounts of dissolved carbon dioxide in the sodium hydroxide solution is not harmful if the solution is to be used for the titration of strong acids, with an indicator such as methyl orange or methyl purple or if extremely high accuracy is not required. In such instances the solution may be stored in a stoppered bottle and poured into the buret as needed. Only rubber stoppers should be used in alkali storage bottles because the alkali tends to cement glass stoppers in place.

After the acid and base solutions have been prepared, it is necessary to standardize them. It is not necessary to use primary standards for both. A volume ratio between the two may be determined, and then only one or the other need be standardized against a primary standard. The determination of this volume ratio serves as a convenient first titration for student work because it is possible for the student to titrate back and forth over the end point to familiarize himself with volumetric techniques and the detection of end points.

Primary Standard Bases. Any one of several primary standard bases may be used for the standardization of the hydrochloric acid solution. Sodium carbonate is frequently chosen. Assuming that methyl orange or methyl purple is the indicator, sodium carbonate reacts stoichiometrically with hydrochloric acid according to the equation

$$2 H^+ + CO_3^= \longrightarrow H_2CO_3$$

Reagent grade sodium carbonate is commercially available for primary standard use. Preferably it should be obtained in small bottles and insofar as practical should not be exposed to the atmosphere. The titration reaction is driven farther to completion, and thereby the end point becomes sharper, if most of the carbonic acid which is formed is removed from the reaction medium. This can be accomplished readily by boiling the solution to decompose the carbonic acid, by evolution of carbon dioxide, just before completing the titration.

The organic base tris(hydroxymethyl)aminomethane is an excellent primary standard. It reacts with hydrochloric acid much as does ammonia, according to the equation

$$H^+ + (CH_2OH)_3CNH_2 \longrightarrow (CH_2OH)_3CNH_3^+$$

This substance is also available in reagent grade purity and presents no particular problems with regard to drying or weighing. The same indicators which are used with sodium carbonate may be used with tris(hydroxymethyl)-aminomethane. There is, of course, no need to boil to remove carbon dioxide near the end point in this titration unless the solvent itself contains considerable dissolved carbon dioxide.

Other primary standards occasionally used for the standardization of hydrochloric acid solutions include calcium carbonate in the form of clear calcite crystals and borax ($Na_2B_4O_7 \cdot 10\ H_2O$). Alternatively, a hydrochloric acid solution may be standardized gravimetrically by precipitating and weighing the anion as silver chloride, although it is generally preferable to standardize an acid directly on the basis of its acidity.

One final method of standardizing the hydrochloric acid solution involves its preparation from constant-boiling hydrochloric acid. When a solution of this acid is boiled, hydrogen chloride and water molecules are distilled away in such a ratio that eventually the remaining solution approaches a definite, known composition. Thereafter the two kinds of molecule will distill off in that particular ratio to each other. The concentration of this constant-boiling solution is greater than that required in most analytical work, but quantitative dilution with distilled water suffices to bring it to a suitable concentration. This procedure is relatively inconvenient, but excellent results can be obtained. Similarly, a standard solution of sulfuric acid can be prepared from constant-boiling sulfuric acid.

Primary Standard Acids. There are several primary standard acids, any one of which may be used to standardize a solution of sodium hydroxide.

Potassium acid phthalate ($KHC_8H_4O_4$) has the advantages of high equivalent weight, stability on drying and ready availability, while it has the disadvantage of being a weak acid so that it is generally suitable for standardization of carbonate-free base solutions only. Sulfamic acid (HNH_2SO_3) is a very good primary standard, being readily available in a pure condition, rather inexpensive and a strong acid. Oxalic acid ($H_2C_2O_4 \cdot 2\,H_2O$) and benzoic acid ($HC_7H_5O_2$) are also occasionally used as primary standard acids, but they are generally less satisfactory than are potassium acid phthalate and sulfamic acid.

It must be emphasized that it is not necessary to standardize both the hydrochloric acid and sodium hydroxide solutions against primary standards. The concentration of either one may be calculated from the volume ratio once the concentration of the other one is known. Therefore, only the hydrochloric acid solution *or* the sodium hydroxide solution, not both, need be standardized against a primary standard.

Laboratory Experiment 10

PREPARATION AND STANDARDIZATION OF APPROXIMATELY 0.2 N SOLUTIONS OF HYDROCHLORIC ACID AND OF SODIUM HYDROXIDE

Reagents

Hydrochloric acid, approximately 0.2 N solution, prepared by diluting 32 ml. stock solution to 2 liters with water

Methyl purple indicator, stock solution

Phenolphthalein indicator, solution containing 0.5 gram phenolphthalein in 100 ml. 95% ethyl alcohol

Sodium carbonate, analytical reagent grade

Sodium hydroxide, approximately 0.2 N solution, prepared by dissolving 16 grams NaOH in water and diluting to 2 liters; store in rubber-stoppered bottle. Note: If carbonate-free solution is desired, stop diluting at half the final volume, add slowly 20 ml. warm 0.25 M barium chloride solution, let stand until supernatant liquid is clear, decant, dilute to final volume, let stand again, and siphon the clear liquid into a storage apparatus similar to Figure 30.

Sulfamic acid, analytical reagent grade

Tris(hydroxymethyl)aminomethane, analytical reagent grade

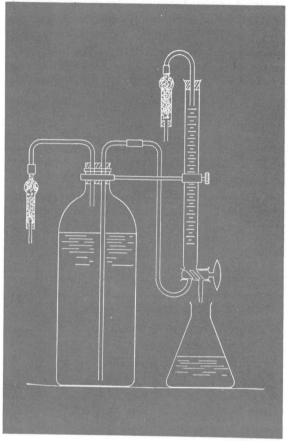

FIGURE 30. Storage bottle and buret assembly for volumetric reagent solutions which must be protected from the atmosphere.

Volume Ratio of Acid to Base. Clean and thoroughly rinse with water two 50 ml. burets. (Do not permit sodium hydroxide to stand in a buret with a glass stopcock any longer than absolutely necessary to perform the titrations.) Rinse each buret with one 10 ml. portion and then two 5 ml. portions of the solution to be used in each, draining the rinse liquids through the tips. Fill each buret so the meniscus is near, but not quite at, the top of the graduation marks. Check the tips to insure freedom from air bubbles. Record the reading of each buret to the nearest hundredth ml. Run about 20 ml. of the acid solution into a 500 ml. Erlenmeyer flask, and add about 60 ml. water from the wash bottle and two drops of methyl purple indicator solution. Run in alkali from the other buret, using the left hand to manipulate the stopcock on the buret (the stopcock should be on the right as illustrated in Figure 28 so that the fingers reach around the buret to manipulate the stopcock) and the right hand to swirl the flask, until the color of the solution changes from its acid to its basic color (purple to green). An intermediate gray coloration is seen during the transition. Wash down the inside of the flask with a little water from a wash bottle, replace the flask under the first buret, and add acid dropwise until the solution turns to its acid color again. In this way, adjust the contents of the titration flask carefully until a drop of either acid or base will cause a definite color change. Select the point at which the first tinge of acid color appears as the end point. Allow at least thirty seconds after concluding the titration for drainage of the glass walls within the burets and then record the buret readings. The quantity of each solution used is merely the difference between initial and final buret readings. Calculate the volume ratio of acid to base by dividing the volume of acid used by the volume of base used. Refill the burets and repeat the titration. Replicate results should agree within two or three parts per thousand.

Standardization of Hydrochloric Acid Solution with Sodium Carbonate. (Only one of the three standardization sections of this experiment need be performed.) Place an unstoppered sample tube containing the Na_2CO_3 in a small beaker and dry in an oven at 110° C. for two hours. Cool, accurately weigh three portions of 0.25 to 0.3 gram each into 500 ml. Erlenmeyer flasks, and carry each through the remainder of the procedure. Add 80 ml. water and 2 drops methyl purple indicator solution. Shake by hand until the salt has dissolved. Fill both burets (HCl and NaOH) and record the readings. Introduce acid from the HCl buret, with shaking of the flask, until the solution just turns purple. At this first color change, heat the titration solution to a gentle boil, to expel carbon dioxide, by rotating the flask over a low Bunsen flame. (A folded piece of paper placed around the neck of the flask serves as a convenient handle.) Cool the flask under running water to room temperature. The indicator will have changed back to its original color if the end point was not overshot. Wash down the inside walls of the flask with a stream of water from the wash bottle. Continue the titration by adding acid from the buret. If too much acid is added, back-titrate the excess with the base solution, but select as the end point the point at which the first acid color appears. Wait about thirty seconds after reaching the final end point for drainage from the inner walls of the burets and record the buret readings. From the titration data, and the acid to base ratio if any sodium hydroxide solution was used, calculate the normality of the acid solution. Replicate results should agree within 2 or 3 parts per thousand. (Instead of weighing out individual portions of the Na_2CO_3, a single sample of about 1.5 grams may be weighed accurately, dissolved, diluted to the mark in a 250 ml. volumetric flask, and 50 ml. aliquots titrated.)

Standardization of Hydrochloric Acid Solution with Tris-(hydroxymethyl)aminomethane. Follow the procedure of the preceding section of this experiment, substituting 0.5 to 0.7 gram portions of tris(hydroxymethyl)aminomethane for the 0.25 to 0.3 gram portions of sodium carbonate, and omitting the boiling and recooling steps near the end point.

Standardization of Sodium Hydroxide Solution with Sulfamic Acid. Accurately weigh three samples of about 0.5 gram each of primary standard sulfamic acid into 300 ml. Erlenmeyer flasks. Add about 150 ml. water to each, shake until the acid dissolves, and add 3 or 4 drops of phenolphthalein indicator solution. Titrate with the sodium hydroxide solution. If necessary, back-titrate any excess of sodium hydroxide solution with the hydrochloric acid solution. Calculate the normality of the sodium hydroxide solution. Replicate results should agree within two or three parts per thousand.

Suggestions for Supplementary Laboratory Work. Study the significance of the proper choice of indicator by using each of the four indicators, phenolphthalein, bromthymol blue, methyl purple and methyl orange, for each of the following titrations: hydrochloric acid vs. sodium hydroxide; hydrochloric acid vs. sodium carbonate; acetic acid (prepared by diluting about 1.2 ml. stock solution with 200 ml. water) vs. sodium hydroxide; hydrochloric acid vs. ammonium hydroxide (prepared by diluting about 1.5 ml. stock solution with 200 ml. water). Run duplicate titrations of each. After your class study of Chapter 11, discuss the significance of your observations.

SELECTED DETERMINATIONS

Determination of Acetic Acid in Vinegar. Vinegar consists predominantly of a dilute solution of acetic acid in water. The chief source of error in the determination of concentration of acetic acid in vinegar is the frequent difficulty in observing the indicator end point in the presence of traces of organic materials which impart the natural color to vinegar. If this interference is prohibitive, the color indicator may be replaced by the potentiometric type of indicator as described in Chapter 20.

Laboratory Experiment 11

DETERMINATION OF ACETIC ACID IN VINEGAR

Reagents

Hydrochloric acid, the solution prepared and standardized as in Experiment 10

Phenolphthalein indicator, solution containing 0.5 gram phenolphthalein in 100 ml. 95% ethyl alcohol

Sodium hydroxide, the solution prepared and standardized as in Experiment 10

Procedure

Weigh a glass-stoppered weighing bottle. Insert about 5 ml. of the vinegar sample and reweigh the bottle. (Both weighings need be accurate only to the nearest milligram because of the large sample weight involved.) Transfer the sample completely to a 300 ml. Erlenmeyer flask and dilute with 80 ml. of previously boiled, distilled water. Add three drops of phenolphthalein solution. Run in standard alkali from a buret until a pink color just persists. If too much base is added, add standard acid dropwise from a second buret until the color disappears, then add more base from the first buret until the indicator color just returns again. Repeat the titration with three separately weighed portions of the vinegar. Calculate the weight percentage $HC_2H_3O_2$ in the sample. Replicate results should agree within about two parts per thousand.

Determination of Available Hydrogen in an Organic Acid. The determination of the percentage of available, or replaceable, hydrogen ion in a solid impure organic acid or acid salt is a very useful type of analysis. If the unknown is a weak acid, it is well to use carbonate-free standard base solution for the titration. Alternatively, the solution being titrated could be boiled at the time the equivalence point is reached so as to remove carbonate at that time as carbon dioxide gas. If much carbonate is present the results tend to be high because the carbon dioxide is an acid to the indicator which must be used in a weak acid vs. strong base titration and will, therefore, use up some of the standard base solution. Some organic acids are somewhat volatile at the customary drying temperature of 110° C., so the instructor must be consulted to ascertain whether or not to dry the unknown sample prior to use.

Laboratory Experiment 12

DETERMINATION OF AVAILABLE HYDROGEN IN AN ORGANIC ACID

Reagents

Hydrochloric acid, the solution prepared and standardized in Experiment 10

Phenolphthalein indicator, solution containing 0.5 gram phenolphthalein in 100 ml. 95% ethyl alcohol

Sodium hydroxide, the solution prepared and standardized in Experiment 10

Procedure

Conduct the determination in triplicate. Accurately weigh samples of 1.0 to 1.4 gram each into 300 ml. Erlenmeyer flasks. Dissolve in 80 ml. water. Add three drops phenolphthalein indicator solution. While swirling the flask, add standard base solution from a buret until a pink color persists. Wash down the inner walls of the flask with a stream of water from a wash bottle. If the pink color vanishes, add more standard base solution. Stop the titration when a pink coloration persists for at least a minute. (If much carbonate is expected—see your instructor—heat gently to boiling and then cool just prior to completing the titration.) The standard acid solution may be used for back-titration if necessary. Calculate the percentage of replaceable hydrogen ion in the sample.

Determination of the Alkaline Value of Soda Ash. Soda ash is impure sodium carbonate. The determination of the alkaline value, that is, of the purity of soda ash is very similar to the standardization of hydrochloric acid with pure sodium carbonate.

Laboratory Experiment 13

DETERMINATION OF THE ALKALINE VALUE OF SODA ASH | |

Reagents

Hydrochloric acid, the solution prepared and standardized in Experiment 10
Methyl purple indicator, stock solution
Sodium hydroxide, the solution prepared and standardized in Experiment 10

Procedure

Conduct the determination in triplicate. Dry the sample at 110° C. for two hours. Accurately weigh samples of about 0.3 to 0.4 gram each into 300 ml. Erlenmeyer flasks. Dissolve in 80 ml. water. Add two drops methyl purple indicator solution. Run in standard acid from a buret until the solution just turns purple. At this first color change, heat the solution to a gentle boil, to expel carbon dioxide, by rotating the flask over a low Bunsen flame. (A folded piece of paper placed around the neck of the flask serves as a convenient handle.) Cool the flask under running water to room temperature. The indicator will have changed back to its original color if the end point was not overshot. Wash down the inside walls of the flask with a stream of water from the wash bottle. Continue the titration by adding acid from the buret. If the end point is over-stepped, back-titrate the excess with the standard alkali solution, but end the titration just on the acid side of the indicator change. Calculate the percentage Na_2CO_3 in the sample.

Kjeldahl Method for Determination of Nitrogen in Organic Materials. Nitrogen in organic compounds may be determined by the Kjeldahl method in which the nitrogen is converted into an ammonium salt, from thence to ammonium hydroxide and, finally, measured by usual volumetric neutralization procedures. The determination is carried out in three steps: digestion, distillation, titration.

1. Digestion. The digestion step serves to decompose the organic material. The decomposition is brought about by heating the sample with concentrated sulfuric acid. The products of the decomposition are, for the most part, gases such as the carbon oxides, sulfur oxides and water vapor. Under suitable conditions all the nitrogen in the organic material is converted to ammonia, which immediately comes into solution in the sulfuric acid as the salt, ammonium sulfate. Many organic substances are only difficultly decomposed, so two additional reagents are often used along with sulfuric acid in the digestion. One is a catalyst, such as selenium, which hastens the decomposition. The other is either potassium sulfate or sodium sulfate, which serves to raise the boiling point of the sulfuric acid. The decomposition is normally accelerated at higher temperatures, and the maximum temperature attainable is set by the boiling point of the digestion medium. There is no appreciable oxidation or reduction occurring in the digestion as herein described. If the nitrogen in the organic specimen happens to be, for example, in an oxidation state greater than it is in ammonia, a preliminary reduction process is required. At the conclusion of the digestion step, all the nitrogen should be present in the digestion container in the form of ammonium ions in a solution very concentrated in sulfuric acid.

2. Distillation. The distillation serves to remove the ammonium ions from the digestion flask by converting them to volatile ammonia gas and collecting that ammonia gas in a separate solution for subsequent measurement. The ammonium ions are initially held in the digestion flask by the acid present, so they may be removed by neutralizing the acid with sodium hydroxide. The solution is very concentrated in sulfuric acid so a considerable amount of sodium hydroxide is required. (Special caution is needed in adding an aqueous solution to sulfuric acid.) As soon as an excess of hydroxyl ion is present, the ammonia will be in the form of ammonium hydroxide, from which ammonia gas is readily liberated by heat. The evolved ammonia gas may be collected by bubbling it into a receiver flask containing a quantity of hydrochloric acid which is known quantitatively and which is certain to be more than enough to neutralize the ammonia arriving during the distillation.

3. Titration. The titration step consists of titrating the hydrochloric acid left over in the receiver flask with a standard solution of sodium hydroxide. Since all the nitrogen is converted into ammonia which reacts with standard hydrochloric acid, the weight of nitrogen in the sample may be calculated from the titration data as follows:

$$\text{mEq. N in sample} = \text{total mEq. acid used} - \text{mEq. acid in excess}$$

or

$$\frac{\text{mg. N in sample}}{14.00} = \underset{\substack{\text{(of std. acid} \\ \text{at start)}}}{N \times \text{ml.}} - \underset{\substack{\text{(of std. base used} \\ \text{in titration)}}}{N \times \text{ml.}}$$

The percentage of nitrogen is found, of course, by dividing the weight of N as found from this equation by the sample weight and multiplying by 100.

There are numerous modifications which have been proposed for this procedure. The catalyst and the conditions of the digestion may be varied. Other titration procedures have been developed. The procedure is widely used for determining the protein content of materials. Although proteins are complex and somewhat varied in composition, they generally contain about 16% nitrogen. Therefore, the percentage protein in the presence of other substances which are nonnitrogenous may be calculated from the results of a Kjeldahl determination by multiplying the observed % N by 1/0.16. This factor, 1/0.16 or 6.25, is accordingly called the *"protein factor."*

Laboratory Experiment 14

DETERMINATION OF NITROGEN BY THE KJELDAHL METHOD

Reagents

Hydrochloric acid, approximately 0.1 N standard solution, prepared from the solution prepared and standardized in Experiment 10 by a 1:1 dilution
Methyl purple indicator, stock solution
Potassium sulfate
Selenium
Sodium hydroxide, approximately 0.1 N standard solution, prepared by a 1:1 quantitative dilution of the solution prepared and standardized in Experiment 10.
Sodium hydroxide, solution approximately 10 M, prepared by dissolving 40 grams NaOH in 100 ml. for each sample
Sulfuric acid, stock solution

Procedure

Conduct the determination in triplicate. Accurately weigh samples of about 0.7 gram each into 500 ml. Kjeldahl flasks. Add 0.1 gram selenium and 10 grams potassium sulfate. Pour in 25 ml. sulfuric acid. Place the flask in a digestion rack, if available, or place it in a hood in an inclined (about 45°) position. Boil gently until the liquid appears clear and no undissolved particles remain; this may require from thirty minutes to a couple of hours, depending upon the particular sample. If foaming is excessive, place a small piece of paraffin in the flask. When the digestion is complete, allow the flask to cool, shaking occasionally. Then, while keeping the flask cool under running water, cautiously and slowly add 100 ml. water and the 100 ml. portion of the sodium hydroxide solution. Set the flask up with a Kjeldahl trap and a water-cooled condenser. Prepare now (or before) a receiver flask with a 50.00 ml. aliquot of the standard acid solution and add two drops methyl purple indicator solution. The end of the condenser must be fitted with an adapter that reaches below the surface of the standard acid in the receiver flask. With the distillation set-up complete, heat the solution in the Kjeldahl flask to boiling (steam distillation may be employed if it is available), and distil over about half of its contents. Disconnect the Kjeldahl flask, then remove the source of heat. Rinse the condenser with distilled water, letting the rinsings run into the receiver flask. Disconnect the receiver flask. Titrate the excess acid in the receiver flask with the standard sodium hydroxide solution. Calculate the percentage N in the sample.

Determination of Total Salt Concentration by Ion Exchange and Acid-Base Titration. The technique of ion exchange was introduced in Chapter 6 as a useful method of accomplishing a separation prior to a measurement by gravimetric or other means. The same technique can be used in conjunction with an acid-base titration to determine the total salt content of a solution. The test solution is passed through a cation exchange column, in which the cations are replaced by hydrogen ions, as described in Chapter 6:

$$E \cdot H + Na^+ \longrightarrow E \cdot Na + H^+$$

and the resultant solution is titrated by a standard solution of sodium hydroxide.

The resin column may be formed in a buret or in a reductor column like the one shown in Figure 47, p. 349. The resin must first be soaked in acid to insure that essentially all of its exchange sites are initially occupied by hydrogens. The resin expands somewhat when wet, so it must be kept covered with water from the time prior to preparation of the column until after the column is finally disassembled. The rate of flow of the test solution through the column must be slow enough to permit intimate contact between the solution and the resin. The effectiveness of the resin gradually decreases from its maximum effectiveness to zero as its exchange sites are used up. Whether or not the effectiveness has been sufficient can be ascertained by a qualitative spot test for a major salt constituent of the test solution on a drop or two of the liquid emerging from the column. If the test solution contains colored ions, the color of the effluent generally reveals whether exchange has been adequate. The resin can be regenerated simply by passing acid through the column.

The initial unknown solution must be neutral. Any acid initially present would be titrated along with the desired hydrogen ions and make the results for total salt content too high. Any basic substances would react with some of the desired hydrogen ions prior to the titration, rendering the results low. This determination does not distinguish between two or more kinds of cations, so the results are expressed in terms of milliequivalents rather than in weight units.

Laboratory Experiment 15

DETERMINATION OF TOTAL SALT CONCENTRATION BY ION EXCHANGE AND ACID-BASE TITRATION

Reagents

Cation exchange resin, Amberlite IR-120
Hydrochloric acid, approximately 1.5 N solution, prepared by diluting 25 ml. stock solution with 200 ml. water
pH paper, "universal" type
Phenolphthalein indicator, solution containing 0.5 gram phenolphthalein in 100 ml. 95% ethyl alcohol
Sodium hydroxide, 0.1 N standard solution, prepared by 1:1 quantitative dilution of the solution prepared in Experiment 10

Procedure

Obtain the sample in a 100 ml. volumetric flask and analyze in 25 ml. aliquot portions. Add about 10 grams of the resin to 200 ml. of the 1.5 N hydrochloric acid in a beaker. Let stand with occasional stirring for 15 minutes. Decant the acid. Wash by decantation several times with water, leaving the resin covered with water. Set up a 50 ml. buret and insert about 5 ml. water. Insert a small plug of glass wool, using a glass rod to push it down against the stopcock. Transfer the resin-suspension to the buret. Maintain the liquid level at least 1 cm. above the resin at all times, and always add water or other liquids gently so as not to stir the resin. Pass water through the column until drops of the effluent and of the initial water are of the same pH as indicated on the pH paper, leaving the liquid level 1 cm. above the resin. Place a 250 ml. Erlenmeyer flask below the column. Insert by pipet a 25 ml. aliquot of the unknown to the column above the resin. Open the stopcock to permit a flow rate of 1 to 2 ml. per minute. When the liquid level is again 1 cm. above the resin, add 25 ml. water and pass it at a slightly higher flow rate. Continue washing with water until a drop of effluent again shows the same pH as the initial water; collect all washings in the Erlenmeyer flask. Add 3 drops phenolphthalein indicator solution to the flask. Titrate with the standard sodium hydroxide solution. Calculate the number of mEq. of salt per ml. of the unknown sample. Replicate results should agree within a few parts per thousand. The resin should be returned to the container provided for it.

REVIEW QUESTIONS

1. Define and characterize the following terms: acid, base, neutralization, hydronium ion.
2. Compare the "proton" and the "electron-pair" concepts of acids and bases, noting clearly both the similarities and the differences.
3. Distinguish between concentrated and strong solutions of chemical reagents.
4. Using the symbol HIn, In–, InOH or In–, indicate (a) the substance imparting color to an acid solution of an indicator which is itself a weak acid, and (b) the acid color form of an indicator that is a weak base.
5. Why is nitric acid not more commonly used as a standard volumetric acid? Why is acetic acid not suitable for this purpose?
6. Why are potassium hydroxide and ammonium hydroxide not more commonly used as standard volumetric bases?
7. List five primary standards suitable for acid and/or base solutions, and indicate whether each is to be used directly for standardizing an acid or a base solution.
8. A student used sodium hydroxide as a primary standard to standardize a solution of hydrochloric acid. Was his reported normality high, low or correct?
9. A standardized solution of sodium hydroxide was permitted to absorb large amounts of carbon dioxide after standardization. Did this make the numerical value of the original normality high, low or correct?
10. In a standardization of hydrochloric acid with sodium carbonate, a student failed to dry the sodium carbonate completely. Did this cause his reported normality to be too high, too low or correct?
11. If in a determination of available hydrogen ion there is an air bubble in the tip of the hydrochloric acid buret (used for back-titration) when the initial reading is taken, and if that air bubble disappears before making the final reading, will the results be high, low or correct, assuming that no other error arises?
12. Why is the solution boiled when determining the end point in an unknown weak acid determination?
13. What is the purpose of each of the following in a Kjeldahl nitrogen determination: selenium; potassium sulfate or sodium sulfate; standard solution of hydrochloric acid?
14. Write a balanced chemical equation for the main titration reaction in a determination of the alkaline value of soda ash.
15. Write balanced equations for all steps in a Kjeldahl nitrogen determination, excluding the initial digestion reaction.

PROBLEMS

1. A 2.5000 gram crystal of calcite, $CaCO_3$, was dissolved in excess hydrochloric acid, the carbon dioxide boiled out and the excess acid titrated with a basic solution. The volume of acid was 45.56 ml., the volume of base used was 2.25 ml. In a separate titration, 43.33 ml. of the base solution neutralized 46.46 ml. of acid. Calculate the normality of the acid and of the base.
2. If constant-boiling hydrochloric acid, at 745 mm. Hg pressure, contains 20.257% HCl, what weight of acid solution must be distilled at this pressure to prepare 1.0000 liter of 1.000 N acid?
3. If a 4.000 gram sample of potassium acid phthalate reacts with 48.37 ml. of a sodium hydroxide solution, what is the normality of the latter?
4. A solution of hydrochloric acid is standardized gravimetrically, with 25.00 ml. of the acid solution yielding 0.4055 gram of silver chloride. What is the normality of the acid?
5. If 50.00 ml. of a sulfuric acid solution yields 0.5111 gram of barium sulfate, to what volume must a liter of the acid solution be diluted to yield a solution which is 0.0500 N?
6. A 1.0000 gram sample of oxalic acid, $H_2C_2O_4 \cdot 2 H_2O$, required 46.00 ml. of a sodium hydroxide solution for titration. What is the normality of the hydroxide solution?
7. A 0.6300 gram sample of a pure organic dibasic acid was titrated with 38.00 ml. of 0.3030 N sodium hydroxide solution, but 4.00 ml. of a 0.2250 N acid solution were needed for back-titration, at which point the original acid was completely neutralized. Calculate the molecular weight of the organic acid.
8. A sample of vinegar weighing 11.400 grams was titrated with 0.5000 N base, 18.24 ml. being required. Calculate the percentage acetic acid in the sample.
9. A 15.64 ml. sample of vinegar of density 1.060 requires 24.84 ml. of a 0.4686 N base solution for titration. Calculate the weight percentage acetic acid in the sample.
10. An impure oxalic acid sample weighing 0.7500 gram is titrated with 21.37 ml. of 0.5066 N base solution. What is the percentage oxalic acid, $H_2C_2O_4 \cdot 2 H_2O$, in the sample?
11. Exactly 2.50 ml. of a sodium hydroxide solution are required for back-titration after 40.00 ml. of 0.5000 N hydrochloric acid solution are added to a solution containing 1.5000 gram of impure calcium oxide. If 1.00 ml. of acid corresponds to 1.25 ml. of base, calculate the percentage purity of calcium oxide, CaO, in the sample.
12. In the analysis of a sample of soda ash the following data were obtained: sample weight = 0.5365 gram; volume of acid added = 45.35 ml.; volume of base used in back titration = 4.36 ml.; normality of acid = 0.1166; normality of base = 0.1243. Calculate the percentage purity of the soda ash, expressing the result in terms of (a) sodium carbonate, (b) sodium oxide, (c) sodium.
13. A 4.000 gram sample of organic material is analyzed for nitrogen by the Kjeldahl method, in which 43.00 ml. of 0.1313 N acid were used as the ammonia collector and 23.66 ml. of 0.1166 N base were used in the titration. Calculate the percentage nitrogen in the sample.
14. A protein material was analyzed for nitrogen by the Kjeldahl method and the following data were obtained: sample weight = 1.4800 gram; acid used to receive ammonia from the distillation, 50.00 ml. of 0.5000 N sulfuric acid; sodium hydroxide solution used in final titration, 36.86 ml. of 0.4962 N solution. Calculate the percentage nitrogen in the sample.

15. A 1.0000 gram sample of impure sodium nitrate is reduced to ammonia, which is distilled into 100.00 ml. of 0.1250 N acid. The excess acid requires 15.25 ml. of 0.1200 N base. What is the percentage sodium nitrate in the sample?

16. The sulfur in a 1.0000 gram sample of steel is burned to sulfur trioxide, SO_3, which is, in turn, absorbed in 50.00 ml. of 0.0100 N alkali solution. The excess of the latter is titrated with 0.0140 N acid, 22.65 ml. being required. What is the percentage of sulfur in the steel?

17. A baking powder sample weighing 5.0000 grams is treated with an excess of dilute sulfuric acid, and the carbon dioxide thus formed is bubbled into a barium hydroxide solution, forming 0.2600 gram of barium carbonate. Calculate the percentage sodium bicarbonate, $NaHCO_3$, in the sample, assuming it is the only ingredient furnishing carbon dioxide.

18. Of what normality should a hydrochloric acid solution be so that the volume in ml. used in titrating a 1/10 aliquot of a soda ash sample should be equal to the percentage of sodium carbonate in the sample, if the sample weighs 10.000 grams?

19. What weight of cream of tartar, impure $KHC_4H_4O_6$, must be taken for analysis in order that each ml. of a 0.1224 N base solution used for titration will correspond to 1% of $KHC_4H_4O_6$?

20. What weight of vinegar should be taken for analysis so that the buret reading will be ten times the percentage of acetic acid when a 0.1000 N alkaline solution is used?

21. What should be the normality of acid used in a Kjeldahl determination so that when a 2.000 gram sample is taken the volume of acid actually required will be the same as the percentage protein in the sample (protein is close to 16.00% nitrogen in most cases)?

22. What weight of soda ash sample should be taken for analysis in order that the volume of 0.1000 N hydrochloric acid required for titration of a 1/5 aliquot portion shall equal the percentage of sodium carbonate in the sample?

23. An acid was standardized against sodium carbonate. Just 37.66 ml. are required to titrate a 0.3663 gram sample. Later it was found that the sodium carbonate was the hydrated form, $Na_2CO_3 \cdot 10\ H_2O$, not the anhydrous form as expected. What were the reported and the correct normalities of the acid?

24. A hydrochloric acid solution is treated with an excess of calcium carbonate, and the weight of the liberated carbon dioxide determined by means of a suitable absorbent. If 100.00 ml. of acid liberates 0.2525 gram of carbon dioxide, what is the normality of the acid?

25. A steel sample weighing 2.0204 grams was taken for a tungsten determination. The tungsten was precipitated as the oxide, WO_3, and treated with 60.00 ml. of 0.1000 N sodium hydroxide solution, which was an excess over that required for the reaction, $WO_3 + 2\ OH^- \rightleftharpoons WO_4^= + H_2O$. The excess base was titrated with 42.33 ml. of 0.1000 N acid solution. What is the percentage tungsten metal in the steel?

SUGGESTIONS FOR ADDITIONAL READING

Items 1, 5, 6, 10, 13, 17, 18, 21, 24, 28 and 30, Appendix 7.

Chapter 11

Neutralization Theory

NEUTRALIZATION theory consists in large part of the application of equilibrium concepts and calculations to acidic, neutral and basic media. The purposes of this chapter are to establish and to illustrate methods for calculating the pH of any aqueous solution containing an acid, a base, a salt or a mixture of two or more of these components, to apply these calculations to the construction of titration curves, to evaluate the curves with respect to feasibility of titration and selection of indicator and, finally, to extend the principles of acid-base titrations to nonaqueous systems.

It is assumed in all of the calculations of this chapter that the solution is at room temperature, 25° C. If some other temperature were to be of interest, it would merely be necessary to use the numerical values of the equilibrium constants which are valid at that temperature. The ionization constant of water is particularly temperature-dependent, ranging from 0.12×10^{-14} at 0° C. through 1.04×10^{-14} (taken as 1.00×10^{-14} for convenience) at 25° C. to 5.66×10^{-14} at 50° C.

It is also assumed in all of the calculations of this chapter that molar concentrations of dissolved species may be used directly in all equilibrium constant equations when, in fact, the effective concentrations or "activities" may be somewhat less. The differences are slight in solutions which are dilute in all components, and correction factors can be used in more rigorous calculations as described in textbooks of physical chemistry.

SOLUTIONS OF STRONG ACIDS OR BASES
AND THEIR SALTS

A strong acid or base is, by definition, one that is fully ionized in solution. With very few exceptions, salts ionize completely in solution. If the salt is a salt of a strong acid and base, such as sodium chloride, its ions remain as such in the solution. If the salt is a salt of a weak acid or weak base (or both), as are sodium acetate and ammonium chloride, its ions will react to some extent with any hydrogen or hydroxyl ions which may be present. In the present section let us consider only solutions of strong acids, strong bases and salts of strong acids and bases.

Strong Acid Solutions.   Since a strong acid solution is, by definition, one in which the acid is fully ionized, the hydrogen ion concentration is equal to the normality. Hydrochloric acid and nitric acid are common strong acids. For example, a tenth-normal solution of hydrochloric acid is tenth-normal in chloride ions and also tenth-normal in hydrogen ions. The term $[H^+]$ designates the concentration in molar units rather than in normal units, but both are numerically identical for a monovalent substance such as the hydrogen ion. The calculation of the pH of a solution of a strong acid is very simple, then, since the hydrogen ion concentration simply equals the normality.

Example I.   Calculate the pH of each of the following solutions: (a) 0.0015 N HCl; (b) 1.000 liter of solution containing 0.1000 gram of HCl.

(a) $$[H^+] = N$$
$$[H^+] = 1.5 \times 10^{-3}$$
$$[H^+] = 10^{-2.82} \quad \text{so} \quad pH = 2.82$$

(b) $$[H^+] = N$$

but $$N \times ml. = \frac{mg.\ HCl}{eq.\ wt.}$$

or $$N = \frac{mg.\ HCl}{ml. \times eq.\ wt.}$$

$$[H^+] = \frac{100.0}{1000 \times 36.47}$$

$$[H^+] = 10^{-2.56} \quad \text{so} \quad pH = 2.56$$

Strong Base Solutions.   In a strong base solution, the hydroxyl ion concentration is equal to the normality in a manner analogous to the situation in a strong acid solution. The pH may, then, be calculated from the hydroxyl ion concentration and the ionization constant of water.

Example 2.   Calculate the pH of a 0.0023 N sodium hydroxide solution.

$$[OH^-] = N$$
$$[OH^-] = 2.3 \times 10^{-3}$$
$$[OH^-] = 10^{-2.64}$$

so $$pOH = 2.64$$
$$pH = 14 - pOH$$
so $$pH = 11.36$$

Solutions of Salts of a Strong Acid and Strong Base.   In considering the acidic or basic behavior of any salt, we must ask ourselves two questions: Does the salt contribute any hydrogen ions or hydroxyl ions to the solution? Does the salt remove from the solvent any of the hydrogen ions or hydroxyl ions already present? The answers to both of these questions are necessarily in the negative if the salt is a salt of a strong acid and a strong base. Therefore, a salt of this type does not influence the acidity or basicity of a solution (other than its effect on the activity coefficients of the hydrogen and hydroxyl ions already present, which effect is being neglected in this discussion). A solution containing no solute other than a salt of a strong acid and strong base, accordingly, has a pH the same as that of the solvent so the pH of such a solution is 7 at room temperature. Addition of such a salt to an acid or base solution does not modify the pH of that acid or base solution.

SOLUTIONS OF WEAK ACIDS OR BASES AND THEIR SALTS

General Methods. A weak acid or base is one which is incompletely ionized. Therefore, the hydrogen ion concentration or the hydroxyl ion concentration is always less than the normality of a weak acid or weak base, respectively. The equilibrium constant for the state of equilibrium developed between ionized and un-ionized forms of the solute serves as a basis for calculations of the pH of the weak acid or weak base solution.

The calculation of the pH of any solution falling into the present category may be accomplished by application of a few fundamental principles. These principles are the same as those employed in other types of mass law problems, including solubility product problems in Chapter 8. First, write chemical equations for the one or more chemical equilibria involved. These chemical equations must include the source of hydrogen ions in the solution, which is either water and/or an acid present as solute, and they must include any additional equilibria involving any substance present in the equation representing this source. There will frequently be only one chemical equation involved, while two and even more may be involved in other cases. Second, write mathematical equations representing each of the separate chemical equations. Third, write additional mathematical equations based upon known reference data and specifications for the particular solution until the total number of equations equals the total number of unknowns involved in those equations. Fourth, solve these equations mathematically for the desired unknown quantity. These four steps are presented not as a recipe for blind calculations but rather as a set of principles to guide in an understanding approach to mass law problems involving weak acid or weak base equilibria. The range of significant problems is so wide that no set of equations can possibly suffice for the solving of the problems, but these principles will serve as an adequate guide in understanding and attacking the varied types of problems. The principles may now be considered with reference to some of the varied types of solutions involving weak acids, weak bases, salts of weak acids or weak bases, and their combinations.

Weak Acid Solutions. Applications of the preceding principles will be illustrated by two examples, in one of which will be included many explanatory comments.

Example 3. Calculate the pH of a 0.10 N solution of acetic acid. Chemical Equation:

$$HC_2H_3O_2 \rightleftharpoons H^+ + C_2H_3O_2^-$$

This dissociation of acetic acid molecules is the source of hydrogen ions. (It is true that a few hydrogen ions come from water dissociation also, but acetic acid is a much stronger acid than is water, so this additional source of hydrogen ions may be neglected as insignificant.)
Mathematical Equations:

(1)
$$K_a = \frac{[H^+][C_2H_3O_2^-]}{[HC_2H_3O_2]}$$

(This one equation has four unknowns, so three more equations must be found from reference data and/or from specifications of this particular solution without introducing any further unknown quantities.)

(2)
$$K_a = 1.75 \times 10^{-5}$$

(From reference data in Appendix 2.) (These equilibria constants are always to be considered to be available for use as desired unless the specific problem calls for calculation of the constants.)

(3)
$$[H^+] = [C_2H_3O_2^-]$$

(The chemical equation tells us these two types of ion come in equal numbers from acetic acid molecules; since we have no other significant source of either type of ion and no other means of removing either type, their molar concentrations are equal.)

(4)
$$[HC_2H_3O_2] = 0.10 - [H^+]$$

(The total concentration of acetic acid is 0.10, so the molar amount un-ionized equals 0.10 minus the molar amount ionized.)
Solving:

$$1.75 \times 10^{-5} = \frac{[H^+][H^+]}{0.10 - [H^+]}$$

(Substituting equations 2, 3, and 4 into 1.)
This is one equation with one unknown, so it may be solved. However, this is a quadratic equation, so it must be solved by the so-called quadratic formula* from which the answer is found to be $[H^+] = 1.32 \times 10^{-3}$ or pH = 2.88.

* An equation of the type $aX^2 + bX + c = 0$ may be solved by the quadratic formula, which is $X = \dfrac{-b \pm \sqrt{b^2 - 4ac}}{2a}$. In this example, the combined arithmetic equation may be rearranged into the form, $[H^+]^2 + 1.75 \times 10^{-5}[H^+] - 1.75 \times 10^{-6} = 0$.
Applying the quadratic formula:

$$[H^+] = \frac{(1.75 \times 10^{-5}) \pm \sqrt{(1.75 \times 10^{-5})^2 - 4(1)(-1.75 \times 10^{-6})}}{2}$$

$[H^+] = 1.32 \times 10^{-3}$ (the other root is negative, an impossible situation)

Alternate Solving Procedure:

The mathematical operations can be simplified considerably by rewriting equation (4) as

$$[HC_2H_3O_2] = 0.10$$

This substitution is, in effect, saying that the numerical value of $[H^+]$ is a negligible quantity in comparison to 0.10 or, in other words, that very nearly all of the acetic acid remains as molecules rather than as ions. A weak acid, is, by definition, one that is only slightly ionized, so this assumption could be expected to be a reasonable one. Ultimately, the validity of this assumption in any particular case can be proven by solving the problem both with and without it. However, this type of assumption is commonly valid, so it will frequently be made in this chapter. Every student of quantitative chemical analysis should learn to make simplifying assumptions when justified, but only when justified. With this change in Equation 4, the combination of Equations 1, 2, 3 and 4 becomes

$$1.75 \times 10^{-5} = \frac{[H^+][H^+]}{0.10}$$

$$[H^+] = 10^{-2.88} \quad \text{or} \quad pH = 2.88$$

The two answers are seen to be the same.

Example 4. Calculate the pH of a solution of 0.25 N formic acid.
Chemical Equation:

$$HCHO_2 \rightleftharpoons H^+ + CHO_2^-$$

Mathematical Equations:

(1) $$K_a = \frac{[H^+][CHO_2^-]}{[HCHO_2]}$$

(2) $$K_a = 1.76 \times 10^{-4}$$

(3) $$[H^+] = [CHO_2^-]$$

(4) $$[HCHO_2] = 0.25 \quad \text{(simplified from } [HCHO_2] = 0.25 - [H^+])$$

Solving:

$$1.76 \times 10^{-4} = \frac{[H^+][H^+]}{0.25} \text{ (substituting 2, 3 and 4 into 1)}$$

$$[H^+] = 10^{-2.18} \quad \text{or} \quad pH = 2.18$$

Weak Base Solutions. Again, two examples will be considered. In both examples the equilibrium between ionized and un-ionized species in a solution of ammonia and water is written as

$$NH_4OH \rightleftharpoons NH_4^+ + OH^-$$

even though the NH_4OH molecule may not exist as a discrete entity. The calculations would be identical if the chemical equation were written in the form

$$NH_3 + H_2O \rightleftharpoons NH_4^+ + OH^-$$

and the [NH$_4$OH] quantity replaced in the calculations by the quantity [NH$_3$]. The water molecule concentration is taken as unity so it need not appear in the numerical calculations.

Example 5. Calculate the pH of a solution of 0.10 N ammonium hydroxide.

Chemical Equations:

$$HOH \rightleftharpoons H^+ + OH^-$$

(This is the only source of hydrogen ions in this solution.)

$$NH_4OH \rightleftharpoons NH_4^+ + OH^-$$

(This represents an additional source of hydroxyl ions and is of significance because hydroxyl ions are produced along with hydrogen ions in the ionization of water molecules.)

Mathematical Equations:

(1) $\qquad K_w = [H^+][OH^-]$ (or $pK_w = pH + pOH$)

(2) $\qquad K_b = \dfrac{[NH_4^+][OH^-]}{[NH_4OH]}$

These two equations include six unknowns, so four more equations are needed without introducing additional unknowns.

(3) $\qquad K_w = 1.0 \times 10^{-14}$

(4) $\qquad K_b = 1.8 \times 10^{-5}$

(5) $\qquad [NH_4^+] = [OH^-]$

(Most of the OH$^-$ ions come from NH$_4$OH since it is a much stronger base than is water, and the second chemical equation shows that NH$_4^+$ and OH$^-$ come in equal quantities.)

(6) $\qquad [NH_4OH] = 0.10$

(Actually, [NH$_4$OH] = 0.10 − [NH$_4^+$], but the simplification will be made as before.)

Solving:

$$1.8 \times 10^{-5} = \frac{[OH^-][OH^-]}{0.10} \quad \text{(substituting 4, 5, 6 into 2)}$$

$$[OH^-] = 1.34 \times 10^{-3} \quad \text{or} \quad pOH = 2.87$$

so $\qquad pH = 11.13$

(Combining the pOH value with equations 1 and 3.)

Example 6. Calculate the pH of a solution of 0.025 N ammonium hydroxide.

Chemical Equations:

$$HOH \rightleftharpoons H^+ + OH^-$$

$$NH_4OH \rightleftharpoons NH_4^+ + OH^-$$

Mathematical Equations:

(1) $\qquad K_w = [H^+][OH^-]$

(2) $\qquad K_b = \dfrac{[NH_4^+][OH^-]}{[NH_4OH]}$

(3) $\qquad K_w = 1.0 \times 10^{-14}$

(4) $\qquad K_b = 1.8 \times 10^{-5}$

(5) $\qquad [NH_4^+] = [OH^-]$

(6) $\qquad [NH_4OH] = 0.025$ (simplified from $[NH_4OH] = 0.025 - [NH_4^+]$)

Solving:

$$1.8 \times 10^{-5} = \frac{[OH^-][OH^-]}{0.025}$$

$$[OH^-] = 6.7 \times 10^{-4} \quad \text{or} \quad pOH = 3.17$$
$$\text{so} \quad pH = 10.83$$

It may be noted that problems such as in Examples 5 and 6 are essentially the same as in Examples 3 and 4 with the additional factor of the ionization of water.

Buffer Solutions. A buffer solution may be defined as a solution containing a weak acid or a weak base and a salt of that acid or base. Two examples of buffer solutions are a solution of acetic acid and sodium acetate and a solution of ammonium hydroxide and ammonium chloride. In the former, a state of equilibrium is established in accordance with the chemical equation

$$HC_2H_3O_2 \rightleftharpoons H^+ + C_2H_3O_2^-$$

This solution differs from a simple solution of acetic acid primarily in that the salt provides an additional source of acetate ions. The salt itself tends to ionize completely in solution, but the acetate ions thus formed enter into the state of equilibrium between acetic acid molecules and hydrogen and acetate ions. Calculations of the pH of a buffer solution are carried out just as in the case of a solution of a weak acid or base by itself, with due consideration being given to the influence of the additional ions from the salt.

Example 7. Calculate the pH of a solution 0.100 N in acetic acid and 0.100 N in sodium acetate.

Chemical Equation:

$$HC_2H_3O_2 \rightleftharpoons H^+ + C_2H_3O_2^-$$

Mathematical Equations:

(1)
$$K_a = \frac{[H^+][C_2H_3O_2^-]}{[HC_2H_3O_2]}$$

(This equation has four unknowns, so three more equations are required without introducing any further unknowns.)

(2) $$K_a = 1.75 \times 10^{-5}$$

(3) $$[C_2H_3O_2^-] = 0.100$$

(This is effectively the concentration of sodium acetate, all of which ionizes in solution and nearly all of which remains ionized.)

(4) $$[HC_2H_3O_2] = 0.100$$

(This is effectively the total acetic acid concentration, nearly all of which is un-ionized because it is a weak acid and, in fact, its ionization is repressed by the presence of the salt.)

Solving:

$$1.75 \times 10^{-5} = \frac{[H^+]\,0.100}{0.100} \quad \text{(substituting 2, 3 and 4 into 1)}$$

$$[H^+] = 1.75 \times 10^{-5} \quad \text{or} \quad pH = 4.76$$

Example 8. Calculate the pH of 100 ml. of a solution containing 0.01 mole of ammonium chloride and 0.02 mole of ammonium hydroxide.

Chemical Equations:

$$HOH \rightleftharpoons H^+ + OH^-$$

$$NH_4OH \rightleftharpoons NH_4^+ + OH^-$$

Mathematical Equations:

(1) $$K_w = [H^+][OH^-] \quad \text{(or } pK_w = pH + pOH)$$

(2) $$K_b = \frac{[NH_4^+][OH^-]}{[NH_4OH]}$$

(These two equations involve six unknowns, so four more equations involving the same unknowns are required.)

(3) $$K_w = 1 \times 10^{-14}$$

(4) $$K_b = 1.8 \times 10^{-5}$$

(5) $$[NH_4^+] = 0.1$$

(This is the molar concentration of NH_4Cl, which is essentially all in the form of the constituent ions.)

(6) $$[NH_4OH] = 0.2$$

(This is the molar concentration of NH_4OH, which is essentially all in the undissociated form.)

Solving:

$$1.8 \times 10^{-5} = \frac{0.1 \times [OH^-]}{0.2} \text{ (substituting 4, 5 and 6 into 2)}$$

$$[OH^-] = 3.6 \times 10^{-5} \quad \text{or} \quad pOH = 4.44$$

$$pH = 9.56 \text{ (from the pOH value and equations 1 and 3)}$$

In all of these calculations it must be remembered that the concentrations in the various mass law equilibrium constant equations are in molar units. If they are known or if they are wanted in some other units, they must be converted so that they are in molar units whenever used directly in the equations.

Some Properties of Buffer Solutions. Let us next consider some of the significant properties of buffer solutions. These properties consist primarily of the unique behavior of a buffer solution upon dilution (or concentration), upon adding acid and upon adding base.

First, consider the effect upon the pH of a buffer solution produced by dilution, that is, by adding water. Taking HA to represent any weak, monobasic acid and BOH to represent any weak, mono-acidic base, the corresponding K_a and K_b equations may be solved for $[H^+]$ and $[OH^-]$ as follows:

$$K_a = \frac{[H^+][A^-]}{[HA]} \qquad K_b = \frac{[B^+][OH^-]}{[BOH]}$$

$$[H^+] = K_a \frac{[HA]}{[A^-]} \qquad [OH^-] = K_b \frac{[BOH]}{[B^+]}$$

In each case, the $[H^+]$ or $[OH^-]$ quantity is equal to a constant multiplied by a ratio which is, in effect, the ratio of acid (or base) concentration to salt concentration. Addition of water dilutes both the acid (or base) and salt concentrations to the same extent so that the ratio is not altered by dilution; likewise, making the solution more concentrated does not alter the ratio. Therefore, a buffer solution resists changes in pH upon dilution or concentration. Actually, the activity coefficients of the molecular and ionic species are dependent upon their concentrations, but they are both usually about equally dependent upon concentration. Hence, no significant error arises from dealing solely with concentrations rather than with activities.

Next, consider the addition of a strong acid or a strong base to a buffer solution. This discussion will include a buffer consisting of a weak acid and its salt, although the treatment would be similar with a weak base-salt buffer. Noting again the generalized chemical equation

$$HA \rightleftharpoons H^+ + A^-$$

we see that addition of hydrogen ions in the form of a strong acid pushes the reaction as written to the left, thus removing hydrogen ions along with anions from the salt. Similarly, the addition of hydroxyl ions in the form of a strong base pulls the reaction as written to the right, causing more weak acid molecules to ionize to replace the hydrogen ions which combined with hydroxyls to form water. In other words, addition of either H^+ or OH^- ions to a buffer shifts the state of equilibrium in such a direction as to minimize the effect of the added H^+ or OH^- ions. Thus, a buffer solution maintains at least an approximately constant pH even though strong acid or strong base is added to it. The pH control is not perfect, however, as may be illustrated by the following example:

Example 9. a. Calculate the pH of 100 ml. of solution containing 0.01 mole $HC_2H_3O_2$ and 0.01 mole $NaC_2H_3O_2$.

Chemical Equation:

$$HC_2H_3O_2 \rightleftharpoons H^+ + C_2H_3O_2^-$$

Mathematical Equations:

(1) $$K_a = \frac{[H^+][C_2H_3O_2^-]}{[HC_2H_3O_2]}$$

(2) $$K_a = 1.75 \times 10^{-5}$$

(3) $$[C_2H_3O_2^-] = 0.1$$

(4) $$[HC_2H_3O_2] = 0.1$$

Solving:

$$1.75 \times 10^{-5} = \frac{[H^+]0.1}{0.1} \quad \text{(combining 1, 2, 3 and 4)}$$

$$[H^+] = 1.75 \times 10^{-5} \quad \text{or} \quad pH = 4.76$$

Example 9. b. Calculate the pH of *a* after adding 10 ml. of 0.1 N HCl.

Chemical Equation:

$$HC_2H_3O_2 \rightleftharpoons H^+ + C_2H_3O_2^-$$

Mathematical Equations:

(1) $$K_a = \frac{[H^+][C_2H_3O_2^-]}{[HC_2H_3O_2]}$$

(2) $$K_a = 1.75 \times 10^{-5}$$

(3) $$[C_2H_3O_2^-] = \frac{9}{110}$$

and

(4) $$[HC_2H_3O_2] = \frac{11}{110}$$

(The initial solution a contained 10 mEq. of $HC_2H_3O_2$ and 10 mEq. of $C_2H_3O_2^-$, all in 100 ml. To this was added 1.0 mEq. of H^+, which would have combined with 1.0 mEq. of the $C_2H_3O_2^-$, leaving 11 mEq. of $HC_2H_3O_2$ and 9 mEq. of $C_2H_3O_2^-$, both now in 110 ml.)
Solving:

$$1.75 \times 10^{-5} = \frac{[H^+](9/110)}{(11/110)}$$

$$[H^+] = 2.14 \times 10^{-5} \quad \text{or} \quad pH = 4.67$$

Example 9. c.   Calculate the pH of a after adding 10 ml. of 0.1 N NaOH.
Chemical Equation:

$$HC_2H_3O_2 \rightleftharpoons H^+ + C_2H_3O_2^-$$

Mathematical Equations:

(1) $$K_a = \frac{[H^+][C_2H_3O_2^-]}{[HC_2H_3O_2]}$$

(2) $$K_a = 1.75 \times 10^{-5}$$

(3) $$[C_2H_3O_2^-] = 11/110$$

and

(4) $$[HC_2H_3O_2] = 9/110$$

(The initial solution a contained 10 mEq. of $HC_2H_3O_2$ and 10 mEq. of $C_2H_3O_2^-$, all in 100 ml. The added 1.0 mEq. of NaOH would have combined with 1.0 mEq. of the $HC_2H_3O_2$, leaving 9 mEq. of $HC_2H_3O_2$ and 11 mEq. of $C_2H_3O_2^-$, all in 110 ml.)
Solving:

$$1.75 \times 10^{-5} = \frac{[H^+](11/110)}{(9/110)}$$

$$[H^+] = 1.43 \times 10^{-5} \quad \text{or} \quad pH = 4.84$$

These calculations reveal that the pH of the buffer, initially 4.76, was changed to only 4.67 and 4.84 by the addition, respectively, of 10 ml. of 0.1 N HCl and 10 ml. of 0.1 N NaOH.

There is a limit to how much acid or base can be added to a given buffer solution before any appreciable change in pH results, and this quantity is designated the *capacity* of the buffer. This limit is set by the initial amount of acid and salt present, since one or the other is used up by the addition of either acid or base. In the preceding example the initial solution contained 10 mEq. of acetate ion, and the strong acid added reacted with this ion. Obviously, addition of 10 mEq. of strong acid would have depleted the supply of acetate ion, and no buffering action would have remained. Calculations similar to that of Example 9 reveal that the pH changes at a gradually increased rate as this limiting capacity is approached.

Buffer solutions are encountered in all neutralization titrations in which one or more of the main reactants is a weak acid or a weak base. Furthermore, buffer solutions are very important in many chemical and biological processes. The near constancy of the pH of a buffer solution upon dilution (or concentration) and upon the addition of acid or base is a very important property of this very important type of solution.

SOLUTIONS OF SALTS OF WEAK ACIDS AND WEAK BASES

The preceding sections have dealt with solutions of the major types with the exception of solutions of a salt of which either the anion or cation can form a weak acid or base. Such salts were considered only in the presence of an additional supply of the weak acid or base. Let us now consider solutions of salts of weak acids or bases.

Salt of a Weak Acid and Strong Base. Sodium acetate, which is a salt of this type, ionizes completely in aqueous solution to form sodium and acetate ions. The only source of hydrogen ions in such a solution is the water ionization, but the acetate ions from the salt will tie up some of the hydrogen ions from the water to form acetic acid molecules. More water molecules will ionize in an effort to replace the hydrogen ions removed by acetate ions, and the solution will definitely contain more hydroxyl ions than hydrogen ions. A solution of a salt of a weak acid and a strong base is basic. The extent of this basicity is determined by the weakness of the acid involved. Calculation of the pH of a solution of a salt of this type is made by application of the very same principles used heretofore in this chapter, as illustrated by Example 10.

Example 10. Calculate the pH of a solution of 0.10 M $NaC_2H_3O_2$. Chemical Equations:

$$HOH \rightleftharpoons H^+ + OH^-$$

(This is the one and only source of hydrogen ions in the solution.)

$$H^+ + C_2H_3O_2^- \rightleftharpoons HC_2H_3O_2$$

(Acetate ions from the sodium acetate combine to some extent with some of the hydrogen ions from water.)

Note: These two chemical equations may be combined (added) into one over-all chemical equation:

$$HOH + C_2H_3O_2^- \rightleftharpoons OH^- + HC_2H_3O_2$$

Mathematical Equations:

(1) $$K_w = [H^+][OH^-]$$

(2) $$K_a = \frac{[H^+][C_2H_3O_2^-]}{[HC_2H_3O_2]}$$

(These two equations include six unknowns, so four more equations are required without introducing any additional unknowns.)

(3) $$K_w = 1 \times 10^{-14}$$

(4) $$K_a = 1.75 \times 10^{-5}$$

(5) $$[C_2H_3O_2^-] = 0.10$$

(This equation assumes that only a very small fraction of the total acetate combines so that most of it is left as acetate ions; this is likely a valid assumption, as there is really only a very limited supply of hydrogen ions with which the acetates can combine.)

(6) $$[OH^-] = [HC_2H_3O_2]$$

(This is true because the only source of either OH^- ions or of $HC_2H_3O_2$ molecules is from the reactions indicated by the chemical equations; the combined chemical equation shows that these two species are formed in equal numbers.)

Solving:

$$[H^+] = \frac{K_w}{[OH^-]}$$

and $$[H^+] = \frac{K_a[HC_2H_3O_2]}{[C_2H_3O_2^-]}$$ (solving 1 and 2 for H^+)

$$\frac{K_w}{[OH^-]} = \frac{K_a[HC_2H_3O_2]}{[C_2H_3O_2^-]}$$ (equating the two expressions for $[H^+]$)

$$\frac{K_w}{[OH^-]} = \frac{K_a[OH^-]}{[C_2H_3O_2^-]}$$ (substituting equation 6 into the equation just preceding)

$$* \quad [OH^-] = \sqrt{\frac{K_w}{K_a}[C_2H_3O_2^-]}$$ (rearranging)

$$[OH^-] = \sqrt{\frac{1 \times 10^{-14}}{1.75 \times 10^{-5}} \times 0.10}$$

$$[OH^-] = 10^{-5.12} \quad \text{or} \quad pOH = 5.12$$

so $$pH = 8.88$$

Equation * is a very useful one which is often used as a starting point in solving problems of this type. It may be made more general by substituting c, the molar concentration of the salt, for $[C_2H_3O_2^-]$, and it is valid for a solution of a salt of a weak acid and a strong base. It is definitely not valid, however, when the solution contains any acid or base other than that formed by hydrolysis of the salt. (Specifically, equation 6 in Example 10 is not valid when any other acid or base is present.)

Salt of a Strong Acid and a Weak Base. This type of solution is analogous to that discussed in the preceding section except that the places of the hydrogen ion and the hydroxyl ion are reversed. Ammonium chloride may be taken as an example. This salt dissociates completely in aqueous solution, in which the dissociation of water provides the only source of hydrogen ions. Water dissociates to form equal numbers of hydrogen and hydroxyl ions, but some of these hydroxyl ions are tied up by ammonium ions from the salt as ammonium hydroxide molecules. The resultant number of hydrogen ions is greater than that of hydroxyl ions, so the solution is definitely acidic. Calculations of pH are similar to those of Example 10.

Example 11. Calculate the pH of a 0.10 N solution of NH_4Cl. Chemical Equations:

$$HOH \rightleftharpoons H^+ + OH^-$$

$$NH_4^+ + OH^- \rightleftharpoons NH_4OH$$

Note that these two chemical equations may be added to give one over-all chemical equation

$$NH_4^+ + HOH \rightleftharpoons NH_4OH + H^+$$

Mathematical Equations:

(1) $$K_w = [H^+][OH^-]$$

(2) $$K_b = \frac{[NH_4^+][OH^-]}{[NH_4OH]}$$

(These two equations contain six unknowns, so four more equations are required involving no additional unknowns.)

(3) $$K_w = 1 \times 10^{-14}$$

(4) $$K_b = 1.8 \times 10^{-5}$$

(5) $$[NH_4^+] = 0.10$$

(The amount of NH_4^+ which combines with OH^- from water is assumed negligible in comparison with the total amount of NH_4^+ from the salt.)

(6) $$[NH_4OH] = [H^+]$$

(from the combined chemical equation, which represents the only source of either species).

Solving:

$$[OH^-] = \frac{K_w}{[H^+]} \quad \text{and}$$

$$[OH^-] = K_b \frac{[NH_4OH]}{[NH_4^+]} \quad \text{(solving 1 and 2 for [OH}^-])$$

$$\frac{K_w}{[H^+]} = \frac{K_b[H^+]}{[NH_4^+]} \quad \text{(equating the two [OH}^-] \text{ expressions and substituting in equation 6)}$$

$$* [H^+] = \sqrt{\frac{K_w}{K_b} [NH_4^+]} \quad \text{(rearranging)}$$

$$[H^+] = \sqrt{\frac{1 \times 10^{-14}}{1.8 \times 10^{-5}} \times 0.10}$$

$$[H^+] = 7.43 \times 10^{-6} \quad \text{or} \quad pH = 5.13$$

Again, equation * is a very useful one, and it is often taken as the starting point in solving problems of this type with $[NH_4^+]$ replaced by the more general quantity c, which is the molar concentration of the salt. It must be emphasized, however, that equation 6 (and therefore equation * also) is valid only for a solution of a salt of a weak base and a strong acid in which there is no other acidic or basic substance present. Careless use of equations such as the starred ones in Examples 10 and 11 can only lead to trouble, whereas any of these problems can be solved by the use of the general principles used throughout this chapter.

Salt of a Weak Acid and a Weak Base. Ammonium formate, NH_4CHO_2, may be taken as an example of a salt of a weak acid and a weak base. This salt ionizes completely in aqueous solution to ammonium ions and formate ions. The hydrogen ions in such a solution must come solely from the dissociation of water molecules, which upon dissociation yield equal numbers of hydrogen ions and hydroxyl ions. Both H^+ ions and OH^- ions from water dissociation are removed to some extent, the former by formate ions to yield formic acid molecules and the latter by ammonium ions to yield ammonium hydroxide molecules. The acidity or the basicity of this salt solution is determined, therefore, by the relative extents to which the ammonium ions and the formate ions are able to tie up the hydrogen ions and hydroxyl ions. These relative quantities are indicated directly by the appropriate K_a and K_b values. If the K_a and the K_b values are equal (assuming the salt to be a uni-univalent one), the solution is neutral. If the K_b value is less than the K_a value, the solution is acidic, while it is basic if the K_a value is less than the K_b value. These qualitative predictions may be verified by quantitative calculations employing the same principles used heretofore in this chapter. However, the setting up of the requisite number of mathematical equations and the resulting mathematical solution in general terms does lead to a useful equation analogous to the starred equations in Examples 10 and 11, from which the pH of a solution of a salt of a weak acid and a weak base may be calculated.

$$[H^+] = \sqrt{\frac{K_aK_w}{K_b}}$$

It will be noted that the pH of such a solution is independent of the concentration of the salt. This equation is not fully exact, but it is adequate for calculations encountered in quantitative analysis.

Example 12. Calculate the pH of a solution of 0.010 M ammonium formate. Applying the preceding equation empirically,

$$[H^+] = \sqrt{\frac{K_aK_w}{K_b}}$$

$$[H^+] = \sqrt{\frac{1.76 \times 10^{-4} \times 1.0 \times 10^{-14}}{1.8 \times 10^{-5}}}$$

$$[H^+] = 10^{-6.50}$$

We have now considered the calculation of the pH of any type of aqueous solution containing a strong acid or a strong base, a strong acid or base plus a salt of a strong acid and base, a weak acid or a weak base, a weak acid or base plus a salt of a weak acid or base, and a salt. Every aqueous solution must fit into one of these categories or, in special cases, into a combination of the categories. General methods of calculation have been described, and these methods have been applied in examples to solutions falling in each of the several categories.

TITRATION CURVES

A neutralization titration curve consists of a graph of pH plotted against volume of added reagent. The curves may be constructed from experimental data as described in Chapter 20, or they may be constructed theoretically from calculated data. The methods required for calculations of theoretical titration curves are solely those used thus far in this chapter along with some stoichiometric considerations as described in Chapter 9. Theoretical titration curves will now be developed and discussed for typical titrations within each of the several possible categories of neutralization titrations.

Strong Acid vs. Strong Base. Assuming that the acid is in the titration vessel to begin with and that the base is added from the buret, the solution initially consists of a strong acid. At all subsequent points prior to the equivalence point, the solution contains strong acid plus a salt of a strong acid and strong base, while the solution contains a strong base plus the salt of a strong acid and strong base beyond the equivalence point. The solution contains merely the salt at the equivalence point. This type of salt neither provides any hydrogen or hydroxyl ions, nor does it combine with any hydrogen or hydroxyl ions from any other source, so the salt exerts no influence whatever upon the pH of the solution. Therefore, pH calculations prior to the equivalence point are similar to Example 1, and beyond the equivalence point to Example 2. At the equivalence point the solution is neutral, with pH of 7, since no acidic or basic components are present.

Example 13. Construct a theoretical titration curve for the titration of 25.00 ml. of 0.1000 N hydrochloric acid by 0.1000 N sodium hydroxide.

0.00 ml. NaOH added:

$$N = [H^+] = 0.1000, \text{ so pH} = 1$$

10.00 ml. added:

mEq. HCl to start $= N \times ml. = 0.1000 \times 25.00 = 2.500$

mEq. HCl used up $=$ mEq. NaOH added $= N \times ml. = 0.1000 \times 10.00$
$$= 1.000$$

mEq. HCl left in solution $= 1.500$

$$[H^+] = N = \frac{\text{mEq. present}}{\text{ml.}} = \frac{1.500}{35.00} = 10^{-1.37} \text{ so pH } 1.37$$

20.00 ml. added:

similarly,   pH $= 1.95$

24.00 ml. added:

similarly,   pH $= 2.69$

24.90 ml. added:

similarly,   pH $= 3.70$

25.00 ml. added: (this is the exact equivalence point)
$$\text{pH} = 7.00$$

25.10 ml. added:

mEq. NaOH total $= N \times ml. = 0.1000 \times 25.10 = 2.510$

mEq. NaOH used up $=$ mEq. HCl total $= 2.500$

mEq. NaOH left $= 0.010$

$$[OH^-] = N = \frac{\text{mEq. present}}{\text{ml.}} = \frac{0.010}{50.10} = 10^{-3.70}$$

so pOH $= 3.70$, or pH $= 10.30$

26.00 ml. added:

similarly,   pOH $= 2.71$, or pH $= 11.29$

30.00 ml. added:

similarly,   pOH $= 2.04$, or pH $= 11.96$

40.00 ml. added:

similarly,   pOH $= 1.64$, or pH $= 12.36$

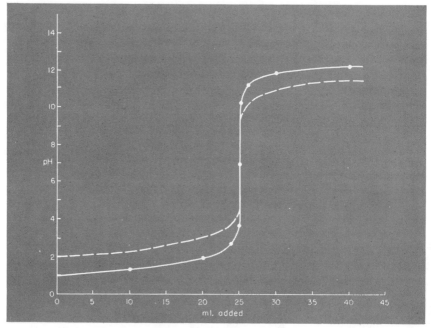

Figure 31. Titration curve: strong acid vs. strong base. 25 ml. 0.1 N hydrochloric acid titrated by 0.1 N sodium hydroxide (solid line); 25 ml. 0.01 N hydrochloric acid titrated by 0.01 N sodium hydroxide (broken line).

These points are plotted in Figure 31. The choice of what points to calculate is arbitrary, but enough points must be calculated so that a smooth curve can be drawn. This means that points must be taken very closely together around the equivalence point, as is evident from the slope of the curve. If the original concentrations are less, 0.0100 for both reagents, for example, the form of the curve is similar but it is slightly displaced as shown by the dotted line in the figure. Interpretation of this graph will be considered later.

Weak Acid vs. Strong Base. Assuming once again that the acid is in the titration vessel to begin the titration, the initial solution is simply that of a weak acid. At subsequent points prior to the equivalence point, the solution contains weak acid and salt of that weak acid. At the equivalence point the solution consists of the salt in water, but this salt hydrolyzes to some extent. Beyond the equivalence point, the solution contains strong base plus the salt; the pH of this latter solution is determined by the strong base present, since the hydroxyl ion resulting from hydrolysis of the salt is negligible in comparison to the amount furnished by the strong base. Accordingly, pH calculation of the initial solution is done as in Examples 3 and 4; of the solution from the initial point to (not including) the equivalence point as in Example 7; of the equivalence point solution as in Example 10, and of the solution beyond the equivalence point again as in Example 2.

Example 14. Construct a theoretical titration curve for the titration of 25.00 ml. of 0.1000 N acetic acid by 0.1000 N sodium hydroxide.

0.00 ml. added:

$$K_a = \frac{[H^+][C_2H_3O_2^-]}{[HC_2H_3O_2]}$$

$$1.75 \times 10^{-5} = \frac{[H^+][H^+]}{0.1000} \text{ (as in Example 3)}$$

$$[H^+] = 10^{-2.88} \quad \text{so} \quad pH = 2.88$$

10.00 ml. added:

mEq. $C_2H_3O_2^-$ = mEq. NaOH used = $10.00 \times 0.1000 = 1.000$ (in 35.00 ml.)
mEq. $HC_2H_3O_2$ = mEq. to start − mEq. used up =
$$25.00 \times 0.1000 - 10.00 \times 0.1000 = 1.500 \text{ (in 35.00 ml.)}$$

$$K_a = \frac{[H^+][C_2H_3O_2^-]}{[HC_2H_3O_2]} \quad \text{or} \quad [H^+] = K_a \frac{[HC_2H_3O_2]}{[C_2H_3O_2^-]}$$

$$[H^+] = 1.75 \times 10^{-5} \frac{1.500/35}{1.000/35}$$

$$[H^+] = 10^{-4.58} \quad \text{so} \quad pH = 4.58$$

20.00 ml. added: similarly, pH = 5.36
24.00 ml. added: similarly, pH = 6.14
24.90 ml. added: similarly, pH = 7.15
25.00 ml. added: (this is the equivalence point)

$$[OH^-] = \sqrt{\frac{K_w}{K_a} [C_2H_3O_2^-]} \quad \text{(as in Example 10)}$$

$$[OH^-] = \sqrt{\frac{1 \times 10^{-14}}{1.75 \times 10^{-5}} \times 0.05}$$

(note that we now have 2.500 mEq. $C_2H_3O_2^-$ in 50.00 ml., so

$$[C_2H_3O_2^-] = \frac{2.500}{50.00} = 0.05)$$

$$[OH^-] = 10^{-5.27}$$

so   pOH = 5.27 or pH = 8.73

26.00 ml. added: pOH = 2.71 or pH = 11.29⎫ (these are identical to corre-
30.00 ml. added: pOH = 2.04 or pH = 11.96⎬ sponding points in Example
40.00 ml. added: pOH = 1.64 or pH = 12.36⎭ 12.)

These points are plotted in Figure 32. This curve differs from that of the strong acid vs. strong base titration in two respects: during the portion of the titration in which unneutralized acid governs the pH, the curve for the weak reagent lies above that for the strong reagent because only a small

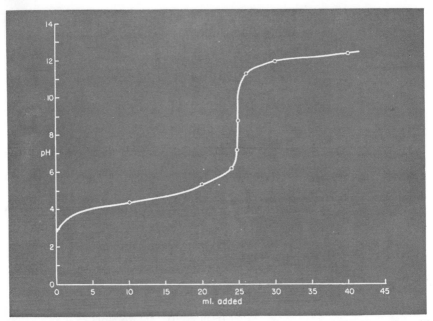

FIGURE 32.   Titration curve: weak acid vs. strong base. 25 ml. 0.1 N acetic acid
titrated by 0.1 N sodium hydroxide.

portion of the weak acid ionizes to furnish hydrogen ions; the pH at the
equivalence point is on the basic side in the titration of a weak acid because
of hydrolysis of the salt present at the equivalence point.

Two modifications may be applied to this curve. If the original reagent
concentrations are less than or greater than 0.1000 N, the curves turn out to
be of the same form but somewhat displaced at the initial point and beyond
the equivalence point. If the weak acid has an ionization constant different
from that of acetic acid, the curve is again of the same form, but the first half
is displaced. This latter factor is illustrated in Figure 33 in which are plotted
titration curves for the titrations of sodium hydroxide against acids of
several different ionization constants.

Weak Base vs. Strong Acid.   Assuming that the base is in the titration
vessel at the start of the titration, the initial solution consists merely of
the weak base, so pH calculation is similar to Example 5. At all subsequent
points prior to the equivalence point, the solution contains the remaining
portion of the weak base plus salt of that weak base, so pH calculation is
similar to Example 8. The pH at the equivalence point is calculated as in
Example 11, because this solution consists of a salt of a weak base and
strong acid. Beyond the equivalence point, the solution contains excess
strong acid plus a salt which does not significantly influence the pH, so the
pH is calculated as in Example 1.

Example 15.   Construct a theoretical titration curve for the titration of
25.00 ml. of 0.1000 N ammonium hydroxide with 0.1000 N hydrochloric acid.

0.00 ml. added:

$$K_b = \frac{[NH_4^+][OH^-]}{[NH_4OH]}$$

$$1.8 \times 10^{-5} = \frac{[OH^-][OH^-]}{0.1000} \quad \text{(as in Example 5)}$$

$$[OH^-] = 10^{-2.87}$$

$$\text{so} \quad pOH = 2.87 \quad \text{or} \quad pH = 11.13$$

10.00 ml. added:

mEq. NH_4^+ = mEq. HCl added = $0.1000 \times 10.00 = 1.000$ (in 35 ml.)
mEq. NH_4OH = mEq. to start — mEq. used up =
$\qquad 0.1000 \times 25.00 - 0.1000 \times 10.00 = 1.500$ (in 35 ml.)

$$K_b = \frac{[NH_4^+][OH^-]}{[NH_4OH]} \quad \text{or} \quad [OH^-] = K_b \frac{[NH_4OH]}{[NH_4^+]}$$

$$[OH^-] = 1.8 \times 10^{-5} \frac{1.500/35}{1.000/35}$$

$$[OH^-] = 10^{-4.57} \quad \text{so} \quad pOH = 4.57 \quad \text{or} \quad pH = 9.43$$

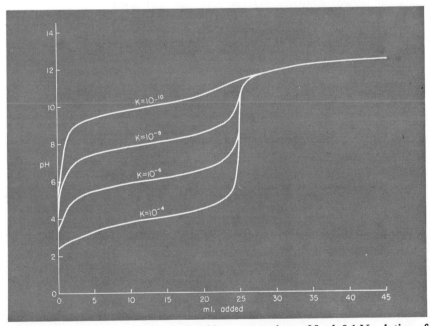

FIGURE 33. Titration curves: weak acids vs. strong base. 25 ml. 0.1 N solution of weak acid of indicated ionization constant titrated by 0.1 N sodium hydroxide.

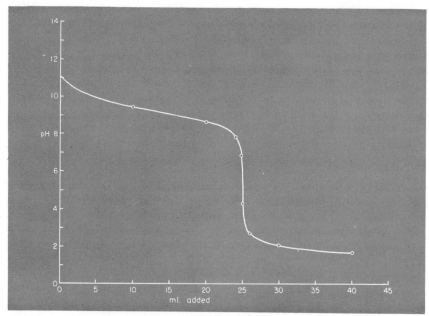

FIGURE 34.   Titration curve: weak base vs. strong acid. 25 ml. 0.1 N ammonium
hydroxide titrated by 0.1 N hydrochloric acid.

20.00 ml. added: similarly, pOH = 5.35   or   pH = 8.65
24.00 ml. added: similarly, pOH = 6.12   or   pH = 7.88
24.90 ml. added: similarly, pOH = 7.14   or   pH = 6.86
25.00 ml. added: (this is the equivalence point)

$$[H^+] = \sqrt{\frac{K_w}{K_b} [NH_4^+]} \quad \text{(as in Example 11)}$$

$$[H^+] = \sqrt{\frac{1 \times 10^{-14}}{1.8 \times 10^{-5}} 0.05}$$ (note that we now have
                                                         2.500 mEq. NH_4^+ in
                                                         50.00 ml., so

$$[NH_4^+] = \frac{2.500}{50.00} = 0.05)$$

$[H^+] = 10^{-5.28}$ so   pH = 5.28
26.00 ml. added:

mEq. HCl present = mEq. total − mEq. used up =
                0.1000 × 26.00 − 0.1000 × 25.00 = 0.1000

$$[H^+] = N = \frac{\text{mEq. present}}{\text{ml.}} = \frac{0.1000}{51.00} = 10^{-2.71}, \quad \text{so} \quad pH = 2.71$$

30.00 ml. added: similarly, pH = 2.04
40.00 ml. added: similarly, pH = 1.64

These data are plotted in Figure 34, which appears to be almost identical to Figure 32 except that it is inverted. If the weak base in this titration had been either more or less highly ionized than ammonium hydroxide, the titration curve would have been found to be displaced analogous to the family of curves of Figure 33.

Weak Acid vs. Weak Base. Assuming that the base is in the titration vessel to begin the titration, the solution initially contains a weak base, the pH of which may be calculated as in Example 5. Prior to and beyond the equivalence point, the remaining weak base and the excess weak acid, respectively, are the main factors in determining the pH of the solution. A salt is also present, so pH calculations are equivalent to Examples 8 and 7 before and after the equivalence point, respectively. The solution at the equivalence point contains principally the salt along with the hydrolysis products of both the anion and cation of the salt, so the pH may be calculated approximately from the special equation used in Example 12. This type of titration is not practical, as will be seen later, so no sample calculations need be listed. However, a typical titration curve for a weak acid vs. weak base titration is shown in Figure 35.

It may be noted from all of the titration curves thus far presented that there are just two general forms of "half-titration curve," one for a strong reagent and one for a weak reagent. Each complete titration curve is composed of some combination of these two. The concentration of a reagent and

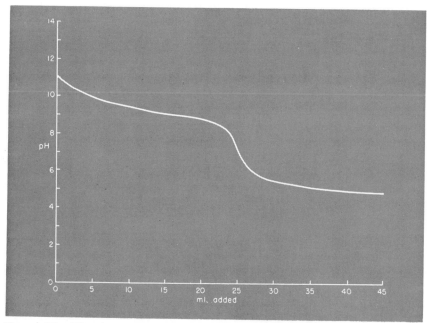

FIGURE 35.   Titration curve: weak base vs. weak acid. 25 ml. 0.1 N ammonium hydroxide titrated by 0.1 N acetic acid.

the magnitude of the K_a or K_b of the weak reagent do not change the general form of the curve but do govern its exact location on the axes.

Salt of Weak Acid vs. Strong Acid.   All of the bases in the titrations considered thus far in this chapter have been hydroxyl bases. It is also possible to titrate the anions of a very weak acid by a strong acid and the cations of a very weak base by a strong base. These are often called displacement titrations. The calculations of points for a titration curve of this type of titration are similar to those already encountered. In the example which follows, the hypothetical salt, NaA, of which A^- is the anion of a weak acid, is titrated by hydrochloric acid. The initial solution is simply that of a salt of a weak acid and strong base, so the pH is calculated as in Example 10. At subsequent points prior to the equivalence point, the solution contains a weak acid plus a salt of that weak acid. At the equivalence point, the solution contains the weak acid (plus the salt NaCl which does not influence the pH). Beyond the equivalence point, the solution contains a weak acid plus a strong acid, so the latter is the predominant source of hydrogen ions.

Example 16.   Construct a theoretical titration curve for the titration of 25.00 ml. of a 0.1000 N solution of the salt, NaA, by 0.1000 N hydrochloric acid. Assume the acid HA to have an ionization constant of 1.00×10^{-10}. 0.00 ml. added:

$$[OH^-] = \sqrt{\frac{K_w}{K_a}[A^-]} \quad \text{(as in Example 10)}$$

$$[OH^-] = \sqrt{\frac{1.00 \times 10^{-14}}{1.00 \times 10^{-10}} \times 0.1000}$$

$$[OH^-] = 10^{-2.50}$$

$$\text{so pOH} = 2.50 \quad \text{or} \quad pH = 11.50$$

10.00 ml. added:

$$
\begin{aligned}
\text{mEq. } A^- \text{ left} \quad &= \text{mEq. } A^- \text{ at start} - \text{mEq. } H^+ \text{ added} \\
\text{mEq. } A^- \text{ left} \quad &= 0.1000 \times 25.00 - 0.1000 \times 10.00 \\
\text{mEq. } A^- \text{ left} \quad &= 1.500 \text{ (in 35.00 ml.)} \\
\text{mEq. HA found} &= \text{mEq. } H^+ \text{ added} \\
\text{mEq. HA found} &= 1.000 \text{ (in 35.00 ml.)}
\end{aligned}
$$

$$K_a = \frac{[H^+][A^-]}{[HA]} \quad \text{or} \quad [H^+] = K_a \frac{[HA]}{[A]}$$

$$[H^+] = 1.00 \times 10^{-10} \frac{1.000/35.00}{1.500/35.00}$$

$$[H^+] = 10.17 \quad \text{or} \quad pH = 10.17$$

20.00 ml. added: similarly, pH = 9.40
24.00 ml. added: similarly, pH = 8.62
24.90 ml. added: similarly, pH = 7.60

25.00 ml. added: (this is the equivalence point)

$$K_a = \frac{[H^+][A^-]}{[HA]}$$

$K_a = 1.00 \times 10^{-10}$

$[H^+] = [A^-]$ (there is no excess of either one)

$[HA] = 0.05$ (we now have 2.500 mEq. in 50.00 ml.)

$[H^+] = 10^{-5.56}$ (combining the four equations)

or pH = 5.65

26.00 ml. added:

mEq. HCl present = mEq. total − mEq. used up

mEq. HCl present = $0.1000 \times 26.00 - 0.1000 \times 25.00$

mEq. HCl present = 0.1000 (in 51.00 ml.)

$$[H^+] = N = \frac{0.1000}{51.00} = 10^{-2.71} \quad \text{or} \quad pH = 2.71$$

30.00 ml. added: similarly, pH = 2.04

40.00 ml. added: similarly, pH = 1.64

These data are plotted in the solid line of Figure 36. If the weak acid of which NaA is a salt were of some other ionization constant, the curve prior to the equivalence point would have been displaced as shown by the broken lines. Titration curves for salts of the type BCl, in which B is the cation of a very weak base, by a strong base would be similar to those of Figure 36 except for an inversion on the pH scale.

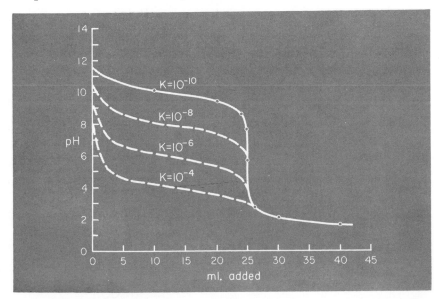

FIGURE 36. Titration curves: salts of weak acid vs. strong acid. 25 ml. 0.1 N solution of salt of weak acid of indicated ionization constant titrated by 0.1 N hydrochloric acid.

Simultaneous or Successive Titration of Two Acids or Bases.
The starting solution in each of the titrations considered thus far in this
chapter has consisted of one acid component or one base component.
Frequently, two or more such components are encountered in practical
situations. Consider a mixture of two acids, HX, and HY, to be titrated by a
strong base. If both are strong acids, the titration is the same as that of
Example 13, as both acids are completely ionized and are identical to each
other insofar as they serve as sources of hydrogen ions. If both are weak acids
and of the same ionization constant, the titration is the same as that of
Example 14, as both acids are again identical as sources of hydrogen ions. If
however, one acid is strong and one weak, or if both are weak but of unequal
strength, the stronger one will tend to react first. The extent to which the
reaction of the stronger one is completed before the second one begins to
react is determined by the relative strengths of the two acids. If this difference
is sufficiently great, the titration curve will show two distinct "breaks,"
one for each of the two successive titrations. How great this difference must
be to provide successful titrations of individual components in mixtures of
acids or of bases will be considered later in this chapter.

The titration of a polybasic weak acid by a strong base is a common
example of the successive titration of two acids. Consider the titration of
sulfurous acid, H_2SO_3, by sodium hydroxide. The acid ionizes in two steps:

$$H_2SO_3 \rightleftharpoons H^+ + HSO_3^- \qquad K_1 = \frac{[H^+][HSO_3^-]}{[H_2SO_3]}$$

$$HSO_3^- \rightleftharpoons H^+ + SO_4^= \qquad K_2 = \frac{[H^+][SO_4^=]}{[HSO_3^-]}$$

The first titration is one of H_2SO_3 by NaOH to form the salt $NaHSO_3$, which
remains in solution as Na^+ and HSO_3^- ions. The second titration is one of
HSO_3^- by NaOH to form the salt Na_2SO_3, which remains in solution predominantly as Na^+ and $SO_3^=$ ions. A titration curve for the titration of
25.00 ml. of 0.1000 M H_2SO_3 by 0.1 N NaOH would show two end points.
Curves for tribasic acid vs. strong base and of polyacidic base vs. strong acid
are analogous.

Another common example of the successive titration of two components
is that of sodium carbonate solution by hydrochloric acid. This titration also
proceeds in two steps, the first involving changing carbonate ions to bicarbonate ions and the second changing bicarbonate ions to carbonic acid
molecules.

$$H^+ + CO_3^= \rightleftharpoons HCO_3^- \qquad K_2 = \frac{[H^+][CO_3^=]}{[HCO_3^-]}$$

$$H^+ + HCO_3^- \rightleftharpoons H_2CO_3 \qquad K_1 = \frac{[H^+][HCO_3^-]}{[H_2CO_3]}$$

If the two acids were of equal strength, the two reactions would proceed
simultaneously. However, K_2 is 4.4×10^{-11} and K_1 is 3.8×10^{-7}, so the one

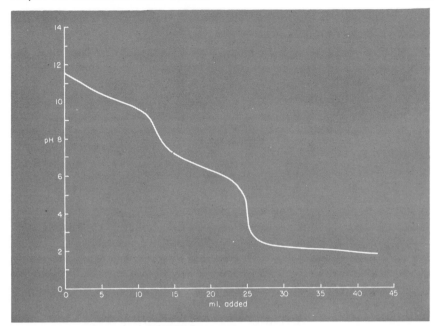

FIGURE 37. Titration curve: dibasic salt vs. strong acid. 25 ml. 0.1 N sodium carbonate titrated by 0.1 N hydrochloric acid.

represented by K_2 goes prior to that of K_1. A typical titration curve for this type of titration is shown in Figure 37. There are two equivalence points, one at a pH of about 8 and one at a pH of about 4, representing the two steps in the titration.

We have now constructed calculated titration curves for the several types of neutralization titration. The same curves can be constructed from experimentally determined data by the methods described in Chapter 20 and included in Experiment 41. Before we consider the significance of the several titration curves which have been constructed thus far, we must consider further the nature of neutralization indicator reactions.

NEUTRALIZATION INDICATORS

A neutralization indicator was described in Chapter 10 as an organic dye that is either a weak acid or base. It exhibits one color form in acid solution and another color form in basic solution, with the two colors arising from the forms of the indicator with and without the proton

$$In_A \rightleftharpoons H^+ + In_B$$
$$\text{(Color A)} \qquad \text{(Color B)}$$

Equilibrium calculations may be applied quantitatively to the reaction of the indicator to provide information concerning the proper choice of an indicator for any specific titration.

Indicator Constants. The equilibrium constant expression for the indicator system as represented by the preceding chemical equation is

$$K_{In} = \frac{[H^+][In_B]}{[In_A]}$$

This constant is called the indicator constant. The equation may be rearranged, as

$$[H^+] = K_{In} \frac{[In_A]}{[In_B]}$$

The substance In_A is of color A and, ideally at least, the intensity of color A is a direct measure of the concentration of In_A in solution (the relationships between intensity of color and concentrations of the colored substances are discussed in detail in Chapter 17). Likewise, substance In_B is of color B and, ideally, the intensity of color B is a direct measure of the concentration of In_B in solution. Therefore, this mathematical expression may be rewritten as

$$[H^+] = K_{In} \frac{(\text{color A intensity})}{(\text{color B intensity})}$$

To the average eye, a solution containing two colored substances, A and B, will appear to be of color A if the A intensity is ten times as great as that of color B, and the solution will appear of color B if the B intensity is ten times greater than that of color A. At intermediate ratios of color intensities, there is an intermediate and often indistinguishable color. Substituting these two color conditions into the preceding equation, we find that

if $[H^+] = K_{In} \times 10$, or more, the solution appears to be color A;

if $[H^+] = K_{In} \times 0.1$, or less, the solution appears to be color B.

These two equations may conveniently be written in pK and pH values, as

color A if pH $= pK_{In} - 1$ or less;

color B if pH $= pK_{In} + 1$ or more

The change in pH required to change the indicator from one color form to the other is two units, and this pH range is centered on the pK_{In} value.

A list of typical indicators, along with the pH range over which each changes from one color form to the other, is given in Table 12. It may be noted that the change ranges are often about two pH units, although quite a few are less. The factor of 10 used in the preceding paragraph is an approximation, of course. The human eye responds more readily to some shades of color than to others, and some substances are naturally more intensely colored than others are, even at the same concentrations. It is very important, however, to emphasize two things: a pH change of two units or nearly so is usually required to produce a visible color change of a neutralization indicator; the pK_{In} value of the indicator itself determines where that change range is located on the pH scale.

Some indicators change from colorless to a color rather than from one color to another. That is to say, either color A or color B may be colorless.

Table 12. Selected Neutralization Indicators

Indicator	Color Change (Lower pH Color Listed First)	Approximate pH Range of Color Change
Picric acid	colorless to yellow	0.1 to 0.8
Paramethyl red	red to yellow	1.0 to 3.0
2,6-Dinitrophenol	colorless to yellow	2.0 to 4.0
Bromphenol blue	yellow to blue	3.0 to 4.6
Congo red	blue to red	3.0 to 5.0
Methyl orange	red to yellow	3.1 to 4.4
Ethyl orange	red to yellow	3.4 to 4.5
Alizarin red S	yellow to purple	3.7 to 5.0
Methyl red	red to yellow	4.2 to 6.2
Methyl purple	purple to green	4.8 to 5.4
Propyl red	red to yellow	4.6 to 6.6
Paranitrophenol	colorless to yellow	5.0 to 7.0
Bromcresol purple	yellow to purple	5.2 to 6.8
Bromthymol blue	yellow to blue	6.0 to 7.6
Brilliant yellow	yellow to orange	6.6 to 8.0
Neutral red	red to amber	6.7 to 8.0
Phenol red	yellow to red	6.7 to 8.4
Metanitrophenol	colorless to yellow	6.7 to 8.6
Phenolphthalein	colorless to pink	8.3 to 10.0
Thymolphthalein	colorless to blue	9.4 to 10.6
Alizarin blue-5	amber and green to blue green	11.0 to 12.0
2,4,6-Trinitrotoluene	colorless to orange	12.0 to 14.0

The pH range necessary to produce a visible end point indication in the one color type of indicator is governed to some extent by the concentration of the indicator, while such is not the case for an indicator which possesses two distinct colors.

Concentration of Indicator. If the concentration of a two-color indicator is increased, the acidic and basic form color intensities are both increased proportionally, and the end point should still be marked by the same intermediate color even though its intensity is similarly increased. However, if the concentration of a colored to colorless indicator is increased, the intensity of the colored form is increased while there is no visible change whatever in the colorless form. Therefore, a relatively concentrated solution of a one-color indicator at a particular pH might appear the same as a more dilute solution of the same indicator at a different pH.

There is one further point in regard to concentration of the indicator. The change of the indicator from one form to another actually uses up or liberates some hydrogen ions. The quantity of hydrogen ions thus consumed or provided ideally must be negligible in comparison to the number provided by the acid involved in the main titration reaction, otherwise a significant error is introduced. The magnitude of this indicator error increases as the concentration of indicator is increased. Therefore, the indicator concentration should not be any larger than required to render the end point change visible. This indicator error is often of slight but measurable magnitude, and this is one reason why experimental end points and theoretical end points often do not coincide perfectly.

Mixed Indicators. A mixed indicator, which generally consists of a conventional indicator with an added organic dye, is sometimes used to increase the apparent sharpness of the visible end point. The added dye may be another indicator, but more commonly it is a substance not affected by pH. A properly selected substance of the latter type serves to block out certain wavelengths of light common to both colors of the indicating substance; essentially, only the components of color A and of color B which differ from each other are observed by the analyst. For example, consider an indicating substance of which color A is blue-green and color B is yellow-green, with an added dye which absorbs green throughout. This mixed indicator would exhibit a color change from blue to yellow, which would be more distinct than the change from blue-green to yellow-green obtained without the added dye.

Mixed indicators may involve even more complex color relationships. Methyl orange and xylene cyanole FF comprise a common mixed indicator. Methyl orange appears yellow in alkaline solution. Xylene cyanole absorbs yellow and orange strongly, so this mixed indicator causes an alkaline solution to appear green. In acid solution methyl orange absorbs in the green region, xylene cyanole still absorbs in the yellow-orange region, and the mixed indicator color is blue-red. In the intermediate region, which is at a pH of about 4 because the pK_{In} value is about 4, the solution appears nearly colorless because of the transmission of complementary colors.

Another mixed indicator, methyl purple, is of tremendous value. Methyl purple consists of methyl red (red below pH 4.2 and yellow above pH 6.2) mixed with an inert blue dyestuff. This mixed indicator not only has a very pronounced color change but it is discernible over a very narrow range of pH values. Methyl purple is purple below pH 4.8, green above pH 5.4, and passes through an intermediate light gray color between 4.8 and 5.4.

Effect of Temperature and Solvent. The data listed in Table 12 concerning neutralization indicators are valid only in aqueous solutions at room temperature, 25° C. Special indicator calibration is needed if a pH is to be measured, or the indicator is to be used, under other conditions. An increase in temperature raises the value of K_w and may also influence the value of K_{In}. Use of another solvent, even of a mixed solvent, alters the K_{In}

value also. Similar effects may be exerted upon the main titration reactants as well.

FEASIBILITY OF TITRATIONS

The construction of theoretical titration curves provides student practice with nearly every useful type of pH calculation. Furthermore, a titration curve gives at a glance very important information concerning whether or not a titration is feasible and, if so, what indicator to use.

Because neutralization indicators require up to two pH units to change from one color form to the other, no neutralization titration is feasible unless the pH changes abruptly by about two or more units around the end point. As seen in Figure 31, strong acid vs. strong base titrations are feasible on this basis unless the reagent concentrations are excessively dilute. The limit of acceptable dilution is set by the facts that water itself is an acid (and a base) and that the acid to be titrated must supply considerably more hydrogen ions than does water. A 10^{-5} N acid or base would likely be an absolute limit, although the random presence in the solutions of dissolved carbon dioxide and/or other acidic or basic components (including the indicator itself) generally sets a practical limit of acceptable dilution at a ten- to hundredfold greater concentration.

The weak acid vs. strong base titration of Figure 32 does have the requisite vertical portion of the titration curve, but the plots of Figure 33 reveal that there is a limit to how weak an acid can be and still have the vertical portion of about two pH units. The concentration of the titrant also influences the magnitude of the "jump" at the equivalence point. As a general rule, the titration of a weak acid vs. a strong base is feasible if the product of the concentration of the titrant and the ionization constant is at least 1×10^{-8}. Thus, using a 0.1 N reagent, the titration is feasible if the ionization constant is 1×10^{-7} or greater; this value is consistent with Figure 33. This general rule must be considered as only very approximate, because some indicators require less of a pH change in order to change color than do others. Also, an error of a few percent may be acceptable in some titrations but not in others. The ionization constant of water is significant in this generalization, as may be seen, for example, from the fact that the upper portion of the curve of Figure 32 is obtained by subtracting each calculated pOH from pK_w.

The weak base by strong acid titration of Figure 34 shows an adequate equivalence point rise in pH. Curves for bases of differing strength would lead to a generalization similar to that of the preceding paragraph, namely: a weak base vs. strong acid titration is feasible if the product of the concentration of the titrant and the ionization constant is at least 1×10^{-8}.

The weak acid vs. weak base titration, Figure 35, is definitely not a useful one because the pH does not undergo a sufficiently wide and sufficiently abrupt change in pH near the equivalence point. If the acid and/or basic strengths were greater, one or both of the halves of the curve of Figure 35 would approach that with the corresponding strong reagent and render the titration more feasible. In practical situations, however, a strong reagent can almost always be chosen as the titrant so that the nonfeasibility of weak acid vs. weak base titrations is not a source of difficulty. Moreover, the electrical conductance method of end point indication, Chapter 20, does not require the abrupt change in pH in the vicinity of the end point.

The displacement titration of the salt of a weak acid by a strong acid, Figure 36, is seen to be feasible as long as the weak acid which is involved is sufficiently weak. Again, the concentration of the titrant is also of significance as it determines how far down is the right half of the curve of Figure 36. In general, this type of titration is feasible if the quotient, concentration of titrant ÷ ionization constant of weak acid equals 10^6 or more. The titration of bicarbonate ion to carbonate and by 0.1 N hydrochloric acid presents an interesting case:

$$\frac{\text{concentration of titrant}}{K_a} = \frac{10^{-1}}{3.8 \times 10^{-7}} = 10^{5.40}$$

This ratio does not quite equal or exceed 10^6; this is why it is necessary in Laboratory Experiments 10 and 13 to boil off the product of the titration reaction in order to drive it to completion and get an accurate end point. The displacement titration of the salt of a weak base by a strong base is similarly feasible if the quotient of the concentration of the titrant divided by the ionization constant of the weak base equals at least 10^6.

Titrations of two or more basic substances by an acid or of two or more acidic substances by a base result in two or more possible end points. In the carbonate titration of Figure 37, for example, there is a pH change around the second end point in the region of pH 4, while there is a less sharp end point earlier around a pH of 10. The titration of sodium carbonate by strong acid is, therefore, quite feasible if the second end point is used (particularly if it is improved by removal of carbon dioxide as already discussed). In addition, the less exact first end point may be used to advantage in some titrations to be described in a later section of this chapter.

In general, it is possible to titrate one base in the presence of another acid if the pK values of the two differ by at least four units. In Figure 33 it is seen that the pH does not rise to 5, for example, until the titration of the acid of $K = 10^{-4}$ is almost complete and that the acid of $K = 10^{-8}$ is just barely started by the time the pH is up to 5. If two acids differ in pK by more than 4 units, the stronger one reacts even more completely before the second one reacts much at all. If two acids differ in pK by less than 4 units, the reaction of the second one is well under way before the reaction of the first one is complete. Similar observations can be made on Figure 36. In the carbonate example, Figure 37, the two bases, carbonate ion and bicarbonate ion, have ionization constants of 4.4×10^{-11} and 3.8×10^{-7}, so their pK's differ by just about four units.

CHOICE OF INDICATORS

The titration curve, along with a listing of indicators as in Table 12, serves directly as the basis for the choice of indicator. The one requirement is that the indicator change from one color to another within the pH interval through which the titration solution passes at its end point. For this discussion, only three indicators will be considered:

methyl orange—red below pH 3.1, yellow above pH 4.4
bromthymol blue—yellow below pH 6.0, blue above pH 7.6
phenolphthalein—colorless below pH 8.3, pink above pH 10.0

For the strong acid vs. strong base titration (solid line of Figure 31), the pH jumps around the equivalence point abruptly from about 3.0 to about 10.0, so any one of the three indicators should suffice. In practice, methyl orange should be used in preference to phenolphthalein, however, for another reason—residual dissolved carbon dioxide acts as an acid to phenolphthalein, while it is essentially neutral to methyl orange. The more dilute strong acid vs. strong base titration (broken line of Figure 31), requires an indicator changing closer to pH 7, so bromthymol blue would be definitely preferable to either of the other two. Methyl orange would indicate a very broad and a very inaccurate end point in the titration of a weak acid vs. a strong base (Figure 32); phenolphthalein would clearly be the best choice of the three indicators being considered. Figure 34 reveals that in this strong acid vs. weak base titration methyl orange would be the best of the three, bromthymol blue would be acceptable but of somewhat questionable value, and phenolphthalein would be of absolutely no use.

In the carbonate titration of Figure 36 methyl orange provides a good indication of the second end point. If an indicator changing sharply right at about pH 8 could be used, the first end point could also be indicated. Actually, phenolphthalein does provide an approximation to this first end point. Since it is a one-color indicator, the change interval is dependent upon such factors as concentration, so the range listed above and in the table is certainly not a precise one. Admittedly, this first end point with phenolphthalein does come a bit too soon, and it is not so sharp as would ordinarily be desired, so it is not useful in work of extremely high accuracy. It is useful, however, in titrations of mixtures of, for example, sodium carbonate and sodium hydroxide by strong acid.

Determination of Carbonate and Hydroxide in Presence of Each Other. When standard acid is added to a solution containing both $CO_3^=$ and OH^- ions, the first two reactions occur simultaneously

$$H^+ + CO_3^= \rightleftharpoons HCO_3^-$$
$$H^+ + OH^- \rightleftharpoons HOH$$

and the completion of these reactions may be marked by the change of phenolphthalein indicator from pink to colorless. Then, as more acid is added, the following reaction occurs:

$$H^+ + HCO_3^- \rightleftharpoons H_2CO_3$$

The completion of this reaction is marked by the characteristic end point color change of methyl orange. The volume of standard acid required for complete neutralization of the carbonate is twice that required to go from the phenolphthalein end point to the methyl orange end point, while the remainder of the standard acid used is equivalent to the amount of hydroxide in the sample. Thus, one "double" titration may be used to determine the amounts of sodium carbonate and sodium hydroxide in the presence of each other.

An alternative procedure is to determine the total basic strength on one portion of the sample (following the same procedure as for the soda ash determination) and then to determine the basic strength of another portion of the sample by a similar titration after precipitation of the carbonate as barium carbonate. If phenolphthalein indicator is used in the latter titration, the insoluble barium carbonate need not be filtered off prior to the titration. Thus, one titration shows the total milliequivalents of base while the other reveals the milliequivalents of hydroxide. This procedure is preferable to the one titration method because the first end point in that one titration method is not very sharp. Mixtures of a carbonate and a bicarbonate may be analyzed in an analogous manner.

TITRATIONS IN NONAQUEOUS SOLVENTS

As already pointed out, a hydrogen ion cannot exist in solution as a free proton. The predominant form of the hydrogen ion in aqueous solution is the hydronium ion, H_3O^+. In other solvents the principal form is similar, with one solvent molecule combined with one proton. In pure acetic acid (frequently designated as glacial acetic acid to prevent confusion with aqueous solutions), the hydrogen ion is in the form of $H_2C_2H_3O_2^+$, which is one proton plus one acetic acid molecule. The titrations of a weak base, NH_3, by a strong acid in each of these two solvents may be represented by the equations:

(a) $H_3O^+ + NH_3 \rightleftharpoons NH_4^+ + H_2O$

(b) $H_2C_2H_3O_3^+ + NH_3 \rightleftharpoons NH_4^+ + HC_2H_3O_2$

Remembering that a base is a proton-acceptor, we may make these equations general by replacing NH_3 by B to represent any weak base.

As each of these reactions proceeds to the right, NH_3 is accepting protons, while the solvent molecule is accepting protons as the reverse reaction proceeds. The extents to which reactions (a) and (b) proceed to completion to the right are determined by the relative strengths as bases (i.e., as proton-acceptors) of NH_3 and H_2O in (a) and of NH_3 and $HC_2H_3O_2$

in (b). We know that acetic acid is a much stronger acid than is water which means, conversely, that water is more basic than is acetic acid. Therefore, the reaction of (b) proceeds more quantitatively from left to right than does (a). The base, NH_3, is effectively a stronger base (a more powerful proton-acceptor) in glacial acetic acid than it is in water. This leads us to the very important conclusion that many bases which are too weak in aqueous medium to be titrated by strong acid can be titrated successfully if the solvent is glacial acetic acid. Other solvents which are similarly less basic (more acidic) than water could also be used.

The use of the acidic solvent not only renders the weak base a stronger base, but it also shifts the titrant strong acid in the same direction. Thus, an acid which is a strong acid in water is not necessarily a strong acid in the glacial acetic solvent. Both hydrochloric and perchloric acids are strong acids in water because they are ionized completely

$$HCl + H_2O \longrightarrow H_3O^+ + Cl^-$$

$$HClO_4 + H_2O \longrightarrow H_3O^+ + ClO_4^-$$

However, in solutions of the same solutes in glacial acetic acid, the ionization is less complete

$$HCl + HC_2H_3O_2 \rightleftharpoons H_2C_2H_3O_2^+ + Cl^-$$

$$HClO_4 + HC_2H_3O_2 \rightleftharpoons H_2C_2H_3O_2^+ + ClO_4^-$$

Hydrochloric acid is actually a rather weak acid in this solvent, while perchloric acid is almost completely ionized. Therefore, perchloric acid is preferable as the strong acid titrant in glacial acetic acid solutions.

Among the bases which are too weak to be titrated by strong acid in water solutions but which can be titrated in a glacial acetic acid solvent are numerous organic amines (compounds with molecules like ammonia but with one or more of the three hydrogen atoms replaced by organic groupings of atoms) and amino acids (titrated as amines because the substances are effectively not acids in this solvent). In addition, anions of some salts, including acetates, bisulfites, bromides, chlorides and others, are sufficiently basic to be titrated by strong acid in displacement titrations.

Consider next the effect of a solvent more basic than water upon the acidic strength of weak acids dissolved in it. Solutions of both hydrochloric and acetic acids in butylamine are ionized completely

$$HCl + C_4H_9NH_2 \longrightarrow C_4H_9NH_3^+ + Cl^-$$

$$HC_2H_3O_2 + C_4H_9NH_2 \longrightarrow C_4H_9NH_3^+ + C_2H_3O_2^-$$

Thus, acetic acid, which is moderately weak in water, is a very strong acid in the more basic solvent. Other acids, which are too weak to be titrated successfully by a strong base in water, are sufficiently strong in butylamine to make their titrations feasible. Other basic solvents are also used, including ethylenediamine, methanol-benzene mixtures and dimethylformamide; although some of these solvents combine with solutes by mechanisms other than by ionization. The titrant must be a base which is strong even in the basic solvent. Sodium and potassium hydroxides, the most common strong base titrants for use in aqueous media, are not sufficiently soluble in some of the other solvents. Sodium methoxide and sodium tetraphenylmethane are frequently used as the titrants in the titrations of weak acids in basic solvents.

Among the acids which are too weak to be titrated in aqueous solutions but are made sufficiently strong by use of a solvent more basic than water are carboxylic acids (some but not all are titratable in water), alcohols, phenols, sulfonamides and a few salts of ammonia and of organic amines.

The solubilities of reactants and of products preclude the usefulness of nonaqueous solvents in some instances. Many of the very weak acids and bases for which nonaqueous titrations are especially applicable are organic compounds for which the nonaqueous solvents are especially suitable. When two or more solvents are equally acceptable from the standpoint of acidity and basicity, the solubilities of the main reactants and their reaction products dictate which solvent is selected.

The pH ranges over which neutralization indicators change color are not directly applicable to titrations in nonaqueous solvents. In fact, the concept of pH must be modified somewhat to apply it to systems other than water. However, several acid-base color indicators, including crystal violet, methyl violet, methyl red and modified methyl orange, have been found empirically to function acceptably in certain nonaqueous titrations. The color reactions are not the same as in water. In addition, several instrumental methods of detecting end points are suitable for nonaqueous systems. The potentiometric method, described in Chapter 20 for titrations in aqueous media, is particularly useful in nonaqueous systems.

No laboratory directions are included in this book for acid-base titrations in nonaqueous solvents. However, good student determinations can be taken directly from the book listed as item 5 in Appendix 7.

REVIEW QUESTIONS

1. Define and characterize the following terms: hydrolysis, buffer solution, pH.
2. Discuss the influence of the solvent upon the strength of an acid. Is hydrochloric acid ever a weak acid? Is acetic acid ever a strong acid?
3. Name specific ingredients of two buffer solutions, one of which maintains a pH somewhere above 7 and the other below 7.
4. What is meant by the term "capacity of a buffer solution"? What limits the capacity of any given buffer solution?
5. Explain with the aid of a generalized equilibrium constant equation how a buffer solution can maintain a constant pH upon dilution.
6. Sketch titration curves for the following titrations, clearly labeling the axes:
   (a) 50 ml. 0.1 N hydrochloric acid titrated by 0.1 N sodium hydroxide.
   (b) 50 ml. 0.001 N hydrochloric acid titrated by 0.001 N sodium hydroxide.
   (c) 50 ml. 0.1 N benzoic acid titrated by 0.1 N sodium hydroxide.
   (d) 50 ml. 0.1 N benzoic acid titrated by 0.1 N ammonium hydroxide.
   (e) 50 ml. 0.1 N hydrochloric acid titrated by 0.1 N ammonium hydroxide.

7. State whether each of the titrations of (6) is feasible and, if so, name a suitable color indicator.
8. Explain in words and in chemical equations why the pH at the end point in a weak acid vs. strong base titration is not equal to 7.
9. In view of hydrolysis effects, is it possible for a solution of a salt of a weak acid and a weak base to have a pH of 7? Explain.
10. What is a mixed indicator? Illustrate.
11. Suggest a procedure for the determination of carbonate and bicarbonate in the presence of each other.
12. Suggest a procedure whereby the approximate ionization constant for an unknown weak acid of the type HA can be determined from an experimentally obtained titration curve, assuming that a pure sample of the unknown acid is available.
13. Consider 100 ml. of 0.1 N acetic acid at 25° C.:
    (a) Will addition of 1 gram of pure acetic acid cause the ionization constant of acetic acid to increase, decrease or remain the same?
    (b) Will addition of 1 gram of sodium acetate cause the pH of the solution to increase, decrease or remain the same?
    (c) Will addition of 1 gram of sodium acetate cause the hydroxyl ion concentration to increase, decrease or remain the same?
14. Consider 50 ml. of 0.1 N ammonium hydroxide at 25° C.:
    (a) Will the end point solution in titration of this solution with 0.1 N hydrochloric acid have a pH of less than 7, equal to 7 or greater than 7?
    (b) Will addition of 1 gram of pure acetic acid cause the pH to increase, decrease or remain the same?
    (c) Will addition of 1 gram of ammonium chloride cause the hydroxyl ion concentration to increase, decrease or remain the same?

PROBLEMS

1. Convert the following pH values to [H^+]: 6.2; 4.3; 11.7.
2. Convert the following pOH values to [H^+]: 3.8; 9.2; 2.6.
3. Convert the following hydrogen ion concentrations (in moles per liter) to pH values: 0.015; 1.5; 2×10^{-5}.
4–15. Calculate the pH of each solution.
    4. 40 ml. of 0.1 M hydrochloric acid.
    5. 40 ml. containing 1.00 gram nitric acid, HNO_3.
    6. 40 ml. containing 12.0 mg. potassium hydroxide, KOH.
    7. 0.025 N sodium hydroxide.
    8. 40 ml. containing 2.0 gram hydrochloric acid and 1.0 gram sodium chloride.
    9. 0.01 M potassium nitrate.
    10. 0.01 M acetic acid.
    11. 40 ml. containing 0.50 gram acetic acid, $HC_2H_3O_2$.
    12. 40 ml. containing 0.50 gram acetic acid and 1.00 gram sodium acetate.
    13. 500 ml. of 0.10 N ammonium hydroxide to which 3.0 grams solid ammonium chloride have been added.
    14. 0.10 M ammonium chloride.
    15. 0.10 M sodium acetate.
16–22. Calculate the pH of the solution obtained by mixing each pair of solutions.
    16. 40 ml. 0.01 M sodium hydroxide and 60 ml. 0.01 M nitric acid.
    17. 20 ml. 0.01 M hydrochloric acid and 30 ml. 0.01 M hydrochloric acid.
    18. 30 ml. 0.010 M acetic acid and 15 ml. 0.010 M potassium hydroxide.

19. 20 ml. 0.20 M acid, whose $K = 1.0 \times 10^{-6}$, and 20 ml. 0.20 M base, whose $K = 1.0 \times 10^{-6}$.
20. 20 ml. 0.20 M hydrochloric acid and 40 ml. 0.10 M sodium hydroxide.
21. 10 ml. 0.10 M hydrochloric acid and 30 ml. 0.10 M ammonium hydroxide.
22. 12.0 ml. 0.10 M sodium hydroxide and 36.0 ml. 0.10 M acetic acid.
23. Calculate the pH of the solution prepared by adding 100 ml. water to 100 ml. of a solution which was 0.10 M in hydrochloric acid and 0.10 M in sodium chloride.
24. Calculate the pH of the solution prepared by adding 100 ml. water to 100 ml. of a solution which was 0.10 M in acetic acid and 0.10 M in sodium acetate.
25. In what molar proportion must acetic acid and sodium acetate be mixed to provide a buffer of pH 6.2?
26. In what molar proportion must ammonium hydroxide and ammonium chloride be mixed to give a buffer of pH 8.4?
27-30. Calculate the pH at (a) the initial point, (b) the point halfway to the equivalence point and (c) the equivalence point in each of the following titrations:
  27. 40 ml. 0.1 N hydrochloric acid titrated by 0.1 N sodium hydroxide.
  28. 40 ml. 0.001 N hydrochloric acid titrated by 0.001 N sodium hydroxide.
  29. 40 ml. 0.1 N benzoic acid titrated by 0.1 N potassium hydroxide.
  30. 40 ml. 0.1 N ammonium hydroxide titrated by 0.1 N hydrochloric acid.
31. A sample contains sodium hydroxide and sodium carbonate. If 20.00 ml. of 0.1000 N acid are needed to titrate it to the phenolphthalein end point and an additional 5.00 ml. to complete the titration from the phenolphthalein end point to the methyl orange end point, how many grams of each constituent are in the sample?
32. A mixture of sodium hydroxide, sodium carbonate and inert ingredients weighing 0.2500 gram was dissolved and divided into two equal aliquots. One aliquot was titrated with 0.1016 N acid using phenolphthalein as indicator and required 22.50 ml. The other aliquot was titrated with the same acid solution but with methyl orange as indicator and required 26.00 ml. Calculate the percentage composition of (a) sodium hydroxide, (b) sodium carbonate and (c) inert ingredients.
33. A 2.000 gram sample containing sodium carbonate and sodium bicarbonate and possibly inert material was dissolved and titrated cold with 0.5000 N hydrochloric acid. When phenolphthalein was the indicator the end point was reached when 24.00 ml. of acid had been added. Methyl orange was then added, and an additional 35.00 ml. acid was required to reach its end point. What were the percentages of sodium carbonate and sodium bicarbonate in the mixture?
34. A mixture, containing 0.5000 gram pure, dry sodium hydroxide and 0.5000 gram pure, dry sodium bicarbonate was dissolved and titrated with 0.5000 N acid. What volume of acid was necessary (a) to arrive at the phenolphthalein end point and (b) to go from the phenolphthalein end point to the methyl orange end point?
35. A mixture contains only sodium carbonate and barium carbonate. If a 1.0000 gram sample requires 50.00 ml. of 0.2500 N hydrochloric acid for complete neutralization, what is the percentage of each component in the mixture?

SUGGESTIONS FOR ADDITIONAL READING

Items 2, 5, 10, 11, 13, 14, 25, 27 and 30, Appendix 7.

Chapter 12

Volumetric

Precipitation Methods

A QUANTITATIVE determination by a volumetric precipitation method is based upon the measurement of the quantity of a standard solution which is required to react in a precipitation reaction with the unknown substance or some derivative of that substance.

COMPARISON BETWEEN GRAVIMETRIC AND VOLUMETRIC PRECIPITATION METHODS

In a gravimetric determination an excess of the precipitating agent is added to the solution of the unknown. In a volumetric precipitation determination the end point in the titration of the solution of the unknown with the standard solution is the point at which neither substance is in excess, that is, the point at which both substances are present in stoichiometrically equivalent amounts. Some means must be provided for the analyst to detect this end point. Chemical indicator systems are considered in this chapter. Some of the electrical and optical indicator systems discussed in Chapters 18 and 20 are also applicable to volumetric precipitation titrations.

Some coprecipitation errors are of significance in volumetric as well as in gravimetric precipitation methods. In a volumetric determination, the experimental work is completed as soon as all of the precipitate has been formed, so coprecipitation causes error only when the coprecipitated substance consumes a significant amount of one of the main reactants. Unfortunately, many coprecipitation phenomena do fall into this category. The unit operations of coagulation, filtration, washing and weighing are necessary in gravimetric but not in volumetric precipitation methods.

TITRATION CURVES

Titration curves for volumetric precipitation titrations are analogous to those for neutralization titrations. Each curve consists of a plot of the concentration of one of the main reactants (generally in a logarithmic quantity) vs. the volume of added reagent. The curves may be constructed either from calculated data or from experimentally measured data. As an example of a typical precipitation titration, consider the titration of 25.00 ml. of 0.1000 M NaCl by a titrating solution of 0.1000 M $AgNO_3$. The curve may be a plot of pCl, defined by the equation

$$[Cl^-] = 10^{-pCl}$$

vs. ml. of standard silver nitrate solution. The methods of calculation of each point for the construction of the curve are somewhat analogous to those used for neutralization titrations. Prior to the equivalence point, unreacted chloride ion is present in the solution, so the pCl may be calculated from the quantity of unreacted chloride ion and the volume. At the equivalence point, the concentrations of chloride and silver ions equal each other, so the pCl may be calculated from the solubility product constant of silver chloride. Beyond the equivalence point, unreacted silver ion is present, so the pCl may be calculated from the quantity of unreacted silver ion, the volume and the solubility product constant.

0.00 ml. $AgNO_3$ added:

$$[Cl^-] = 0.1000$$

$$[Cl^-] = 10^{-1.00}, \text{ so pCl} = 1.00$$

10.00 ml. added:

mEq. Cl^- left = mEq. Cl^- at start − mEq. Cl^- used up by Ag^+
mEq. Cl^- left = 25.00 × 0.1000 − 10.00 × 0.1000
mEq. Cl^- left = 1.500

$$[Cl^-] = \frac{\text{mEq. } Cl^- \text{ left}}{\text{ml.}}$$

$$[Cl^-] = \frac{1.500}{35.00}$$

$$[Cl^-] = 10^{-1.37}, \text{ so pCl} = 1.37$$

20.00 ml. added: similarly, pCl = 1.95
24.00 ml. added: similarly, pCl = 2.69
24.90 ml. added: similarly, pCl = 3.70
25.00 ml. added (this is the exact equivalence point):

$$K_{sp} = [Ag^+][Cl^-]$$

$$K_{sp} = 1.56 \times 10^{-10}$$

$$[Ag^+] = [Cl^-] \text{ (true at equivalence point only)}$$

$$1.56 \times 10^{-10} = [Cl^-]^2$$

$$[Cl^-] = 10^{-4.90}, \text{ so pCl} = 4.90$$

25.10 ml. added:

mEq. Ag$^+$ present = mEq. Ag$^+$ added − mEq. Ag$^+$ used up by Cl$^-$
mEq. Ag$^+$ present = 25.10 × 0.1000 − 25.00 × 0.1000
mEq. Ag$^+$ present = 0.0100

$$[Ag^+] = \frac{mEq.\ Ag^+\ present}{ml.}$$

$$[Ag^+] = \frac{0.0100}{50.10}$$

$$[Ag^+] = 10^{-3.70}$$

but

$$[Cl^-] = \frac{K_{sp}}{[Ag^+]}$$

$$[Cl^-] = \frac{1.56 \times 10^{-10}}{10^{-3.70}}$$

$$[Cl^-] = 10^{-6.11},\ so\ pCl = 6.11$$

25.00 ml. added: similarly, pCl = 7.10
30.00 ml. added: similarly, pCl = 7.77
50.00 ml. added: similarly, pCl = 8.33

The curve for this titration is shown in Figure 38. The curve could have

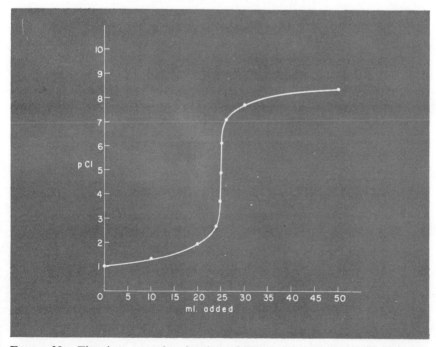

FIGURE 38.   Titration curve for titration of 25 ml. 0.1 N sodium chloride with
0.1 N silver nitrate.

consisted of a plot of pAg, defined by the equation

$$[Ag^+] = 10^{-pAg}$$

vs. ml. of added silver nitrate. The solubility product equation

$$K_{sp} = [Ag^+][Cl^-]$$

may be written in terms of pCl and pAg and the numerical value of the constant, as

$$9.81 = pAg + pCl$$

Thus, each pAg value is 9.81 minus the corresponding pCl value, and the curve would look like that shown except for an inversion.

This titration curve reveals that the end point indicator must be a substance which will reveal a certain level of chloride (or silver) ion concentration. Such indicators are available for this particular titration and for a number of others. However, a lack of suitable indicators is a significant limiting factor in the broader applicability of volumetric precipitation methods of analysis.

In these titrations it is desirable to have as abrupt, or steep, a change in the titration curve at the equivalence point as possible. This consideration was also encountered in the preceding chapter. In general, the abruptness of the rise in the precipitimetry titration curve is greater for a very insoluble compound than for a slightly soluble one.

VOLHARD METHOD

Determination of Silver. The Volhard method, as originally developed for the determination of silver, involves the titration of a solution containing the silver ion with a standard solution of either potassium thiocyanate or ammonium thiocyanate, and the formation of a deep-red-colored ferric thiocyanate complex with the first excess of thiocyanate ion in the titration vessel. The end point is thus marked by the appearance of a colored ion in the solution. The primary reaction in the titration is

$$Ag^+ + SCN^- \longrightarrow AgSCN$$

and the indicator reaction is

$$Fe^{+++} + SCN^- \rightleftharpoons Fe(SCN)^{++}$$

The indicator is usually added to the titrated solution prior to the start of the titration in the form of a solution of ferric alum. It should be noted that, as thiocyanate ions are added from the buret, the thiocyanate ions have the possibility of reacting either with silver ion or with ferric ion. The success of the method requires that, with both ferric and silver ions competing for the thiocyanates, the silver ion will win until the silver ion concentration is reduced to its equivalence point value.

The necessary relationships may be demonstrated by means of the equilibrium constants for the primary and the indicator reactions. The K_{sp} for silver thiocyanate is 1.16×10^{-12}, so the silver ion and thiocyanate ion concentrations are each equal to 1.08×10^{-6} at the true equivalence point in the primary titration reaction. The desire is, then, to use sufficient ferric ion for the color of the $Fe(SCN)^{++}$ complex to become visible when the thiocyanate ion concentration becomes as large as 1.08×10^{-6} molar. Empirical experiment has revealed that the complex imparts noticeable color when its concentration reaches about 10^{-5} molar. The ferric ion concentration necessary to cause the red color to appear just at the proper point in the titration is calculated as follows:

$$K = \frac{[Fe^{+++}][SCN^-]}{[FeSCN^{++}]}$$

$$K = 8.0 \times 10^{-3}$$

$$[SCN^-] = 1.08 \times 10^{-6}$$

$$[FeSCN^{++}] = 10^{-5}$$

$$8.0 \times 10^{-3} = \frac{[Fe^{+++}]1.08 \times 10^{-6}}{10^{-5}}$$

$$[Fe^{+++}] = 0.074$$

This means that the red color of the $FeSCN^{++}$ ion just becomes visible at the theoretical end point in the silver thiocyanate titration if the ferric ion concentration is 0.074 molar. This calculation must be considered only as a very approximate one, however, particularly because of individual variation and uncertainty in the value used for the minimum detectable concentration of the complex ion.

This titration may be performed only in an acidic medium. Silver ion would react in alkaline medium to form insoluble silver oxide

$$2\,Ag^+ + 2\,OH^- \longrightarrow Ag_2O + H_2O$$

The silver ions must be available for reaction with thiocyanate ions for the titration to proceed properly. Furthermore, ferric ions would be precipitated as a hydrous oxide and thus be unavailable for the indicator reaction unless the medium were distinctly acidic.

Determination of Chloride. Although the Volhard procedure is primarily a method for the determination of silver, it may be modified to permit the determination of any ion that forms an insoluble silver salt. In principle, two general modifications are possible, the direct and the indirect methods.

In the direct method, the ion being determined is precipitated as the silver salt by the addition of excess silver nitrate, the precipitate is coagulated, filtered, washed and redissolved. The liberated silver ion may then be titrated with standard thiocyanate solution. From the amount of silver found in the redissolved precipitate, the corresponding amount of the unknown substance in the original solution may be calculated.

The indirect method is much more commonly used, particularly for determinations of chloride and other halides. It involves the addition of an amount of standard silver nitrate solution that is known, and which is known to be in excess, to the solution containing the unknown anion, removal of the precipitate formed, and titration of the remaining silver ion with standard thiocyanate solution. From the total amount of silver nitrate originally used and the amount found to be left over after precipitation of the unknown ion, it is possible to calculate the amount of silver ion used up by the unknown and thus the amount of the unknown substance originally present. Chloride may be successfully determined by this indirect Volhard procedure even when in the presence of reasonable concentrations of a number of the metallic ions, including copper, antimony, arsenic, lead, iron, manganese, cobalt and nickel.

It is ordinarily necessary to remove the silver chloride precipitate from the reaction medium before titration of the excess silver ion with thiocyanate because silver chloride is more soluble than is silver thiocyanate. If allowed to remain during the final titration, the silver chloride would redissolve as thiocyanate ion is introduced. Thus, some silver ions would have reacted, in effect, both with chloride and with thiocyanate so that the resulting titration data would be useless. The removal of silver chloride may be accomplished by filtration or, more easily, by shaking the suspension with nitrobenzene. Nitrobenzene coats the precipitate particles so that they are removed from the possibility of further reaction even though they remain in the titration vessel. When the indirect Volhard procedure is used for the determination of an anion which forms a silver salt less soluble than silver thiocyanate, the primary precipitate need not be removed as it will remain nonreactive during the final titration. Such is the case with silver bromide and silver iodide.

Laboratory Experiment 16

DETERMINATION OF CHLORIDE BY THE INDIRECT VOLHARD METHOD

Reagents

Ammonium thiocyanate, approximately 0.1 N solution, prepared by dissolving 7.6 grams NH_4SCN in water and diluting to one liter

Ferric alum, solution saturated with ferric alum and made 1 N in nitric acid

Nitric acid, stock solution

Nitrobenzene

Silver nitrate, approximately 0.1 N standard solution as a primary standard, prepared by drying and accurately weighing 8.5 grams reagent grade $AgNO_3$, dissolving in water and diluting to the mark in a 500 ml. volumetric flask

Procedure

Standardization of Ammonium Thiocyanate Solution. Fill one buret with the ammonium thiocyanate solution and another with the standard silver nitrate solution. Run about 25 ml. of silver nitrate solution into a 300 ml. Erlenmeyer flask, and dilute to 100 ml. with water. Add 5 ml. ferric alum solution. Titrate with ammonium thiocyanate solution until the first lasting tinge of brownish-red color is seen. Calculate the normality of the ammonium thiocyanate solution.

Chloride Determination. Conduct the determination in triplicate. Dry the sample at 110° C. for one hour. Weigh accurately individual portions of 0.3 gram each into 300 ml. Erlenmeyer flasks. Dissolve in 100 ml. water. Add 1 ml. nitric acid and 5 ml. ferric alum solution. Introduce a quantity of silver nitrate solution known to be in excess (30–40 ml. should suffice). Add 15 ml. nitrobenzene, stopper the flask, and shake vigorously by hand until the precipitate is completely coated with a film of nitrobenzene. Titrate the excess silver nitrate which remains in solution with ammonium thiocyanate solution until the first lasting tinge of brownish-red color appears. Calculate the percentage Cl in the sample.

MOHR METHOD

In the Mohr method for chloride, the chloride ion is precipitated as silver chloride by titration with standard silver nitrate solution in the presence of a small amount of chromate ion. The end point is marked by the appearance of a colored precipitate of silver chromate, which forms with the first excess of titrating agent after practically all of the chloride ion is precipitated. The primary and indicator reactions may be represented, in order, by the following two chemical equations:

$$Ag^+ + Cl^- \longrightarrow AgCl$$

$$2\,Ag^+ + CrO_4^= \longrightarrow Ag_2CrO_4$$

The success of this method depends upon the fact that, if both chromate ion and chloride ion are in appreciable concentration and are competing for silver ions, the chloride will win. This fact may be demonstrated by calculations based upon the two appropriate solubility product constants.

The K_{sp} for silver chloride is 1.56×10^{-10}, so the chloride ion concentration and also the silver ion concentration are each $10^{-4.90}$, or 1.25×10^{-5}, at the true equivalence point, as shown earlier in this chapter. The desire is, then, for the indicator to function as soon as the chloride ion concentration is reduced from its initial value to 1.25×10^{-5} molar, that is, as soon as the silver ion concentration is raised to 1.25×10^{-5} molar. Silver chromate just begins to precipitate when its K_{sp}, 9×10^{-12}, is just exceeded by the product of its ions, each raised to the proper power. The chromate ion concentration needed to cause silver chromate to precipitate at a silver ion concentration of 1.25×10^{-5} molar is calculated as follows:

$$K_{sp} = [Ag^+]^2[CrO_4^=]$$

$$K_{sp} = 9 \times 10^{-12}$$

and $$[Ag^+] = 1.25 \times 10^{-5}$$

so $$9 \times 10^{-12} = (1.25 \times 10^{-5})^2 [CrO_4^=]$$

$$[CrO_4^=] = 0.058$$

This means that silver chromate just begins to precipitate at the theoretical end point in the silver chloride titration if the chromate ion concentration is 0.058 molar.

There is a measureable indicator error in the Mohr titration for several reasons. In the first place, the chromate ion in solution is yellow-colored, and this tends to conceal the appearance of the first small traces of the colored precipitate. In the second place, the human eye requires that a finite amount of the colored precipitate form before it is recognizable. The first factor renders a lower concentration of indicator desirable, while the second factor renders a higher concentration of indicator preferable so that the colored precipitate will begin to form slightly before the true end point. A compromise is necessary, and the first factor is dominant in choosing the optimum indicator concentration. A chromate ion concentration of about 0.002 molar is usually employed. With such a low indicator concentration, the colored precipitate fails to start forming until slightly beyond the true end point, and the end point is further overshot before a noticeable quantity of silver chromate is present. The difference between the true end point and the experimental end point is commonly as great as a couple of tenths of a milliliter of a 0.1 N standard silver nitrate solution. Because of the end point error in a Mohr titration, an indicator blank should be run for each analysis or set of analyses and the corresponding indicator correction applied to the data for subsequent titrations.

The Mohr titration must be carried out in a solution which is either neutral or just barely acidic. An alkaline medium is prohibited again by the insolubility of silver oxide. A strongly acidic solution is not satisfactory because the excess hydrogen ions remove the chromate ions so they are no longer available as such to react to form silver chromate.

$$CrO_4^= + H^+ \rightleftharpoons HCrO_4^-$$

or

$$2\,CrO_4^= + 2\,H^+ \rightleftharpoons Cr_2O_7^= + H_2O$$

The necessity of maintaining the solution at or near neutrality in the Mohr method for the determination of chloride is a serious disadvantage of this method as compared to the indirect Volhard procedure.

The Mohr method is satisfactory for the determination of bromide as well as of chloride. However, iodide and thiocyanate do not give satisfactory results, probably because of strong ion adsorption effects before and at the end point.

Laboratory Experiment 17

DETERMINATION OF CHLORIDE BY THE MOHR METHOD

Reagents

Potassium chromate, solution containing 2.0 gram K_2CrO_4 per 100 ml. solution

Silver nitrate, approximately 0.1 N solution, prepared by dissolving 8.5 grams $AgNO_3$ in water and diluting to 500 ml.

Sodium chloride, analytical reagent grade

Procedure

Standardization of Silver Nitrate Solution. Conduct the standardization in triplicate. Dry the sodium chloride at 110° C. for one hour. Weigh accurately individual portions of about 0.2 gram each into 300 ml. Erlenmeyer flasks. Dissolve in 50 ml. water. Add 2 ml. potassium chromate solution. Titrate with the silver nitrate solution until the first lasting appearance of the colored precipitate, which is silver chromate. The background for viewing the titration flask should be white—a white titration stand or a sheet of glazed white paper. Calculate the normality of the silver nitrate solution. (Note that no indicator blank has been used. A self-correction for the indicator error is provided if the silver nitrate solution is both standardized and used only in Mohr chloride titrations, and if the volumes used each time are approximately the same. If the solution is to be used for any other purpose, a "blank" consisting of about the same volume of water and of chromate as in the preceding titration and a few tenths gram of finely divided calcium carbonate to simulate the white precipitate of silver chloride should be titrated. The volume of silver nitrate solution used in this "blank" titration should be subtracted from the observed amount required in this and subsequent Mohr titrations of chloride.)

Chloride Determination. Follow the same procedure as in the preceding standardization of the silver nitrate solution with primary standard sodium chloride, except use about 0.4 gram samples of the unknown. Calculate the percentage Cl in the sample.

ADSORPTION INDICATOR METHODS

Some organic dyes are more readily adsorbed by colloidal precipitates on one side of the equivalence point than on the other. In some specific cases, the dye undergoes a change in color in the process of being adsorbed. A dye of this type may serve as an indicator. The practical applications of this type of indicator are rather few in number and are very specific in application, yet the few useful ones are of considerable importance.

To review some properties of colloidally dispersed particles as discussed in Chapter 8, a colloidal particle generally attracts to itself a primary adsorbed ion layer consisting primarily of whichever lattice ion is present in excess in the surrounding liquid. Thus, for example, the primary ion layer adsorbed on silver chloride consists of chloride ions before the equivalence point in a titration of chloride by standard silver nitrate solution, while the primary adsorbed ion layer is of silver ions beyond the equivalence point. In turn, a secondary ion layer is attracted more or less tightly, and the sign of the ions in the secondary layer must be opposite to that of the primary layer ions.

Consider now the titration of chloride by standard silver nitrate with some dye, dichlorofluorescein, present in the titration vessel. This dye consists in the solid state of the salt, sodium dichlorofluoresceinate. It ionizes in solution to sodium ions and dichlorofluoresceinate ions, Ind^-. The latter are anions of a weak acid

$$H^+ + Ind^- \rightleftharpoons H\,Ind$$

Unless the pH is unduly high, the indicator is dominantly in solution in the form of the undissociated acid molecules. As soon as the titration is begun, some solid silver chloride is present in the titration vessel. At all points prior to the equivalence point, chloride ion is present in excess, so the primary ion layer consists of chloride ions and the secondary ion layer of any available cations, such as sodium ion, hydrogen ion, etc. Beyond the equivalence point, excess silver nitrate is present in the titration vessel, so the primary adsorbed ion layer is composed of silver ions, and the secondary ion layer of negative ions. This secondary ion layer will include an appreciable number of the indicator anions, causing a shift in the equilibrium represented by the preceding chemical equation to the left. The indicator molecules impart a yellow-green color to the solution, while the indicator ions adsorbed as counter ions on the precipitate particles are pink. Thus, the end point is marked by the change from a green solution to a pink precipitate. In practice, the particles of precipitate are kept sufficiently dispersed so that the observed change appears to be one of green to pink throughout the entire contents of the titration vessel. This method of determining chloride is commonly called the Fajans method.

In this example, dichlorofluorescein has been considered as an indicator for the chloride by silver nitrate titration. Several other indicators have been developed for this and for other precipitation titrations. Eosin and fluorescein both of which are chemically similar to dichlorofluorescein, are useful indicators. Fluorescein is applicable to silver halide precipitations, but only if the pH is held within the approximate limits of 6 to 7 because fluorescein is itself a weaker acid than is dichlorofluorescein. A pH as low as about 4 is acceptable with dichlorofluorescein. Eosin is suitable with precipitations of silver halides and silver thiocyanate in solutions as acidic as pH 3 or 4. Fluorescein is reportedly also suitable for precipitations of lead hydroxide and dichlorofluorescein for lead sulfate. Each of these three indicators is an acidic dye, that is, the anion is responsible for the color characteristics. Several basic dyestuffs, principally rhodamine and related substances, have also been developed as adsorption indicators for use in strongly acidic solutions.

Since the color on one side of the equivalence point appears on the surface of the particles of the main precipitate, it is desirable to have as large a surface area as possible. This means that the individual particles should be kept very small and they should be kept dispersed throughout the suspending solution. It should be noted that these desirable features are exactly opposite to those deemed desirable in gravimetric analysis. Dextrin is used as a protective colloid in the determination of chloride by the adsorption indicator method to help insure the desired physical characteristics of the precipitate.

Laboratory Experiment 18

DETERMINATION OF CHLORIDE BY THE ADSORPTION INDICATOR METHOD

Reagents

Dextrin

Dichlorofluorescein indicator, solution containing 0.1 gram dichlorofluorescein per 100 ml. of 70% alcohol

Silver nitrate, approximately 0.1 N solution; prepared by dissolving
8.5 gram $AgNO_3$ in water and diluting to 500 ml.

Sodium chloride, reagent grade

Procedure

Standardization of Silver Nitrate Solution. Conduct the
standardization in triplicate. Dry the sodium chloride at 110° C.
for one hour. Weigh accurately individual portions of about 0.2
gram each into 300 ml. Erlenmeyer flasks. Dissolve in 50 ml. water.
Add about 0.4 ml. dichlorofluorescein solution and 0.1 gram dextrin.
Titrate, with vigorous swirling, with the silver nitrate solution to the
first lasting appearance of a pink tinge on the particles of precipitated
silver chloride, taking care to keep the flask out of direct sunlight. A white background, either a white titration stand or a
sheet of glazed white paper, should be used as the background in
viewing the titration flask. Calculate the normality of the $AgNO_3$
solution.

Chloride Determination. Follow the same procedure as in
the preceding standardization of the silver nitrate solution with
primary standard sodium chloride, except use about 0.4 gram samples
of the unknown. If the unknown contains carbonate, add acetic acid
(1 part stock solution diluted with 3 parts water) dropwise, after the
dilution to 50 ml., until the solution is just acid to litmus paper.
Calculate the percentage Cl in the sample.

Suggestions for Supplementary Laboratory Work. The
several volumetric methods for the determination of chloride can
readily be compared with one another, because some of the solutions
required for one can also be used for another. Prepare a silver nitrate
solution as a primary standard (Experiment 16). Prepare a sodium

chloride solution as a primary standard (about 2.9 grams of reagent grade NaCl accurately weighed, dissolved and diluted quantitatively to 500 ml.). Standardize the silver nitrate solution vs. the sodium chloride solution by the adsorption indicator method (Experiment 18) and also by the Mohr method (Experiment 17). Prepare and standardize a thiocyanate solution by the Volhard method (Experiment 16), and then restandardize the silver nitrate solution vs. the sodium chloride solution by the Volhard method (Experiment 16). Compare the silver nitrate standardization data as obtained by taking it as a primary standard and as obtained in the three methods of comparison to the standard sodium chloride solution. Also repeat silver nitrate vs. sodium chloride titrations with 2 ml. nitric acid (stock solution) present by the Mohr method and by the adsorption method; explain the results which are obtained. Finally, use any one of the three methods for the determination of the chloride content of your unknown sample.

EXTERNAL INDICATOR METHODS

External indicator methods are possible for many determinations, although they are desirable only when no suitable internal indicators are available. An external indicator is a reagent which will react with one of the constituents involved in a titration to give a precipitate or a colored substance. This type of indicator provides a qualitative test for one of the main reactants. It is not added directly to the solution being titrated, but instead a drop of that solution is withdrawn periodically throughout the titration and mixed with the indicator on a spot test plate.

The method is slow and tedious, because the titration must be stopped and a drop withdrawn for test at frequent intervals. A prior knowledge of the approximate end point will, of course, minimize the number of spot tests which must be performed during a titration. External indicators are used only in titrations for which no good internal indicators are available.

STOICHIOMETRIC CALCULATIONS

Calculations encountered in volumetric precipitation methods of analysis are of two kinds, stoichiometric and mass law, just as are calculations in other branches of quantitative analysis. Mass law problems involving solubility product constants are of significance, but they have been covered in principle in Chapter 8 so will not be discussed further here. Stoichiometric problems here, as in all of volumetric analysis, are approached by means of the three relationships given in Chapter 9:

(1)   mEq. = mEq.

(2)   mEq. = N × ml.

(3) $mEq. = \dfrac{mg.}{eq.\ wt.}$

In volumetric precipitation reactions, the equivalent weight equals the formula weight divided by the positive or negative valence of the ion from that formula which is involved in the precipitation reaction. Thus, the equivalent weight of silver nitrate equals its formula weight, because the silver ion which is involved in the precipitation reaction has a positive valence of one.

Example 1. Exactly 8.4273 grams of primary standard silver nitrate are dissolved in water and diluted to the mark in a 500 ml. volumetric flask. Calculate the normality of the solution.

$$mEq.\ AgNO_3\ weighed\ out = mEq.\ AgNO_3\ in\ solution$$

$$\frac{mg.\ AgNO_3}{eq.\ wt.} = N \times ml.$$

$$\frac{8427.3}{169.89} = N \times 500.0$$

$$N = 0.09921$$

Example 2. A 0.4273 gram sample of a soluble salt was analyzed by the adsorption indicator method, requiring 25.26 ml. of 0.1000 N silver nitrate solution. Calculate the percentage Cl in the sample.

$$mEq.\ Cl = mEq.\ AgNO_3$$

$$\frac{mg.\ Cl}{eq.\ wt.} = N \times ml.$$

$$\frac{mg.\ Cl}{35.457} = 0.1000 \times 25.26$$

$$mg.\ Cl = 0.1000 \times 25.26 \times 35.457$$

but $\% Cl = \dfrac{mg.\ Cl \times 100}{mg.\ sample}$

$$\% Cl = \frac{0.1000 \times 25.26 \times 35.457 \times 100}{427.3}$$

$$\% Cl = 20.96$$

Example 3. Chlorine was determined in a 0.4273 gram sample by an indirect Volhard procedure, in which 40.00 ml. of 0.1068 N silver nitrate solution was used, and 10.21 ml. of 0.1230 N ammonium thiocyanate was required in the back-titration. What is the percentage Cl in the sample?

$$\text{mEq. Cl} + \text{mEq. NH}_4\text{CNS} = \text{mEq. AgNO}_3$$

$$\frac{\text{mg. Cl}}{\text{eq. wt.}} + N \times ml. = N \times ml.$$

$$\frac{\text{mg. Cl}}{35.457} + 0.1230 \times 10.21 = 40.00 \times 0.1068$$

$$\text{mg. Cl} = (40.00 \times 0.1058 - 0.1230 \times 10.21)35.457$$

but
$$\% \text{ Cl} = \frac{\text{mg. Cl} \times 100}{\text{mg. sample}}$$

$$\% \text{ Cl} = \frac{(40.00 \times 0.1068 - 0.1230 \times 10.21)35.457 \times 100}{427.3}$$

$$\% \text{ Cl} = 25.03$$

REVIEW QUESTIONS

1. Contrast gravimetric and volumetric precipitation methods on several significant points.
2. Write chemical equations for the primary and indicator reactions in the Mohr and the Volhard methods.
3. In a chloride determination by the modified Volhard method, a student failed to coat the precipitated silver chloride completely with nitrobenzene. Was his result high, low or correct?
4. Explain why it is not necessary to remove the precipitated silver iodide before the final titration in an iodide determination by the modified Volhard procedure.
5. In the Mohr method for chloride, why must the solution not be acidic, and why must it not be basic?
6. In a determination of chloride by the Mohr method, a student added the correct amount of indicator, made the solution distinctly acid and titrated. Was the percentage of chloride he obtained high, low or correct?
7. Make sketches of the precipitate in a Fajans chloride determination both before and after the equivalence point showing the relative positions and composition of the primary adsorbed ion layer and the counter ion layer.
8. Contrast the desirability of coagulating the precipitate in a Fajans determination and in a gravimetric determination.

PROBLEMS

1–4. Calculate the pBr (defined as $[Br^-] = 10^{-pBr}$) of each of the following solutions.
1. 40 ml. of 0.2 M sodium bromide.
2. 40 ml. of 0.2 M sodium bromide to which 20 ml. of 0.1 M silver nitrate has been added.

3. 40 ml. of 0.2 M sodium bromide to which 20 ml. of 0.4 M silver nitrate has been added.

4. 40 ml. of 0.2 M sodium bromide to which 20 ml. of 0.5 M silver nitrate has been added.

5. A sample of rock salt contains 99.36% sodium chloride. What volume of 0.0963 N silver nitrate is required to precipitate the chloride from a 0.1987 gram sample?

6. What volume of 0.2000 N potassium thiocyanate is required to precipitate the silver from a solution containing 0.4623 gram of silver nitrate?

7. A soluble salt mixture contains not more than 75% sodium sulfate. What is the maximum volume of a barium chloride solution containing 50 grams of $BaCl_2 \cdot 2\ H_2O$ per liter that would be required to precipitate the sulfate from a 1.0000 gram sample?

8. If 25.00 ml. of a sodium chloride solution was required for the precipitation of the silver from the solution resulting from dissolving 0.2365 gram of metallic silver, 98.00% pure, what was the normality of the sodium chloride solution?

9. An oxalic acid solution is 0.5000 N as an acid. What is its normality when used for the precipitation of calcium as the oxalate?

10. What must be the normality of a solution of potassium thiocyanate in order that 25.00 ml. will precipitate the silver from a coin containing 98.00% silver and weighing 0.5000 gram?

11. What is the percentage of iodide in a 2.145 gram sample of a mixture of sodium iodide and sodium carbonate that, analyzed by the modified Volhard process, required 3.22 ml. of 0.1212 N potassium thiocyanate solution after the addition of 50.00 ml. of 0.2429 N silver nitrate?

12. For the analysis of a commercial solution of silver nitrate, a 2.0752 gram sample was weighed out, diluted to 100.00 ml., a 50.00 ml. aliquot withdrawn and titrated with 35.55 ml. of a thiocyanate solution of which 1.00 ml. corresponds to exactly 5.0 mg. of silver, Ag. What was the weight percentage of silver nitrate in the original solution?

13. A solution contains both hydrochloric acid and potassium chloride. A 25.00 ml. aliquot required 31.73 ml. of sodium hydroxide solution for titration. Another 25.00 ml. aliquot required 42.37 ml. of silver nitrate solution for titration by the adsorption indicator method. Just 1.00 ml. of the alkali solution corresponds to 1.00 ml. of 0.05 M sulfuric acid, and 1.00 ml. of the silver nitrate solution corresponds to 0.0100 gram of silver, Ag. What is the concentration in equivalents per liter of each component, HCl and KCl, in the original solution?

14. A 1.0000 gram sample of a salt mixture contains 2.00% moisture and is known to contain in addition only potassium bromide and potassium chloride. It requires for complete halide titration, 25.20 ml. of 0.5111 N silver nitrate solution. What is the percentage composition of the original sample?

15. A 25.00 ml. portion of a silver nitrate solution was treated with an excess of sodium chloride solution, the precipitate was coagulated, filtered, washed and found to weigh 0.3520 gram. Then 22.00 ml. of the same original silver nitrate was found to react with 11.00 ml. of a thiocyanate solution. What were the normalities of the silver nitrate and the thiocyanate solutions?

16. A sample is known to contain only sodium hydroxide, sodium chloride and water. A 6.700 gram sample was dissolved and diluted to the mark in a 250 ml. volumetric flask. A one-tenth aliquot required 22.22 ml. of 0.4976 N hydrochloric acid for titration to the phenolphthalein end point. Another one-tenth aliquot was titrated by the modified Volhard method, using 35.00 ml. of 0.1117 N silver nitrate and 4.63 ml. of 0.0962 N thiocyanate for the back-titration. The percentage moisture was determined by difference. What was the percentage composition of the original sample?

17. A mixture contains only lithium chloride and barium bromide. A 1.0000 gram sample was treated with 50.00 ml. of 0.2500 N silver nitrate, the excess being titrated with 16.25 ml. of 0.2428 N thiocyanate. What was the percentage composition of the sample?

18. A 0.5000 gram sample was analyzed for arsenic by oxidizing the arsenic to arsenate, precipitating silver arsenate, Ag_3AsO_4, dissolving that precipitate in nitric acid and titrating with 0.1000 N thiocyanate solution, 45.45 ml. being required. What was the percentage arsenic, As, in the sample?

19. A 0.5000 gram sample of impure potassium chlorate, $KClO_3$, was reduced to the chloride and precipitated by titration with 0.1020 N silver nitrate solution, 25.20 ml. being required. What is the percentage purity of the original sample?

20. To 10.00 ml. of a sodium chloride brine are added 50.00 ml. of 0.6200 N silver nitrate solution. Then 13.00 ml. of 0.1510 N ammonium thiocyanate is required for back-titration. Calculate the weight in grams of sodium chloride per liter of the brine.

SUGGESTIONS FOR ADDITIONAL READING

Items 1, 10, 13, 17, 18 and 30, Appendix 7.

Chapter 13

Volumetric
Complex Formation Methods

A QUANTITATIVE determination by a volumetric complex formation method is based upon a reaction in which a complex ion is formed. For a reaction of this type to be suitable, it must fulfill the four requirements listed in Chapter 9 for all volumetric titration reactions: (1) it must be one definite reaction; (2) the reaction must proceed to completion or nearly so; (3) it must proceed rapidly; (4) an indicator must be available.

With respect to the first requirement, a majority of the pairs of atoms or ions which can combine to form a complex can do so to form more than one complex. For example, mercuric and chloride ions can form the species $HgCl^+$, $HgCl_2$, $HgCl_3^-$ and $HgCl_4^=$. This fact alone does not necessarily preclude use of the system in volumetric analysis, because the reactions are generally stepwise. If any one species is sufficiently stable to permit fulfillment of the other requirements, particularly the second and the fourth, the system can still be used in volumetric analysis.

Many reactions in which a complex ion is formed fail to meet the second requirement. However, the cyanide complexes with certain metal ions, including nickel, silver and mercuric, are sufficiently stable for the reactions in which they are formed to proceed to quantitative completion. The Liebig method for the determination of cyanide by titration with silver nitrate is described in detail in this chapter. Much research work has been done in recent years on complexing agents with which a metal ion may react in such a way that the metal ion forms a ring structure with two or more parts of the same complexing molecule or ion. Many of these complexes are extremely stable and are thus very useful in quantitative analysis. The use of ethylene diamine tetraacetate as a complexing agent of this type is described in some detail in this chapter.

With respect to the third requirement, reactions in which complex ions are formed generally do take finite periods of time, but failure to go sufficiently rapidly is of less frequent occurrence than failure to meet the other three requirements. The fourth of the listed requirements, the availability of an indicator, is met to some extent for most of the reactions in which the other requirements are fulfilled. However, a considerable amount of intensive research has necessarily gone into the development of indicating systems, and further developments along this line may be anticipated in the future.

LIEBIG METHOD

The Liebig method for the determination of cyanide consists of the titration of cyanide by a standard solution of silver nitrate. A complex ion is formed in the primary titration reaction

$$Ag^+ + 2\ CN^- \longrightarrow Ag(CN)_2^-$$

The secondary or indicator reaction involves the formation of a white precipitate, silver cyanide,

$$Ag^+ + Ag(CN)_2^- \longrightarrow Ag[Ag(CN)_2]$$

The silver and cyanide ions are the only ingredients for both reactions.

The equivalent weight of silver ion in the primary reaction equals its formula weight, and the normality and molarity of the silver nitrate solution are numerically equal to each other. Two formula weights of cyanide ion are required to react with one equivalent weight of silver ion in the primary reaction, so the equivalent weight of cyanide ion is twice its formula weight. Thus, the normality of the cyanide solution for this system equals one-half its molarity. This is one of the relatively few instances in which an equivalent weight is greater than a molecular weight and a normality is numerically less than a molarity.

Titration Curve. A titration curve for the main titration reaction of the Liebig method consists of a plot of either pAg or pCN, defined respectively by the equations:

$$[Ag^+] = 10^{-pAg} \quad \text{and} \quad [CN^-] = 10^{-pCN}$$

vs. the volume of added silver nitrate solution. It is more meaningful to use pAg than pCN, because the silver ion is common to both the primary reaction and the indicator reaction. In the calculations which follow, the primary titration reaction alone is considered first, and then further calculation is made to show the modification caused by the indicator reaction.

Prior to the equivalence point in the titration of cyanide by silver ion, no silver ions are present except those resulting from the dissociation of the complex ion, so the calculation of pAg must be based upon the dissociation constant:

$$K_d = \frac{[Ag^+]\ [CN^-]^2}{[Ag(CN)_2^-]}$$

$$\text{or} \quad [Ag^+] = \frac{[Ag(CN^-)_2^-] \times 1 \times 10^{-21}}{[CN^-]^2} \quad \text{(rearranging and inserting numerical value for } K_d)$$

The concentrations of $Ag(CN)_2^-$ and of CN^- are determined by the amounts of the initial cyanide which are reacted and unreacted, respectively.

At the equivalence point the cyanide and silver ion concentrations equal each other when expressed in equivalent (not in molar) quantities, so the pAg may again be calculated from the dissociation constant. Beyond the equivalence point, apart from the secondary reaction, the pAg would be determined simply by the amount of excess silver nitrate which has been introduced.

Consider now the titration of 25.00 ml. of 0.2000 M (0.1000 N) cyanide solution by 0.1000 M silver nitrate solution.

0.00 ml. added: no silver ion is present at all, so $pAg = -\infty$
1.00 ml. added:

mEq. CN^- left = mEq. CN^- at start $-$ mEq. CN^- used up
mEq. CN^- left = 25.00 × 0.1000 $-$ 1.00 × 0.1000
mEq. CN^- left = 2.400

$$[CN^-] = \frac{2.400}{26.00} \times 2 = 0.185 \quad \text{(factor of 2 converts from N to M)}$$

mEq. $Ag(CN)_2^-$ formed = mEq. Ag^+ used up
mEq. $Ag(CN)_2^-$ formed = 1.00 × 0.1000
mEq. $Ag(CN)_2^-$ formed = 0.1000

$$[Ag(CN)_2^-] = \frac{0.1000}{26.00} = 0.00385$$

$$[Ag^+] = \frac{[Ag(CN)_2^-] \times 1 \times 10^{-21}}{[CN^-]^2}$$

$$= \frac{0.00383 \times 1 \times 10^{-21}}{(0.185)^2}$$

$$[Ag^+] = 10^{-21.95} \quad \text{so} \quad pAg = 21.95 \text{ or } 22.0$$

  5.00 ml. added: similarly, pAg = 20.4
10.00 ml. added: similarly, pAg = 19.8
20.00 ml. added: similarly, pAg = 18.4
24.00 ml. added: similarly, pAg = 16.9
24.90 ml. added: similarly, pAg = 14.9
25.00 ml. added:

mEq. CN^- present = mEq. Ag^+ present (this is the equivalence point)

$$[CN^-] = [Ag^+] \times 2 \quad \text{(factor of 2 converts from normalities to}$$
$$\text{molarities)}$$

mEq. $Ag(CN)_2^-$ formed = mEq. Ag^+ used up

mEq. $Ag(CN)_2^-$ formed $= 2.500$

$$[Ag(CN)_2^-] = \frac{2.500}{50.00} = 0.0500$$

$$1 \times 10^{-21} = \frac{[Ag^+] \, [CN^-]^2}{[Ag(CN)_2^-]} \text{ (the dissociation constant)}$$

$$1 \times 10^{-21} = \frac{[Ag^+] \, [(Ag^+) \times 2)]^2}{0.0500}$$

$$[Ag^+] = 10^{-7.63} \quad \text{so} \quad pAg = 7.6$$

25.10 ml. added:

mEq. Ag^+ present $=$ mEq. Ag^+ added $-$ mEq. Ag^+ used up

mEq. Ag^+ present $= 25.00 \times 0.1000 - 25.00 \times 0.1000$

mEq. Ag^+ present $= 0.0100$

$$[Ag^+] = \frac{0.0100}{50.10} = 10^{-3.7} \text{ so } pAg = 3.7$$

28.00 ml. added: similarly, $pAg = 2.7$
30.00 ml. added: similarly, $pAg = 2.0$
40.00 ml. added: similarly, $pAg = 1.6$
50.00 ml. added: similarly, $pAg = 1.5$

The curve resulting from these calculations is shown in Figure 38. It has been assumed in these calculations that all cyanide which has not reacted with silver ion is present in the form of free cyanide ion, even though hydrocyanic acid, HCN, is a weak acid. The assumption is justified, however, by the fact that the poisonous nature of the undissociated acid makes mandatory a sufficiently high pH to keep the acid predominately dissociated. (No student procedure is given in this book for this determination because of the danger associated with the handling of cyanides.)

Now let us re-examine the calculations and the curve to ascertain the effect of the indicator reaction. The precipitation of silver cyanide commences as soon as the concentrations of silver ion and of the complex become sufficiently great to exceed the solubility product constant

$$K_{sp} = [Ag^+] \, [Ag(CN)_2^-]$$

The molar concentration of the complex is 0.0500 at the equivalence point, and it differs only slightly for a few ml. prior to and beyond the equivalence point (for example, it may be shown by calculation that it is 0.0444 at 20.00 ml.). The silver ion concentration required to initiate precipitation of silver cyanide may be calculated as follows:

$$K_{sp} = [Ag^+] \, [Ag(CN)_2^-]$$
$$K_{sp} = 2.2 \times 10^{-12}$$
$$[Ag(CN)_2^-] = 0.0500$$
$$2.2 \times 10^{-12} = [Ag^+] \times 0.0500$$
$$[Ag^+] = 4.4 \times 10^{-11} \text{ or } pAg = 10.4$$

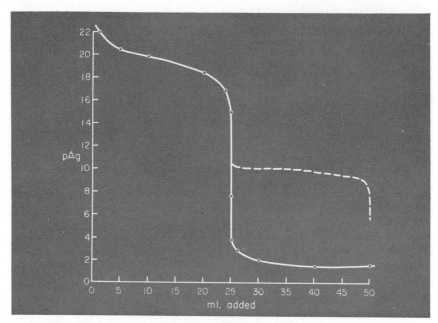

FIGURE 39.   Titration curve for titration of 25 ml. 0.1 N cyanide solution by 0.1 N silver nitrate solution (see text).

Therefore, the white precipitate which marks the end point begins to form when the pAg is about 10.4, which is seen from Figure 39 to come very close to the equivalence point. As more silver ions are added in the titration, more precipitate forms and the pAg remains at this approximate value as shown by the broken line of Figure 39. When essentially all of the soluble complex has been changed to the insoluble silver cyanide, addition of more silver ions causes the pAg to decrease rapidly. Specific points for plotting the broken line may be calculated from the K_{sp} for the precipitate and the molar concentration of complex remaining at each point.

Further Considerations.   A practical difficulty arises in this method from the presence of local concentrations of silver ion sufficient to cause a temporary formation of precipitate where the titrating drops fall into the titrated solution. These premature formations of precipitate tend to obscure the true end point, particularly because the precipitate tends to dissolve only slowly once it does form. A somewhat better end-point indication is obtained if ammonium hydroxide and potassium iodide are added to the solution prior to the titration. The ammonia complexes silver ion sufficiently to prevent the precipitation of silver cyanide. But the main titration reaction still proceeds quantitatively, and silver iodide precipitates as the equivalence point is reached.

A somewhat analogous procedure is useful for the titration of nickel with a standard solution of potassium cyanide. A trace of solid silver iodide is added to an ammoniacal solution of nickel. A cyanide solution is then introduced from a buret, reacting with the nickel ammonia complex as long as any remains; then the first excess of cyanide ion reacts with the silver iodide to dissolve it. The disappearance of the turbidity caused by the presence of silver iodide marks the end point. The primary and indicator reactions are, respectively:

$$Ni(NH_3)_4^{++} + 4\ CN^- \longrightarrow Ni(CN)_4^= + 4\ NH_3$$
$$AgI + 2\ CN^- \longrightarrow Ag(CN)_2^- + I^-$$

The success of this general method requires that the complex ion which is formed in the main reaction dissociate to such a slight extent that there is not enough cyanide ion present from the standard solution to start the indicator reaction until an excess of that reagent is added from the buret. The general method has been applied to a few other determinations.

ETHYLENE DIAMINE TETRAACETIC ACID AS A TITRATING AGENT

The organic acid ethylene diamine tetraacetic acid is representative of a group of reagents which form very stable complexes with a number of metal ions and which have been developed for use as titrating agents in volumetric analysis. The acid has the empirical formula, $H_4C_{10}H_{12}O_8N_2$, and the structural formula

$$
\begin{array}{ccc}
\text{HOOC—CH}_2 & & \text{CH}_2\text{—COOH} \\
& \diagdown \qquad \diagup & \\
& \text{N—CH}_2\text{—CH}_2\text{—N} & \\
& \diagup \qquad \diagdown & \\
\text{HOOC—CH}_2 & & \text{CH}_2\text{—COOH}
\end{array}
$$

Only the four hydrogen atoms on the $-COOH$ groups are ionizable as hydrogen ions. The name of the compound is often abbreviated E.D.T.A. and its empirical formula as H_4Y; these abbreviations will be used in the discussions which follow.

Acidic Characteristics of E.D.T.A. We must consider briefly the characteristics of E.D.T.A. as an acid before we discuss the ways in which it is used in volumetric analysis. The ionization of E.D.T.A. occurs stepwise:

$$H_4Y \rightleftharpoons H^+ + H_3Y^- \qquad K_1 = 1.0 \times 10^{-2}$$
$$H_3Y^- \rightleftharpoons H^+ + H_2Y^= \qquad K_2 = 2.0 \times 10^{-3}$$
$$H_2Y^= \rightleftharpoons H^+ + HY^\equiv \qquad K_3 = 6.3 \times 10^{-7}$$
$$HY^\equiv \rightleftharpoons H\ H^+ + Y^\equiv \qquad K_4 = 5.0 \times 10^{-11}$$

The distribution of E.D.T.A. among its completely undissociated form and its four dissociated forms varies considerably with the pH. The distribution at any particular pH may be calculated from the ionization constants. For example, let us insert a pH value of 10 into the four ionization constants and calculate the percentage distribution among the five forms at this pH.

$$K_1 = \frac{[H^+][H_3Y^-]}{[H_4Y]}$$

$$1.0 \times 10^{-2} = \frac{10^{-10}[H_3Y^-]}{[H_4Y]}$$

or $\qquad [H_4Y] = [H_3Y^-] \times 10^{-8} \qquad$ (equation 1)

$$K_2 = \frac{[H^+][H_2Y^=]}{[H_3Y^-]}$$

$$2.0 \times 10^{-3} = \frac{10^{-10}[H_2Y^=]}{[H_3Y^-]}$$

or $\qquad [H_3Y^-] = [H_2Y^=] \times 5 \times 10^{-8} \qquad$ (equation 2)

$$K_3 = \frac{[H^+][HY^\equiv]}{[H_2Y^=]}$$

$$6.3 \times 10^{-7} = \frac{10^{-10}[HY^\equiv]}{[H_2Y^=]}$$

or $\qquad [H_2Y^=] = [HY^\equiv] \times 1.6 \times 10^{-4} \qquad$ (equation 3)

$$K_4 = \frac{[H^+][Y^\equiv]}{[HY^\equiv]}$$

$$5.0 \times 10^{-11} = \frac{10^{-10}[Y^\equiv]}{[HY^\equiv]}$$

or $\qquad [HY^\equiv] = [Y^\equiv] \times 2 \qquad$ (equation 4)

The concentration of $HY^\equiv$ is twice that of $Y^\equiv$ (equation 4), while the concentration of $H_2Y^=$ is only 1.6 ten-thousandths as great as that of $HY^\equiv$ (equation 3). The concentrations of H_3Y^- and H_4Y are relatively much smaller (equations 2 and 1). So E.D.T.A. at pH 10 is almost entirely in the $Y^\equiv$ and $HY^\equiv$ forms, and is about 33 % $Y^\equiv$ and 67 % $HY^\equiv$. The approximate percentage distributions at pH values from 1 to 12, all calculated similar to that at pH 10, are tabulated in Table 13. The chief component is seen to be

Table 13. Approximate Percentage Distribution of E.D.T.A. at Various pH's

Form	pH											
	1	2	3	4	5	6	7	8	9	10	11	12
H_4Y	91	46	3	0	0	0	0	0	0	0	0	0
H_3Y^-	9	46	32	5	0	0	0	0	0	0	0	0
$H_2Y^=$	0	8	65	94	94	61	14	2	0	0	0	0
$HY^\equiv$	0	0	0	1	6	39	86	98	95	67	17	2
$Y^\equiv$	0	0	0	0	0	0	0	0	5	33	83	98

$H_2Y^=$ in the pH range of 4 to 6, while $HY^\equiv$ is the predominant form at pH 7 to 10.

Complexes of E.D.T.A. with Metals. The complexes which E.D.T.A. forms with metal ions are typically of the type $MY^=$, with M representing the metal ion (assumed in this formula to be divalent). Complexes of sufficient stability to be useful in analytical chemistry are formed with most of the metals except the alkali metals, the platinum metals and the small highly charged ions such as boron and beryllium. The dissociation constants for several are listed in Appendix 3. Each constant represents the dissociation of the complex into its components

$$MY^= \rightleftharpoons M^{++} + Y^\equiv$$

Because the $Y^\equiv$ anion enters into combination with one or more hydrogen ions, to an extent dependent upon the pH, a chemical equation for the over-all formation and dissociation of the complex must include one or more of the acid ionizations. For example, at pH 10 the predominate species of E.D.T.A. are $HY^\equiv$ and $Y^\equiv$, as listed in Table 13, so the reaction at pH 10 of E.D.T.A. with calcium ion involves the two systems:

$$HY^\equiv \rightleftharpoons H^+ + Y^\equiv \qquad \text{for which } K_4 = \frac{[H^+][Y^\equiv]}{[HY^\equiv]}$$

$$\text{and } Ca^{++} + Y^\equiv \rightleftharpoons CaY^= \qquad \text{for which } K_d = \frac{[Ca^{++}][Y^\equiv]}{[CaY^=]}$$

The two chemical equations may be added together

$$Ca^{++} + HY^\equiv \rightleftharpoons CaY^= + H^+ \qquad \text{for which } K = \frac{K_4}{K_d} = \frac{[CaY^=][H^+]}{[Ca^{++}][HY^\equiv]}$$

This over-all equilibrium constant equation will be used subsequently in this chapter in the calculation of a titration curve for a direct titration of metal ions by E.D.T.A.

Solutions of E.D.T.A. Ethylene diamine tetraacetic acid is not soluble in water. However, the disodium salt is readily soluble and is commercially available as the dihydrate, $Na_2H_2Y \cdot 2 H_2O$. This substance generally serves as the starting material in the preparation of standard solutions for analytical use. When the hydrate is dissolved in water, the chief components of the solution are sodium ion and $H_2Y^=$ ion, so the pH is slightly over 4, as would be predicted from Table 13. Most titrations are carried out in solutions buffered at higher pH values, as will be seen from the calculations of titration curves.

DIRECT TITRATIONS OF METAL IONS BY E.D.T.A.

The determination of a metal ion by direct titration with a standard solution of E.D.T.A. may be illustrated by a detailed consideration of the titration of calcium in a medium buffered at pH 10 and with sufficient buffer capacity to maintain the pH. The over-all titration reaction is, as already shown,

$$Ca^{++} + HY^= \rightleftharpoons CaY^= + H^+$$

Titration Curve. The titration curve consists of a plot of pCa vs. ml. of E.D.T.A. solution added, and the curve may be constructed by calculations similar to those conducted for other types of titration. Prior to the equivalence point, the pCa is calculated directly from the quantity of unreacted calcium ion. At the equivalence point, the only calcium ions present are those resulting from the incompleteness of the main titration reaction, so the pCa may be calculated from the equilibrium constant which is, as already shown,

$$K = \frac{K_4}{K_d} = \frac{[CaY^=][H^+]}{[Ca^{++}][HY^=]}$$

Beyond the equivalence point, excess E.D.T.A. reagent is present and the only calcium ions present are again those resulting from the slight dissociation of the complex, so the equilibrium constant is again used in calculations of pCa.

Consider the titration of 20.00 ml. 0.1000 N calcium ion, buffered at pH 10 and diluted to 100.00 ml. with water, by 0.1000 N E.D.T.A. solution

0.00 ml. added: 2.000 mEq. Ca^{++} in 100.00 ml., so

$$[Ca^{++}] = \frac{2.000}{100.00} \times \frac{1}{2} \qquad \text{(factor of } \tfrac{1}{2} \text{ converts N to M)}$$

$$[Ca^{++}] = 10^{-2.00} \text{ so pCa} = 2.00$$

1.00 ml. added:

mEq. Ca^{++} left = mEq. Ca^{++} initially − mEq. Ca^{++} used up
mEq. Ca^{++} left = 20.00 × 0.1000 − 1.00 × 0.1000
mEq. Ca^{++} left = 1.900

$$[Ca^{++}] = \frac{1.900}{101.00} \times \frac{1}{2}$$

$$[Ca^{++}] = 10^{-2.03} \text{ so pCa} = 2.03$$

5.00 ml. added: similarly, pCa = 2.13
10.00 ml. added: similarly, pCa = 2.34
19.00 ml. added: similarly, pCa = 3.38
19.90 ml. added: similarly, pCa = 4.38

20.00 ml. added: (this is the exact equivalence point)

$$\frac{K_4}{K_d} = \frac{[CaY^=][H^+]}{[Ca^{++}][HY^=]}$$

$$[CaY^=] = \frac{2.000}{120.00} \times \frac{1}{2} \qquad (2.000 \text{ mEq. in } 120.00 \text{ ml.})$$

$$[H^+] = 10^{-10}$$

$$K_d = 2.5 \times 10^{-11}$$

$$K_4 = 5.0 \times 10^{-11}$$

$$[Ca^{++}] \times \tfrac{2}{3} = [HY^=]$$

(Note that, at the equivalence point, equivalent amounts of Ca^{++} and unreacted E.D.T.A. are present, but that only 2/3 of the total E.D.T.A. at pH 10 is $HY^=$, Table 13.)

$$[Ca^{++}] = 10^{-6.10} \text{ (combining 6 preceding equations}$$
$$\text{and solving for } [Ca^{++}])$$

so $pCa = 6.10$

20.10 ml. added:

mEq. $HY^=$ = (mEq. E.D.T.A. total − mEq. E.D.T.A. used by Ca^{++})$\tfrac{2}{3}$
    (factor of $\tfrac{2}{3}$ because $\tfrac{2}{3}$ of E.D.T.A. is $HY^=$)
mEq. $HY^=$ = $(20.10 \times 0.1000 - 20.00 \times 0.1000)\tfrac{2}{3}$
mEq. $HY^=$ = 0.0067
and mEq. $CaY^=$ = mEq. Ca^{++} used up
mEq. $CaY^=$ = 20.00×0.1000
mEq. $CaY^=$ = 2.000

$$\frac{K_4}{K_d} = \frac{[CaY^=][H^+]}{[Ca^{++}][HY^=]}$$

$$\frac{5.0 \times 10^{-11}}{2.5 \times 10^{-11}} = \frac{\dfrac{2.000}{120.10} \times \dfrac{1}{2} \times 10^{-10}}{[Ca^{++}]\dfrac{0.0067}{120.10} \times \dfrac{1}{2}} \qquad \begin{array}{l}\text{(substituting appropriate}\\ \text{values into preceding}\\ \text{equation)}\end{array}$$

$$[Ca^{++}] = 10^{-7.83} \text{ so } pCa = 7.83$$

21.00 ml. added: similarly, pCa = 8.22
25.00 ml. added: similarly, pCa = 8.92
30.00 ml. added: similarly, pCa = 9.32
40.00 ml. added: similarly, pCa = 9.54

The curve resulting from these calculations is shown in Figure 40.

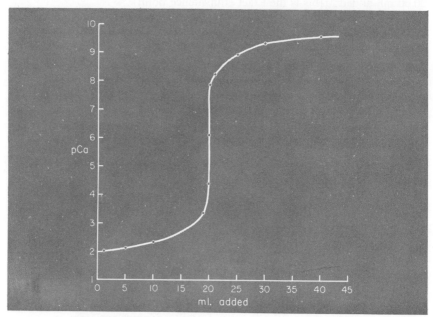

Figure 40.   Titration curve for titration of 20 ml. 0.1 N calcium solution, buffered
at pH 10 and diluted to 100 ml., by 0.1 N E.D.T.A. solution.

Variables in the Titration. Before considering the subject of
indicators, let us note qualitatively how the curve would differ for other
similar titrations. Prior to the equivalence point, the points are determined
solely by the concentration of unreacted calcium ion. So the first half of the
curve would be the same at other pH values and even for metals other than
calcium at the same initial concentration. For more dilute initial calcium
solution, however, the first half would be displaced upward, for there would
be fewer calcium ions per unit volume and thus higher pCa at each point;
in addition, of course, the equivalence point would be displaced laterally. At
and beyond the equivalence point, the effects of several variables can be noted
directly by rearranging the $\dfrac{K_4}{K_d}$ equation as follows:

$$[Ca^{++}] = \frac{[CaY^=][H^+] \times K_d}{K_4 \times [HY^=]}$$

Titration of a metal which forms a complex more stable (smaller K_d value)
than calcium would result in a lower metal ion concentration or a higher pM
(M for the metal) at each point at and beyond the equivalence point, so the
second half of the curve would be displaced upward. Titration of a metal
which forms a less stable complex (larger K_d value) would similarly displace the
second half of the curve downward. The effect of a change in pH is

complicated because not only $[H^+]$ but also $[HY^=]$ is influenced by pH. However, it may be shown that a higher pH (lower $[H^+]$ value) decreases $[Ca^{++}]$ and thus increases pCa at each point at and beyond the equivalence point.

Indicators. The indicator for this titration must be one which responds within the approximately vertical portion of the titration curve. The organic dye, eriochrome black T., is a common indicator for the direct titration of several metals by a standard solution of E.D.T.A. The principles may be illustrated with reference to the magnesium titration. This dye consists primarily of a trivalent anion, which may be abbreviated as $In^=$, and which, at pH 10, is in solution principally in the form $HIn^=$. The dye can form a complex with magnesium

$$Mg^{++} + HIn^= \rightleftharpoons MgIn^- + H^+$$
$$\text{(blue)} \qquad\qquad \text{(wine red)}$$

for which the equilibrium constant is 2.75×10^{-5}:

$$2.75 \times 10^{-5} = \frac{[MgIn^-][H^+]}{[Mg^{++}][HIn^=]}$$

or

$$2.75 \times 10^5 = \frac{[MgIn^-]}{[Mg^{++}][HIn^=]} \text{ (at pH 10.)}$$

The concentrations of $MgIn^-$ and of $HIn^=$ are proportional to the intensities of red color and of blue color, respectively, so

$$2.75 \times 10^5 = \frac{\text{(red color intensity)}}{[Mg^{++}](\text{blue color intensity})}$$

or

$$[Mg^{++}] = 10^{-5.44} \times \frac{\text{(red color intensity)}}{\text{(blue color intensity)}}$$

The human eye recognizes the mixture of blue and red colors as one color alone if one intensity is about ten or more times the intensity of the other. Thus, the indicator imparts to the solution a red color if the pMg is 4.44 or less and a blue color if 6.44 or higher. As shown on the curve of Figure 40, this change range is suitable for the titration of calcium by E.D.T.A.; it is likewise suitable for the titration of magnesium.

The titration curves are so similar for calcium and magnesium that their sum may be determined if both are present. When calcium alone is to be determined, a small amount of magnesium may be added and the same indicator used. If the magnesium is added directly to the E.D.T.A. solution prior to standardization, no further consideration need be paid in the stoichiometric calculations to the presence of magnesium.

The equations for the main titration reaction and for the indicator reaction in the calcium determination are, respectively,

$$Ca^{++} + HY^= \longrightarrow CaY^= + H^+$$

$$HY^= + MgIn^- \longrightarrow MgY^= + HIn^=$$
$$\text{(red)} \text{(blue)}$$

The pH is rather critical. At a value above 10, magnesium ion enters into a side reaction, precipitation as its hydroxide, and the desired $HIn^=$ blue color shifts at least partially into a different form, $In^=$, which is orange. At lower pH, the indicator dye holds magnesium ion too loosely to maintain the $MgIn^-$ red form prior to the equivalence point.

Determination of the Total Hardness of Water. An especially useful application of the ethylene diamine tetraacetic acid reagent is in the determination of the total hardness of water. The hardness of water is due to dissolved calcium and magnesium salts, the concentrations of which vary widely from one water to another. Results are generally calculated as if all the hardness were due to dissolved calcium carbonate. In the procedure which follows, some magnesium ion is inserted directly into the E.D.T.A. solution to insure proper indicator action even with waters of little or no magnesium content. The titration is not affected by considerable concentrations of salt, but even traces of copper, cobalt, nickel, permanganate and, in some cases, iron cause interference. The interference arises partially from preventing proper indicator action and partially by permitting direct reaction with the reagent in the same way that calcium and magnesium ions react. Whenever poor, indistinct indicator end points are obtained, the difficulty probably lies in the presence of one or more of these interfering metal ions. The procedure which follows includes use of hydroxylamine hydrochloride, which reduces some of the potential interferences to less objectionable lower oxidation states. Further elimination of interferences may be accomplished by use of sodium cyanide to tie up the interfering metals as their cyanide complexes. (Do not use cyanide, however, without specific directions and authorization from your instructor.)

Laboratory Experiment 19

DETERMINATION OF THE TOTAL HARDNESS OF WATER

Reagents

Ammonium chloride-ammonium hydroxide buffer, solution containing 7 grams NH_4Cl and 60 ml. ammonium hydroxide (stock solution) diluted to 100 ml. with water

Calcium chloride, standard solution prepared as primary standard, prepared by weighing accurately 1 gram analytical reagent grade $CaCO_3$, dissolving it in a little dilute hydrochloric acid and diluting it to the mark in a one liter volumetric flask (if the weight is exactly 1.000 gram, then 1.000 ml. of this standard soluton corresponds to 1.000 mg. $CaCO_3$)

E.D.T.A. solution, prepared by dissolving 3.75 grams of the disodium salt of ethylene diamine tetraacetic acid dihydrate and 0.1 gram $MgCl_2 \cdot 2 H_2O$ in water and diluting to one liter

Eriochrome black T. indicator, solution containing 0.5 gram eriochrome black T. and 4.5 grams hydroxylamine hydrochloride in 100 ml. methyl alcohol

(Note: Hach Chemical Company, Ames, Iowa, markets a combination buffer, indicator and inhibitor which may be used to simplify the preparation and use of these reagents in this determination.)

Procedure

Standardization of E.D.T.A. Solution with Calcium Chloride Solution. Pipet a 25 ml. sample of the standard calcium chloride solution into a 300 ml. Erlenmeyer flask. Add 1 ml. buffer solution and mix. Add four drops indicator solution. Titrate with the E.D.T.A. solution until the end point, which is marked by a change of color from red to blue. Repeat until successive results are in substantial agreement. Calculate the concentration of the E.D.T.A. solution, preferably in terms of mg. $CaCO_3$ which react per ml. of E.D.T.A. solution.

Water Hardness Determination. Pipet a 50.0 ml. portion of the water sample into a 300 ml. Erlenmeyer flask. Add buffer and indicator and titrate as in the standardization procedure. If the volume of standard E.D.T.A. solution required is either too large or too small for convenient and accurate measurement, use smaller or larger aliquots of the sample solution for subsequent titrations. Repeat until successive results are in substantial agreement. Calculate the mg. $CaCO_3$ in the size of aliquot titrated, and then the hardness of the water sample in terms of parts per million, assuming all the hardness to be due to calcium carbonate.

Determination of Zinc. The dye eriochrome black T. also forms complexes with several other metal ions of stabilities suitable for use as indicators in their titrations by E.D.T.A. For example, zinc may be titrated in the same way as magnesium and calcium. Zinc and the indicator anion form two complexes, $ZnIn^-$ and $ZnIn_2^=$, but the principle of operation is similar.

Laboratory Experiment 20

DETERMINATION OF ZINC BY DIRECT TITRATION WITH ETHYLENE DIAMINE TETRAACETATE

Reagents

Ammonium chloride—ammonium hydroxide buffer, solution containing 7 grams NH_4Cl and 60 ml. stock ammonium hydroxide diluted to 100 ml. with water.

E.D.T.A., approximately 0.01 M standard solution as a primary standard, prepared by drying at 80° C. and accurately weighing about 0.9 gram of $Na_2H_2C_{10}H_{12}O_8N_2\cdot2\ H_2O$ and diluting to the mark in a 250 ml. volumetric flask

Eriochrome black T. indicator, solution containing 0.1 gram eriochrome black T. and 1.0 gram hydroxylamine hydrochloride in 10 ml. methyl alcohol. ("Calmagite" may alternatively be used as the indicator.)

Procedure

Submit a 100 ml. volumetric flask to your instructor for the unknown, which will contain not more than 0.07 gram Zn in its entirety, and analyze triplicate 25 ml. aliquots. Pipet each 25 ml. aliquot into a 300 ml. Erlenmeyer flask. Add about 100 ml. water, 4 ml. of the buffer solution and 4 drops of the indicator solution. Titrate with standard E.D.T.A. solution until the indicator color just changes from pink to blue. Calculate the weight of zinc in the entire sample issued.

Suggestion for Supplementary Laboratory Work. Run triplicate titrations on a standard zinc solution and calculate the normality of the E.D.T.A. solution from the data. Discuss the probable reasons for the agreement or lack of agreement between the two normalities (as primary standard and as determined with the standard zinc solution).

E.D.T.A. TITRATIONS USING ACID-BASE INDICATORS

Hydrogen ion is liberated in the reaction between a metal ion and E.D.T.A. at all pH values except those so high that the predominant form of E.D.T.A. is the $Y^{\equiv}$ ion. When a solution of $Na_2H_2Y \cdot 2 H_2O$ is used, the pH is about 4.5, so the predominant form is $H_2Y^=$ and two moles of hydrogen ion are liberated for every one mole of metal ion which is complexed:

$$M^{++} + H_2Y^= \longrightarrow MY^= + 2 H^+$$

It is of interest to consider determining the quantity of metal ion initially present by causing it to react with an excess of E.D.T.A. and titrating the liberated hydrogen ion with a standard alkali solution.

The change in pH in the vicinity of the equivalence point in the titration with alkali is not very great. The liberated hydrogen is, at the start of the titration, in the form of H_3Y^- to a considerable extent, rather than in the form of free hydrogen ion, so the pH is only slightly lower than that before the hydrogen ion was liberated. Furthermore, the excess hydroxyl ions added beyond the equivalence point do not remain as such but cause much of the $H_2Y^=$ which was left over from the initial reaction to change to H_3Y^-, so the pH never does get very high. Best results are obtained if the excess $H_2Y^=$ used in complexing the metal is held to a minimum and if a very sharp acid-base indicator is used.

It is possible to determine cobalt, nickel, copper, zinc, cadmium, mercury and lead by this procedure. If more than one of these metal ions are present, the sum is determined. The procedures have found some usefulness but are generally less satisfactory than the E.D.T.A. methods employing other indicator systems.

BACK-TITRATION METHODS USING E.D.T.A.

Some metal ions cannot be determined by the direct titration method because the high pH required for complete reaction and for adequate internal indicator reaction would result in precipitation of the metal ion as a hydroxide or hydrous oxide. A back-titration method has been developed in which the unknown metal ion is caused to react with an excess of a standard solution of E.D.T.A. at a pH sufficiently low to prevent hydroxide precipitation; the solution is then buffered at a higher pH, and the excess E.D.T.A. is titrated with a standard solution of zinc or magnesium ions using an indicator suitable for the zinc or magnesium titration. The stoichiometric calculation is based upon

mEq. unknown = mEq. E.D.T.A. − mEq. Zn or Mg

In this way the unknown metal ion is, at the higher pH, already complexed with E.D.T.A., so it neither precipitates as a hydroxide nor interferes with the desired indicator action. Some of the $MY^=$ complexes do slowly release metal to the indicator, but even so no difficulty arises so long as the titration is performed with reasonable speed.

This back-titration method is applicable to the determinations of cobalt, nickel, copper, aluminum, iron, titanium and a few other metals. The procedure which follows is for the determination of nickel.

Laboratory Experiment 21

DETERMINATION OF NICKEL BY BACK-TITRATION METHOD USING ETHYLENE DIAMINE TETRAACETATE

Reagents

Ammonium chloride—ammonium hydroxide buffer, the solution prepared in Experiment 20.

E.D.T.A., the standard solution prepared as a primary standard in Experiment 20.

Eriochrome black T. indicator, the solution prepared in Experiment 20. ("Calmagite" may alternatively be used as the indicator.)

Magnesium nitrate, approximately 0.01 M solution, prepared by dissolving approximately 1.3 grams $Mg(NO_3)_2 \cdot 6\ H_2O$ in 300 ml. water, adding 0.5 ml. concentrated nitric acid and diluting to 500 ml.

Procedure

Standardize the magnesium solution by the procedure of Experiment 20, substituting magnesium for zinc throughout.

Submit a 100 ml. volumetric flask to your instructor for the unknown, which will contain not more than 0.06 gram nickel in its entirety, and analyze triplicate 25 ml. aliquots. Pipet each 25 ml. aliquot into a 300 ml. Erlenmeyer flask. Add about 100 ml. water. Introduce from a buret 30 ml. standard E.D.T.A. solution. Add 4 ml. buffer solution and 4 drops indicator solution. Titrate with standard magnesium solution until the indicator color changes to a purplish-pink. The end point is not readily reversible, so stop as soon as a permanent change is developed. Calculate the weight of nickel in the entire sample issued.

REVIEW QUESTIONS

1. Write chemical equations for the primary and the indicator reactions in the Liebig method and in the determination of the total hardness of water.
2. What is the equivalent weight of the cyanide ion in terms of its formula weight when titrated by the Liebig method.
3. In view of the fact that E.D.T.A. forms complexes with so many cations, state and explain two means whereby it can be made quite selective.
4. Account for (descriptively, at least) the general stability of E.D.T.A. complexes compared with other types of complexes with the same cations.
5. Why is a pH of 10 needed in the titration to determine the total hardness of water?
6. Why cannot the direct titration method, using a standard solution of E.D.T.A., be used for determining nickel?
7. Suggest a method, either direct or indirect, for determining sulfate by use of E.D.T.A. in a titration.

PROBLEMS

1–4. Calculate the pAg and the pCN of each of the following solutions. (Consider the possible formation of a precipitate as well as a complex. Assume the pH to be high enough so that no undissociated HCN forms.)
   1. 40.0 ml. of 0.0100 M sodium cyanide
   2. 40.0 ml. of 0.0100 M sodium cyanide to which 10.0 ml. of 0.0100 M silver nitrate has been added.
   3. 40.0 ml. of 0.0100 M sodium cyanide to which 30.0 ml. of 0.0100 M silver nitrate has been added.
   4. 40.0 ml. of 0.0100 M sodium cyanide to which 100.0 ml. of 0.0100 M silver nitrate has been added.
   5. Calculate the molar concentrations of H_4Y, H_3Y^-, $H_2Y^=$, $HY^\equiv$ and $Y^\equiv$ in a 0.1000 M solution of E.D.T.A. at a pH of 4.00.
6–7. Calculate the pZn in each of the following solutions, each of which is buffered at a pH of 10.5.
   6. 20.0 ml. of 0.100 M zinc solution to which 10.0 ml. of 0.100 M E.D.T.A. has been added.
   7. 20.0 ml. of 0.1000 M zinc solution to which 40.0 ml. of 0.100 M E.D.T.A. has been added.
   8. What is the percentage purity of an impure sample of sodium cyanide, a 2.000 gram sample of which required 25.00 ml. of a 0.2500 N silver nitrate solution for titration by the Liebig method?
   9. What should be the normality of a silver nitrate solution so that each 1.00 ml. will correspond to 1.00 mg. cyanide ion in a Liebig titration?
   10. A standard solution of calcium chloride was prepared by dissolving 0.2000 gram of calcium carbonate in a little hydrochloric acid and diluting to the mark in a 250 ml. volumetric flask. A 25.00 ml. aliquot required 22.62 ml. of a solution of E.D.T.A. for titration. What was the concentration of the E.D.T.A. solution in terms of mg. calcium carbonate equivalent to 1.00 ml. E.D.T.A. solution?
   11. What is the total hardness in parts of calcium carbonate per million of a water sample, 50.00 ml. of which required 28.60 ml. of an E.D.T.A. solution, each ml. of which corresponds to 1.00 mg. calcium carbonate?

12. What weight of disodium ethylene diamine tetraacetate dihydrate should be taken to make 500.00 ml. of a 0.0100 M solution?

13. Calculate the percentage zinc in a 0.2000 gram sample which required 24.18 ml. of 0.0100 M E.D.T.A. for titration? (Assume that nothing in the unknown except zinc reacts with E.D.T.A.)

14. A 1.000 ml. aliquot of a nickel solution is diluted with water and treated with 15.00 ml. of 0.0100 M E.D.T.A., the excess of which is titrated with 4.30 ml. of a 0.0150 M solution of a magnesium salt. Calculate the molarity of the nickel solution.

SUGGESTIONS FOR ADDITIONAL READING

Items 1, 10, 13, 14, 23 and 30, Appendix 7.

Chapter 14

Oxidation-Reduction

Methods—Principles and Theory

OXIDATION-REDUCTION methods of analysis, commonly called redox methods, are the most widely used volumetric analytical methods. Both neutralization and volumetric precipitation methods are very important within their realms of usefulness, but many substances, especially metals, cannot be analyzed satisfactorily by either of those two types of determination. Redox methods are, however, of much wider applicability for the determinations of many substances. The principles and theory underlying redox reactions are considered in this chapter, and some practical analytical applications are described in Chapters 15 and 16.

INTRODUCTORY PRINCIPLES

Definitions. Oxidation is the loss of electrons, and reduction is the gain of electrons. This loss or gain of electrons by a substance undergoing oxidation or reduction may be considered, respectively, as a gain or loss of positive oxidation state. Therefore, oxidation may also be defined as a gain of positive oxidation state, and the loss of such oxidation state is reduction.

The substance which is reduced, that is, the substance which causes another substance to be oxidized, is the oxidizing agent. The substance which causes another substance to be reduced, thereby becoming oxidized itself, is the reducing agent. In terms analogous to those used in defining acid and base in Chapter 10, a reducing agent is an electron-donor, and an oxidizing agent is an electron-acceptor.

Two factors are of particular significance in considering any individual oxidation or reduction process. The quantity factor deals with the number of electrons involved per unit (atom, ion, molecule, etc.) of the substance involved and is of significance in all redox stoichiometric considerations. The intensity factor deals with how readily the substance gives up or takes on electrons and is of significance in considerations such as assessing the completeness of any reaction and selecting an indicator. These two factors, the quantity factor and the intensity factor, will now be considered in turn.

Quantity Factor. A simple example of an oxidation process is the loss of two electrons by a stannous ion to form a stannic ion, as shown by the equation

$$Sn^{++} \rightleftharpoons Sn^{++++} + 2e$$

This reaction is, like all other redox reactions, reversible; a stannic ion can, under the proper conditions, gain two electrons to become a stannous ion. This reverse reaction is an example of a reduction process. A further simple example of a reduction process is the gain of an electron by a ferric ion to become a ferrous ion, as shown by the equation

$$Fe^{+++} + e \rightleftharpoons Fe^{++}$$

or $$2\,Fe^{+++} + 2e \rightleftharpoons 2\,Fe^{++}$$

Again the reaction is reversible.

Electrons cannot exist as free electrons in solution, so oxidation cannot take place without a corresponding reduction, and no substance can be reduced without some other substance simultaneously being oxidized. For this reason, the above equations must be considered partial reaction equations. These two partial reaction equations may be combined to yield a complete redox reaction equation

$$Sn^{++} + 2\,Fe^{+++} \rightleftharpoons Sn^{++++} + 2\,Fe^{++}$$

This equation states that in the forward direction a stannous ion gives up two electrons to form a stannic ion, those two electrons, in turn, being taken on by two ferric ions which become two ferrous ions. It is important to note that the number of electrons lost by one substance must exactly equal the number gained by the other. The tin is oxidized and the iron is reduced in this reaction going from left to right. Since tin is oxidized by ferric iron, the ferric iron is termed an *oxidizing agent*; similarly, stannous tin is the *reducing agent*. Ferric iron and stannic tin are the most highly oxidized forms involved in this reaction of the iron and the tin, respectively, so these two substances are called *oxidants*; similarly, ferrous iron and stannous tin are called *reductants*.

Some substances are oxidized or reduced by a change of one electron per atom or ion, while others require that two or even more electrons be involved for each atom undergoing oxidation or reduction. As examples, ferrous ion is oxidized by a loss of one electron per atom to form ferric ion, a stannic ion requires two electrons to form stannous ion, and a manganous ion requires the loss of five electrons to become Mn^{+7} (actually in the form of MnO_4^-).

In acid-base reactions, the quantity factor is the number of protons involved per unit (ion or molecule) of the reacting substance. Most acid-base reactions in which the quantity factor is greater than one proceed in a step-wise fashion. For example, in the titration of carbonate ion with an acid, nearly every carbonate accepts one proton before any get two. However, redox reactions generally do not proceed in this stepwise manner. In the reduction of permanganate ion by titration in acid medium with a reducing agent, for example, each permanganate ion which reacts accepts five electrons to become a manganous ion, even while other permanganate ions remain. The specific mechanisms by which redox reactions occur are often complex, but it is possible in only a relatively few cases to stop a reduction or an oxidation at any one of two or more oxidation states merely by variation in amount of titrant introduced.

Intensity Factor. In order for any redox reaction to be suitable as the basis of a method of quantitative analysis, that reaction must go practically to completion; that is, the reverse reaction must be experimentally negligible. This intensity factor deals with how readily substances give up or take on electrons.

In the preceding example the forward reaction between ferric ions and stannous ions was described in an incomplete manner, because nothing was said as to whether most, some, or only a few ions would react when ferric ions and stannous ions are brought together. The degree of completeness of a redox reaction is described qualitatively by the difference of *electron affinity*, or electron attraction, of each of the two substances competing for the electrons. In the present example, the degree to which the reaction goes to completion in either direction is described by the relative attractions which the iron and tin systems have for the electrons involved in the possible transfer. In this example, stannous tin has a much weaker electron affinity than does ferrous ion, so the reaction goes nearly to completion to the right. Substances with relatively strong or intense electron affinity are substances that are relatively intense oxidizing agents, or are relatively easily reduced themselves.

Table of Oxidants and Reductants. In Table 14 are listed many oxidants and reductants with partial reaction equations and with information on both the quantity and intensity factors for each. The number of electrons involved is indicated as a part of each equation. It must be remembered that a complete, practical reaction equation consists of two of these partial equations, as neither oxidation nor reduction can take place without the other. The *standard electrode potential*, $E°$, for each half-reaction is also given in the table. This electrode potential is a quantitative measure of the intensity factor for a redox reaction. This concept will be discussed in detail subsequently in this chapter. Suffice it to state here that the more positive an electrode potential is, the more strongly does that substance function as an oxidizing agent.

Table 14. Standard Oxidizing Potentials*

$E°$	Half-Reaction Equation
1.77	$1/2\ H_2O_2 + H^+ + e \rightleftharpoons H_2O$
1.70	$Ce^{++++} + e \rightleftharpoons Ce^{+++}$ (in $HClO_4$)
1.68	$PbO_2 + 4\ H^+ + SO_4^{--} + 2\ e \rightleftharpoons PbSO_4 + 2\ H_2O$
1.61	$Ce^{++++} + e \rightleftharpoons Ce^{+++}$ (in HNO_3)
1.59	$MnO_4^- + 4\ H^+ + 3\ e \rightleftharpoons MnO_2 + 2\ H_2O$
1.51	$MnO_4^- + 8\ H^+ + 5\ e \rightleftharpoons Mn^{++} + 4\ H_2O$
1.45	$BrO_3^- + 6\ H^+ + 5\ e \rightleftharpoons 1/2\ Br_2 + 3\ H_2O$
1.45	$Ce^{++++} + e \rightleftharpoons Ce^{+++}$ (in H_2SO_4)
1.45	$ClO_3^- + 6\ H^+ + 6\ e \rightleftharpoons Cl^- + 3\ H_2O$
1.42	$BrO_3^- + 6\ H^+ + 6\ e \rightleftharpoons Br^- + 3\ H_2O$
1.36	$1/2\ Cl_2 + e \rightleftharpoons Cl^-$
1.35	$ClO_4^- + 8\ H^+ + 8\ e \rightleftharpoons Cl^- + 4\ H_2O$
1.30	$1/2\ Cr_2O_7^{--} + 7\ H^+ + 3\ e \rightleftharpoons Cr^{+++} + 7/2\ H_2O$
1.25	$Tl^{+++} + 2\ e \rightleftharpoons Tl^+$
1.23	$MnO_2 + 4\ H^+ + 2\ e \rightleftharpoons Mn^{++} + 2\ H_2O$
1.23	$Ce^{++++} + e \rightleftharpoons Ce^{+++}$ (in HCl)
1.23	$1/2\ O_2 + 2\ H^+ + 2\ e \rightleftharpoons H_2O$ (in acid solution)
1.20	$IO_3^- + 6\ H^+ + 5\ e \rightleftharpoons 1/2\ I_2 + 3\ H_2O$
1.09	$IO_3^- + 6\ H^+ + 6\ e \rightleftharpoons I^- + 3\ H_2O$
1.06	$1/2\ Br_2 + e \rightleftharpoons Br^-$
0.96	$NO_3^- + 4\ H^+ + 3\ e \rightleftharpoons NO + 2\ H_2O$
0.92	$Hg^{++} + e \rightleftharpoons 1/2\ Hg_2^{++}$
0.81	$Ag^+ + e \rightleftharpoons Ag$
0.80	$1/2\ Hg_2^{++} + e \rightleftharpoons Hg$
0.77	$Fe^{+++} + e \rightleftharpoons Fe^{++}$
0.75	$SbO_4^{---} + 2\ H^+ + 2\ e \rightleftharpoons SbO_3^{---} + H_2O$
0.70	$C_6H_4O_2 + 2\ H^+ + 2\ e \rightleftharpoons C_6H_4O_2H_2$ (quinhydrone electrode)
0.68	$1/2\ O_2 + H^+ + e \rightleftharpoons 1/2\ H_2O_2$
0.60	$MnO_4^- + 2\ H_2O + 3\ e \rightleftharpoons MnO_2 + 4\ OH^-$
0.56	$AsO_4^{---} + 2\ H^+ + 2\ e \rightleftharpoons AsO_3^{---} + H_2O$
0.54	$1/2\ I_2 + e \rightleftharpoons I^-$
0.50	$MoO_3 + 4\ H^+ + e \rightleftharpoons MoO^{+++} + 2\ H_2O$
0.4	$PtCl_6^{--} + 2\ e \rightleftharpoons PtCl_4^{--} + 2\ Cl^-$
0.40	$1/2\ O_2 + H_2O + 2\ e \rightleftharpoons 2\ OH^-$
0.36	$Fe(CN)_6^{---} + e \rightleftharpoons Fe(CN)_6^{----}$
0.36	$VO^{++} + 2\ H^+ + e \rightleftharpoons V^{+++} + H_2O$
0.34	$Cu^{++} + 2\ e \rightleftharpoons Cu$
0.33	$UO_2SO_4 + 4\ H^+ + SO_4^{--} + 2\ e \rightleftharpoons U(SO_4)_2 + 2\ H_2O$
0.338	0.1 N calomel electrode
0.280	1.0 N calomel electrode
0.246	saturated calomel electrode
0.22	$AgCl + e \rightleftharpoons Ag + Cl^-$
0.17	$Cu^{++} + e \rightleftharpoons Cu^+$
0.17	$SO_4^{--} + 4\ H^+ + 2\ e \rightleftharpoons H_2SO_3 + H_2O$
0.15	$Sn^{++++} + 2\ e \rightleftharpoons Sn^{++}$
0.14	$S + 2\ H^+ + 2\ e \rightleftharpoons H_2S$

* The direction in which the half-reaction equations are written and the signs listed for the $E°$ values are somewhat arbitrary. Unfortunately, not all authors make the same arbitrary choices and considerable confusion results. The main requirement is that some self-consistent basis be used in tabulating and using these data. The system of electrochemical conventions used in this table and throughout this book adheres to that adopted in 1953 at the Stockholm meeting of the International Union of Pure and Applied Chemistry.

Table 14. Standard Oxidizing Potentials (Continued)

$E°$	Half-Reaction Equation
0.10	$TiO^{++} + 2\,H^+ + e \rightleftharpoons Ti^{+++} + H_2O$
0.0000	$H^+ + e \rightleftharpoons 1/2\,H_2$
−0.13	$Pb^{++} + 2\,e \rightleftharpoons Pb$
−0.14	$Sn^{++} + 2\,e \rightleftharpoons Sn$
−0.25	$Ni^{++} + 2\,e \rightleftharpoons Ni$
−0.40	$Cd^{++} + 2\,e \rightleftharpoons Cd$
−0.41	$Cr^{+++} + e \rightleftharpoons Cr^{++}$
−0.44	$Fe^{++} + 2\,e \rightleftharpoons Fe$
−0.49	$CO_2 + H^+ + e \rightleftharpoons 1/2\,H_2C_2O_4$
−0.60	$Cr^{++} + 2\,e \rightleftharpoons Cr$
−0.76	$Zn^{++} + 2\,e \rightleftharpoons Zn$
−0.83	$H_2O + e \rightleftharpoons 1/2\,H_2 + OH^-$
−1.18	$Mn^{++} + 2\,e \rightleftharpoons Mn$
−2.71	$Na^+ + e \rightleftharpoons Na$
−2.87	$Ca^{++} + 2\,e \rightleftharpoons Ca$
−2.89	$Sr^{++} + 2\,e \rightleftharpoons Sr$
−2.90	$Ba^{++} + 2\,e \rightleftharpoons Ba$
−2.92	$K^+ + e \rightleftharpoons K$
−2.92	$Rb^+ + e \rightleftharpoons Rb$
−3.04	$Li^+ + e \rightleftharpoons Li$

OXIDATION-REDUCTION EQUATIONS

Stoichiometric calculations in neutralization, precipitation and complex formation work are based in large part upon the completed and balanced chemical equations for the reactions involved, and the same thing holds true for redox calculations. Some equations can be balanced by mere inspection. However, many redox equations cannot feasibly be balanced this way and others may even be balanced in a way that appears correct but is, in fact, not correct unless a more systematic procedure is employed. Several systematic procedures have been developed, but all are more or less equivalent to the following:

STEP 1.   Write the formulas of the main reactants on the left and their corresponding products on the right. There is ultimately only one way to ascertain the products of any particular combination of reactants and that is by experiment. However, it is often, perhaps usually, possible to predict what the products are for any particular reaction from tables and generalizations of chemical knowledge, all of which are, in turn, based upon experiments of other persons. In writing the formulas of the main reactants and products, it is advisable to write each in the form in which it predominantly exists. Thus, an ionized salt would be written ionically, and any undissociated molecule would be written molecularly. A weak acid would be written as a molecule since it exists predominantly as molecules rather than as ions.

STEP 2. Break the equation of Step 1 down into its constituent partial reaction equations and balance each separately by inspection or by reference to Table 14. Each of these equations will be the same as (or the reverse of) one of the equations in Table 14, assuming the substances involved are listed. Usually there will be just two equations at this point. If there are more, because two or more substances are going through either oxidation or reduction, combine them at this point so there remain two equations only, one representing a gain of electrons and one a loss of electrons.

STEP 3. Multiply each of the equations of Step 2 by an integer so that the total number of electrons gained in one equals the total number lost in the other.

STEP 4. Add the equations of Step 3. If one substance appears on both sides, combine. If the coefficients of all substances are all divisible by the same integer, divide all by that integer. This leaves the completely balanced equation.

With considerable practice, the student may be able to perform some of these steps in his head without writing them down, but the over-all steps remain the same. The operation of Step 3 is the distinctive part of balancing a redox equation; in fact, it is an arithmetical application of the principle that the number of electrons gained must equal the number lost in the complete reaction. It must be emphasized again that writing and balancing an equation does not prove that the reaction either does or does not go to completion.

Example 1. The reaction between Sn^{++} and Fe^{+++} ions.

STEP 1. $$Sn^{++} + Fe^{+++} \rightleftharpoons Sn^{++++} + Fe^{++}$$

(The choice of products is based upon experience or, more likely, upon other people's experiences as listed in Table 14.)

STEP 2. $$Sn^{++} - 2\,e \rightleftharpoons Sn^{++++}$$
$$Fe^{+++} + e \rightleftharpoons Fe^{++}$$

STEP 3. $$1(Sn^{++} - 2\,e \rightleftharpoons Sn^{++++})$$
$$2(Fe^{+++} + e \rightleftharpoons Fe^{++})$$

STEP 4. $$Sn^{++} - 2\,e + 2\,Fe^{+++} + 2\,e \rightleftharpoons Sn^{++++} + 2\,Fe^{++}$$
or $$Sn^{++} + 2\,Fe^{+++} \rightleftharpoons Sn^{++++} + 2\,Fe^{++}$$

Example 2. The reaction between solutions of $KMnO_4$ and of $FeSO_4$.

STEP 1. $$MnO_4^- + Fe^{++} \rightleftharpoons Mn^{++} + Fe^{+++}$$

STEP 2. $$MnO_4^- + 8\,H^+ + 5\,e \rightleftharpoons Mn^{++} + 4\,H_2O$$
$$Fe^{++} - e \rightleftharpoons Fe^{+++}$$

STEP 3. $$1(MnO_4^- + 8\,H^+ + 5\,e \rightleftharpoons Mn^{++} + 4\,H_2O)$$
$$5(Fe^{++} - e \rightleftharpoons Fe^{+++})$$

STEP 4.
$$MnO_4^- + 8\,H^+ + 5\,e + 5\,Fe^{++} - 5\,e \rightleftharpoons Mn^{++} + 4\,H_2O + 5\,Fe^{+++}$$
or $$MnO_4^- + 8\,H^+ + 5\,Fe^{++} \rightleftharpoons Mn^{++} + 4\,H_2O + 5\,Fe^{+++}$$

Example 3. The reaction between Sn^{++} and $Cr_2O_7^=$.

STEP 1. $\quad\quad\quad Sn^{++} + Cr_2O_7^= \rightleftharpoons Sn^{++++} + Cr^{+++}$

STEP 2. $\quad\quad\quad Sn^{++} - 2\,e \rightleftharpoons Sn^{++++}$
$Cr_2O_7^= + 14\,H^+ + 6\,e \rightleftharpoons 2\,Cr^{+++} + 7\,H_2O$

STEP 3. $\quad\quad\quad 6(Sn^{++} - 2\,e \rightleftharpoons Sn^{++++})$
$2(Cr_2O_7^= + 14\,H^+ + 6\,e \rightleftharpoons 2\,Cr^{+++} + 7\,H_2O)$

STEP 4. $\;6\,Sn^{++} - 12\,e + 2\,Cr_2O_7^= + 28\,H^+ + 12\,e \rightleftharpoons$
$6\,Sn^{++++} + 4\,Cr^{+++} + 14\,H_2O$

or $\quad 3\,Sn^{++} + 1\,Cr_2O_7^= + 14\,H^+ \rightleftharpoons 3\,Sn^{++++} + 2\,Cr^{+++} + 7\,H_2O$

Example 4. The reaction of solid Cu_2S and HNO_3 solution to form $Cu(NO_3)_2$ solution, NO_2 gas and solid sulfur.

STEP 1. $\quad\quad\quad Cu_2S + NO_3^- \rightleftharpoons Cu^{++} + NO_2 + S$

STEP 2. $\quad\quad\quad NO_3^- + 2\,H^+ + e \rightleftharpoons NO_2 + H_2O$
$Cu^+ - e \rightleftharpoons Cu^{++}$
$S^= - 2\,e \rightleftharpoons S$

(The two equations representing losses of electrons must be combined into one, recognizing that the Cu^+ and the $S^=$ come as Cu_2S, with $2\,Cu^+$ to every one S.)

$$Cu_2S - 4\,e \rightleftharpoons 2\,Cu^{++} + S$$

STEP 3. $\quad\quad 4(NO_3^- + 2\,H^+ + e \rightleftharpoons NO_2 + H_2O)$
$1(Cu_2S - 4\,e \rightleftharpoons 2\,Cu^{++} + S)$

STEP 4. $\;4\,NO_3^- + 8\,H^+ + 4\,e + 1\,Cu_2S - 4\,e \rightleftharpoons$
$4\,NO_2 + 4\,H_2O + 2\,Cu^{++} + S$

or $\quad 4\,NO_3^- + 8\,H^+ + Cu_2S \rightleftharpoons 4\,NO_2 + 4\,H_2O + 2\,Cu^{++} + S$

ELECTROCHEMICAL CELLS

A quantitative treatment of the intensity factor in oxidation-reduction reactions must be based upon the concept of galvanic electrochemical cells. The cell diagrammed in Figure 41 is one of the simpler types of cell. One beaker contains a solution of some zinc salt in which a strip of metallic zinc is partially immersed, while the other beaker contains a solution of a cupric salt into which is dipped a piece of metallic copper. The salt bridge which connects the two beakers is merely a conducting solution; a common form consists of an inverted U-tube filled with KCl solution and gelatin, the latter to prevent leakage. The purpose of the salt bridge is to provide a pathway for the migration of ions from one beaker to the other.

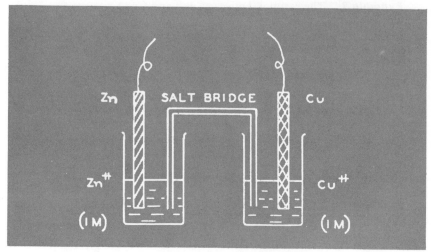

FIGURE 41.   A simple type of electrochemical cell.

In the left-hand beaker a reaction might occur

$$Zn^{++} + 2\,e \rightleftharpoons Zn$$

The reaction

$$Cu^{++} + 2\,e \rightleftharpoons Cu$$

may possibly take place in the right-hand beaker. These two equations indicate that no net reaction takes place in either beaker unless electrons are either delivered to or removed from that beaker. There is a possibility, however, that a reaction could take place in each beaker if the two metal strips are connected by means of a conducting wire so that the electrons released in one beaker could travel through the wire to the other beaker and there be consumed. In other words, an over-all reaction could take place in accordance with the equation

$$Cu^{++} + Zn \rightleftharpoons Cu + Zn^{++}$$

The direction in which this reaction does go is determined by whether the copper or the zinc has a greater attraction for the electrons.

Experimentally, it has been found that electrons flow through the external circuit from the zinc to the copper. This means that copper has a greater electron affinity than does zinc and that the over-all reaction proceeds from left to right as written. The magnitude of this difference in electron affinity can be measured by connecting a suitable voltmeter between the two metal strips; in the present example a potential difference of 1.1 volts is found. By convention in this book, the electrode of greater affinity for electrons will be considered as the positive one. Therefore, the electron affinity of copper is 1.1 volts more positive than that of zinc.

This complete reaction consists of one oxidation process in which electrons are lost and one reduction process in which electrons are consumed. One of the two processes takes place in each beaker, so each is called a *half-cell* and each process is called a half-cell reaction. No reaction can take place in a half-cell by itself; yet any two half-cells present a possibility of a complete redox reaction when properly connected together.

A half-cell need not consist of a metallic strip dipped into a solution of ions of that metal. In the pair of half-cells shown in Figure 42, the left-hand portion consists of a solution of some ferric salt into which is dipped an inert platinum electrode, while another platinum electrode is dipped into a solution of a stannous salt in the right-hand portion. In practice, the left-hand beaker would necessarily contain at least a few ferrous ions and the right-hand one some stannic ions also. Possible reactions in the two half-cells are

$$Fe^{+++} + e \rightleftharpoons Fe^{++}$$

and

$$Sn^{++++} + 2 e \rightleftharpoons Sn^{++}$$

Neither reaction can occur alone, since electrons can be neither created nor destroyed in any complete chemical or electrochemical reaction. Yet if the two electrodes are connected externally by a metallic conductor as shown, both half-cell reactions occur simultaneously with those electrons released in one half-cell being carried through the external wire to the others. Experimentally, it has been found that the left half-cell receives electrons from the right, so the iron system has a greater electron affinity than does the tin system. It has further been found that the potential between the two platinum wires is typically about 0.6 volt in this combination of half-cells.

Although it is impossible to measure any single electrode or half-cell potential by itself, it would be very valuable to have some method of expressing quantitatively the potential of a single electrode. The values of

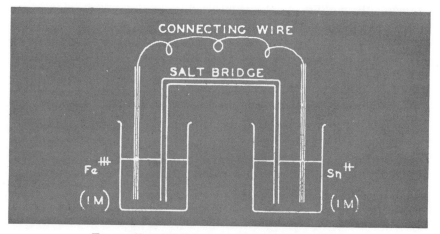

FIGURE 42. Another type of electrochemical cell.

1.1 volt and 0.6 volt mentioned above are useful in describing each of the cells involved, but they reveal nothing concerning other possible combinations of half-cells, such as an iron vs. copper set-up. A basis for a tabulation of single electrode potentials has been established by arbitrarily selecting one electrode or half-cell as a standard of reference, assigning it the value of exactly 0.0000 volts, and expressing all other electrode potentials relative to this one.

The electrode which has been selected as this defined standard is the *standard hydrogen electrode.* This electrode, or half-cell, consists of hydrogen gas under one atmosphere of pressure surrounding a piece of metallic platinum covered with a coating of spongy, black platinum and bathed in a solution 1.0 molar in hydrogen ion concentration. (Strictly speaking, it should have a hydrogen ion activity, rather than molarity, of unity.) The electrode reaction for this electrode is

$$H^+ + e \rightleftharpoons 1/2\ H_2$$

or
$$2\ H^+ + 2\ e \rightleftharpoons H_2$$

The potential of any other half-cell reaction may be determined by measuring its potential relative to that of the standard hydrogen electrode as zero.

THE NERNST EQUATION

Statement of the Equation. The standard oxidizing potentials listed in Table 14 are those potentials which would be observed for each half-cell, relative to the standard hydrogen electrode, if that half-cell is at standard conditions. Standard conditions have been defined to include the following: concentrations of all ionic species which enter into the electrode reaction are one molar (strictly speaking, the activities rather than the molarities should be unity); the pressure of any gas involved in the electrode reaction is one atmosphere; the temperature is 25° C.

Theoretical and experimental work has led to the development of an equation relating the potential of an electrode under other than standard conditions to the potential of that electrode in standard conditions. With this equation it is possible to calculate any electrode, or half-cell, potential from the standard potentials which are listed in Table 14. This very important equation is designated the *Nernst equation.* As used throughout this book, the Nernst equation may be stated in the form

$$E = E° + \frac{0.059}{n} \log \frac{[Ox]^a}{[Red]^b}$$

for the electrode whose chemical reaction may be represented as

$$a \cdot Ox + n \cdot e \rightleftharpoons b \cdot Red$$

$E°$ is the potential of the electrode under standard conditions and is as listed in Table 14, and E is the potential under other conditions. The factor 0.059 includes the temperature factor, so the equation in this form is valid at 25° C. only. This temperature will be assumed throughout this book whenever the Nernst equation is employed. This equation is, in a sense, a mass law equation for this type of reaction. As in other mass law equations, concentration factors must be expressed in standard units. Thus, dissolved ionic and molecular concentrations are in molarities, and gas concentrations in atmospheres pressure. The concentration of water molecules is taken as unity, just as it is in the equation for the ionization constant of water, and concentrations of solids not in solution are also taken as unity just as they are in equations for solubility product constants.

One further item of explanation must be given in the statement of the Nernst equation. If any substance other than the oxidant itself or the reductant itself enters into the reaction, its concentration raised to the appropriate power must be included along with that of the oxidant or reductant in the Nernst equation. This point will become clear from the example which follows:

Example 5. Write Nernst equations for each of the half-cells indicated in the left-hand column.

$$Cu^{++} + 2\,e \rightleftharpoons Cu \qquad E = 0.34 + \frac{.059}{2} \log [Cu^{++}]$$

$$2\,H^+ + 2\,e \rightleftharpoons H_2 \qquad E = 0.00 + \frac{0.59}{2} \log \frac{[H^+]^2}{[H_2]}$$

$$Sn^{++++} + 2\,e \rightleftharpoons Sn^{++} \qquad E = 0.15 + \frac{.059}{2} \log \frac{[Sn^{++++}]}{[Sn^{++}]}$$

$$Cr_2O_7^= + 14\,H^+ + 6\,e \rightleftharpoons \qquad E = 1.30 + \frac{.059}{6} \log \frac{[Cr_2O_7^=][H^+]^{14}}{[Cr^{+++}]^2}$$
$$2\,Cr^{+++} + 7\,H_2O$$

$$MnO_4^- + 8\,H^+ + 5\,e \rightleftharpoons \qquad E = 1.51 + \frac{.059}{5} \log \frac{[MnO_4^-][H^+]^8}{[Mn^{++}]}$$
$$Mn^{++} + 4\,H_2O$$

Each of the chemical equations could be multiplied or divided by an integer without changing the value of E derived from the Nernst equation. For example, the hydrogen electrode could be written as

$$H^+ + e = 1/2\,H_2$$

instead of as in the example above. The corresponding Nernst equation would be

$$E = 0.00 + \frac{.059}{1} \log \frac{[H^+]}{[H_2]^{\frac{1}{2}}}$$

which is mathematically identical with that listed in Example 5.

It is of interest to check the definition of $E°$ with the Nernst equation. If the concentration of each substance involved is unity, the quantity following "log" in each of the Nernst equations in the examples listed becomes unity. The log of one is zero, so under these conditions each Nernst equation reduces to

$$E = E° + 0$$

Thus, the definition of $E°$ and the statement of the Nernst equation are entirely consistent with each other. Furthermore, the E value becomes more positive as the concentration of the oxidized form is increased; this fact is consistent with the listing of the stronger oxidants with higher (more positive) values in Table 14.

Calculation of Half-Cell Potentials. Several examples will now be undertaken to illustrate the direct application of the Nernst equation to the calculation of half-cell, or electrode, potentials. As is customary, the standard hydrogen electrode will be taken as the reference standard.

Example 6. Calculate the potential of a Pt wire dipping into a solution 0.10 M in Sn^{++} and 0.01 M in Sn^{++++}

$$E = E° + \frac{.059}{2} \log \frac{[Sn^{++++}]}{[Sn^{++}]}$$

$$E = 0.15 + \frac{.059}{2} \log \frac{0.01}{0.10}$$

$$E = 0.15 + \frac{.059}{2} \log 10^{-1}$$

$$E = 0.15 + \frac{.059}{2} (-1)$$

$$E = 0.15 - .03$$

$$E = 0.12$$

Example 7. Calculate the potential of a hydrogen electrode in which the pH is 5.0 and the hydrogen gas pressure is one atmosphere.

$$E = E° + \frac{.059}{2} \log \frac{[H^+]^2}{[H_2]}$$

$$E = 0.00 + \frac{.059}{2} \log \frac{(10^{-5})^2}{1}$$

$$E = -0.295$$

Example 8. Calculate the potential of a Pt wire dipping into a solution which is 0.10 M in $Cr_2O_7^=$, 0.10 M in Cr^{+++}, and the pH of which is 2.0.

$$E = E^\circ + \frac{.059}{6} \log \frac{[Cr_2O_7^=][H^+]^{14}}{[Cr^{+++}]^2}$$

$$E = 1.30 + \frac{.059}{6} \log \frac{(10^{-1})(10^{-2})^{14}}{(10^{-1})^2}$$

$$E = 1.30 + \frac{.059}{6} \log (10^{-27})$$

$$E = 1.03$$

Calculation of Complete Cell Potentials. Each potential calculated in Examples 6, 7 and 8 was the potential of a complete cell consisting of the standard hydrogen electrode (E = 0.00) as the other half-cell. Calculations of complete cell potentials in which neither electrode is the standard hydrogen electrode may be determined readily by calculating the potential of each half-cell relative to hydrogen as zero and then taking the difference between the two. The proper way to combine the two half-cell potentials to obtain the complete cell potential may be facilitated by the construction of "linear graphs" as illustrated in Figure 43. The standard hydrogen electrode is placed at E = 0.00, and the two half-cell potentials relative to the standard hydrogen electrode are placed on the diagram with plus values above and minus values below. The difference between any two electrodes can be seen readily.

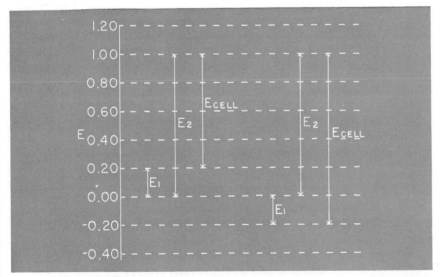

FIGURE 43. Diagram to illustrate the combination of two half-cell potentials to form one complete cell potential. Left, half-cell potentials of 0.20 and 1.00 combine to form E_{cell} of 0.80. Right, half-cell potentials of −0.20 and 1.00 combine to form E_{cell} of 1.20.

Example 9. Calculate the potential difference between two Pt wires, one dipping into a solution 0.10 M in Fe^{+++} and 0.010 M in Fe^{++}, and the other 0.010 M in Sn^{++++} and 0.10 M in Sn^{++}, both beakers being connected by a suitable salt bridge. Which way would electrons flow through a wire connecting the two Pt wires?

Fe^{+++}/Fe^{++} half-cell:

$$E = E° + \frac{.059}{1} \log \frac{[Fe^{+++}]}{[Fe^{++}]}$$

$$E = 0.77 + .059 \log \frac{(10^{-1})}{(10^{-2})}$$

$$E = 0.83$$

Sn^{++++}/Sn^{++} half-cell:

$$E = E° + \frac{.059}{2} \log \frac{[Sn^{++++}]}{[Sn^{++}]}$$

$$E = 0.15 + \frac{.059}{2} \log \frac{(10^{-2})}{(10^{-1})}$$

$$E = 0.12$$

One electrode is $+0.83$ and the other $+0.12$, both relative to the standard hydrogen electrode, so this cell potential is the difference, or *0.71 with the ferric-ferrous half-cell as positive.* The more positive electrode attracts electrons, so *electrons will flow through an external wire from the stannic-stannous beaker to the ferric-ferrous beaker.*

Example 10. Calculate the potential of a cell consisting of two hydrogen electrodes, in one of which the pH is 1.0 and in the other of which it is 3.0, and in both of which the hydrogen gas pressure is one atmosphere.

$$E = E° + \frac{.059}{2} \log \frac{[H^+]^2}{[H_2]}$$

with pH of 1.0:

$$E = 0.00 + \frac{.059}{2} \log \frac{(10^{-1})^2}{1}$$

$$E = -0.059$$

with pH of 3.0:

$$E = 0.00 + \frac{.059}{2} \log \frac{(10^{-3})^2}{1}$$

$$E = -0.177$$

The over-all cell potential is the difference between -0.059 and -0.177, or *0.118 with the half-cell of pH 1.0 the positive one.*

Note that each statement of over-all cell potential must include not only a number but also must include a statement of which electrode, or half-cell, is the positive one.

EQUILIBRIUM CONDITIONS

Equilibrium Established by Flow of Electrons through External Circuit. Consider next what happens when an external wire is connected between the two half-cells and electrons are permitted to flow spontaneously for a period of time. The more positive electrode receives the electrons from the less positive one. Taking the cell of Example 9 in this discussion, the ferric-ferrous half-cell receives electrons, so these electrons must be consumed by the reaction

$$Fe^{+++} + e \longrightarrow Fe^{++}$$

Accordingly, the $[Fe^{+++}]$ value gradually decreases and the $[Fe^{++}]$ value increases correspondingly. According to the Nernst equation, these changes will make the electrode potential become less positive. At the same time a reaction to liberate electrons proceeds in the other half-cell

$$Sn^{++++} + 2\,e \longleftarrow Sn^{++}$$

with the $[Sn^{++++}]$ value increasing and the $[Sn^{++}]$ value decreasing. These changes cause the potential of this electrode to become more positive. Therefore, as the reactions proceed, the potential of the electrode which was initially $+0.83$ volt becomes less positive, and the potential of the electrode which was initially $+0.12$ becomes more positive. The current flow will continue until the electrode potentials equal each other, at which time no further net current flows in either direction and the reactants in both half-cells are in equilibrium with each other.

The over-all chemical equation representing the entire cell may be found by combining the two half-cell chemical equations, as

$$2\,Fe^{+++} + Sn^{++} \longrightarrow 2\,Fe^{++} + Sn^{++++}$$

At the state of equilibrium, the potentials of the two half-cells are equal, so

$$0.77 + \frac{.059}{1} \log \frac{[Fe^{+++}]}{[Fe^{++}]} = 0.15 + \frac{.059}{2} \log \frac{[Sn^{++++}]}{[Sn^{++}]}$$

This equation may be simplified by combining the numbers on one side and the concentration expressions on the other.

$$0.77 - 0.15 = \frac{.059}{2} \log \frac{[Sn^{++++}]}{[Sn^{++}]} - \frac{.059}{1} \log \frac{[Fe^{+++}]}{[Fe^{++}]}$$

$$0.77 - 0.15 = \frac{.059}{2} \log \frac{[Sn^{++++}]}{[Sn^{++}]} - \frac{.059}{2} \log \frac{[Fe^{+++}]^2}{[Fe^{++}]^2}$$

$$0.77 - 0.15 = \frac{.059}{2} \left(\log \frac{[Sn^{++++}]}{[Sn^{++}]} - \log \frac{[Fe^{+++}]^2}{[Fe^{++}]^2} \right)$$

$$\frac{(0.77 - 0.15) \times 2}{.059} = \log \frac{[Sn^{++++}][Fe^{++}]^2}{[Sn^{++}][Fe^{+++}]^2}$$

$$10^{21.0} = \frac{[Sn^{++++}][Fe^{++}]^2}{[Sn^{++}][Fe^{+++}]^2}$$

$$1.0 \times 10^{21} = K_{eq.}$$

Note that the right side of this last equation is the equilibrium constant for the over-all reaction and that the only data required for the calculation of the numerical value of this equilibrium constant are the E° values for the half-reactions. The E° values for many half-reactions have been tabulated, as in Table 14, and, in fact, these E° values can be re-measured quite easily in the laboratory. This represents one of the best and at the same time one of the simplest methods of determining numerical values of equilibrium constants for redox reactions. It is also possible to calculate equilibrium constants for some other types of reactions as well, as will be illustrated later in Example 13.

Equilibrium Established by Reaction within One Vessel. Next, consider two of the half-cells combined into one beaker. Following through with the cell of Example 9 again, this would mean that the ferric-ferrous solution and the stannic-stannous solution would be poured together in the same beaker. *Exactly the same reaction would proceed as did proceed in the separate half-cells when they were connected with an external wire and salt bridge.* The ferric-ferrous system has the more positve potential so takes electrons away from the stannic-stannous system. The only difference is that the ferric and stannous ions can meet directly and exchange electrons rather than pass them from the latter to the former through an external wire. A state of equilibrium is eventually established, just as when the two half-cells were in separate containers and suitably connected. Even though this particular reaction, between ferric and stannous ions, does not reach equilibrium as rapidly as some do, because of cation-cation repulsion, many ionic reactions do proceed very quickly to equilibrium. A platinum wire dipping into this one beaker would assume the potential of the ferric-ferrous system which is, when a state of equilibrium exists in the solution, identical with the potential of the stannic-stannous system.

Calculation of Equilibrium Constants. The steps required to calculate the equilibrium constant of any redox reaction from electrochemical data are as follows: (1) write the over-all chemical reaction for which a constant is desired; (2) write the separate half-reactions involved, conventionally writing each in the form used in Table 14; (3) write Nernst equations for each of these half-reactions; equate these two Nernst equations to each other, a condition necessarily valid at equilibrium; (4) combine the numbers on one side and the concentration expressions on the other. This process must, without exception, lead either to the equilibrium constant or to its reciprocal; if it does not, an error must have been made in the arithmetic work. One additional comment is in order—the combination of terms in Step 4 always requires that the n value for each half-reaction be the same. This may be accomplished mathematically either in Step 3 or in Step 4, remembering the property of logarithms that

$$\frac{0.059}{1} \log \frac{[A]}{[B]} = \frac{0.059}{2} \log \frac{[A]^2}{[B]^2}$$

and so forth.

Example 11. Calculate the equilibrium constant for the reaction,

$$Cr_2O_7^= + 14\ H^+ + 6\ Fe^{++} \rightleftharpoons 2\ Cr^{+++} + 6\ Fe^{+++} + 7\ H_2O.$$

half-reactions: $Cr_2O_7^= + 14\ H^+ + 6\ e \rightleftharpoons 2\ Cr^{+++} + 7\ H_2O,$

for which $\qquad E = 1.30 + \dfrac{.059}{6} \log \dfrac{[Cr_2O_7^=][H^+]^{14}}{[Cr^{+++}]^2}$

and $\quad Fe^{+++} + e \rightleftharpoons Fe^{+++},$

for which $\qquad E = 0.77 + \dfrac{.059}{1} \log \dfrac{[Fe^{+++}]}{[Fe^{++}]}$

or $\qquad E = 0.77 + \dfrac{.059}{6} \log \dfrac{[Fe^{+++}]^6}{[Fe^{++}]^6}$

at equilibrium,

$$1.30 + \frac{.059}{6} \log \frac{[Cr_2O_7^=][H^+]^{14}}{[Cr^{+++}]^2} = 0.77 + \frac{.059}{6} \log \frac{[Fe^{+++}]^6}{[Fe^{++}]^6}$$

combining terms, $\dfrac{(1.30 - 0.77)6}{.059} = \log \dfrac{[Fe^{+++}]^6[Cr^{+++}]^2}{[Fe^{++}]^6[Cr_2O_7^=][H^+]^{14}}$

$$10^{53.9} = K_{eq.}$$

Example 12. Calculate the equilibrium constant for the reaction,

$$AsO_3^= + H_2O + I_2 \rightleftharpoons AsO_4^= + 2\ H^+ + 2\ I^-.$$

half-reactions: $AsO_4^= + 2\ H^+ + 2\ e \rightleftharpoons AsO_3^= + H_2O,$

for which $\qquad E = 0.56 + \dfrac{.059}{2} \log \dfrac{[AsO_4^=][H^+]^2}{[AsO_3^=]}$

and $\qquad I_2 + 2\ e = 2\ I^-,$ for which $E = 0.54 + \dfrac{.059}{2} \log \dfrac{[I_2]}{[I^-]^2}$

at equilibrium:

$$0.56 + \frac{.059}{2} \log \frac{[AsO_4^=][H^+]^2}{[AsO_3^=]} = 0.54 + \frac{.059}{2} \log \frac{[I_2]}{[I^-]^2}$$

combining terms: $\dfrac{(0.56 - 0.54)2}{.059} = \log \dfrac{[I_2][AsO_3^=]}{[I^-]^2[AsO_4^=][H^+]^2}$

$$0.68 = \log \frac{1}{K_{eq.}} \quad *$$

$$10^{0.68} = \frac{1}{K_{eq.}}$$

$$K_{eq.} = 10^{-0.68}$$

or $\qquad K_{eq.} = 0.21$

* Note that, if the numbers had been grouped on the right instead of on the left in the preceding step, this step would have come out as $\log K_{eq.} = -0.68$. It is possible to anticipate on which side the numbers should be grouped so that $K_{eq.}$, instead of $\dfrac{1}{K_{eq.}}$, is obtained at this point.

Example 13. Calculate the solubility product constant of silver chloride from these two half-reactions:

$$Ag^+ + e \rightleftharpoons Ag, \qquad E° = 0.81$$
$$AgCl + e \rightleftharpoons Ag + Cl^-, \quad E° = 0.22$$

over-all reaction:

$$Ag^+ + Cl^- \rightleftharpoons AgCl$$

half-reaction:

$$Ag^+ + e \rightleftharpoons Ag, \text{ for which } E = 0.81 + .059 \log [Ag^+]$$

$$AgCl + e \rightleftharpoons Ag + Cl^-, \text{ for which } E = 0.22 + .059 \log \frac{1}{[Cl^-]}$$

at equilibrium:

$$0.81 + .059 \log [Ag^+] = 0.22 + .059 \log \frac{1}{[Cl^-]}$$

combining terms: $\qquad \dfrac{0.81 - 0.22}{.059} = \log \dfrac{1}{[Cl^-][Ag^+]}$

$$10.0 = \log \frac{1}{K_{sp}}$$

$$10^{10.0} = \frac{1}{K_{sp}}$$

or $\qquad\qquad\qquad\qquad K_{sp} = 1.0 \times 10^{-10}$

Calculation of the Equilibrium Potential. The equilibrium potential was used as the basis of the calculation in each of the three preceding examples, but that potential was not actually calculated. In some types of work it is useful to know just what that potential is. It may be calculated from either of the two Nernst equations written for it. That is, in Example 11, the equilibrium potential, $E_{eq.}$, can be calculated from either of the two equations:

$$E_{eq.} = 0.77 + \frac{.059}{1} \log \frac{[Fe^{+++}]}{[Fe^{++}]}$$

or $\qquad E_{eq.} = 1.30 + \dfrac{.059}{6} \log \dfrac{[Cr_2O_7^=][H^+]^{14}}{[Cr^{+++}]^2},$

while in Example 12, the $E_{eq.}$ value can be calculated either from

$$E_{eq.} = 0.56 + \frac{.059}{2} \log \frac{[AsO_4^=][H^+]^2}{[AsO_3^=]}$$

or from $\qquad E_{eq.} = 0.54 + \dfrac{.059}{2} \log \dfrac{[I_2]}{[I^-]^2}$

It will be noted that, in any case, certain quantities must be known before the numerical value of the equilibrium potential can be ascertained. In practical situations, the analyst will usually have available sufficient data for him to use only one of the two Nernst equations for that potential, so the nature of the available information usually dictates which of the two will be used.

Example 14. Calculate the potential of a Pt wire dipping into a solution of ferrous sulfate undergoing titration by dichromate at the point at which just one-half of the ferrous has been changed to ferric.

$$E = 0.77 + \frac{.059}{1} \log \frac{[Fe^{+++}]}{[Fe^{++}]}$$

We have data on $[Fe^{+++}]$ and $[Fe^{++}]$, so will use this one of the two possible equations:

$$E = 0.77 + .059 \log 1$$

Since $[Fe^{+++}] = [Fe^{++}]$, the ratio $\frac{[Fe^{+++}]}{[Fe^{++}]} = 1$, regardless of what the total volume is and regardless of what else may be in solution.

$$E = 0.77$$

Example 15. Calculate the potential of a Pt wire dipping into an equilibrium mixture formed by mixing 20 ml. of a 0.2 N Fe^{++} solution with 20 ml. of a 0.08 N $Cr_2O_7^=$ solution.

We have 4.0 mEq. of Fe^{++} and 1.6 mEq. $Cr_2O_7^=$ initially. The latter would have reacted with 1.6 mEq. of the former, forming 1.6 mEq. of Fe^{+++} and leaving 2.4 mEq. of Fe^{++}, all in 40 ml., so

$$[Fe^{+++}] = \frac{1.6}{40} \quad \text{and} \quad [Fe^{++}] = \frac{2.4}{40}$$

$$E = 0.77 + .059 \log \frac{[Fe^{+++}]}{[Fe^{++}]}$$

$$E = 0.77 + .059 \log \frac{1.6/40}{2.4/40}$$

$$E = 0.76$$

Calculation of Completeness of Reaction. At the theoretical equivalence point in any redox titration, the main reactants have been brought together in stoichiometric quantities. The concentration of either one of the reactants which remains unreacted at this point is a measure of the extent to which the desired reaction has gone to completion. It is possible to calculate this quantity with the aid of the equilibrium constant for the reaction. This may be illustrated by two examples.

Example 16. Calculate the concentration of ferrous ion remaining as such in a solution formed by mixing 20.00 ml. of 0.2000 N Ce(IV) with 20.00 ml. of 0.2000 N Fe^{++}, sulfuric acid being present.

We have 4.000 mEq. of Fe^{++} and 4.000 mEq. of Ce^{++++} initially, which react to form very nearly 4.000 mEq. Fe^{+++} and 4.000 mEq. Ce^{+++}, all in 40.00 ml.

Calculate the equilibrium constant by the methods of Examples 11, 12 and 13 (the work will not be shown here).

$$\frac{[Fe^{+++}][Ce^{+++}]}{[Fe^{++}][Ce^{++++}]} = 10^{11.5}$$

Now write additional mathematical equations until the number of equations equals the number of unknowns contained therein, and then combine the equations to obtain the desired information.

$$[Fe^{+++}] = \frac{4.000}{40.00} = 0.1000$$

$$[Ce^{+++}] = \frac{4.000}{40.00} = 0.1000$$

$$[Fe^{++}] = [Ce^{++++}]$$

Equivalent amounts were used and reacted so equivalent amounts remain.

$$\frac{0.1000 \times 0.1000}{[Fe^{++}][Fe^{++}]} = 10^{11.5}$$

$$[Fe^{++}] = 1.8 \times 10^{-7}$$

Example 17. Calculate the concentration of ferrous ion remaining as such in a solution formed by mixing 20.00 ml. of 0.2000 N MnO_4^- with 20.00 ml. of 0.2000 N Fe^{++}, the pH of the resulting solution being 1.0.

We have 4.000 mEq. of Fe^{++} and 4.000 mEq. of MnO_4^- initially, which react to form very nearly 4.000 mEq. Fe^{+++} and 4.000 mEq. Mn^{++}, all in 40.00 ml.

$$\frac{[Fe^{+++}]^5[Mn^{++}]}{[Fe^{++}]^5 MnO_4^-][H^+]^8} = 10^{62.7} \quad \text{(Calculated as in Examples 11, 12, 13.)}$$

$$[Fe^{+++}] = \frac{4.000}{40.00} = 0.1000$$

$$[Mn^{++}] = \frac{4.000}{40.00 \times 5} = 0.0200 \quad \begin{array}{l}\text{(Molarity of } Mn^{++} \\ \text{is one-fifth its} \\ \text{normality in this} \\ \text{reaction.)}\end{array}$$

$$\frac{[Fe^{++}]}{5} = [MnO_4^-] \quad \begin{array}{l}\text{(Equivalent amounts remain, so} \\ \text{normalities are equal, but} \\ \text{molarity of } MnO_4^- \text{ is one-fifth} \\ \text{its normality in this reaction.)}\end{array}$$

$$\frac{(0.1000)^5 \times 0.0200}{[Fe^{++}]^5 \times \dfrac{[Fe^{++}]}{5} \times (10^{-1.0})^8} = 10^{62.7}$$

$$[Fe^{++}] = 7.6 \times 10^{-11}$$

The extremely low values of the ferrous ion concentration in Examples 16 and 17, when compared with the much larger ferric ion concentration, show that both of these reactions do go far to completion.

Calculation of Potential at the Equivalence Point. The method of calculating the potential when stoichiometrically equivalent amounts of reagents have been brought together can be based upon the appropriate Nernst equations as in Examples 14 and 15 along with the calculation of the amount of one reactant remaining as in Examples 16 and 17.

Example 18. Calculate the potential of Pt wire dipping into the solution in Example 16.

$$E = 0.77 + .059 \log \frac{[Fe^{+++}]}{[Fe^{++}]}$$

$$[Fe^{+++}] = 0.1000 \quad \text{(as in example 17)}$$

$$[Fe^{++}] = 1.8 \times 10^{-7} \text{ (as in example 17)}$$

so

$$E = 0.77 + .059 \log \frac{0.1000}{1.8 \times 10^{-7}}$$

$$E = 1.11$$

Note that, even though the ferrous ion concentration is extremely small, it is not equal to zero. Otherwise, the equilibrium constant would be infinite rather than of a finite value.

TITRATION CURVES

The preceding several examples along with associated discussions have illustrated the fact that a platinum wire dipping into a redox titration solution can serve as an indicating electrode to show the progress of the titration. A redox titration curve consists of a plot of the potential of this electrode vs. the volume of added reagent. Titration curves may be plotted from experimental data obtained by methods to be described in Chapter 20 or from data calculated by the methods of this chapter. Points before and after the equivalence point are calculated similar to Examples 14 and 15, while the equivalence point is handled as in Examples 16 and 17. The calculations which follow are for a titration of 20 ml. of 0.2000 N Fe^{++} solution with 0.2000 N Ce^{++++} solution, all in sulfuric acid medium:

0.00 ml. added: no calculation will be made for this point, because we do not know the Fe^{+++} ion concentration other than to know it is very small.

2.00 ml. added: mEq. Fe^{+++} = mEq. Ce^{++++} added
$$= 2.00 \times 0.2000 = 0.400$$
mEq. Fe^{++} = mEq. Fe^{++} to start − mEq. Fe^{++} used up
$$= 4.000 − 0.400 = 3.600$$

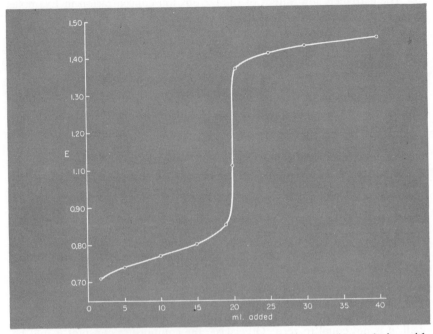

FIGURE 44.   Titration curve for titration of 20 ml. 0.2 N ferrous iron solution with
0.2 N ceric sulfate solution.

so
$$\frac{[Fe^{+++}]}{[Fe^{++}]} = \frac{0.400}{3.600} = 0.111$$

$$E = 0.77 + .059 \log \frac{[Fe^{+++}]}{[Fe^{++}]}$$

$$E = 0.77 + .059 \log 0.111$$
$$E = 0.71$$

5.00 ml. added: similarly, $E = 0.74$
10.00 ml. added: similarly, $E = 0.77$
15.00 ml. added: similarly, $E = 0.80$
19.00 ml. added: similarly, $E = 0.85$
20.00 ml. added: this is the equivalence point, and is identical with Example
16, so

$$E = 1.11$$

21.00 ml. added: mEq. Ce^{++++} = mEq. Ce^{++++} added − mEq. Ce^{++++}
reacted

$$= 4.200 - 4.000 = 0.2000$$

$$\text{mEq. } Ce^{+++} = \text{mEq. } Ce^{++++} \text{ reacted} = 1.000$$

so
$$\frac{[Ce^{++++}]}{[Ce^{+++}]} = \frac{0.2000}{4.000} = 0.0500$$

$$E = 1.45 + .059 \log \frac{[Ce^{++++}]}{[Ce^{+++}]}$$

$$E = 1.45 + .059 \log 0.0500$$
$$E = 1.37$$

25.00 ml. added: similarly, $E = 1.41$
30.00 ml. added: similarly, $E = 1.43$
40.00 ml. added: similarly, $E = 1.45$

These points are plotted in Figure 44. The general appearance of this curve is similar to that of a neutralization‚ titration curve. The potential changes very abruptly as the titration passes through the equivalence point. The potentials in this titration curve have all been calculated relative to the usual standard hydrogen electrode. If some other reference is desired, the y-axis would merely be shifted up or down, depending on the relative values of the desired reference electrode and the standard hydrogen electrode.

A titration curve may be calculated in the same way for any other redox titration. In Figure 45 are shown titration curves for reducing agents of several different strengths, all by ceric sulfate solution. If the oxidizing agent were of lesser or greater strength, the curve beyond the equivalence point would have been displaced downward or upward, respectively. It is clear that the larger the difference in $E°$ values of the two main reactants, the larger will

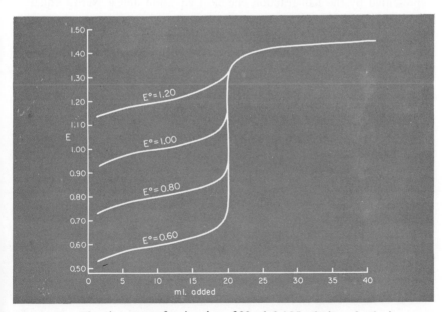

FIGURE 45. Titration curves for titration of 20 ml. 0.1 N solution of reducing agent of indicated $E°$ value by 0.1 N cerate solution.

be the vertical portion of the curve in the vicinity of the end point. The hydrogen ion is a reactant in some titrations so, of course, its concentration appears in the corresponding Nernst equations in the preparation of calculated titration curves.

OXIDATION-REDUCTION INDICATORS

There are several types of indicators for oxidation-reduction titrations. Some colored reagents may serve as their own indicators. For example, even a small amount of potassium permanganate imparts a distinct purple tinge to a solution, so the appearance of this color due to unreacted permanganate in a titration vessel marks the end point of a permanganate titration. Several physicochemical methods of end point detection are of value; a few are described in Chapter 20. For some titrations a specific qualitative test reagent is used as an external spot-test indicator. However, most redox titrations employ an additional substance which serves as an internal color indicator by changing color as the titration passes through the equivalence point. This type of indicator is, in many respects, analogous to the internal neutralization type of indicator.

A redox color indicator is a substance which itself can undergo an oxidation-reduction reaction. Its oxidized and reduced forms must differ in color from each other. The nature of the indicator reaction may be represented by the half-reaction chemical equation and a Nernst equation as follows:

$$Ox + n\,e \rightleftharpoons Red$$
$$\text{(color A)} \qquad \text{(color B)}$$

$$E = E^\circ + \frac{.059}{n} \log \frac{[Ox]}{[Red]}$$

in which Ox and Red are the oxidized and reduced forms, respectively, of the indicator. These equations assume that no hydrogen ion enters into the half-reaction. This assumption is not necessarily valid for all indicators, but it is adequate for the present discussion. Since the oxidized and reduced forms differ in color from each other, and since the intensity of color of a colored substance is (ideally, at least) directly proportional to its concentration, this Nernst equation may be rewritten as

$$E = E^\circ + \frac{.059}{n} \log \frac{\text{color A intensity}}{\text{color B intensity}}$$

As in the case of neutralization indicators, the indicator will appear to be color A if the A/B intensity ratio equals or exceeds 10, while it will appear to be color B if the ratio is equal to or less than 0.1. thus,

$$\text{color A if } E = E^\circ + \frac{.059}{n} \log 10$$

$$E = E^\circ + \frac{.059}{n}$$

and $\qquad$ color B if $E = E^\circ + \dfrac{.059}{n} \log 0.1$

$$E = E^\circ - \frac{.059}{n}.$$

Table 15. Selected Oxidation-Reduction Indicators

Indicator	Color change upon oxidation	E°
Methylene blue	blue to colorless	0.53
Diphenylamine	colorless to violet	0.76
Diphenylbenzidine	colorless to violet	0.76
Ba diphenylamine sulfonate	colorless to red-violet	0.84
Na diphenylbenzidine sulfonate	colorless to violet	0.87
2,2′-bipyridyl ferrous sulfate	red to faint blue	0.97
Eriogreen	red-yellow to rose	0.99
Erioglaucine	red-yellow to rose	1.00
5-methyl-1,10-phenanthroline ferrous sulfate (methyl ferroin)	red to faint blue	1.02
1,10-phenanthroline ferrous sulfate (ferroin)	red to faint blue	1.06
N-phenanthranilic acid	colorless to pink	1.08
5-nitro-1,10-phenanthroline ferrous sulfate (nitro-ferroin)	red to faint blue	1.25
Ruthenium tripyridyl nitrate	yellow to colorless	1.25

At intermediate potentials, the indicator will appear to be intermediate between color A and color B. Two conclusions may be drawn: a redox indicator requires a potential change of $2 \times \dfrac{.059}{n}$ or a maximum of about 0.12 volt to change from one color form to the other; this color change range is centered on the E° value of the indicator.

In Table 15 are listed several redox indicators along with the E° value and other significant information about each one. The hydrogen ion concentration influences the color change of some redox indicators. Some indicators are not reversible, so these Nernst equation considerations are not properly applicable. In a few cases either color A or color B (but not both) is colorless.

FEASIBILITY OF TITRATION AND SELECTION OF INDICATOR

A titration curve provides direct information concerning whether the titration is feasible or not and, if so, what indicator should be used. The curve should have a vertical rise in the region of the equivalence point of at least 0.12 volt, and the indicator selected should be one whose $E°$ is well within this vertical rise. For the titration of Figure 44, 1,10-phenanthroline ferrous sulfate would be very good as an indicator, as would several others listed in Table 15. However, for titrations in which the $E°$ values of the two main reactants lie closer together, Figure 45, the choice of indicator is more limited. In fact, if the two $E°$'s differ by only 0.25 volt, the rise at the equivalence point is hardly adequate, although a very approximate end point could be obtained if an indicator of suitable $E°$ were available.

It may be concluded from Figure 45 that titrations are feasible in quantitative work if the $E°$ values of the two reactants differ by more than about 0.20 volt. The $E°$ for the reducing agent is the potential existing experimentally when the concentrations of its oxidized and reduced forms are equal, which is true half-way to the end point; the $E°$ of the oxidizing agent is the observed potential at a volume 100% beyond the end point. Whenever hydrogen ion enters into a half-reaction equation, this generalization concerning the feasibility of a titration must be based upon potentials corrected for the effect of the hydrogen ion concentration rather than directly upon the $E°$. For example, if permanganate were the titrant for the titrations of Figure 45, and if the pH were two throughout, the E at 100% beyond the equivalence point would be

$$E = 1.51 + \frac{.059}{5} \log \frac{[MnO_4^-] \, 10^{-2}}{[Mn^{++}]}$$

$$E = 1.32$$

Thus, titrations would generally be feasible if the $E°$ of the reducing agent were at least 0.20 volt less than 1.32, not than 1.51.

The feasibility of a particular titration may be decided much more rigorously by calculations with Nernst equations of the potential range over which the indicator must change color in order to obtain some predetermined accuracy. Consider again the titration of Figure 44, and assume that the maximum end point error which is acceptable is one part per thousand. That is, the indicator must change color between 99.9% and 100.1% of the volume of titrant at the exact equivalence point. Calculation of the potentials at these volumes of titrant, by the same methods used in calculating the points plotted in Figure 44, come out to be 0.94 and 1.28 volts. Thus, any indicator changing color completely within this potential region would result in an end point indicator error of less than one part per thousand.

Consider next the titration of a mixture of two reducing agents by a strong oxidizing agent. For example, if the two reducing agents have $E°$ values of 0.60 and 1.00, the plots of Figure 45 show that the first one is titrated to practical completion before the potential rises high enough to begin the titration of the second one. A stepwise titration curve would result, much as in the titration of two acids of differing strengths by a strong base as described in Chapter 11. If, however, the two reducing agents were of the same strength (same $E°$), they would be titrated simultaneously rather than successively. In order for one reducing agent to be titrated successfully in the presence of another reducing agent, the $E°$'s of these two must differ by at least 0.20 volt. The oxidizing agent must, of course, be sufficiently strong as described in the preceding paragraphs. In Figure 46 is shown the titration curve of two oxidizing agents, Ce(IV) and Tl^{+++}, to Ce^{+++} and Tl^+, respectively, by a standard solution of Fe^{++}. Cerium(IV) is the stronger of the two oxidizing agents so it reacts first. The first end point is observable but is not sharp because the $E°$ values of the cerium and thallium systems differ by just 0.20 volt. The second end point is much sharper because the thallium and iron systems differ in $E°$ by almost 0.50 volt.

Many practical titration systems involve the presence in the titrating solution of some component which alters the concentration of one of the main reactants or products by complexation. For example, phosphate ion complexes ferric ion and, if present during a titration of ferrous ion by an oxidizing agent, keeps the ferric ion concentration very low throughout the entire titration. The generalizations made in this section of this chapter concerning the feasibility of titrations must include consideration of the effects of these components upon the effective potentials whenever such complexing agents are present.

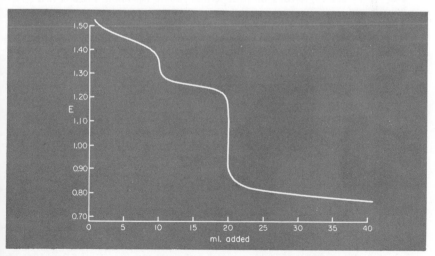

FIGURE 46.   Titration curve for titration of mixture of Ce(IV) and Tl^{+++} (1 mEq. each) by 0.1 N Fe^{++} solution.

REVIEW QUESTIONS

1. Define oxidation and reduction.
2. Distinguish between a solution of a strong oxidizing agent and a concentrated solution of an oxidizing agent.
3. Balance the following equations:
   a. $Al + H^+ \rightarrow Al^{+++} + H_2$
   b. $H_2AsO_3^- + Ce^{++++} + H_2O \rightarrow H_2AsO_4^- + Ce^{+++} + H^+$
   c. $SCN^- + MnO_4^- + H^+ \rightarrow SO_4^= + CN^- + H_2O + Mn^{++}$
   d. $ClO_3^- + Cl^- + H^+ \rightarrow Cl_2 + H_2O$
   e. $ClO_3^- + H_2S + H^+ \rightarrow S + Cl^- + H_2O$
   f. $H_2S + Br_2 + H_2O \rightarrow SO_4^= + H^+ + Br^-$
   g. $Cr^{+++} + MnO_2 + H_2O \rightarrow Mn^{++} + CrO_4^= + H^+$
   h. $Zn + OH^- \rightarrow ZnO_2^= + H_2$
   i. $BrO_3^- + I^- + H^+ \rightarrow Br^- + I_2 + H_2O$
   j. $NO_2^- + Al + OH^- + H_2O \rightarrow NH_3 + AlO_2^-$
4. From the data of Table 14, arrange the following in order of decreasing strength as oxidizing agents: I_2; MnO_4^-; $Cr_2O_7^=$; Sn^{++++}; Fe^{+++}.
5. How is the intensity factor in redox reactions actually measured?
6. What is a half-cell? a standard cell?
7. State the Nernst equation and apply it mathematically to two or three half-cells of your choice.
8. Is it possible for two copper-cupric ion half-cells to have different potentials? Explain by means of chemical equations and by means of Nernst equations.
9. What does the numerical value of an equilibrium constant indicate concerning the completeness of a reaction?
10. In 4 to 6 N acid, arsenate oxidizes iodide quantitatively to free iodine, but in a bicarbonate buffered medium, iodine quantitatively oxidizes arsenite to arsenate. Explain by means of chemical equations and by means of Nernst equations.
11. Sketch on the same axes titration curves for the titrations of (a) ferrous ion with dichromate and (b) ferrous ion with permanganate, assuming all other factors to be constant.
12. Consider a platinum wire dipping into 100 ml. of a solution containing 0.01 mole ferric ion and 0.01 mole ferrous ion. What will be the effect of each of the following upon the potential of this half-cell:
    a. Addition of 50 ml. water?
    b. Addition of some soluble ferrous salt?
    c. Addition of a few ml. of a permanganate solution?
13. Name some common internal oxidation-reduction indicators.
14. Of what practical significance is the $E°$ value of an oxidation-reduction indicator?

PROBLEMS

1–3. Calculate the potential relative to the standard hydrogen electrode of each half-cell:
   1. A silver wire dipping into a 0.015 M solution of silver nitrate.
   2. A strip of metallic nickel dipping into a 0.028 M solution of nickel chloride, $NiCl_2$.
   3. A hydrogen electrode with one atmosphere gas pressure and 5.0×10^{-3} M hydrochloric acid.

4–5. Calculate the potential relative to the saturated calomel electrode of each half-cell:

4. A platinum wire dipping into a solution 10^{-2} M in $Fe(CN)_6^=$ and 10^{-2} M in $Fe(CN)_6^\equiv$.

5. A platinum wire dipping into a solution 10^{-1} M in $Cr_2O_7^=$, 10^{-1} M in Cr^{+++} and 10^{-2} M in H^+.

6–8. Calculate the potential of each whole cell:

6. Two hydrogen electrodes, both with one atmosphere gas pressure, one with pH 1.0 and the other with pH 4.0.

7. A normal calomel electrode connected to a silver wire dipping into a solution of 0.0050 M silver nitrate.

8. Two platinum wires, one dipping into a solution 10^{-1} M in Fe^{+++} ion and 10^{-3} M in Fe^{++} ion, and the other dipping into a solution 10^{-3} M in $Cr_2O_7^=$ ion, 10^{-2} M in Cr^{+++} ion and at a pH of 1.5.

9–12. Complete and balance the following equations and calculate the equilibrium constant for each:

9. $Ce^{++++} + Fe(CN)_6^\equiv \rightleftharpoons Ce^{+++} + Fe(CN)_6^=$ (in H_2SO_4 medium)

10. $Pb + Sn^{++++} \rightleftharpoons Pb^{++} + Sn^{++}$

11. $Fe^{++} + MnO_4^- + H^+ \rightleftharpoons Fe^{+++} + Mn^{++}$

12. $Fe^{++} + Cu^{++} \rightleftharpoons Fe^{+++} + Cu^+$

13. When a hydrogen half-cell with one atmosphere gas pressure was connected to a normal calomel half-cell, the potential was 0.500 volts with the calomel side positive. Calculate the pH of the solution in the hydrogen half-cell.

14. Calculate the pH of a dichromate half-cell in which $[Cr_2O_7^=] = [Cr^{+++}] = 0.0100$ and of which the potential is $+1.02$ volt relative to the standard hydrogen electrode.

15–17. Calculate the potential of a platinum wire dipping into each of the following solutions:

15. The solution resulting from mixing 20.0 ml. 0.100 M ferrous chloride solution with 20.0 ml. 0.010 M ceric chloride, the solution being 10^{-1} M in hydrochloric acid at equilibrium.

16. The solution resulting from mixing 20.0 ml. 0.100 M ferrous chloride solution with 20.0 ml. 0.010 M dichromate solution, the pH being 1 at equilibrium.

17. The solution resulting from mixing 20.0 ml. 0.100 M ferrous chloride solution with 20.0 ml. 0.010 M permanganate solution, the pH being 1 at equilibrium.

18. Calculate the molar concentration of $Cr_2O_7^=$ ion in a solution prepared by mixing 20.00 ml. of 0.0500 N $Cr_2O_7^=$ with 30.00 ml. of 0.100 M ferrous solution, if the pH of the resultant solution equals zero.

19. Calculate the molar concentration of stannic ion in a solution prepared by mixing 100.0 ml. of 0.0100 N stannous chloride with 100.0 ml. of 0.0200 N dichromate solution, the pH being 1.00.

20–23. Consider the titration of 40.00 ml. of 0.2000 N arsenite solution with 0.2000 N iodine solution, the medium being buffered at pH 7.00 throughout.

20. Calculate the molar concentration of unreacted arsenite ion at the equivalence point.

21. Calculate the potential of a platinum wire dipping into the solution at the equivalence point.

22. Calculate the molar concentration of arsenate ion if 80.00 ml. of iodine is used.

23. Calculate the molar concentration of arsenite ion if 80.00 ml. of iodine is used.

24–27. Consider the titration of 40.00 ml. 0.2000 N stannous chloride solution with 0.2000 N dichromate solution, assuming the pH to be 0.0 throughout.

24. Calculate the concentration of unreacted stannous ion at the equivalence point.

25. Calculate the potential of a platinum wire dipping into the solution at the equivalence point.

26. Calculate the concentration of stannous ion when 20.00 ml. of dichromate is used.

27. Calculate the concentration of stannic ion when 20.00 ml. of dichromate is used.

28. Calculate and plot a complete titration curve for the titration of Problem 20, taking the pH as 7.00 throughout. (Calculate and plot as many points as are needed to obtain a smooth curve.)

SUGGESTIONS FOR ADDITIONAL READING

Items 2, 9, 10, 11, 14, 25, 27 and 30, Appendix 7.

Chapter 15

Oxidation-Reduction Methods Using Permanganate, Dichromate and Cerium(IV)

In most oxidation-reduction methods of analysis, a reduced form of the substance being determined is titrated with a standard solution of an oxidizing agent. The most common standard oxidizing agents are potassium permanganate, potassium dichromate, cerium(IV) and iodine. The first three of these reagents will be considered in this chapter, while methods involving iodine will be described in Chapter 16.

OXIDIZING POWER

Some oxidizing agents are more powerful than are others, as indicated by the E° values of Table 14. Likewise the reduced forms of some substances are more easily oxidized than are reduced forms of others. For any particular titration, the oxidizing agent must be at least strong enough to fulfill two requirements. First, it must be strong enough to react to practical completion with the substance being titrated, as discussed in detail in Chapter 14. Second, the oxidizing agent must not be so powerful that it is able to react with any component of the solution being titrated other than the desired component. Permanganate, dichromate and cerium(IV) are all rather powerful oxidizing agents, while iodine is a much weaker one; this is the reason why the first three are being considered together.

There is more than one standard potential listed in Table 14 for permanganate. The potential 1.51 is listed for the half-reaction

$$MnO_4^- + 8\,H^+ + 5\,e \rightleftharpoons Mn^{++} + 4\,H_2O$$

for which the corresponding Nernst equation is

$$E = 1.51 + \frac{.059}{5} \log \frac{[MnO_4^-][H^+]^8}{[Mn^{++}]}$$

Also, the potential 1.59 is listed for the half-reaction

$$MnO_4^- + 4\ H^+ + 3\ e \rightleftharpoons MnO_2 + 2\ H_2O$$

for which the corresponding Nernst equation is

$$E = 1.59 + \frac{.059}{3} \log \frac{[MnO_4^-][H^+]^4}{1}$$

The primary difference between these two half-reactions is the extent of the reduction of the permanganate ion. The product of the second one, manganese dioxide, is insoluble in neutral or in alkaline medium but is not formed in acidic solution. Therefore, in acid medium this product is not obtained, but rather the permanganate ion is reduced all the way down to the manganous ion, Mn^{++}. In alkaline medium, permanganate ion reduces only to the plus four valence state and its product is insoluble manganese dioxide. The hydrogen ion concentration plays a large role in the oxidizing power of permanganate, as indicated by the Nernst equations above. It should be noted that the conditions required for stopping the permanganate reduction at the manganese dioxide stage necessarily signify a much weaker oxidizing power than do the conditions under which the half-reaction product is the manganous ion.

Except for some reactions of permanganate with organic materials, potassium permanganate is usually used in acid medium to yield manganous ion. Accordingly, the $E°$ value is 1.51 volts, and the half-reaction product is the manganous ion.

The only common half-reaction undertaken by dichromate is

$$Cr_2O_7^= + 14\ H^+ + 6\ e \rightleftharpoons 2\ Cr^{+++} + 7\ H_2O$$

for which the corresponding Nernst equation is

$$E = 1.30 + \frac{.059}{6} \log \frac{[Cr_2O_7^=][H^+]^{14}}{[Cr^{+++}]^2}$$

The $E°$ value is less than that of permanganate, but it still signifies a rather powerful oxidizing agent. Once again the hydrogen ion concentration enters into the Nernst equation, this time to the fourteenth power as written. In alkaline medium the chromic ion, Cr^{+++}, forms an insoluble hydrous oxide and the nature of the dichromate ion also is shifted to the chromate ion. Accordingly, dichromate as an oxidizing agent is almost invariably employed in acid medium, and its reaction product is the chromic ion, Cr^{+++}.

For the simple half-reaction equation

$$Ce^{++++} + e \rightleftharpoons Ce^{+++}$$

four separate $E°$ values are listed in Table 14. These are 1.70 in perchloric acid, 1.61 in nitric acid, 1.45 in sulfuric acid and 1.23 in hydrochloric acid. This influence of the medium upon the oxidizing power of the cerium(IV) ion is very real, even though it would not be expected from the simple half-reaction equation as written. It seems apparent that the cerium(IV) ion does not exist simply as Ce^{++++}, but that it is at least partially complexed in solution. Nitrate ion quite definitely does complex cerium(IV) to some extent, and even hydroxyl ion from water can participate in formation of the complex ion, $Ce(OH)^{+++}$. Because of these complexes, it is customary to write the quadrivalent cerium ion as "cerium(IV)," thus signifying the oxidation state but not implying anything specific concerning the actual ionic species. The stabilities of such complexes as do exist influence the availability of ceric ions and so influence the oxidizing power of cerium(IV). This type of influence of acid upon an oxidizing power is entirely different from that encountered with permanganate and dichromate. With cerium(IV) the nature of the acid (i.e., its anion) influences the oxidizing power, while with dichromate and permanganate the amount of acid (i.e., the hydrogen ion concentration) influences the oxidizing power. Cerium salts are used as oxidizing agents almost exclusively in acid media.

In summary, permanganate is a more powerful oxidizing agent than is dichromate, although the pH influences the strength of both, and the oxidizing power of cerium(IV) ranges from much greater than that of permanganate to slightly less than that of dichromate, depending upon the nature of the acid environment.

COLORS OF OXIDIZED AND REDUCED FORMS

The colors of the oxidized and reduced forms of a standard oxidizing agent are of significance in end point detection. If the color of a small amount of the oxidized form can be detected in the presence of a much larger amount of the reduced form, the agent can serve as its own indicator when used to titrate other substances. When a regular internal color indicator is employed, its color change must be detected in the presence of oxidized and reduced forms of the standard titrating agent, so once again the colors of the oxidized and reduced forms of the oxidizing agent are of significance. In every specific application, consideration must also be given to the possibility of the end point color change being masked by some other colored substance in the solution being titrated.

Solutions of potassium permanganate are so intensely colored that one drop of a 0.1 N solution imparts a perceptible color to a hundred milliliters of water. The reduction product of permanganate in acid solution, Mn^{++}, is practically colorless in reasonable concentrations. The theoretical end point in a titration with standard permanganate solution is the point just beyond which the first slight trace of unreacted permanganate ion persists in the titration flask. Therefore, the color imparted to the solution by the first trace of excess reagent may be taken as the end point, permanganate thus acting as its own indicator.

The intense purple color of permanganate necessitates a different method of reading burets. Ordinarily the broad lower part of the meniscus should be read, but this part is not even visible from the side with permanganate solution in the buret. Therefore, the top of the meniscus must be read. No appreciable error need be introduced if initial and final buret readings are made in the same manner.

The oxidized form of cerium(IV) is yellow and the reduced form is colorless. A cerium solution can serve as its own indicator but only for relatively inexact work. The yellow color is not sufficiently intense for the analyst to recognize it until an excessive amount is present. That is, the true end point must be passed by an appreciable amount before the experimental end point is observed. This moderate yellow color does not interfere in the least with recognition of the color changes of internal redox indicators, and good indicators are readily available for cerate titrations.

Both the oxidized and reduced forms of dichromate are colored fairly intensely. Dichromate solutions are yellow, and chromic solutions are distinctly green. The passing of the end point in a titration with dichromate is characterized by the persistence of the first trace of excess dichromate ion in the titration vessel. This slight excess doubtless does give a yellow coloration to the solution, but that coloration is completely masked by the green color of the chromic ions which have been formed prior to that point in the titration. Therefore, dichromate cannot serve as its own indicator. Furthermore, the indicator to be used must be one whose color change is so distinct that it can be recognized in the presence of the other colored ions necessarily present in the solution at and near the end point. Fortunately, suitable indicators are available.

PREPARATION OF STANDARD SOLUTIONS

Potassium Permanganate. Potassium permanganate is not a primary standard, chiefly because its solutions become somewhat decomposed right after preparation. Therefore, it is necessary to prepare a solution of approximately the desired strength, let it stand for a period of time, then standardize it against some primary standard reducing agent or against a reducing agent solution which has previously been standardized against a primary standard oxidizing agent.

The instability of a freshly prepared permanganate solution arises from the facts that permanganate is a powerful oxidizing agent and that distilled water contains some organic matter which is oxidizable. Since the reaction between permanganate and organic matter in the distilled water from which the solution is prepared cannot conveniently be eliminated, it should be allowed to proceed to completion, or nearly so, prior to standardization of the solution. After the solute is dissolved, the solution should be heated to hasten this decomposition and allowed to stand a day or two. The solution is approximately neutral, so the permanganate ion reduces only to the plus four valence state of insoluble manganese dioxide. This precipitate must be removed by filtration, otherwise it would enter into further reaction when the solution is subsequently used in acid medium and it would also tend to catalyze further decomposition. The filtration should be through an asbestos mat in a Gooch crucible or Buchner funnel, not through filter paper, since the paper could cause further decomposition of the permanganate solution. Solutions of potassium permanganate should be stored in dark bottles and kept out of bright light as much as is conveniently possible.

A standard solution of any reducing agent which reacts quantitatively with permanganate may be used for standardization purposes. Among the primary standard reducing agents which are suitable for this purpose are arsenious oxide (As_2O_3), sodium oxalate ($Na_2C_2O_4$), and pure iron wire.

Arsenious oxide must be dissolved in alkaline solution:

$$As_2O_3 + 2\ OH^- + H_2O \longrightarrow 2\ H_2AsO_3^-$$

but it may then be acidified and titrated with permanganate in accordance with the equation

$$2\ MnO_4^- + 5\ H_3AsO_3 + 6\ H^+ \longrightarrow 2\ Mn^{++} + 5\ H_3AsO_4 + 3\ H_2O$$

The arsenite ion, $AsO_3^=$, forms the weak acid ions, $HAsO_3^=$, $H_2AsO_3^-$ and H_3AsO_3, and the arsenate ion does similarly. Thus, the equation as written does not necessarily represent completely the true form of the arsenite and arsenate ions, but it suffices for stoichiometric purposes.

Sodium oxalate is readily soluble in acid, in which it exists predominantly in the form of undissociated oxalic acid molecules. These are titrated with permanganate, presumably in accordance with the equation

$$2\ MnO_4^- + 5\ H_2C_2O_4 + 6\ H^+ \longrightarrow 2\ Mn^{++} + 10\ CO_2 + 8\ H_2O$$

This reaction involves a rather complex mechanism, and results that are reproducible and stoichiometric are obtained only when the titrated solution is at or slightly above 70° C. However, results are very good when the empirical conditions are fulfilled.

Ordinary iron wire is not pure enough for use as a primary standard, but a specially purified grade may be purchased for this purpose. The wire is dissolved in acid and titrated from the ferrous to the ferric state with the permanganate solution. The reaction involved in the titration will be discussed in some detail in conjunction with the determination of unknown quantities of iron in ores. The primary standard wire can be obtained with sufficiently constant cross section that it can be measured by a ruler instead of by weighing it out. The regular weighing method is required for the most accurate work, however.

Potassium Dichromate.   Potassium dichromate may be obtained in a sufficiently pure condition to make possible its use as a primary standard.

It is also readily soluble in water, and its solutions are quite stable over long periods of time. In some analytical work, dichromate solutions are standardized against known samples which are chemically similar to the unknown samples which are to be analyzed. Nevertheless, potassium dichromate may serve as a primary standard in most work, including much precise work.

Cerium(IV). Ammonium hexanitrato cerate, $(NH_4)_2Ce(NO_3)_6$, is a good primary standard for the direct preparation of standard cerium(IV) solutions. However, cerium(IV) solutions are generally prepared from sulfatoceric acid, $H_2Ce(SO_4)_3$, from ammonium sulfatocerate, $(NH_4)_4Ce$-$(SO_4)_4 \cdot 2 H_2O$, or from hydrous ceric oxide, $CeO_2 \cdot xH_2O$, all of which are commercially available. The solution which is prepared must be acidic, as ceric salts hydrolyze to insoluble substances in neutral or alkaline media. Sulfuric acid solutions of cerium(IV) are stable over extended periods of time, while solutions in nitric acid and in perchloric acid decompose slowly and solutions in hydrochloric acid are unstable (unless the acid is very dilute). No particular difficulty is encountered in titrating other substances which are in hydrochloric acid media, however.

Primary standard reducing agents suitable for standardizing cerium(IV) solutions include the three discussed for permanganate, namely, arsenious oxide, sodium oxalate and iron wire. A catalyst is required for rapid reaction between sulfatocerate and arsenious oxide, and osmium tetroxide is usually employed for this purpose. The reaction with sodium oxalate proceeds readily at room temperature in 2 N perchloric acid. Additional primary standards for the standardization of cerate solutions include Oesper's salt, $FeC_2H_4(NH_3)_2(SO_4)_2 \cdot 2 H_2O$, and Mohr's salt, $Fe(NH_4)_2(SO_4)_2 \cdot 6 H_2O$. These are readily soluble and are suitable for the standardization of solutions of permanganate and of dichromate also.

INDICATORS

No indicator other than the reagent itself is required with permanganate, unless the reagent is very dilute (for example, 0.01 N or less), in which case ferrous 1,10-phenanthroline as an internal indicator is advantageous. Some permanganate reactions, including the one with oxalate, proceed rather slowly. Thus, there may be a momentary appearance of the end point color before the true end point is reached. Even the correct end point color fades slowly, so the point at which the first definite tinge of permanganate color persists in the titration vessel for thirty seconds should be taken as the end point.

The common indicator for cerium(IV) titrations is the ferrous 1,10-phenanthroline complex. This indicator is initially in the reduced form, $Fe(C_{12}H_8N_2)_3^{++}$, and is oxidized by the first excess of cerium(IV) in the titration vessel to the oxidized form, $Fe(C_{12}H_8N_2)_3^{+++}$. The color change is from an intense red to a faint blue. The E° value of this indicator is 1.06, which value is very good, for example, in titrations of ferrous iron with cerate in sulfuric acid.

Potassium dichromate is not sufficiently strong as an oxidizing agent to permit the use of an indicator with an E° value as high as that of ferrous 1,10-phenanthroline, unless the hydrogen ion concentration is unduly high. Barium diphenylamine sulfonic acid, with an E° value of 0.84, is a good indicator for dichromate titrations. The color change from reduced form to oxidized form is from colorless to deep purple. The purple coloration is sufficiently intense to be discernible even in the greenish chromic solution in which the end point must be detected.

SELECTED APPLICATIONS

Determination of Iron. Iron is perhaps the most frequently encountered element in industrial analysis so its determination is of considerable practical as well as pedagogical importance. Several of the factors involved in an iron determination are also encountered in other analytical determinations. Therefore, a detailed study of the iron redox determination is of much value. The standard oxidizing agent may be dichromate, permanganate or cerium(IV), although some steps differ in accordance with which one is used.

A volumetric iron determination generally consists of the following major steps: (1) dissolution of the sample; (2) reduction of all ferric ion to ferrous ion and removal of the excess of whatever reducing agent is employed for that purpose; (3) addition of special reagents to insure that the one proper reaction will occur during the subsequent titration; (4) titration of the ferrous solution with a standard permanganate, cerate or dichromate solution.

Dissolution of the sample. The steps taken to dissolve a sample must be selected to fit the particular specimen involved. Occasionally, a water-soluble iron salt is encountered, but most unknown iron samples are either metal alloys or iron oxides which are not directly soluble in water. Iron alloys are generally soluble in acid. Iron itself is soluble in nitric acid, hydrochloric acid or sulfuric acid, while one or another of these serves satisfactorily to dissolve most iron alloys.

Hot hydrochloric acid is usually effective in dissolving iron ores, while neither nitric acid nor sulfuric acid is satisfactory. A sample that is finely pulverized dissolves more readily than one in the form of larger chunks, but even then an hour or more may be required to complete the solution. During the dissolving period, the acid may be heated near the boiling point, but iron would be lost as fairly volatile ferric chloride if the solution were permitted to evaporate. A small amount of stannous chloride hastens the dissolving process by reducing the ferric ions to ferrous ions as rapidly as they come into solution. In extreme cases, fusion of the ore sample with a flux of sodium carbonate or potassium acid sulfate is necessary to render the sample soluble.

Phosphoric acid also dissolves most iron ore samples, but an insoluble precipitate of an iron phosphate of indefinite composition may form. A 1:1 mixture of perchloric and phosphoric acids serves as an excellent solvent for iron ores; a ten- to fifteen-minute period of heating near the boiling point is generally sufficient. Perchloric acid is a powerful oxidizing agent when hot, and explosive reaction may occur when the concentrated acid is heated in the presence of organic material. Therefore, it is essential that this reagent be employed very carefully and that student use be limited to carefully prescribed procedures. No particular danger exists if perchloric acid is used properly.

Most iron ores contain some silica which will not dissolve upon treatment with hot hydrochloric acid. This residue is not harmful in the iron determination. The silicious residue may be distinguished readily from any remaining particles of iron oxide, because the silica is lighter than the iron oxide, both in color and in density.

After the sample is dissolved, the iron will be either all or partly in the ferric form. Dissolving of iron alloys and of ferrous oxides yields some ferric ion through air oxidation, unless the process of dissolving the sample is carried out in an oxygen-free environment. Many iron ores are of ferric oxide and others are of mixed ferric and ferrous oxides.

Reduction of ferric ions to ferrous ions. The eventual titration will require that the iron be in the ferrous form at the start of the titration. Thus, all ferric ions in the dissolved sample must be reduced prior to the final titration. Several different reducing agents have been developed for this purpose. In each case, an excess of the reducing agent must be used to insure that all the ferric ions are reduced, and then that excess must be removed so that it would not also eventually react with the standard oxidizing agent in the main titration.

Ferric ion may be reduced with stannous chloride in the presence of hydrochloric acid, and the excess may be removed by mercuric chloride. The desired reactions are

$$2\ Fe^{+++} + Sn(II) \xrightarrow{\ HCl\ } 2\ Fe^{++} + Sn(IV)$$

and $\qquad Hg^{++} + Sn(II) + 2\ Cl^- \xrightarrow{\ HCl\ } Hg_2Cl_2 + Sn(IV)$

The amount of stannous chloride used is quite critical. If not enough, some iron will not be reduced to the ferrous form; if too much, the second reaction will be replaced, at least partially, by the reaction

$$2\ Hg^{++} + Sn(II) \xrightarrow{\ HCl\ } Hg + Sn(IV)$$

Free mercury would react to a significant extent with the oxidizing agent in the subsequent titration, so its presence must be avoided. However, solid mercurous chloride does not interfere, so its presence is not harmful. Fortunately, the ferric ion is colored yellow, so stannous chloride may be added dropwise until this color disappears. One or two drops additional are then added to insure a slight excess of the stannous chloride reagent. If the process is carried out properly, a fine white precipitate of mercurous chloride appears when the mercuric chloride is added. If too much stannous chloride was used, this precipitate will be grayish or even black from finely divided free mercury; the sample must be discarded if this error occurs. This method of reducing ferric ion to ferrous ion is suitable only in hydrochloric acid solution, probably because the tin ions are complexed by the chloride ion.

Alternatively, this preliminary reduction of iron may be accomplished by zinc metal:

$$2\ Fe^{+++} + Zn \longrightarrow 2\ Fe^{++} + Zn^{++}$$

This zinc is commonly used either in the form of a wire spiral or in the form of a Jones reductor (Figure 47). This reductor consists of a glass tube packed with granulated zinc. The ferric solution to be reduced is simply poured in the top, and it comes out the bottom as a ferrous solution. No special step is required to remove the excess reducing agent, as none of the zinc is able to flow along with the iron solution. If a spiral is used, it is simply withdrawn

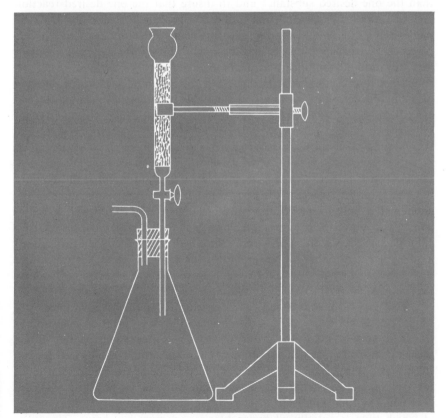

FIGURE 47.   Jones reductor assembly.

from the sample solution when reduction of the iron is complete. The column or the spiral should, of course, be washed to insure that none of the iron solution is lost, the washings being added to the iron solution.

A metallic silver reductor is also frequently useful, chloride ion also being a reactant,

$$Fe^{+++} + Ag + Cl^- \longrightarrow Fe^{++} + AgCl$$

Other usable metallic reductors include cadmium and aluminum. Any of these can be used in the form of a column similar to the Jones reductor, or they may be used in the form of a wire coil which is dipped into the ferric solution and withdrawn after the reduction of ferric to ferrous ions is completed.

Even though all of these reductors are sufficiently powerful to reduce ferric to ferrous quantitatively, not all are of equal strength. When other reducible substances in addition to ferric ion are present, the reductor must be selected judiciously so that only the desired reduction reaction will occur.

Addition of special reagents. Some special reagents are required in some redox titrations to prevent the reaction of the oxidizing agent with other than the one desired substance and to insure that the one desired reaction goes quantitatively to completion. An example of the former is the Zimmermann-Reinhardt (Z-R) reagent in permanganate titrations of iron in the presence of hydrochloric acid, and the use of phosphoric acid in the dichromate titration of iron illustrates the latter.

When ferrous iron in the presence of hydrochloric acid is titrated with one of the oxidizing agents, there are two possible reactions of oxidation:

$$Fe^{+++} + e \longleftarrow Fe^{++}, \quad \text{for which } E° \text{ is } 0.77$$

$$Cl_2 + 2 e \longleftarrow 2 Cl^-, \quad \text{for which } E° \text{ is } 1.36$$

Dichromate is powerful enough as an oxidizing agent to oxidize the iron but not the chloride. Likewise the cerium(IV) E° value in this medium is low enough that only iron is oxidized during the titration. However, permanganate is a powerful enough oxidizing agent to react to some extent with chloride as well as with ferrous iron. Since hydrochloric acid is often needed as the solvent in preparing an unknown for analysis, particularly iron ore unknowns, a possible source of error is introduced in titrations of iron by permanganate.

Two general methods have been developed for the elimination of this error. One is to remove the hydrochloric acid prior to titration by evaporation with sulfuric acid. The latter acid has a higher boiling point, so the former comes off first when a solution containing both is partially evaporated. In this procedure, some sulfuric acid is added to the hydrochloric solution of the sample, and this solution is heated until white fumes of sulfur oxide are evolved. The fumes indicate the beginning of evaporation of sulfuric acid, at which time essentially all hydrochloric acid must be absent. The other method calls for the use of the Zimmermann-Reinhardt reagent and subsequent titration right in the presence of the hydrochloric acid.

The Z-R reagent consists of manganous sulfate, phosphoric acid and sulfuric acid. The manganous ion in the presence of phosphoric acid somehow serves to weaken the oxidizing power of permanganate so that it is no longer strong enough to react with chloride ion. Possibly these portions of the reagent combine with permanganate ion as it is in temporary or localized excess prior to the equivalence point to form a complex ion in which manganese is in an intermediate oxidation state. This complex is still able to oxidize ferrous iron to ferric iron, and the stoichiometry of the desired reaction is not upset. The phosphate also complexes the ferric ion, effectively keeping the ferric ion concentration very low no matter how far the titration has progressed. This effect may be illustrated by the Nernst equation for the ferric-ferrous system:

$$E = E^\circ + .059 \log \frac{[Fe^{+++}]}{[Fe^{++}]}$$

The degree of completion to which the main titration reaction goes is determined by the difference in E values for this and the permanganate half-reactions; making this one low throughout the entire titration is of value in offsetting the weakening of the oxidizing power of the permanganate system. Sulfuric acid is used in the Z-R reagent merely to keep the other components in solution.

The Zimmermann-Reinhardt reagent is not needed in its entirety in the titration of iron by dichromate. The manganous sulfate would be of no consequence whatever. Phosphoric acid may still be employed advantageously to complex the ferric ion as formed, aiding in driving the desired reaction to completion. An iron by cerium(IV) titration likewise does not require the Z-R reagent. The phosphoric acid may or may not be used.

Titration.   The final titration of ferrous ion may be performed with permanganate, dichromate or cerium(IV). As indicated in comparing these reagents throughout this chapter, there are some advantages and disadvantages of each, but excellent results are obtainable with all three. The titration should be carried to completion very soon after reduction of all iron to the ferrous state, as ferrous solutions are slowly oxidized by atmospheric oxygen.

Laboratory Experiment 22

DETERMINATION OF IRON IN AN ACID-SOLUBLE SALT
OR ORE BY DICHROMATE TITRATION

Reagents

Diphenylamine indicator, solution prepared by dissolving 0.3 gram
barium diphenylamine sulfonate in 100 ml. water, adding 0.5
gram Na_2SO_4, letting stand, and then decanting the clear liquid
Hydrochloric acid, stock solution
Mercuric chloride, solution containing 50 grams $HgCl_2$ per liter of
water
Phosphoric acid, stock solution
Potassium dichromate, approximately 0.1 N standard solution as a
primary standard, prepared by drying and accurately weighing
about 2.45 grams reagent grade $K_2Cr_2O_7$, dissolving in water
and diluting to the mark in a 500 ml. volumetric flask
Stannous chloride, solution containing 15.0 grams of iron-free
$SnCl_2 \cdot 2 H_2O$ per 100 ml. of 6 N hydrochloric acid (prepare this
solution fresh within a day or two of the time to be used)

Procedure

Conduct the determination in triplicate. Dry the sample at
110° C. for one hour. Accurately weigh individual portions of 0.5
gram each (consult instructor for possible change in size of sample)
into 600 ml. beakers. Add 10 ml. hydrochloric acid and warm gently.
If the sample dissolves readily, proceed to the addition of stannous
chloride. If the sample does not dissolve readily, cool again, add an
additional 10 ml. hydrochloric acid and gently heat over a sand bath
or burner. Do not boil lest iron be lost as volatile $FeCl_3$. A few
drops of stannous chloride and/or an additional 10 ml. of hydrochloric acid may be added during the digestion if dissolution is
extremely slow, although an hour or longer may be required with
some ore samples. Continue this digestion until no heavy black
particles are seen in the residue; some white or gray-white silica
particles may remain. (Beyond this point, carry each of the replicate
samples separately and quickly through the final titration.) Add
stannous chloride solution dropwise with stirring to the hot sample
solution until the yellow color is discharged. Add an excess of two
drops of the stannous chloride solution. Dilute to 100 ml and cool

to room temperature. Add 10 ml. of mercuric chloride solution rapidly with stirring. A white precipitate should form. (If it is gray or black or if no precipitate forms, an incorrect amount of stannous chloride has been used and the sample must be discarded.) Dilute to 250 ml. with water. Add 10 ml. phosphoric acid and 0.5 ml. diphenylamine indicator solution. Titrate with standard dichromate solution to the end point, which is marked by deep violet color imparted to the solution by the indicator in the presence of the first drop of excess dichromate solution. Calculate the percentage Fe in the sample.

Suggestions for Supplementary or Alternate Laboratory Work. The solution of potassium dichromate can be standardized by titration against primary standard ferrous ethylenediammonium sulfate, $FeC_2H_4(NH_3)_2(SO_4)_2 \cdot 4 H_2O$ or against primary standard electrolytic iron wire. This standardization can serve either as a check on, or as an alternative to, the preparation of the dichromate solution as its own primary standard. Use individual portions of about 1 gram of the ferrous salt or 0.2 gram of iron wire. Both the ferrous salt and the iron wire are soluble in dilute hydrochloric acid and may then be titrated directly by the dichromate solution.

Laboratory Experiment 23

DETERMINATION OF IRON IN AN ORE BY PERMANGANATE TITRATION

Reagents

Hydrochloric acid, stock solution

Mercuric chloride, solution containing 50 grams $HgCl_2$ per liter of water

Potassium permanganate, approximately 0.1 N solution, prepared by dissolving 3.3 grams $KMnO_4$ in warm water, diluting to one liter, shaking thoroughly, letting stand overnight or longer, and filtering through a washed asbestos mat in a Buchner funnel

Sodium oxalate, analytical reagent grade

Sulfuric acid, 1 volume stock solution diluted with 18 volumes water (always add acid to water, never vice versa)

Stannous chloride, solution containing 150 grams of iron-free $SnCl_2 \cdot 2 H_2O$ per liter of 6 N hydrochloric acid (prepare this solution fresh within a day or two of the time used)

Zimmermann-Reinhardt reagent, solution prepared by dissolving 70 grams $MnSO_4 \cdot 4\,H_2O$, in 500 ml. water, adding with stirring 125 ml. sulfuric acid (stock solution) and 125 ml. phosphoric acid (stock solution), and diluting to one liter

Procedure

Standardization of Permanganate Solution with Sodium Oxalate. Conduct the standardization in triplicate. Dry the sodium oxalate at 110° C. for two hours. Accurately weigh individual portions of 0.2 gram each into 300 ml. Erlenmeyer flasks. Dissolve in 100 ml. sulfuric acid. Heat the solution nearly to boiling. Titrate with the permanganate solution until a pink coloration appears and lasts for thirty seconds, keeping the solution above 70° C. throughout the titration. Calculate the normality of the permanganate solution.

Iron Determination. Conduct the determination in triplicate. Dry the sample at 110° C. for one hour. Accurately weigh individual portions of 0.7 gram each into 600 ml. beakers. Add 20 ml. hydrochloric acid. Gently heat over a sand bath or burner to dissolve the sample. Do not boil lest iron be lost as volatile $FeCl_3$. Continue this digestion until no heavy black particles are seen in the residue; some white or gray-white silica particles may remain. Add stannous chloride solution dropwise with stirring to the hot sample solution until the yellow color is discharged. (Beyond this point, carry each of the replicate samples separately and immediately through the final titration.) Add an excess of two drops of the stannous chloride solution. Dilute to 100 ml., and cool to room temperature. Add 10 ml. of mercuric chloride solution rapidly with stirring. A white precipitate should form. (If it is gray or black or if no precipitate forms, an incorrect amount of stannous chloride was used and the sample must be discarded.) Dilute to 300 ml. with water. Add 25 ml. of the Zimmermann-Reinhardt reagent. Titrate with permanganate solution. Calculate the percentage Fe in the sample.

Laboratory Experiment 24

DETERMINATION OF IRON IN AN ORE BY CERIUM(IV) TITRATION

Reagents

Arsenious oxide, analytical reagent grade

Cerium(IV), approximately 0.1 N solution in sulfuric acid, prepared by placing 20 grams ceric hydroxide in a large beaker, adding slowly with stirring a warm sulfuric acid solution obtained by adding 80 ml. sulfuric acid (stock solution) to 300 ml. water, cooling, transferring to a one liter glass-stoppered bottle, and diluting to one liter

Ferrous 1,10-phenanthroline indicator, solution containing 0.7 gram $FeSO_4 \cdot 7 H_2O$ and 1.5 gram orthophenanthroline monohydrate per 100 ml. solution

Hydrochloric acid, stock solution

Mercuric chloride, solution containing 50 grams $HgCl_2$ per liter of water

Osmium tetroxide, solution containing 0.1 gram osmium tetroxide per 40 ml. 0.1 N sulfuric acid

Sodium hydroxide, solid

Stannous chloride, solution containing 150 grams iron-free $SnCl_2 \cdot 2H_2O$ per liter of 6 N hydrochloric acid (prepare this solution fresh within a day or two of the time needed)

Sulfuric acid, 1 volume stock solution diluted with 3 volumes water

Procedure

Standardization of Cerium(IV) Solution with Arsenious Oxide. Conduct the standardization in triplicate. Dry the arsenious oxide at 110° C. for two hours. Weigh accurately individual portions of 0.25 gram each into 400 ml. beakers. Add 25 ml. water and 2 grams sodium hydroxide. Warm gently and stir as needed to dissolve. Add 100 ml. water, 25 ml. sulfuric acid, two drops osmium tetroxide solution as a catalyst, and two drops of ferrous 1,10-phenanthroline indicator solution. Titrate with the cerium(IV) solution to the end point, which is marked by a color change from pink to pale blue. Calculate the normality of the cerium(IV) solution.

Iron Determination. Follow the procedure for the preparation of the sample solution of the unknown in the iron determination in

Experiment 22 through the dilution to 250 ml. Add two drops of ferrous 1,10-phenanthroline indicator solution. Titrate with cerium-(IV) solution. Calculate the percentage Fe in the sample.

Laboratory Experiment 25

DETERMINATION OF IRON IN A SOLUBLE SALT BY JONES REDUCTOR AND PERMANGANATE TITRATION

Reagents

Mercuric nitrate, solution containing 2 grams $Hg(NO_3)_2$ per 100 ml. solution

Nitric acid, stock solution

Potassium permanganate, the standard solution prepared and standardized in Experiment 23

Sulfuric acid, 1 volume stock solution diluted with 16 volumes water

Zinc, 20 to 30 mesh

Procedure

Preparation of Jones Reductor. Obtain a glass tube of the type illustrated in Figure 47, about 2 cm. in diameter and long enough to hold a 25 to 35 cm. column of zinc. Place a pad of glass wool at the bottom and a perforated porcelain plate upon that. Connect the outlet tube at the bottom to a 500 ml. Erlenmeyer flask through one hole of a two-hole rubber stopper; fit a glass tube in the other hole for connection to a suction line. In a separate beaker place 300 grams pure zinc, and add 300 ml. of mercuric nitrate solution and 2 ml. nitric acid. Stir the mixture for five or ten minutes, and remove the liquid by decantation. Wash the zinc several times with water by decantation. The zinc should now be amalgamated and should have a bright, silvery luster. Fill the reductor tube with water. Slowly pour in the amalgamated zinc until the column is packed. Wash by pouring through 500 ml. water, and from this time on keep the column filled with water (or other liquid as needed). Prior to each use of the Jones reductor, wash with sulfuric acid until a 100 ml. portion of the wash liquid does not decolorize two drops of standard permanganate solution. The rate of applied suction should be such that about 50 ml. of liquid are drawn through per minute whenever the reductor is in use.

Iron Determination. Conduct the determination in triplicate. Dry the sample at 110° C. for one hour. Accurately weigh individual portions of 1 gram each into 300 ml. beakers. Add 150 ml. sulfuric acid and warm gently until dissolved. Pass this solution through the prepared reductor column at the flow rate of about 50 ml. per minute; when the solution is in the column and the liquid level is just slightly above the upper zinc level, close the stopcock, pour about 50 ml. of sulfuric acid into the beaker and from thence into the column as the flow is resumed. In this way, pass four 50 ml. wash portions through the reductor. Remove the suction flask, and immediately titrate its contents with standard permanganate solution. Calculate the percentage Fe in the sample.

Determination of Calcium. The volumetric determination of calcium represents a very useful type of indirect oxidation-reduction method of analysis. The calcium ion is precipitated as calcium oxalate, which is washed and filtered. This precipitate is then dissolved in acid, the oxalate becoming oxalic acid. This oxalic acid is then titrated with standard permanganate solution. The titration determines the amount of oxalate which, in turn, is equivalent to the amount of calcium in the initial sample. Any metal ion which forms an insoluble oxalate may be determined similarly by this procedure.

The procedure may be outlined by a series of chemical equations illustrating each step. (The initial unknown will be assumed to contain calcium as calcium carbonate.)

STEP 1. Dissolve the sample in acid

$$CaCO_3 + H^+ \longrightarrow Ca^{++} + HCO_3^-$$

STEP 2. Precipitate Ca^{++} with excess oxalate and ammonium hydroxide

$$Ca^{++} + C_2O_4^= + H_2O \overset{OH^-}{\longrightarrow} CaC_2O_4 \cdot H_2O$$

STEP 3. After filtering and washing to remove excess $C_2O_4^=$, dissolve in acid

$$CaC_2O_4 \cdot H_2O + 2\,H^+ \longrightarrow Ca^{++} + H_2C_2O_4 + H_2O$$

STEP 4. Titrate with $KMnO_4$

$$2\,MnO_4^- + 5\,H_2C_2O_4 + 6\,H^+ \longrightarrow 2\,Mn^{++} + 10\,CO_2 + 8\,H_2O$$

The precipitated calcium oxalate must not be contaminated with coprecipitated oxalates. A purer precipitate is obtained if an oxalate solution is added to an acid solution of the calcium unknown and then the solution slowly neutralized with ammonium hydroxide than if the precipitate is formed by adding the oxalate solution directly to a neutral or ammoniacal solution of the calcium.

Although calcium does not enter directly into the final titration, it is stoichiometrically related to the amount of oxalic acid titrated. One calcium ion corresponds to one molecule of oxalic acid which, in turn, loses two electrons upon subsequent reaction with permanganate. Thus, the equivalent weight of calcium is one-half its atomic weight.

Zinc may be determined by a similar procedure. The precipitate of zinc oxalate should be formed in 70% acetic acid solution.

Laboratory Experiment 26

VOLUMETRIC DETERMINATION OF CALCIUM

Reagents

Ammonium hydroxide, 1 volume stock solution diluted with 10 volumes water, freshly filtered before use

Ammonium hydroxide, 1 volume stock solution diluted with 30 volumes water

Ammonium oxalate

Asbestos fibers, aqueous suspension

Hydrochloric acid, stock solution

Methyl orange indicator, solution containing 0.02 gram methyl orange per 100 ml. solution

Potassium permanganate, the standard solution prepared and standardized in Experiment 23

Sulfuric acid, 1 volume stock solution diluted with 19 volumes water

Procedure

Preparation of Gooch Crucible. Place a Gooch crucible in a suction filtering assembly. Before applying suction, pour in sufficient well-shaken asbestos suspension to form a mat 2 to 5 mm. thick. (The proper amount of asbestos to be used must be found by experiment.) Allow the suspension to stand for two or three minutes so the larger particles will settle to the bottom. The liquid should preferably fill about two-thirds of the crucible for good settling. Gently apply suction to form an even layer of asbestos on the bottom of the crucible. With suction pour through about 100 ml. water to wash through any loose, fine particles. Remove the crucible by disconnecting the tubing from the side arm of the flask, then turn off the suction. (After the crucible is prepared, it is not advisable to pour anything into it unless suction is being applied, or the mat may become torn and allow precipitates to pass through.)

   Calcium Determination. Conduct the determination in triplicate. Dry the sample at 110° C. for one hour. Accurately weigh individual portions of 0.5 gram each into 400 ml. beakers. Add 20 ml. water and 5 ml. hydrochloric acid. If the sample does not dissolve readily, cover the beaker with a watch glass and heat gently to get it into solution. Dilute to 200 ml. with water. Heat to boiling. Add slowly with stirring an amount of ammonium oxalate calculated to be sufficient on the assumption that the sample is entirely $CaCO_3$. Add the ammonium hydroxide solution (1:10 dilution) slowly from a buret until the liquid tests alkaline to methyl orange. Digest the resultant suspension for ten minutes over a low flame or on a sand bath, then let it stand for at least twenty-four hours. Filter through an unweighed Gooch crucible prepared as described in the preceding section of this experiment. Wash the precipitate in the filtering crucible with about 100 ml. ammonium hydroxide (1:30 dilution). Remove the crucible from the filtering assembly and place in a clean 400 ml. beaker. Add enough sulfuric acid to cover the crucible; about 200 ml. generally suffices. Heat nearly to boiling. Immediately titrate the liberated oxalic acid with standard permanganate solution, simply leaving the crucible in the beaker during the titration. Calculate the percentage CaO in the sample.

The Determination of Available Oxygen in Higher Oxides of Manganese and Lead. Lead dioxide, either PbO_2 or Pb_3O_4, or manganese dioxide may be determined by reduction with a measured excess of standard oxalate or arsenite solution, followed by titration of that excess with standard permanganate solution. The reaction between oxalate in acid solution and manganese dioxide, for example, proceeds according to the chemical equation

$$MnO_2 + H_2C_2O_4 + 2\,H^+ \longrightarrow Mn^{++} + 2\,H_2O + 2\,CO_2$$

Laboratory Experiment 27

DETERMINATION OF AVAILABLE OXYGEN IN PYROLUSITE

Reagents

Potassium permanganate, the standard solution prepared and
standardized in Experiment 23
Sodium oxalate, analytical reagent grade
Sulfuric acid, 1 volume stock solution diluted with 6 volumes water

Procedure

Conduct the determination in triplicate. Dry the sample and
the sodium oxalate at 110° C. for one hour. Accurately weigh
individual portions of the sample of 0.5 gram each into 300 ml.
Erlenmeyer flasks. Accurately weigh individual portions of the
sodium oxalate of about one gram each into the same flasks. Add
about 100 ml. sulfuric acid. Heat gently over a burner or on a sand
bath, with occasional shaking, until all dark colored particles are
dissolved; a white or light brown residue may remain. Dilute to
200 ml. with water. Heat to 70° C. and titrate the excess oxalate
remaining with permanganate solution. Calculate the percentage
MnO_2 in the sample.

Determination of Hydrogen Peroxide. Hydrogen peroxide is
oxidized to free oxygen by permanganate in acid solution

$$5 H_2O_2 + 2 MnO_4^- + 6 H^+ \longrightarrow 5 O_2 + 2 Mn^{++} + 8 H_2O$$

This reaction may be made the basis of a method for the determination of
the concentration of a solution of hydrogen peroxide. A little manganous
ion added before the titration commences makes the reaction proceed more
smoothly.

Laboratory Experiment 28

DETERMINATION OF CONCENTRATION OF HYDROGEN PEROXIDE SOLUTION

Reagents

Potassium permanganate, the standard solution prepared and standardized in Experiment 23

Sulfuric acid, stock solution

Procedure

Accurately weigh a small, stoppered flask. Add about 2 ml. of the unknown peroxide solution, and reweigh the flask. Rinse the sample into a 300 ml. Erlenmeyer flask which contains 2 or 3 ml. sulfuric acid in 75 ml. water. Titrate immediately with the permanganate solution. Calculate the percentage H_2O_2 in the sample.

STOICHIOMETRIC CALCULATIONS

Stoichiometric calculations in redox work make use of the same three short equations used in neutralization work:

mEq. = mEq., by identity, or at a true equivalence point;

mEq. = N × ml.;

$$mEq. = \frac{mg.}{eq.\ wt.}$$

The equivalent weight is equal to the formula weight divided by the number of electrons which that formula weight accounts for in the reactions. In reality, one equivalent of an oxidizing or reducing agent is the weight of that substance corresponding to one gram-atom of electrons transferred. Thus, the equivalent weights of $K_2Cr_2O_7$, $KMnO_4$ and $CeSO_4$, assuming each is used in acid medium, are 1/6, 1/5, 1/1 times the formula weights, respectively. It must be recognized clearly that an equivalent weight is tied directly to a reaction. Potassium permanganate, for example, can have equivalent weights of 1/3 or 1/5 of its formula weight, depending upon whether it is reduced to the quadrivalent or to the divalent state in the reaction of interest.

When one particular change in oxidation state is much more frequently encountered than another, that one may be assumed to be the one involved unless designated otherwise. Thus the phrase "tenth normal permanganate solution" means, unless stated differently, that the solution is one-tenth normal when used in acid solution with the oxidation state of the manganese changing from $+7$ to $+2$. Whenever any uncertainty may arise, the specific reaction should be stated.

Several examples of redox stoichiometric calculations, typical of those encountered in student laboratory work, follow:

Example 1. What is the normality of a potassium dichromate solution prepared by dissolving 4.1890 grams of reagent grade $K_2Cr_2O_7$ in water and diluting to the mark in a one liter volumetric flask?

$$\text{mEq. } K_2Cr_2O_7 \text{ weighed out} = \text{mEq. } K_2Cr_2O_7 \text{ in solution}$$

$$\frac{\text{mg. } K_2Cr_2O_7}{\text{eq. wt.}} = N \times \text{ml.}$$

$$\frac{4\ 189.0}{294.21 \div 6} = N \times 1000.0$$

$$N = 0.08543$$

Example 2. What is the normality of a potassium permanganate solution if 31.62 ml. were required to titrate a 0.3455 gram sample of reagent grade $Na_2C_2O_4$?

$$\text{mEq. } KMnO_4 = \text{mEq. } NaC_2O_4$$

$$N \times \text{ml.} = \frac{\text{mg. } Na_2C_2O_4}{\text{eq. wt.}}$$

$$N \times 31.62 = \frac{345.5}{134.01 \div 2}$$

$$N = 0.1631$$

Example 3. Calculate the normality of a ferrous sulfate solution, 26.42 ml. of which required for titration 38.20 ml. of a 0.1025 N solution of permanganate.

$$\text{mEq. } FeSO_4 = \text{mEq. } KMnO_4$$

$$N \times \text{ml.} = N \times \text{ml.}$$

$$N \times 26.42 = 0.1025 \times 38.20$$

$$N = 0.1482$$

Example 4. Calculate the percentage of iron in an ore, a 0.8964 gram sample of which required 40.76 ml. of 0.1134 N ceric sulfate solution for titration.

$$\text{mEq. Fe in ore} = \text{mEq. ceric sulfate}$$

$$\frac{\text{mg. Fe}}{\text{eq. wt.}} = \text{N} \times \text{ml.}$$

$$\frac{\text{mg. Fe}}{55.85} = 0.1134 \times 40.76$$

but
$$\% \text{ Fe} = \frac{\text{mg. Fe} \times 100}{\text{mg. sample}}$$

so
$$\% \text{ Fe} = \frac{0.1134 \times 40.76 \times 55.85 \times 100}{896.4}$$

$$\% \text{ Fe} = 28.80$$

Example 5. A 0.6416 gram sample containing calcium was analyzed by the permanganate procedure; 41.73 ml. of 0.1230 N permanganate solution was used, and a back-titration with 4.76 ml. of 0.2935 N ferrous sulfate solution was needed. Calculate the percentage Ca in the sample.

$$\text{mEq. Ca} = \text{mEq. KMnO}_4 - \text{mEq. FeSO}_4$$

$$\frac{\text{mg. Ca}}{\text{eq. wt.}} = \text{N} \times \text{ml.} - \text{N} \times \text{ml.}$$

$$\frac{\text{mg. Ca}}{40.08 \div 2} = 0.1230 \times 41.73 - 0.2935 \times 4.76$$

but
$$\% \text{ Ca} = \frac{\text{mg. Ca} \times 100}{\text{mg. sample}}$$

so
$$\% \text{ Ca} = \frac{(0.1230 \times 41.73 - 0.2935 \times 4.76)(40.08 \div 2) \times 100}{641.6}$$

$$\% \text{ Ca} = 11.67$$

REVIEW QUESTIONS

1. State one significant advantage each of dichromate, cerium(IV) and permanganate over the other two.
2. Compare dichromate, cerium(IV) and permanganate as standard oxidizing agents on several significant points.
3. Why must the manganese dioxide formed on decomposition of permanganate by organic matter be removed by filtration prior to standardization?
4. Name three primary standard substances that may be used to standardize a permanganate solution.
5. How does the oxidizing power of cerium(IV) solutions vary with the presence of the acid anions, chloride, nitrate, perchlorate and sulfate?

6. Of what advantage is standardization of a dichromate solution with primary standard iron wire over using the dichromate directly as a primary standard?
7. Orthophenanthroline is a good indicator for titrations with cerium(IV) but not for titrations with dichromate. Explain.
8. In the iron determination by permanganate, why is an acidic medium needed? Why is an excessive acidity to be avoided?
9. How could it be visually recognized in the subsequent steps of the analysis that each of the following errors had been made in the permanganate determination of iron?
   a. Insufficient stannous chloride added.
   b. No Zimmermann-Reinhardt reagent added.
10. Write balanced chemical equations for all chemical reactions in a dichromate determination of iron, beginning with a sample of impure ferric oxide, Fe_2O_3.
11. Is the Zimmermann-Reinhardt reagent needed in its entirety in the iron by dichromate titration? Explain.
12. Would the normality obtained for a cerium(IV) solution be too high, too low or correct if it was standardized against iron wire which was assumed to be 100 per cent pure but which actually contained 1% of inert impurities?
13. Would the percentage iron obtained be too high, too low or correct if the ferrous solution was allowed to stand for several hours just prior to titration?
14. Would the percentage calcium obtained in a volumetric determination be too high, too low or correct if the calcium oxalate precipitate was not washed thoroughly prior to redissolving and titration with permanganate?
15. State one advantage and one disadvantage of the volumetric calcium determination in comparison to the gravimetric calcium procedure.
16. Write balanced chemical equations for all chemical reactions in the volumetric calcium procedure beginning with a sample of impure calcium carbonate, $CaCO_3$.

PROBLEMS

1. What is the normality for use in an acid medium of a permanganate solution containing 1.700 gram $KMnO_4$ in 400 ml.?
2. What is the normality of a dichromate solution, 1.00 ml. of which is equivalent to 0.0050 gram iron?
3. What is the normality of a permanganate solution, 35.00 ml. of which is equivalent to 0.2500 gram of 98.0% pure calcium oxalate?
4. How many ml. of water must be added to one liter of a solution containing 5.6000 grams of potassium dichromate to make the resulting solution 0.1000 N?
5. What weight of pure potassium dichromate must be taken to make exactly two liters of a solution, 1.00 ml. of which is to be equivalent to 5.0 mg. iron?
6. How many grams of potassium dichromate should be weighed out to make 500 ml. of approximately 0.1 N solution?
7. How many ml. of 0.1000 M hydrogen sulfide will react with 35.00 ml. of 0.1400 N permanganate solution? (unbalanced equation: $MnO_4^- + H_2S + H^+ \rightarrow Mn^{++} + S + H_2O$)
8. How many mg. of hydrogen peroxide will react with 35.00 ml. of 0.1400 N permanganate solution?
9. If 40.00 ml. of a solution of oxalic acid can be titrated with 35.00 ml. of 0.5000 N sodium hydroxide solution, and if 30.00 ml. of the same oxalic acid solution react with 60.00 ml. of permanganate solution, what is the normality of the permanganate solution?

10. What is the per cent purity of a sample of impure $H_2C_2O_4 \cdot 2 H_2O$ if a 0.4006 gram sample requires 28.62 ml. of a permanganate solution, of which 1.00 ml. contains 5.98 mg. $KMnO_4$?

11. What is the per cent purity of a sample of impure ferric oxide if a 1.009 gram sample required, in the usual procedure, 36.63 ml. of 0.0996 N cerium (IV) solution?

12. A 0.4055 gram sample of an iron salt after suitable reduction was titrated with 30.33 ml. of a standard dichromate solution which contained 2.445 grams of pure $K_2Cr_2O_7$ in 500.0 ml. Calculate the percentage iron in the salt.

13. A certain solution contains about 5.5 grams $K_2Cr_2O_7$ in 1500 ml. What weight of pure $FeSO_4 \cdot (NH_4)_2SO_4 \cdot 6 H_2O$ should be taken for standardization so as to require about 35 ml. of the dichromate solution?

14. A ceric sulfate solution is standardized against iron wire that is 98.70% pure. If the weight of wire taken is 0.1875 gram and if 41.20 ml. of the cerium (IV) solution is required in the titration, what is the normality of the ceric sulfate solution?

15. What is the percentage iron in an ore, if a 0.4250 gram sample requires 26.70 ml. of 0.0850 N permanganate for titration by the usual procedure?

16. A slag sample is known to contain all of its iron in the forms FeO and Fe_2O_3. A 1.0000 gram sample is dissolved and the total iron reduced by stannous chloride. The solution is then titrated with 0.1100 N permanganate, 28.20 ml. being required. Another sample, weighing 1.5000 gram, is dissolved in a nitrogen atmosphere to prevent oxidation during dissolving, and is immediately titrated by the 0.1100 N permanganate, 15.60 ml. being required. Calculate the percentages (a) total iron, (b) FeO and (c) Fe_2O_3.

17. A solution of permanganate was standardized by weighing 0.2626 gram As_2O_3, dissolving, acidifying and titrating with permanganate, 41.37 ml. being required. What was the normality?

18. To a sample of pyrolusite weighing 0.5000 gram, 0.7070 gram of sodium oxalate was added. After the reaction had gone to completion, 30.30 ml. of 0.1133 N permanganate was required to titrate the excess oxalate. Calculate the percentage MnO_2 in the pyrolusite.

19. A 25 ml. pipet-full of a hydrogen peroxide solution was transferred to a 250 ml. volumetric flask and diluted to the mark. A 25 ml. pipet-full of this solution was treated with sulfuric acid and titrated with 0.1366 N permanganate, 37.37 ml. being required. Calculate the number of grams of H_2O_2 per 100 ml. of original solution.

20. The manganese in a 10.000 gram sample of steel was oxidized to permanganate and treated with 40.00 ml. of a 0.1000 N ferrous sulfate solution. Then 10.66 ml. of a 0.0300 N permanganate solution was required to titrate the excess ferrous sulfate. Calculate the percentage Mn in the steel sample.

21. If 36.46 ml. of 0.1068 N sodium hydroxide is needed to neutralize the acid formed when 37.88 ml. of permanganate is treated with sulfur dioxide ($2 MnO_4^-$ $+ 5 H_2SO_3 \rightarrow 2 Mn^{++} + 4 H^+ + 5 SO_4^= + 3 H_2O$) and the excess sulfur dioxide is removed by boiling, what volume of 0.1136 N ferrous sulfate solution would be oxidized by 43.68 ml. of the permanganate solution?

22. What weight of iron ore should be taken for analysis so that the volume of 0.1000 N ceric sulfate solution will be numerically the same as the percentage of iron in the ore?

23. A solution of permanganate of which 1.00 ml. corresponds to 0.0134 gram sodium oxalate in the usual acidic titration was used in alkaline medium for the determination of manganese: $3 Mn^{++} + 2 MnO_4^- + 4 OH^- \rightarrow 5 MnO_2 + 2 H_2O$. What is the manganese equivalent of 1.00 ml. of the permanganate solution?

24. A sample of a mixture of oxalic acid, $H_2C_2O_4 \cdot 2 H_2O$, and sodium oxalate was dissolved in 1.0000 liter of water. Then a 25.00 ml. aliquot was neutralized by 25.37 ml. of 0.1064 N sodium hydroxide solution. A 50.00 ml. aliquot, after being acidified, was oxidized by 74.86 ml. of 0.1377 N permanganate solution. Calculate the weights of $H_2C_2O_4 \cdot 2 H_2O$ and of $Na_2C_2O_4$ in the mixture.

25. A sample of pyrolusite weights 0.5000 gram and contains 75.00 per cent manganese dioxide. Oxalic acid crystals and sulfuric acid were added; the mixture was heated until all the pyrolusite had reacted. The resultant solution required 29.66 ml. of 0.1000 N permanganate to oxidize the excess oxalic acid. What was the weight of oxalic acid crystals, $H_2C_2O_4 \cdot 2 H_2O$, added?

26. What weight of potassium dichromate must be used to make 1.0000 liter of solution such that when it is used for iron determinations with 1.0000 gram samples, the buret reading in ml. will equal the percentage of iron in the sample?

27. If 35.00 ml. of a ferrous sulfate solution require 26.00 ml. of dichromate solution for titration; and if 1.00 ml. of the latter is equivalent to 0.0060 gram iron, what volume of water should be added to 300.0 ml. of the ferrous sulfate solution to make it exactly 0.0400 N.?

28. A 0.1000 gram sample of a pure oxide of an element, containing 51.05% of the element, atomic weight 50.95, was dissolved and reduced. The resulting solution required 20.42 ml. of a 0.10000 N dichromate to oxidize the ion to a valence state of 5. What was the valence state of the element when in the reduced form?

29. What is the normality of a solution as an oxidizing agent if it was prepared by dissolving 5.0000 grams of $K_2Cr_2O_7$ and 5.0000 grams K_2CrO_4 to make 1.0000 liter of solution?

30. If 5.00 ml. of a commercial hydrogen peroxide solution, of density 1.010, requires 18.40 ml. of 0.1212 N permanganate solution for titration, what is the percentage by weight of H_2O_2 in the solution?

SUGGESTIONS FOR ADDITIONAL READING

Items 1, 6, 9, 17, 18, 24 and 28, Appendix 7.

Chapter 16

Oxidation-Reduction
Methods Involving Iodine

INTRODUCTION

THE STANDARD oxidizing potential for the half-reaction

$$I_2 + 2\ e \rightleftharpoons 2\ I^-$$

is 0.54 volt. This potential is far less than that of any of the three oxidizing agents described in Chapter 15. Nevertheless, iodine is sufficiently powerful as an oxidizing agent to react quantitatively with some reduced substances. Moreover, the iodide ion is easily enough oxidized to permit its quantitative reaction with some powerful oxidizing agents. Thus, there are two major classifications of the use of iodine methods: the direct methods in which iodine acts as a standard oxidizing agent; and the indirect methods in which iodine is formed by reaction of iodide with some oxidizing agent.

Direct Methods. Because iodine has a standard potential of only 0.54 volt, it can react quantitatively only with substances whose effective potentials are much lower. Among the substances which can be oxidized quantitatively are H_2S, Sn^{++} and H_2SO_3. Chemical equations for these three reactions are, respectively:

$$I_2 + H_2S \longrightarrow 2\ H^+ + 2\ I^- + S$$
$$I_2 + Sn^{++} \longrightarrow 2\ I^- + Sn^{++++}$$
$$I_2 + H_2SO_3 + H_2O \longrightarrow SO_4^= + 2\ I^- + 4\ H^+$$

The standard potentials listed in Table 14 are, for the three reducing agents in order, 0.14, 0.15 and 0.17 volts. Reaction of each with iodine is quantitative, and each may be titrated successfully with standard iodine solution.

Arsenite ion may also be titrated quantitatively to arsenate ion with standard iodine solution under certain conditions,

$$AsO_3^= + I_2 + H_2O \longrightarrow AsO_4^= + 2\ I^- + 2\ H^+$$

The standard potential for the arsenate/arsenite system is 0.56 volt, which is actually higher than that of the iodine/iodide system. It would appear from these standard potentials that the reaction between arsenite and iodine would be far from complete. It must be remembered that the standard potentials are those which exist when the concentrations of all reacting species are one molar. Hydrogen ion is a reactant in the arsenate/arsenite half-reaction

$$AsO_4^= + 2\,H^+ + 2\,e \rightleftharpoons AsO_3^= + H_2O$$

so the hydrogen ion concentration appears in the Nernst equation

$$E = 0.56 + \frac{.059}{2} \log \frac{[AsO_4^=][H^+]^2}{[AsO_3^=]}$$

If the hydrogen ion concentration is made much less than one molar, the actual electrode potential is lowered considerably. For example, if the pH is 7 and the arsenate and arsenite ion concentrations are kept equal, the E value is

$$E = 0.56 + \frac{.059}{2} \log \frac{[AsO_4^=](10^{-7})^2}{[AsO_3^=]}$$

$$E = 0.15$$

This value, 0.15 volt, is sufficiently less than that of the iodine/iodide system to permit the iodine vs. arsenite reaction in neutral medium to go quantitatively to completion. The fact that both arsenate and arsenite ions are anions of weak acids has been neglected in the preceding calculation. At a pH of 7, arsenite is present dominantly as H_3AsO_3 rather than as $AsO_3^=$, and arsenate is largely in the $HAsO_4^=$ form rather than $AsO_4^=$. Therefore, the calculation must be considered as only an approximation, but the conclusion is still quite valid—the iodine vs. arsenite reaction does go quantitatively to completion in neutral medium.

Trivalent antimony may also be oxidized quantitatively to pentavalent antimony by standard iodine solution. The titrated solution must again be approximately neutral throughout the titration; also, both the oxidized and the reduced forms of antimony are complexed with tartrate ion throughout the titration.

Indirect Methods. Many strong oxidizing agents are capable of changing iodide ion quantitatively to free iodine. Among these substances may be listed MnO_4^-, $Cr_2O_7^=$, BrO_3^-, and Cu^{++}, with the reactions proceeding as indicated by the equations:

$$10\,I^- + 2\,MnO_4^- + 16\,H^+ \longrightarrow 2\,Mn^{++} + 5\,I_2 + 8\,H_2O$$

$$6\,I^- + Cr_2O_7^= + 14\,H^+ \longrightarrow 2\,Cr^{+++} + 3\,I_2 + 7\,H_2O$$

$$6\,I^- + BrO_3^- + 6\,H^+ \longrightarrow Br^- + 3\,I_2 + 3\,H_2O$$

$$4\,I^- + 2\,Cu^{++} \longrightarrow 2\,CuI + I_2$$

The standard potentials as listed for these four substances are, in order, 1.51, 1.30, 1.45 and 0.17. The first three are well above the iodine/iodide standard potential of 0.54, so will readily react quantitatively to oxidize iodide to free iodine.

The reaction between iodide and cupric ion proceeds to completion also, but only because the curprous ions are removed as solid cuprous iodide. The effective potential of the cupric/cuprous system in the presence of iodide ion may be calculated from the standard potential and the solubility product for cuprous iodide, as follows:

$$Cu^{++} + e \rightleftharpoons Cu^+$$

and
$$Cu^+ + I^- \rightleftharpoons CuI$$

$$E = 0.17 + \frac{.059}{1} \log \frac{[Cu^{++}]}{[Cu^+]}$$

but
$$[Cu^+][I^-] = K_{sp} = 5.06 + 10^{-12}$$

or
$$[Cu^+] = \frac{10^{-11.30}}{[I^-]}$$

$$E = 0.17 + .059 \log \frac{[Cu^{++}][I^-]}{10^{-11.30}}$$

$$E = 0.17 + .059 \log ([Cu^{++}][I^-] (10^{11.30}))$$

$$E = 0.17 + .059 \log [Cu^{++}][I^-] + 0.67$$

$$E = 0.84 + .059 \log [Cu^{++}][I^-]$$

The 0.84 potential is above the standard potential of the iodine system, 0.54 volt, but the difference is not so great as is usually desired. The reaction between iodide and cupric ion does, however, go adequately far toward completion for most analytical purposes.

In each of these reactions between iodide and a strong oxidizing agent, iodine is formed as one of the products of the reaction. This iodine may, in turn, be measured by titration with a standard solution of sodium thiosulfate

$$I_2 + 2 S_2O_3^= \rightleftharpoons S_4O_6^= + 2 I^-$$

The principles of the direct and the indirect methods of analysis involving iodine may now be summarized. Direct methods are for the determination of substances which are easily oxidized, and the procedure consists essentially of a direct titration of that substance with a standard solution of iodine. Indirect methods are for the determination of substances which are themselves strong oxidizing agents, and the procedure consists of (1) reacting that substance with an excess of iodide ion to liberate iodine and (2) titration of the liberated iodine with a standard solution of sodium thiosulfate. The titration end point in a direct method is marked by the appearance of free iodine in the titration vessel, and, in an indirect method, by the disappearance of free iodine.

INDICATORS

Starch. Conventional internal redox indicators are not used in iodine titrations because of the availability of starch, a very sensitive internal indicator which is specific for iodine. Free iodine forms a very intense blue color with colloidally dispersed starch, and this coloration serves very well for the indication of the presence of iodine. In fact, the sensitivity and other good features of this indicator are in large part responsible for the popularity of methods of analysis involving iodine. This blue color appears at the end point in the titration in a direct iodine method, while it disappears at the titration end point in an indirect iodine procedure. The starch-iodine color probably results from an adsorption of iodine upon the surface of the colloidally dispersed starch particles, although the full mechanism is still a subject of some speculation.

Several general precautions should be taken in the use of starch as an indicator for iodine. The starch should not be present in the titrated solution unless the free iodine concentration is rather low, as large amounts of iodine are released only slowly by starch. This means that the indicator should not be added until shortly before the end point in the titration of an indirect iodine method. This point may be ascertained by a preliminary, rough titration or, in most instances, the intensity of the natural color of iodine in solution will reveal the approach of the end point. In a direct titration with standard iodine solution, the indicator may be added at the start of the titration, since no free iodine is present in the titrated solution until the end point is passed.

Starch suspensions must be stored in such a manner as to prevent undue exposure to air and to any possible source of bacterial action, as either can cause decomposition of starch. Various preservatives, such as 0.1 gram furoic acid to 100 milliliters starch suspension, help to minimize bacterially induced decomposition, although it is usually preferable to prepare a fresh suspension at least within a day or two of the time it is to be used. The starch indicator should be used only at or near room temperature, as the sensitivity of the starch-iodine end point indication decreases at higher temperatures. Acid decomposes starch through a hydrolysis reaction, so starch should not be used in extremely acid solution nor should it be allowed to remain very long even in solutions of moderate acid concentration.

Extraction Method. A second type of end point indication is sometimes used to detect the presence or absence of free iodine. A non-miscible liquid, generally carbon tetrachloride or carbon disulfide, is added to the titrated solution. This organic layer settles to the bottom. Free iodine is more soluble in the organic layer than in the water layer, so any iodine which may be present will tend to concentrate in the lower layer. The typical iodine color may be recognized readily in this layer. The titrated solution must be thoroughly shaken after each addition of titrating solution, it must be allowed to settle, and the organic layer must be viewed for the presence or absence of the iodine color before further addition of reagent. The extraction method of end point detection is less convenient and more time-consuming than is the starch method, but both methods yield excellent results. The extraction method is most commonly employed in those titrations in which the conditions needed for satisfactory use of starch are not attainable.

pH CONSIDERATIONS

Very careful pH control is frequently required in titrations involving iodine. The reasons for this requirement vary from one situation to another, but several generalizations are possible.

Effect of pH on Iodine. Alkali attacks free iodine, as illustrated by the equations:

$$I_2 + 2 OH^- \rightleftharpoons I^- + IO^- + H_2O$$

$$3 IO^- \rightleftharpoons 2 I^- + IO_3^-$$

These side reactions prevent the satisfactory use of iodine in alkaline solution.

Effect of pH on Thiosulfate. Strong acids attack thiosulfate with the formation of unstable free thiosulfuric acid, which slowly decomposes into a sulfite and free sulfur in accordance with the equation

$$H^+ + S_2O_3^= \rightleftharpoons HS_2O_3^- \rightleftharpoons HSO_3^- + S$$

Thus, thiosulfate is unstable in the presence of strong acids. Fortunately, this reaction is not extremely rapid, so thiosulfate can be used in titrating solutions of iodine in moderately acid solutions if the titrations are carried out in such a manner that there is no significant excess of thiosulfate present at any time.

The desired quantitative reaction between thiosulfate and iodine proceeds in accordance with the equation

$$I_2 + 2 S_2O_3^= \rightleftharpoons 2 I^- + S_4O_6^=$$

This reaction is not quantitative in alkaline solution, as the oxidation of thiosulfate proceeds partially to sulfate under such conditions.

Effect of pH and Oxygen on Iodide. Iodide ion must not be used in strongly acid solution because of a considerable "oxygen error" which may be introduced. Atmospheric oxygen is able to react with iodide in acid solution.

$$O_2 + 4 H^+ + 4 I^- \rightleftharpoons 2 I_2 + 2 H_2O$$

This factor effectively eliminates the use of a strongly acidic solution for all titrations involving iodine, since iodide ion is present at the experimental end point in both direct and indirect procedures. It has been noted in the equations given earlier in this chapter for the first reaction in typical indirect methods of analysis involving iodine that hydrogen ion is frequently a reactant in this first reaction. Thus, iodine must be liberated in these reactions in an acid medium, and the subsequent titrations with thiosulfate must be consummated quickly without any unnecessary exposure to the atmosphere.

Effect of pH on Other Reactants. The standard potential of the iodine-iodide half-reaction is not appreciably influenced by the pH, since hydrogen ion does not directly enter into the reaction. However, iodine is frequently used to titrate substances, the potentials of which are influenced by the hydrogen ion concentration. This factor has already been encountered in the case of the titration of arsenite by iodine, for which calculations earlier in this chapter revealed that quantitative reaction can be expected only when the pH is at or near seven. Similar effects of pH upon other reactants are encountered both in direct and in indirect methods of analysis involving iodine.

Since the pH is so critical in many titrations involving iodine, special methods of driving a reaction to completion are sometimes necessary. The addition of a reagent to form a complex ion or an insoluble precipitate with one or more of the products is occasionally useful as, for example, in the determination of copper discussed earlier. In some indirect determinations, the free iodine is distilled away and collected in a separate reservoir as it is formed.

PREPARATION AND STANDARDIZATION
OF SOLUTIONS

Iodine. Iodine is generally not used as a primary standard because it is difficult to obtain in a pure, dry form. In addition, the solid has an appreciable vapor pressure, so accurate weighing is difficult. Therefore, a solution of approximately the desired concentration is prepared and then standardized against some primary standard.

Free iodine is quite insoluble in water, yet it dissolves quite readily in the presence of an excess of iodide ion. Probably the iodine goes into solution as a complex ion,

$$I_2 + I^- \rightleftharpoons I_3^-$$

Dissolved iodine is often represented in chemical equations and even in tables such as Table 14 as I_2, whereas it more likely is dissolved as I_3^-. This discrepancy does not alter any stoichiometric considerations, nor does the excess iodide ion interfere with the reactions in any way. In the preparation of a solution of iodine, it is preferable to mix the solid iodine and potassium iodide in a relatively small volume of water until solution is complete, and then to dilute with water to the desired volume. In this manner the iodine is dissolved in the presence of a higher concentration of iodide ion than would be the case if an equal amount of potassium iodide were used in the entire volume of liquid to bring about solution.

Iodine solutions are unstable in the presence of air, light and heat, both because of volatility of iodine from solution and because of light-induced decomposition. Therefore, an iodine solution should be stored in a dark, tightly-stoppered bottle.

Arsenious oxide is the primary standard most commonly used for the standardization of a solution of iodine. This standardization presents an interesting series of reactions. As in the permanganate standardization, Chapter 15, arsenious oxide is brought into solution in water made basic by sodium carbonate or sodium hydroxide

$$As_2O_3 + 6 \, OH^- \longrightarrow 2 \, AsO_3^{=} + 3 \, H_2O$$

Hydrochloric acid is added to neutralize any remaining basicity, since the medium must be neutral for the titration. The main titration reaction is

$$AsO_3^{=} + I_2 + H_2O \longrightarrow AsO_4^{=} + 2 \, I^- + 2 \, H^+$$

The arsenite and arsenate are represented as trivalent anions, although in neutral medium they undoubtedly exist to appreciable extent as other ions, as already discussed. Hydrogen ion is formed in the main titration reaction, and this would prevent this reaction from going to completion. Therefore, sodium bicarbonate must be present to remove the hydrogen ions as rapidly as formed

$$H^+ + HCO_3^- \longrightarrow H_2CO_3 \longrightarrow H_2O + CO_2$$

Sodium Thiosulfate. Sodium thiosulfate is not a primary standard, owing principally to its uncertain water of hydration. So a solution must be prepared of approximately the desired strength, and then it must be standardized against some primary standard or against a previously standardized iodine solution.

Sodium thiosulfate crystals are readily soluble in water. The water should preferably be boiled shortly before use, and the solution should be stored in a well-stoppered bottle. Carbon dioxide absorbed from the atmosphere would acidify the solution enough to cause slow decomposition of the solution, as already discussed. Some bacteria also induce the decomposition of thiosulfate.

A previously standardized iodine solution will suffice as a secondary standard for the standardization of a solution of sodium thiosulfate. Some strong oxidizing agents, such as potassium dichromate and potassium iodate, may serve as primary standards for the standardization of thiosulfate solutions through the indirect method of analysis involving iodine. The end point in copper determinations by the indirect iodine method is not so clear nor exact as might be desired, so pure copper wire is best used as the primary standard when copper is the substance to be determined subsequently.

SELECTED APPLICATIONS

Determination of Arsenic. Arsenic in impure arsenious oxide may be determined by the direct method involving iodine. The reactions were discussed with reference to the use of arsenious oxide as a primary standard for iodine solutions.

Laboratory Experiment 29

DETERMINATION OF ARSENIC IN IMPURE ARSENIOUS OXIDE BY IODINE TITRATION

Reagents

Arsenious oxide, analytical reagent grade

Hydrochloric acid, stock solution

Iodine, approximately 0.1 N solution, prepared by dissolving 6.5 grams pure I_2 crystals and 10 grams KI together in 20 ml. water without heating, and diluting to 500 ml. (Store in a dark place.)

Sodium bicarbonate

Sodium carbonate

Starch suspension, prepared by rubbing 0.5 gram "soluble" starch into a paste with a small amount of cold water, slowly pouring it into 50 ml. boiling water, and boiling for two minutes (Prepare fresh each day.)

Procedure

Standardization of Iodine Solution. Conduct the standardization in triplicate. Dry the arsenious oxide at 110° C. for two hours. Weigh accurately individual portions of 0.15 gram each into 300 ml. Erlenmeyer flasks. Add 1 gram sodium carbonate and 15 ml. water and heat until completely dissolved. Dilute to 100 ml. and cool to room temperature. Add 2 ml. hydrochloric acid, 10 grams sodium bicarbonate and 2 or 3 ml. starch suspension. Titrate immediately with the iodine solution until a blue tint is obtained which persists for at least thirty seconds. Calculate the normality of the iodine solution.

Arsenic Determination. Follow same procedure as in the preceding paragraph, but use individual samples of 0.30 gram each of the unknown. Calculate the percentage As in the sample.

Determination of Antimony in Stibnite. Stibnite is a naturally occurring ore containing antimony trisulfide, silica and small amounts of a few other substances. The antimony content of a stibnite ore may be determined by a direct iodine procedure. The antimony trisulfide is brought into solution by digestion with hydrochloric acid in the presence of excess potassium chloride

$$Sb_2S_3 + 6\ H^+ + 8\ Cl^- \longrightarrow 2\ SbCl_4^- + 3\ H_2S$$

The excess chloride ion is necessary to prevent the loss of antimony as antimony trichloride, which is rather volatile. Silica will not dissolve completely, but its presence will not interfere with subsequent steps. Hydrogen sulfide gas is one of the products of this dissolving process, and the cessation of its evolution is a convenient indication of complete solution of the antimony trisulfide. The solution must not be permitted to evaporate to dryness during this digestion procedure lest the loss of volatile antimony trichloride become significant.

After the antimony sulfide is completely dissolved, the solution must be made approximately neutral and buffered there. The requirement of a pH of about 7 throughout the entire titration arises for the very same reason as it did in the titration of arsenite with iodine solution—the reaction between iodine and trivalent antimony or arsenic proceeds to completion only when the pH is about 7. Unfortunately, antimony ions tend to hydrolyze to form an insoluble basic salt if the pH is as high as about 7; fortunately, this tendency is quite completely eliminated by the addition of tartaric acid. The trivalent and pentavalent antimony ions are kept in solution as complex ions, perhaps in the dominant forms of $SbOC_4H_4O_6^-$ and $SbO_2C_4H_4O_6^-$, respectively. The reaction between trivalent antimony and iodine is not adversely influenced by this complexing agent. The reaction of the main titration is as indicated by the equation

$$I_2 + SbOC_4H_4O_6^- + H_2O \longrightarrow 2\ I^- + SbO_2C_4H_4O_6^- + 2\ H^+$$

with the hydrogen ions being removed, as formed, by the buffering ingredients.

Laboratory Experiment 30

DETERMINATION OF ANTIMONY IN A STIBNITE ORE BY IODINE TITRATION

Reagents

  Arsenious oxide, analytical reagent grade
  Hydrochloric acid, stock solution
  Iodine, approximately 0.1 N solution, prepared and standardized as
      in Experiment 29

Methyl orange indicator, solution containing 0.02 gram methyl orange per 100 ml. solution
Potassium chloride
Sodium bicarbonate
Sodium carbonate
Sodium hydroxide, solution containing 40 grams NaOH per 100 ml. solution
Starch suspension, prepared as in Experiment 29
Tartaric acid, pulverized

Procedure

Conduct the determination in triplicate. Dry the sample at 110° C. for one hour. Accurately weigh individual portions of 0.6 gram each into 300 ml. Erlenmeyer flasks. Add 0.3 gram potassium chloride and 10 ml. hydrochloric acid. Cover with a watch glass and heat gently on a sand bath until no black particles remain and no further hydrogen sulfide is evolved. Be sure that enough hydrochloric acid is present at all times to keep the bottom of the flask completely covered with liquid. Stopper the flask and allow to stand overnight or longer. Add about 2.5 grams tartaric acid and another 5 ml. hydrochloric acid and renew the digestion for fifteen minutes. Add water gradually until the solution volume is about 100 ml. Note carefully whether or not any orange-red precipitate of antimony trisulfide appears during this dilution—if so, stop and heat gently until it goes back into solution before resuming the dilution to 100 ml. Cool to room temperature, if necessary, and neutralize to the methyl orange end point with the sodium hydroxide solution, then add one drop hydrochloric acid. Add sodium bicarbonate until an excess remains undissolved on the bottom of the flask. Add 2 or 3 ml. starch suspension, and titrate at once with the standard iodine solution until a blue tint is obtained which persists for at least thirty seconds. Calculate the percentage Sb in the sample.

Sulfides. Sulfides may be determined by a direct iodometric procedure. The sulfide is evolved, by treatment of the sample with acid, as hydrogen sulfide. The evolved gas is collected in an ammoniacal solution containing cadmium ions or zinc ions. The sulfide is now in the form of cadmium sulfide or zinc sulfide and has been separated from all other components of the original sample. This solution is then acidified to reform hydrogen sulfide which will, ideally at least, remain in solution long enough for a quick titration with standard iodine solution

$$I_2 + H_2S \longrightarrow 2\,H^+ + 2\,I^- + S$$

This procedure is especially useful for the determination of sulfur in steel. The accuracy is not so great as usually expected in quantitative analysis, but it is adequate for some purposes.

Laboratory Experiment 31

DETERMINATION OF SULFUR IN IRON AND STEEL

Reagents

Ether

Hydrochloric acid, 1 volume stock solution diluted with 1 volume water

Iodine, the standard solution prepared and standardized in Experiment 29

Starch suspension, prepared as in Experiment 29

Zinc sulfate, solution containing 20 grams $ZnSO_4 \cdot 6\,H_2O$ in 100 ml. water and 100 ml. ammonium hydroxide (stock solution)

Procedure

Prepare a generating flask by fitting a 250 ml. flask with a two-hole stopper bearing a thistle tube extending nearly to the bottom of the flask and a delivery tube leading into another 250 ml. flask. In the latter flask, place 50 ml. water and 10 ml. of the ammoniacal zinc sulfate solution. Wash a 5 gram sample of the unknown with ether, let it dry, and weigh it to the nearest milligram. Place it in the generating flask, and cover with water. Introduce 50 ml. hydrochloric acid through the thistle tube. Heat gently until the sample is dissolved, then boil for one minute additional. Disconnect the receiving flask. Rinse the delivery tube, letting the rinsings run into the receiving flask. To the solution in the receiving flask, add 2 or 3 ml. freshly prepared starch indicator suspension and 40 ml. hydrochloric acid. Titrate immediately with the standard iodine solution. Calculate the percentage S in the original sample.

Copper. Copper may be determined by the indirect iodine procedure, the two main reactions proceeding according to the equations

$$4\,I^- + 2\,Cu^{++} \longrightarrow 2\,CuI + I_2$$

$$I_2 + 2\,S_2O_3^= \longrightarrow S_4O_6^= + 2\,I^-$$

As already discussed, this procedure is less quantitative and more empirical than is ordinarily desired in quantitative analysis. However, good results may be obtained, particularly if the thiosulfate solution is standardized against primary standard copper wire by the same procedure. The method is often used for the determination of copper in ores. Such ores often contain iron, arsenic and antimony, all of which interfere in the reactions unless proper precautions are taken. Interference from ferric iron may be prevented by complexing it with fluoride ion as $FeF_6^=$, while antimony and arsenic do not interfere if they are first oxidized to the pentavalent forms.

Bleaching Powder. Bleaching powder bears the chemical formula, $CaCl(ClO)$, in which the two anions, Cl^- and ClO^- are both bonded to the same calcium ion. When the powder is dissolved in water and acidified, free chlorine is liberated

$$CaCl(ClO) + 2\,H^+ \longrightarrow Ca^{++} + Cl_2 + H_2O$$

Chlorine is a very effective bleaching and disinfecting agent, and the strength of any sample of bleaching powder may be expressed as the per cent available chlorine.

Free chlorine and iodide ion react, as

$$Cl_2 + 2\,I^- \longrightarrow 2\,Cl^- + I_2$$

and this reaction serves as the basis of an analytical method for the determination of the strength of bleaching powder. The bleaching powder is acidified in the presence of excess potassium iodide, liberating free iodine. The latter may then be titrated with standard thiosulfate solution. The method is a typical indirect method of analysis involving iodine.

Laboratory Experiment 32

DETERMINATION OF AVAILABLE CHLORINE IN BLEACHING POWDER

Reagents

Acetic acid, stock solution
Hydrochloric acid, stock solution
Iodine, the standard solution prepared and standardized in Experiment 29

Potassium iodate, analytical reagent grade

Potassium iodide

Sodium thiosulfate, approximately 0.1 N solution, prepared by placing 900 ml. freshly boiled distilled water in a one-liter, glass-stoppered bottle, inserting the stopper loosely and allowing to cool, and adding 25 grams reagent grade $Na_2S_2O_3 \cdot 5\ H_2O$, shaking occasionally until dissolved

Starch suspension as prepared in Experiment 29

Procedure

(Use either standardization procedure; it is not necessary to do both.)

Standardization of Thiosulfate Solution with Standard Iodine Solution. Fill one buret with the thiosulfate solution and one with the iodine solution. Run about 40 ml. thiosulfate solution into a 400 ml. flask. Dilute to 200 ml. with water. Add 2 or 3 ml. freshly prepared starch suspension. Titrate with the iodine solution until the first, reasonably permanent appearance of a blue color. Repeat with at least three titrations. Calculate the normality of the thiosulfate solution.

Standardization of Thiosulfate Solution with Potassium Iodate. Conduct the standardization in triplicate. Dry the potassium iodate at 110° C. for one hour. Accurately weigh individual portions of 0.15 gram each into 300 ml. Erlenmeyer flasks. Add 50 ml. water and 2 grams potassium iodide and shake occasionally until dissolved. Add 15 ml. water containing 1 ml. hydrochloric acid. Immediately begin the titration of the liberated iodine with the thiosulfate solution. When the yellow color imparted to the solution by free iodine becomes quite faint, add 2 ml. of freshly prepared starch suspension. Complete the titration to the disappearance of the blue color. Calculate the normality of the thiosulfate solution.

Available Chlorine Determination. Conduct the determination in triplicate. Accurately weigh out individual portions of the bleaching powder sample weighing one gram each. Rub in a mortar with small portions of water until the sample is thoroughly pulverized. Rinse the sample from the mortar into a 250 ml. Erlenmeyer flask. Dilute to 100 ml. Add 2 grams potassium iodide and 15 ml. acetic acid. Begin the titration with the thiosulfate solution. When the yellow color imparted to the solution by free iodine becomes quite faint, add 2 ml. starch suspension. Complete the titration to the disappearance of the blue color. Calculate the percentage Cl in the sample.

THE USE OF IODATE AND BROMATE AS OXIDIZING AGENTS

Potassium Iodate.   A number of applications of iodate as an oxidizing agent have been developed which do not fit into the classification of iodine methods either as direct or as indirect. If a suitable reductant is titrated with iodate in acid medium, the first iodate ion is reduced to free iodine which, upon reaction with additional iodate, becomes positive univalent iodine. The positive univalent iodine ion is not stable as such, but is stable in complex form with chloride ion, bromide ion, cyanide ion or acetone as, respectively ICl, IBr, ICN and I-acetone. The net reaction in the presence of hydrochloric acid is

$$IO_3^- + 6\,H^+ + 4\,e + Cl^- \longrightarrow ICl + 3\,H_2O$$

Indicators.   Several types of indicator may be used. Even though iodate is reduced only to positive univalent iodine ion in the net reaction, free iodine is formed as an intermediate substance. So the disappearance of free iodine marks the end point. Starch may be used in some applications, but the extraction indicator is more widely useful in iodate titrations. Either carbon tetrachloride or chloroform works well as the immiscible liquid, and it is colored purple by free iodine before the end point and yellow by iodine monochloride, for example, after the end point.

Several internal dye indicators have also been developed. A suitable indicator must be stable in the presence of iodine, iodine monochloride and, usually, rather high concentrations of hydrochloric acid. The indicator must, of course, undergo characteristic color change with the first excess of potassium iodate in the titrated solution. Amaranth, brilliant ponceau 5R and naphthol blue black are three suitable color indicators, the color of each undergoing a marked change at the end point.

Laboratory Experiment 33

DETERMINATION OF ARSENIC IN IMPURE ARSENIOUS OXIDE BY IODATE TITRATION

Reagents

Amaranth indicator, solution containing 0.05 gram amaranth per 100 ml. water
Hydrochloric acid, stock solution

Potassium iodate, standard solution prepared as primary standard: accurately weigh about 5 grams reagent grade KIO_3; dissolve in water and dilute to the mark in a one-liter volumetric flask; calculate the normality of the solution

Sodium hydroxide, solid

Procedure

Conduct the determination in triplicate. Dry the sample at 110° C. for one hour. Accurately weigh individual portions of about 0.2 gram each into 400 ml. beakers. Dissolve in 5 ml. water and 0.5 gram sodium hydroxide. Add 35 ml. hydrochloric acid and dilute to 100 ml. with water. Begin the titration with the standard iodate solution. When most of the iodine color has disappeared, add 0.5 ml. amaranth indicator solution, and complete the titration. The end point is marked by a color change from red to light yellow. Calculate the percentage As in the sample.

Preoxidation with Iodine Monochloride. Several reducing agents may be titrated by direct titration with potassium iodate. Some other reducing agents are not sufficiently powerful to reduce even the first portion of iodate below the positive univalent stage. In such instances, no free iodine is formed anytime in the titration, so the indicator system fails. A useful method for the titration of such reducing agents is to react the reducing agent first with an excess of iodine monochloride, which is quantitatively reduced by the agent as

$$2 \, ICl + 2 \, e \rightleftharpoons I_2 + 2 \, Cl^-$$

Then this liberated iodine may be titrated with the standard iodate solution as described above. This step of preoxidation with iodine monochloride extends the realm of usefulness of iodate as a standard oxidizing agent considerably.

Preoxidation with Iodine Monobromide. When iodine monobromide is substituted for the monochloride, the reaction may be carried out satisfactorily with a lower hydrogen ion concentration than is required with the monochloride. The bromide may be introduced initially in the form of potassium bromide. Iodine monobromide preoxidations may even be carried out in basic solution, so the method is applicable for the determinations of several organic constituents, such as formaldehyde. The final titration with iodate must, however, always be made in acid solution.

Potassium Bromate. Potassium bromate is a more powerful oxidizing agent than is potassium iodate, as indicated by the standard oxidizing potentials. Yet the intermediate steps cannot be controlled so effectively in bromate titrations. The reduction of bromate by bromide ion, for example, goes quantitatively to free bromine

$$5\ Br^- + BrO_3^- + 6\ H^+ \longrightarrow 3\ Br_2 + 3\ H_2O$$

The use of potassium bromate as an oxidizing agent may be illustrated by one example, the direct titration of arsenite ion. The main reaction proceeds according to the equation

$$3\ AsO_3^{=} + BrO_3^- \xrightarrow{\ HCl\ } 3\ AsO_4^{=} + Br^-$$

The first excess of bromate then reacts with some of the bromide ion present to yield free bromine, according to the preceding chemical equation. The free bromine can decompose a dye such as methyl orange or methyl red, so the end point is made visible. This type of indicator action is not reversible, and no advance warning of the approach of the end point is given.

Fluorescein may also be used to advantage as the indicator in bromometric titrations. The titrated solution appears greenish yellow early in the titration, gradually changing to a brownish yellow as the end point is approached. A characteristic red-brown color appears when the end point is finally reached. The color reaction may occur rather slowly, so it is advisable to wait fifteen seconds after each addition of titrating agent. This indicator has two advantages over methyl orange and methyl red for titrations with potassium bromate: there is less danger of premature irreversible indicator decomposition due to temporary local concentrations of excess bromate; there is some advance warning of the approach of the end point.

REVIEW QUESTIONS

1. Why are iodometric methods so useful even though iodine itself is such a weak oxidizing agent?
2. Distinguish clearly with examples and balanced chemical equations between direct and indirect methods involving iodine.
3. Starch may be added at the start of the titration in a direct iodine procedure but not until shortly before the end point of the titration in an indirect iodine procedure.
4. Explain what is the function of potassium iodide in the preparation of a solution of iodine?
5. Explain why direct iodine titrations are carried out in approximately neutral solutions.
6. What difficulty arises if the acidity is too high in the titration of liberated iodine with thiosulfate?
7. List two primary standard substances of interest in methods of analysis involving iodine.
8. Write balanced chemical equations for all chemical reactions in the determination of antimony with iodine, starting with a sample of impure antimony trisulfide, Sb_2S_3.

9. Write balanced chemical equations for the determination of copper by a method involving iodine, starting with metallic copper.
10. Would the percentage copper obtained by an indirect iodine procedure be made too high, too low or correct if starch was added too soon in the titration?
11. Would the percentage antimony in stibnite obtained by a direct iodine procedure be made too high, too low or correct if potassium chloride was not used and the solution was heated to boiling to dissolve the sample?
12. Would the normality obtained for an iodine solution be made too high, too low or be correct if insufficient buffering capacity is available during a standardization titration with arsenious oxide?

PROBLEMS

1. If 37.37 ml. of an iodine solution is required to oxidize the solution prepared from 0.5000 gram of arsenious oxide, what is the normality of the iodine solution?
2. A 8.0000 gram sample of pure arsenious oxide was dissolved and diluted to the mark in a 500 ml. volumetric flask. A 25.00 ml. aliquot was removed and titrated in the regular procedure with an iodine solution, 38.90 ml. being required. What is the normality of the iodine solution?
3. A 0.1875 gram sample of pure potassium dichromate is dissolved, acidified and treated with an excess of potassium iodide. The liberated iodine is titrated with a thiosulfate solution, 39.80 ml. being required. What is the normality of the thiosulfate solution?
4. If 1.00 ml. of a dichromate solution is equivalent to 2.5 mg. iron, and if 40.00 ml. of the same dichromate solution liberates iodine equivalent to 22.00 ml. of a thiosulfate solution, what is the normality of the latter?
5. A 11.30 ml. sample of a tincture of iodine preparation required 39.26 ml. of 0.1136 N thiosulfate for titration. What is the concentration of iodine in the sample expressed in grams per 100.0 ml.?
6. If 1.00 ml. of an iodine solution is equivalent to 1.0 mg. arsenic and if a 1.0000 gram stibnite sample requires 37.24 ml. of iodine solution for titration, what is the purity of the stibnite in terms of (a) percentage antimony and (b) percentage antimony trisulfide?
7. A sample of impure sodium thiosulfate weighing 20.430 grams was dissolved in water and diluted quantitatively to the mark in a 500 ml. volumetric flask. A 25.00 ml. aliquot required 38.38 ml. of 0.0500 N iodine solution for titration. What is the percentage $Na_2S_2O_3 \cdot 5 H_2O$ in the sample?
8. If a solution of hydrogen sulfide in water required twice its volume of 0.1366 N iodine solution to oxidize the sulfide ion, how many grams of hydrogen sulfide were dissolved in one liter of solution?
9. The sulfur from a steel sample is evolved as hydrogen sulfide and finally titrated with standard iodine solution. If a 5.000 gram steel sample requires 10.10 ml. of iodine solution, and if 1.00 ml. of the latter is equivalent to 0.004945 gram arsenious oxide, what is the percentage sulfur in the steel?
10. From the following data, calculate the percentage of copper in an ore sample: 0.7146 gram sample; 36.69 ml. thiosulfate solution required; 1.00 ml. of the thiosulfate solution corresponds to 0.0006 gram potassium bromate.
11. A 0.7500 gram sample of a copper sulfide ore is analyzed by the copper method involving iodine. If 44.70 ml. of a 0.1234 N thiosulfate solution is required, what is the percentage copper sulfide, CuS, in the sample?

12. What weight of copper ore must be taken for analysis so that each 1.00 ml. of 0.1500 N thiosulfate solution represents 1.00 per cent copper in the sample?

13. A sample of bleaching powder weighing 3.500 grams was mixed with water and diluted to 500.0 ml. A one-tenth aliquot was removed and, after suitable treatment, required 33.36 ml. of 0.1000 N sodium arsenite solution. Another one-tenth aliquot required 39.66 ml. thiosulfate solution. What was the normality of the thiosulfate solution?

14. A 0.6750 gram sample of bleaching powder is analyzed by the usual method involving liberated iodine and a standard thiosulfate solution. If 33.60 ml. of a 0.2000 N thiosulfate solution is required, what is the percentage available chlorine in the sample?

15. A certain oxidizing agent has a molecular weight of 250.0. A 0.3125 gram sample is caused to liberate iodine from an excess of potassium iodide. The liberated iodine is titrated with 0.1250 N thiosulfate solution, 20.00 ml. being required. How many electrons are gained per molecule of the oxidizing agent in this reaction?

16. A 0.4250 gram sample of Paris green (an arsenic-containing insecticide) is boiled with hydrochloric acid and a reducing agent. All the arsenic is expelled as arsenic trichloride, $AsCl_3$, which is collected and titrated with 0.0750 N iodine solution, 35.60 ml. being required. Calculate the percentage arsenic as As_2O_3 in the sample.

17. To determine lead in a lead ore, the lead from a 0.6848 gram sample was first precipitated as lead chromate, $PbCrO_4$. This precipitate then reacted with an excess of iodide ion to liberate enough iodine to require for titration 79.62 ml. of a thiosulfate solution containing 17.985 grams $Na_2S_2O_3 \cdot 5\,H_2O$ per liter. What is the percentage Pb in the sample?

18. From a 0.5604 gram sample of a copper ore, the copper was precipitated as cuprous thiocyanate, CuSCN. The precipitate was treated with hydrochloric acid and titrated with a solution containing 10.701 grams KIO_3 per liter, 40.18 ml. being required ($4\,CuSCN + 7\,IO_3^- + 14\,H^+ + 7\,Cl^- \rightarrow 4\,Cu^{++} + 4\,SO_4^= + 7\,ICl + 4\,HCN + 5\,H_2O$). What is the percentage Cu in the sample?

SUGGESTIONS FOR ADDITIONAL READING

Items 1, 6, 9, 17, 18 and 28, Appendix 7.

Part Four

OPTICAL METHODS

Chapter 17

Colorimetric Methods

COLORIMETRIC methods of analysis are based upon measurements of the light-absorbing characteristics of test solutions. Qualitative determinations and a few quantitative ones involve observation of what colors of light are, or are not, absorbed. Most quantitative determinations consist of measurements, either absolute or by comparison, of the extent to which the test solution absorbs light of a particular color. This chapter consists primarily of a consideration of quantitative methods.

Colorimetric procedures have been used for many years. Yet numerous advances have been made in recent years in developing new and better (with respect to sensitivity and selectivity) color-producing reagents, in devising instruments for making optical measurements and in establishing new analytical procedures. Colorimetric determinations are possibly used more widely in modern analytical laboratories than any other type of determination.

Colorimetric methods of analysis are widely applicable, as indicated by the fact that one or more colorimetric procedures have been developed for the determination of nearly every element in the periodic table. The procedures are frequently rapid and simple. The necessary apparatus may be extremely simple, although many elaborate and expensive instruments are also in common use.

Very small amounts of constituents of samples may, in many instances, be determined quantitatively with considerable accuracy by colorimetric procedures. A solution concentration of 10^{-6} or even 10^{-7} molar is sometimes adequate for a colorimetric determination; conventional gravimetric and volumetric methods are useless in dealing directly with such minute amounts of material. The results of quantitative determinations by colorimetric procedures are typically accurate within 1 or 2% of the amount of constituent present, and in some instances much more accurate results can be obtained.

PRINCIPLES

The essential principle of the colorimetric method may be considered on the basis of the block diagram of Figure 48. The light from the source includes light of many colors and is called polychromatic (many colored) light. In

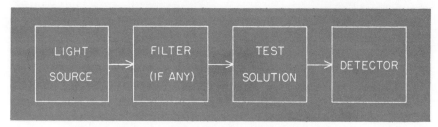

FIGURE 48.   Block diagram for a colorimeter.

some work, polychromatic light is used as such, but in more refined quantitative work a filter or other monochromator is interposed in the light path to permit only a certain range of colors of light to pass on to the solution. The filter may simply consist of a plate of colored glass, which absorbs light of some colors to a greater extent than other colors, preferentially passing light of those colors from the source which are least absorbed. A grating or a prism may be used as a monochromator by spreading out the light striking it into a spectrum; the system is designed physically so that only the desired portion of that spectrum is permitted to pass on to the test solution and the detector. The monochromator could be placed between the sample and the detector rather than as shown in Figure 48. The light which emerges from the filter or other monochromator, or directly from the source if there is no monochromator, is permitted to pass to the test solution, and that portion which is not absorbed by the solution passes on to the detector for measurement. The detector may be the human eye, although photoelectric cells are widely used. The relationships between the composition and physical arrangement of the test solution and the fraction of incident light absorbed may be expressed mathematically by the Lambert and Beer laws, which we will now consider in turn.

Lambert Law.   The Lambert law relates the ratio, of the intensity of light transmitted by a medium to the intensity of light incident upon that medium, to the thickness of that medium. This law may be stated in words as follows: when monochromatic light passes through a transparent medium (i.e., a medium in which the portion of incident light which is transmitted is too great to be negligible), the rate of decrease of intensity with the thickness of the medium is proportional to the intensity of the light. There are various ways of expressing this law mathematically, but perhaps the most useful, and at the same time one of the simplest, is in the form

$$\log \frac{I_0}{I} = k \, b$$

in which I_0 is the intensity of light falling upon the system, I is the intensity of light transmitted through the system, k is a number whose magnitude is determined by the nature of the absorbing medium and the wavelength (color) of the light, and b is the thickness of the medium. In Figure 49 are indicated the meanings of I_0, I and b. There are no known exceptions to the Lambert law.

Beer Law. The Beer law deals with solutions of solutes which absorb light and relates the ratio, of the intensity of light transmitted by a solution to the intensity of light incident upon that solution, to the concentration of the solute. This law may be stated in words as follows: when monochromatic light passes through a solution of a colored solute, the rate of decrease of intensity with the concentration of the solute is proportional to the intensity of the light. The Beer law may be stated in the mathematical form

$$\log \frac{I_0}{I} = k' c$$

in which I_0 and I are as defined above, k' is again a number the magnitude of which is determined by the nature of the solute and the wavelength of light employed, and c is the concentration of solute.

Although there are only few, if any, real failures of the Beer law, it is applicable only to certain concentration ranges for most substances and is not applicable at all to some practical systems. Apparent departures from this law are generally encountered when the colored solute undergoes a change in degree of ionization, hydration or dissociation upon dilution or concentration. For example, the degree of dissociation of a weak acid changes with its concentration, so it should be expected that the Beer law will not be applicable to a solution of a weak acid in which color is imparted to the solution by the anion of the weak acid. Dilution of a potassium chromate solution may cause a shift in the position of equilibrium between chromate ion and dichromate ion, so chromate solutions generally fail to follow the Beer law unless the pH is sufficiently high to keep essentially all of the anions in the chromate form. The degree of complexing of a colored ion generally alters its light-absorbing characteristics, so the Beer law is not applicable if the degree of complexing varies throughout the range of concentrations involved. The Beer law is generally applicable only to solutions of relatively low concentrations of solutes, as the activity coefficients generally decrease

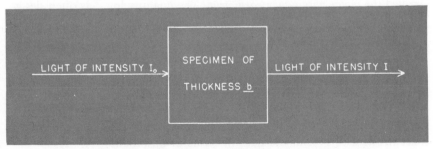

FIGURE 49.   Diagram to show relationships between I_0, I and b.

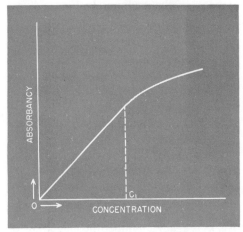

FIGURE 50. Relationship between absorbancy and concentration of the absorbing substance.

from unity as the concentration is increased. Another reason for the frequent apparent inapplicability of the law arises from the fact that it specifies the use of monochromatic light, while the light employed experimentally is never purely monochromatic and frequently departs very widely from such a condition.

Combined Lambert-Beer Law.   The Lambert law and the Beer law may be combined into a single law which serves as a basis for much of colorimetric analysis. This law may be stated mathematically as

$$\log \frac{I_0}{I} = a\,b\,c,$$

in which I_0, I, b and c are as defined above, and a, the absorbancy coefficient, combines the k factors of the two laws. Since the intensity quantities, I_0 and I, appear in ratio form, any units of light intensity may be used, even completely empirical units being fully satisfactory. Most frequently the thickness quantity, b, is expressed in centimeters and the concentration factor, c, in grams of solute per 1 000 grams of solution; the corresponding absorbancy coefficient is designated the *specific absorbancy coefficient*. If c is expressed in molar units and b again in centimeters, the corresponding value is called the *molar absorbancy coefficient*. The quantity $\log \frac{I_0}{I}$ is often designated the *absorbancy* and given the symbol A; some colorimeters are calibrated directly in absorbancy units.

The Lambert-Beer law is applicable, of course, only when its component parts are applicable. Since there are no known exceptions to the Lambert law, all apparent inapplicabilities of the combined law are due to the concentration factor. The applicability of the law may be tested for any particular system by measuring the absorbance for each of a series of solutions of known concentration. A plot of the data in terms of absorbancy, A, versus concentration, c, yields a straight line passing through the origin if the law is applicable. More often than not, a plot of the data over a wide range of concentration of a colored ionic solute yields a graph such as that of Figure 50, signifying that the law is applicable only up to concentration c_1. The apparent departures at higher concentrations are frequently due to a decreasing activity coefficient of the solute with increasing concentration.

Some experimental methods (described in the next section of this chapter) require calculations based upon the Lambert-Beer law, while others do not. It is frequently possible to conduct satisfactory colorimetric determinations even when the system departs from this fundamental law of absorption. The chief requirements in analysis are that the light-absorbing properties be measurable and that they be measurable reproducibly.

EXPERIMENTAL METHODS

Experimental methods of colorimetric analysis may be classified into three groups: standard series determinations, variable depth methods, direct intensity measurements. In practice, each of the three normally requires the use of one or more standards, so all practical colorimetric methods are really comparison methods.

Standard Series Methods. The term *standard solution* has earlier been defined as a solution of known concentration. In a colorimetric determination by the standard series method, several standard solutions are prepared, the color in each is developed by treatment with reagents as necessary, and then the color or the intensity of color of the unknown is compared with that of each of the standards. Assuming that all of the standard solutions are alike in all significant respects other than concentration of the colored material, the concentration of the unknown will approximate that of the standard which it most nearly matches.

Standard series determinations may be performed very simply by using test tubes and viewing the solutions horizontally with illumination from the rear. However, special tubes called Nessler tubes have been designed for this purpose. These tubes are of clear glass with polished, flat bottoms and are normally used in a Nessler rack which permits vertical viewing through the full depth of the tubes. The accuracy and precision of the results are determined partially by the thickness of the solution through which the light must pass, so vertical viewing is distinctly advantageous over horizontal viewing. The unknown solution is inserted successively between pairs of the standards, and the concentration of the most closely matching standard is taken as equal to the unknown concentration. If desired, a second series of standards may be prepared of concentrations very close to that of the unknown as determined by the first standard series comparison in order to achieve more precise results. The standard solutions must, of course, be of such concentrations that at least one is more and one less concentrated than the unknown solution.

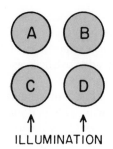

ILLUMINATION

FIGURE 51.   Diagram to illustrate the Walpole technique (see text).

In many instances it has been found feasible to use permanent color standards rather than actual standard solutions. These standards may be in the form of colored glass or even, in some cases, of colored markings on paper. Standards of these types are effectively secondary standards, as they must in turn be standardized against standard solutions to be of any value.

The necessity frequently arises to determine one colored substance in a solution possessing a color from some other source. If the interfering color is very intense, determination by simple colorimetry is not feasible. However, interference from other colored substances in moderate amounts may be minimized by means of the Walpole technique. With reference to Figure 51, A, B, C and D are similar glass cylinders in an enclosed chamber constructed so that illumination may enter from the rear and be viewed from the front, one portion after transmission through A and C and the other portion through B and D. Cylinder A contains the colored solution to be measured (i.e., the unknown solution plus the necessary color-forming reagents), while tube B contains one of the standard solutions with which A is to be compared. Cylinder C contains solvent only, usually water, while D contains the unknown solution without the color-forming reagents. All cylinders or tubes must be of the same diameter. Thus, any difference in the color or the intensity of color transmitted through A-C and that through B-D must be due to a difference in concentration of the unknown colored substance between A and B and not due to any secondary source of color originally present in the solution of the unknown. Each of a series of standards may be inserted, in turn, in position B until the matching one is found.

The standard series method of colorimetric analysis does not involve any Lambert-Beer law calculation. Thus, the applicability of the law is of no concern in this type of colorimetric determination. Furthermore, the standard series method may be used for those determinations in which shades of color, rather than intensities of color, are to be compared; the colorimetric determination of pH discussed later in this chapter illustrates this type.

Variable Depth Methods.   Several standards are used with constant viewing depth in a standard series determination, but the variable depth procedure requires only one standard solution and some arrangement for varying the depth of solution viewed. Results are calculated with the aid of the Lambert-Beer law. The law may be applied to the standard and to the unknown, with subscripts s and x, respectively, as follows:

$$\log \frac{I_{os}}{I_s} = a_s c_s b_s \quad \text{and} \quad \log \frac{I_{ox}}{I_x} = a_x c_x b_x$$

Using the same incident light intensity for both,

$$I_{os} = I_{ox}$$

The apparatus is made in such a way that both b_s and b_x may be adjusted. When this adjustment is made so that $I_s = I_x$, then

$$\log \frac{I_{os}}{I_x} = \log \frac{I_{ox}}{I_x}$$

so

$$a_s c_s b_s = a_x c_x b_x$$

Since the standard and the unknown are both of the same substance, and light of the same spectral distribution is used throughout,

$$a_s = a_x$$

Therefore,

$$c_s b_s = c_x b_x$$

or

$$c_x = c_s \frac{b_s}{b_x}$$

This last equation is the basis of variable depth colorimetric determinations. The experimental apparatus accordingly requires use of one standard and one unknown in containers of variable depth, and a means of viewing the two simultaneously with similar illuminations upon both. The depths are adjusted until the intensity of the light transmitted through one is equal to that through the other. Calculation is made by means of the last equation given.

Many color comparators of the variable depth type have been developed. Even though none of the variable depth devices is now used so widely as are the instruments employing photocells (next section), a study of this type provides familiarity with the principles underlying colorimetric methods of analysis. The variable depth method may be illustrated by brief discussion of two types, the Hehner cylinders and the Duboscq colorimeter. The Hehner cylinders are employed in pairs, one for the standard solution and one for the unknown solution. Each cylinder (Figure 52) is equipped with a glass stopcock 2 or 3 cm. from the bottom, has a uniform bore and is equipped with a flat, carefully ground, clear glass bottom. The cylinders are placed in a box so arranged that light is transmitted from the base up through the cylinders. With the standard solution in one cylinder and the unknown in the other, the volumes are adjusted by drawing off through the stopcock some of the darker appearing solution until the transmitted intensities appear equal to the observer's eye. From the matched depths of the two and the concentration of the standard solution, the concentration of the unknown may be calculated with the simple equation which has just been derived. The standard solution

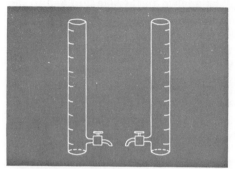

FIGURE 52.   Hehner cylinders.

may contain a concentration of the colored material either greater or less than that of the unknown solution.

The Duboscq colorimeter is an improved form of the Hehner cylinder device with two distinct constructional differences. First, in the Duboscq instrument, Figure 53, no solution need be added nor withdrawn during the adjustment to equal transmission, but rather the effective depth is adjusted by raising or lowering the cups containing the solutions around glass plungers one of which dips into each solution; the thickness of each solution through which light is transmitted is merely the distance from the bottom of each cup to the bottom of its plunger. Second, light transmitted through both solutions is combined in such a way that one-half of the field observed in the eye-piece consists of light transmitted through each solution; this device permits easy and precise comparison of the two.

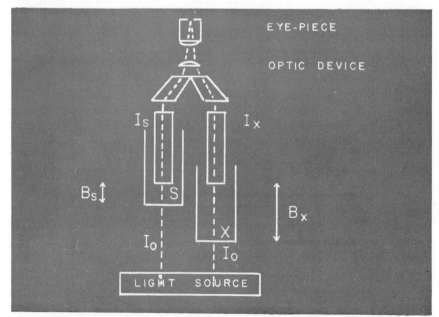

FIGURE 53.   Optical diagram of a Duboscq colorimeter (see text).

Direct Intensity Measurement Methods. In both the standard series methods and the variable depth methods already described, the human eye serves as the detector and each observation is a direct comparison of light transmitted through two or more solutions. The human eye is able to make quite accurate comparisons of light intensity to determine whether or not they are equal but is unable to make adequately meaningful individual quantitative measurements of intensity or of intensity ratios. However, several types of photoelectric tubes and cells make possible the direct measurement of light intensity.

The measurement of the light transmittancy characteristics of a single solution is complicated by the facts that the solvent itself or some additional, undesired component, may absorb some light and that some light is reflected at each glass-air interface. These effects may be compensated for in methods other than direct intensity measurements by the Walpole technique, but their influence may be significant when measurements are to be made upon a single solution.

The errors from solvent absorption and from reflection may readily be eliminated by taking as the I_0 value not the intensity of light incident upon the test solution but rather the intensity of light transmitted through a solution of zero concentration (i.e., of solvent alone) held in the same or an equivalent cell and with light of the same intensity incident upon that cell. Thus, any apparent absorbancy due either to the solvent or to the container would be offset.

Some photoelectric instruments employ a split beam of light in such a manner that one beam is incident upon the test solution and the other upon a similar cell containing solvent only. The comparison of the intensities of light transmitted through the two cells may be made electrically, physically with an

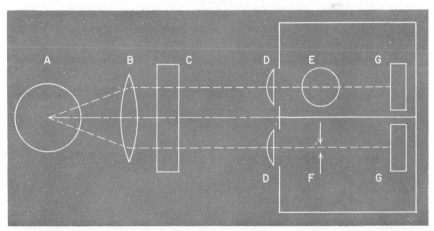

FIGURE 54. Optical diagram of Klett-Summerson colorimeter. Light from the source (A) passes through lens (B) and filter (C); then one-half follows the upper path through lens (D) and test solution (E) to photocell (G) and the other half follows the lower path through lens (D) and the adjustable shutter (F) to photocell (G).

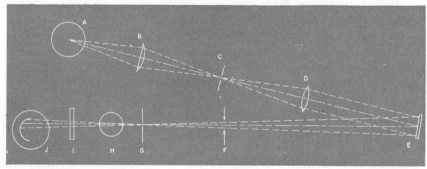

FIGURE 55. Optical diagram of Bausch and Lomb Spectronic colorimeter. Light from the source (*A*) passes through lens (*B*), entrance slit (*C*) and lens (*D*) to the grating (*E*), then through an adjustable light controller (*F*), exit slit (*G*) and test solution (*H*) through filter (*I*) to phototube (*J*).

adjustable shutter in the path of the light coming through the solvent, or each intensity may be noted separately. Several types of photoelectric colorimeters are commercially available. Complete optical diagrams are shown in Figure 54 for a filter type colorimeter and in Figure 55 for one using a grating to render the light more nearly monochromatic.

It is not necessary to use any absolute intensity units, since only a ratio of intensities is involved in the Lambert-Beer law calculations. Any consistent,

Table 16. Suggestions for Filter Colors

Solution Color	Filter Color
purple	green
orange to red	blue to blue-green
yellow	blue
violet to red	purple
blue	red

even though purely empirical, units may be employed for the intensity quantity. In many instruments, the ratio of $I \div I_0$ (as percentage transmission) is read directly, and/or the log of the ratio $I_0 \div I$ (absorbancy) is read.

Since any colored solution will absorb some colors of light more readily than others, most sensitive determinations may be accomplished if the colors of light employed are those most readily absorbed by the test solution. Filters provide only a first, broad approximation to monochromatic (single color) light, but the approximation is sufficiently good for many purposes. The filter should preferentially transmit light in the wavelength region of minimum transmission of the solution undergoing test in order to achieve highest sensitivity in the use of a filter photometer. The choice of filter to use may be accomplished purely empirically, by use of Table 16 or by a spectrophotometric test as described in Experiment 35.

SELECTED APPLICATIONS

One or more colorimetric methods have been developed for the quantitative determination of nearly every one of the elements, and many of these procedures are of considerable practical usefulness in the analyses of both inorganic and organic substances. Nearly every element, ion and molecule is either colored itself, can react with a colored substance or can react to form a colored substance, and each of these situations presents the possibility of a colorimetric determination. Because there are so many practical examples of useful colorimetric determinations using conventional techniques, those discussed here have, of necessity, been chosen quite arbitrarily.

Colorimetric Measurement of pH. Many indicators are satisfactory color-producing reagents for the colorimetric measurement of pH. Two-color indicators serve better than do one-color indicators. This means that the observer may note, or compare, shades of color rather than intensities as is normally done in other quantitative colorimetric determinations. The pH determination can consist of the following steps: prepare a series of standard buffer solutions; select an indicator which exhibits an intermediate color in the pH region of the unknown; add a fixed amount of indicator to each standard and unknown solution; observe which standard buffer solution matches the unknown most closely in shade of color. An approximate knowledge of the pH of the unknown is required in advance, but this can be ascertained readily with a wide range pH indicator.

There are numerous modifications of the colorimetric method of measuring pH. The standards may be in the form of colored markings on paper and the indicator may be used in the form of strips of paper impregnated with the indicating substance. The pHydrion papers are very useful, with both wide range and narrow range papers being available. Standard buffer solutions, and also tablets from which standard buffer solutions may be prepared readily, are commercially available. The Walpole technique is often useful in colorimetric pH determinations.

Most colorimetric methods are not suitable for pH measurement unless the unknown solution possesses some buffering capacity. Because the indicator itself is an acid or a base, addition of an indicator to an unbuffered solution would actually change the pH of the solution unless the indicator solution happened to be at the same pH as did the unknown. Although a special colorimetric procedure has been devised to avoid this source of error, pH measurements of unbuffered or slightly buffered solutions are usually made by the potentiometric method discussed in Chapter 20.

Colorimetric Determination of Ammonia. The quantitative determination of ammonia may be based upon the intensity of color produced when an alkaline potassium mercuric iodide solution is added to solution containing ammonium ion. The reagent is named the Nessler reagent, and the reaction proceeds according to the equation

$$2(HgI_2 \cdot 2 KI) + 2 NH_3 \longrightarrow NH_2Hg_2I_3 + 4 KI + NH_4I$$
$$\text{(colored)}$$

The colored substance is colloidal in nature and flocculates upon long standing. The method is applicable to the determination of ammonium salts, to the determination of nitrogenous substances which may be reduced to ammonia, and is especially useful for the determination of small amounts of nitrogen. All water used in preparing standard solutions and the Nessler reagent must be free of ammonia.

Laboratory Experiment 34

COLORIMETRIC DETERMINATION OF AMMONIA USING NESSLER TUBES

Reagents

Ammonium chloride, 10 standard solutions covering the range 0.000 to 0.050 mg. NH_3 per ml.; prepare a more concentrated solution by direct weight of NH_4Cl, and dilute portions quantitatively to prepare each standard. (Make all measurements accurate within 1%.)

Nessler reagent: dissolve 50 grams KI in 50 ml. cold water; add a saturated solution of mercuric chloride until a faint precipitate persists; add 400 ml. clear 9 N solution of potassium hydroxide or sodium hydroxide; dilute to 1 liter; remove the clear liquid by decantation, discarding the residue.

Procedure

Place each standard and unknown solution in a Nessler tube, filling each to the mark. Add 1 ml. Nessler reagent to each. After ten minutes, observe the tubes vertically to determine which standard matches the unknown most closely. If the unknown should fall beyond the most concentrated standard, either prepare additional standards or quantitatively dilute another portion of the unknown to bring it within the range of the standards. Report your answer as mg. NH_3 per ml. of the unknown solution.

Colorimetric Determination of Iron. Many color-producing reagents have been developed for the colorimetric determination of iron. Orthophenanthroline is one of the best; it forms an intensely colored orange-red complex with ferrous ion. The color is stable for long periods of time and is particularly useful for dilute solutions containing up to about five parts per million of iron.

Laboratory Experiment 35 includes the preparation of an absorbancy spectrum of the colored complex; the choice of what color of light to use for the remainder of the experiment is made from the spectrum. The spectrum consists of a plot of absorbancy vs. wavelength, as illustrated in Figure 56. The sensitivity of a quantitative determination is greatest at the wavelength at which the absorbancy is greatest, A on Figure 56, and this wavelength is generally selected. If a wavelength at which the curve is far from horizontal,

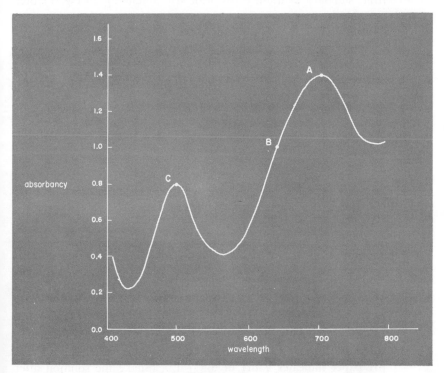

Figure 56.   A hypothetical absorbancy spectrum (see text).

as at B, were to be chosen, a slight random variation in setting the instrument at that wavelength would introduce an unnecessary source of error. This source of error is less significant with a colorimeter which employs filters than with one using a monochromator of continuously variable wavelength. If a wavelength at a lower peak of the curve, as at C, were to be chosen, the determination would be less sensitive but a wider range of concentrations could be included than at A.

Laboratory Experiment 35

DETERMINATION OF IRON USING A PHOTOELECTRIC COLORIMETER

Reagents

Hydroquinone, solution containing 1 gram hydroquinone in 100 ml. of sodium acetate buffered at pH 4.5

Iron, standard solution of an iron salt containing 50 mg. Fe/liter solution

Orthophenanthroline, solution containing 0.3 gram orthophenanthroline per 100 ml. water, warmed to dissolve

pH paper, to cover the approximate range 3.0 to 5.0

Sodium acetate, solution containing 16 grams $NaC_2H_3O_2$ per 100 ml. solution

Special Apparatus

Bausch and Lomb Spectronic Colorimeter. (Any type of colorimeter may be used; the instructor will provide alternative operating directions if some other type is provided.)

Procedure

Obtain four 100 ml. volumetric flasks. Give one to your laboratory instructor for your unknown. Into the other three flasks, pipet 2, 6 and 10 ml., respectively, of the standard iron solution. Add about 50 ml. water to each flask. Add sodium acetate solution dropwise to each flask (only a few drops needed) until the pH paper indicates a pH of 3.5 ± 1.0. (Shake the solution after each addition and touch the pH paper to the solution wetting the stopper of the flask.) Add 4 ml. of the hydroquinone solution and 4 ml. of the orthophenanthroline solution to each flask. Dilute to 100 ml. and let stand for 10 minutes. Then obtain an absorbancy spectrum of the iron-phenanthroline complex, prepare a calibration curve and determine the total mg. Fe in your sample in accordance with the following paragraphs:

General Operating Directions for the Spectronic Colorimeter. Turn on instrument with left front knob and allow to "warm up" for several minutes. Set wavelength dial to desired value. With the sample compartment empty, adjust the left front knob so the meter pointer reads infinite optical density (same as zero % transmission). Insert a sample tube containing water, and adjust the right front knob so that the meter pointer reads zero optical density (same as 100% transmission). Replace the sample tube containing water with one containing the test solution and read the optical density on the meter with no further adjustments.

Obtaining an Absorbancy Spectrum. Use one sample tube containing water and one containing the most concentrated standard solution. At each 25 millimicron interval throughout the available range of wavelengths, measure the optical density of the standard solution. If the instrument has been allowed to "warm up" sufficiently, the adjustment of the left front knob with no sample tube in place so the meter pointer reads infinite optical density should remain fixed throughout the entire experiment. However, the adjustment of the right front knob with water as the sample must be repeated at each wavelength. Plot the data in terms of absorbancy (optical density and absorbancy are synonymous) vs. wavelength. Select from the plot the wavelength of maximum absorbancy and use this wavelength alone in the remainder of the experiment.

Preparation of Calibration Curve and Determination of Unknown. Measure the optical density of each standard and of your unknown, all at the wavelength of maximum absorbancy as found from the work of the preceding paragraph. Use the same sample tube for all measurements, rinsing it with each solution before filling with that solution for measurement. Run duplicate or triplicate measurements on separate fillings with each solution. From the data on the three standards, prepare a calibration chart in terms of absorbancy vs. mg. Fe in the sample. From the data on the unknown and the chart, ascertain the mg. Fe in your unknown.

Colorimetric Determination of Phosphate. Phosphate ion in aqueous solution reacts with ammonium molybdate to form ammonium molybdiphosphate, $(NH_4)_3[P(Mo_3O_{10})_4]$. This compound can be reduced to form an intensely colored compound, called molybdenum blue, which may be measured colorimetrically to provide a determination of the phosphate. Molybdenum blue is not a stoichiometrically well-defined compound, and it bears the average formula $MoO_{2.5-3} \cdot \times H_2O$. Both of the two main chemical reactions can yield the "wrong" products unless they are carried out under carefully prescribed conditions, including the acidity, the amount of ammonium molybdate reagent used and the temperature. Excess ammonium molybdate remaining after the first reaction tends to be reduced in part to molybdenum blue in the second reaction, so even the time of reduction should be controlled reproducibly.

This procedure is typically used in determining phosphate in concentrations up to about twenty parts per million. Similar procedures may be used to determine silicates and arsenates, and the procedure may be turned around to determine molybdenum in samples of unknowns.

Laboratory Experiment 36

DETERMINATION OF PHOSPHATE USING A PHOTO-ELECTRIC COLORIMETER

Reagents

Ammonium molybdate, 5% solution in 1 N sulfuric acid. (Dissolve 5.0 g. reagent grade ammonium molybdate in 80 ml. water and add to this solution one containing 2.8 ml. concentrated sulfuric acid in 20 ml. water. If a white residue forms, discard and prepare a new solution.)

Hydroquinone, 0.5% solution containing 1 drop concentrated sulfuric acid per 100 ml.

Potassium dihydrogen phosphate, standard solution, prepared by dissolving 0.7020 gram potassium hydrogen phosphate in water, add 10 ml. of 10 N sulfuric acid, dilute to 1 liter and mix (each ml. contains 0.16 mg. P)

Sodium sulfite, 11% aqueous solution

Special Apparatus

Bausch and Lomb Spectronic Colorimeter. (Any type of colorimeter may be used; the instructor will provide alternative operating directions if some other type is provided.)

Procedure

Obtain four 100 ml. volumetric flasks. Give one to your laboratory instructor for your unknown. Into the other three flasks, pipet 2, 6 and 10 ml., respectively, of the standard phosphate solution. Add enough water to each of the four to make the total volume at least 50 ml. Add to each in order, and with constant mixing, 10 ml. of the ammonium molybdate solution, 10 ml. of the hydroquinone solution, and 10 ml. of the sodium sulfite solution. Dilute to the mark and mix well. Allow to stand 30 minutes. Then obtain an absorbancy spectrum, prepare a calibration curve and determine the total mg. in your sample according to the following paragraphs.

General Operating Directions for the Spectronic Colorimeter. Follow second paragraph of procedure of Experiment 35.

Obtaining an Absorbancy Spectrum. Follow third paragraph of procedure of Experiment 35.

Preparation of Calibration Curve and Determination of Unknown. Follow fourth paragraph of procedure of Experiment 35. The calibration chart should be a plot of absorbancy vs. mg. P in the sample. The answer will be in mg. P in the unknown.

Colorimetric Determination of Lead with Separation by Extraction. One of the most useful methods of separating one component from all others in a solution is extraction into a solvent which is immiscible with the original solvent. For the separation to be complete, the desired component should be removed quantitatively into the new solvent and all other components should remain quantitatively in the first solvent. Several important aspects of separation by extraction may be illustrated by brief considerations of certain colorimetric procedures for the determinations of lead and nickel.

Lead ion reacts with the organic reagent diphenylthiocarbazone to form a colored complex which can be extracted quantitatively from an aqueous medium into chloroform, and colorimetric measurement can be made upon the chloroform layer. The reagent, which is customarily designated by the shorter name, dithizone, bears the empirical formula $C_{13}H_{12}N_4S$.

Dithizone reacts with several metal ions in addition to lead, including copper, zinc, silver, cadmium and mercury, so the selectivity of the reaction is rather poor. However, the selectivity of the extraction step may be varied somewhat at will by judicious selection of the pH of the aqueous phase and of what organic liquid is used. For example, the mercury-dithizone complex may be extracted at any pH above 2, while the lead-dithizone complex is extracted quantitatively only within the pH range 9 to 11. It is also possible to enhance the selectivity of the extraction by use of another complexing agent in the aqueous phase which would preferentially retain one or more components during the extraction.

Dithizone is not directly soluble in water, but it can be used in the form of a solution in chloroform. This solution is green in color. As would be expected from the solubility relationships, excess dithizone which remains after the reaction with lead ion passes into the chloroform layer during the extraction of the lead-dithizone complex. Therefore, the excess reagent must be removed prior to color-measurement of the chloroform phase, or compensation must be made for it by a procedure in which light-absorbing properties are measured at two different wavelengths of light.

The extraction of lead from aqueous medium into chloroform is reversible. If the organic liquid containing the lead-dithizone complex is subsequently shaken with an aqueous nitric acid solution, the lead is returned to the water phase. This procedure is useful if some type of measurement other than colorimetric is to follow the separation. The colorimetric procedure is preferable for determining small amounts of lead.

Colorimetric Determination of Nickel with Separation by Extraction. The organic reagent dimethylglyoxime reacts with nickel ion in aqueous solution to form a precipitate:

$$Ni^{++} + 2\ H_2C_4H_6N_2O_2 \longrightarrow Ni(HC_4H_6N_2O_2)_2 + 2\ H^+$$

The precipitate is very intensely colored red. Colorimetric measurement of the amount of nickel present could be made upon the aqueous suspension if no other colored components were present. The reaction in which the precipitate forms is very highly selective, particularly in ammoniacal medium, but some other metal ions often encountered along with nickel in practical situations are colored. For example, the determination of nickel in the presence of copper is of practical importance, and the cupric ion is itself intensely colored, especially if in ammoniacal solution. Fortunately, however, the red precipitate can be extracted quantitatively into an organic liquid. The solubility of the precipitate in chloroform is about 50 micrograms per ml., and the intense red color is retained.

Laboratory Experiment 37

DETERMINATION OF NICKEL IN A COPPER SALT BY EXTRACTION AND COLORIMETRY

Reagents

Buffer solution, prepared by dissolving 60 grams $NaC_2H_3O_2$ and 1.2 ml. glacial acetic acid in 200 ml. water

Chloroform

Dimethylglyoxime, solution prepared by dissolving 1 gram $H_2C_4H_6O_2N_2$ in 100 ml. ethanol

Hydroxylamine hydrochloride

Nickel, standard solution of a nickel salt containing 100 mg. Ni per liter

Sodium tartrate

Sodium thiosulfate

Special Apparatus

Bausch and Lomb Spectronic Colorimeter. (Any type of colorimeter may be used; the instructor will provide alternative operating directions if some other type is provided.)

Procedure

Obtain six 50 ml. Erlenmeyer flasks and rubber stoppers. In three, place 0.1, 0.3 and 0.5 gram of your unknown, weighed to the closest 0.001 gram, and dissolve in 10 ml. water. Into the other three flasks, pipet 1, 2 and 4 ml, respectively, of the standard nickel solution, and add water to make the volume approximately 10 ml. in each. To each of the six flasks, add 0.5 gram sodium tartrate, 2.5 grams sodium thiosulfate, 5 ml. buffer solution, 50 mg. hydroxylamine hydrochloride and 2 ml. dimethylglyoxime solution. Shake vigorously after each addition. Add 5.00 ml. chloroform and shake vigorously for one minute. Let stand until the layers separate. Transfer most of the chloroform layer to the colorimeter sample tube by means of a medicine dropper. Then obtain an absorbancy spectrum of the colored complex, prepare a calibration curve and determine the percentage of Ni in your unknown in accordance with the following paragraphs:

General Operating Directions for the Spectronic Colorimeter. Follow second paragraph of procedure of Experiment 35, but use a sample tube containing chloroform instead of water for the zero optical density setting.

Obtaining an Absorbancy Spectrum. Follow third paragraph of procedure of Experiment 35, using one sample tube containing chloroform and one obtained with any of the standard solutions.

Preparation of Calibration Curve and Determination of Unknown. Measure the optical density of each standard and of your unknown, all at the wavelength of 400 or 500 mμ. Run duplicate or triplicate measurements on each solution. From the data on the three standards, prepare a calibration chart in terms of absorbancy vs. mg. Ni in the sample. From the data on the unknown and the chart, ascertain the mg. Ni in your unknown. Convert the answer to percentage of Ni in your original sample. (Note: The unknowns consist of stock samples of cupric salts in various grades of purity.)

REVIEW QUESTIONS

1. Discuss the general applicability of colorimetric methods of analysis.
2. State the Lambert-Beer law in a mathematical equation, and clearly define each term used.
3. How can the Lambert-Beer law be tested for a particular system?
4. For what purpose is the Walpole technique used?
5. Describe the construction of the cups of a Duboscq colorimeter.
6. Compare the three general methods of colorimetric analysis on any three significant points.
7. Describe an experiment to determine the wavelength at which the most sensitive quantitative determination for a particular substance could be made by a colorimetric procedure. Is this always the most desirable wavelength to use? Explain.
8. With reference to Figure 56, draw on one set of axes plots of absorbancy vs. concentration at the three wavelengths, A, B and C.

SUGGESTIONS FOR ADDITIONAL READING

Items 3, 4, 18, 19, 20, 22, 28 and 29, Appendix 7.

Chapter 18

Spectrophotometry and Other Optical Methods

THE VARIOUS portions of the electromagnetic spectrum, diagramed in Figure 57, have all been employed to some extent in quantitative analysis. In the preceding chapter were described colorimetric and simple spectrophotometric methods of analysis based upon absorption of radiation in the visible portion of the spectrum. Further absorption methods include spectrophotometry in which the light employed is in the infrared or ultraviolet portions of the

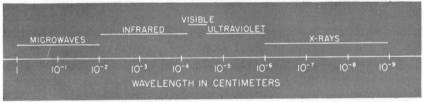

FIGURE 57. Diagramatic representation of the electromagnetic spectrum.

spectrum as well as in the visible region. Methods in addition to absorption methods, employing visible and ultraviolet light, include the following: emission spectrography, in which the sample emits, rather than absorbs, light; turbidimetry and nephelometry, in which the specimen removes a portion of the light incident upon it by reflection or by scattering rather than by absorption; fluorimetry, in which a portion of the light energy absorbed by a specimen is re-emitted as light energy of a longer wavelength. The x-ray portion of the spectrum is also very widely used in analysis, with the methods including diffraction methods in addition to absorption and emission methods.

SPECTROPHOTOMETRY—VISIBLE, ULTRAVIOLET AND INFRARED

General Considerations. All spectrophotometers are basically similar to the colorimeter represented in the block diagram of Figure 48. A spectrophotometer, in contrast to a simple filter photometer, uses a prism or a grating as the monochromator. The use of a prism or grating permits use of a much narrower band of wavelengths than do most filters. The monochromator is usually continuously adjustable so that any desired portion of the spectral range within the limits of the instrument may be selected at will.

Spectrophotometric data are useful both for qualitative and for quantitative determinations. Many substances absorb light of some colors more readily than of other colors, and a color absorption spectrum of the substance is characteristic of that particular substance. As described in Chapter 17, this spectrum consists of a plot of absorbancy, or some related quantity, versus wavelength. The magnitude of the absorbancy at a fixed wavelength of any particular substance is a measure of the concentration of that substance, and this is the basis of quantitative determinations. As already described, the maximum sensitivity in a quantitative determination is obtained at a wavelength of maximum absorption, but the range of concentrations which may be covered is relatively narrow at this wavelength.

Some spectrophotometers are commercially available in which the color absorption spectrum is measured and recorded automatically. These instruments have extended the practical use of light absorption methods tremendously.

Ultraviolet Spectrophotometry. For experiments involving the absorption of ultraviolet light rather than merely of visible light, the light source must emit suitable ultraviolet light, the container which holds the test solution and also certain other optical components of the instrument must be made of materials which transmit ultraviolet light readily, and the detector must be specially designed to respond to ultraviolet light. Accordingly, the light source, the optical material of construction and the detector in an ultraviolet spectrophotometer usually consist of a hydrogen discharge lamp, quartz, and a photoelectric cell inside of a quartz or nonex glass bulb, respectively. The three corresponding items in a spectrophotometer designed primarily for visible light are usually a tungsten incandescent light bulb, optical glass, and a photoelectric cell in a conventional glass bulb, respectively. The optical components and, to some extent, the detectors employed with ultraviolet light are also suitable for visible light. Therefore, some commercial instruments, including the Beckman model DU for which an optical diagram is shown in Figure 58 are designed for use throughout both the ultraviolet and visible regions with two interchangeable light sources and two detectors. It must be recognized, furthermore, that the dividing lines between the several portions of the electromagnetic spectrum are quite arbitrary and that some instruments classified nominally for use in the visible portion do extend somewhat into longer and shorter wavelength portions as well.

The use of ultraviolet light extends the realm of useful applicability of spectrophotometry tremendously. Many solutions which are quite transparent to visible light exhibit absorption properties in the ultraviolet portion of the spectrum. This phenomenon is frequently encountered with both organic and inorganic substances. In some cases it has been possible to correlate the ultraviolet light-absorbing characteristics of organic substances with their structures. Conversely, the structures of newly synthesized organic compounds can in some instances be worked out from absorption spectra in conjunction with other types of information.

The usefulness of an absorption spectrum for qualitative identification is, however, somewhat limited in dealing with mixtures, since the mixture spectrum consists of a composite of the spectra of the individual components. Unless the individual spectra are much sharper than those usually encountered in both visible and ultraviolet spectrophotometry, these individual spectra usually overlap considerably in the spectrum of the mixture. Spectrophotometric data are much more useful for quantitative analyses. The type of plot of Figure 50 serves as the basis of quantitative determinations. Special procedures have been developed to render spectrophotometric data useful in quantitative determinations even in the case of overlapping spectra. These procedures are based upon the fact that, if two or more constituents contribute to the absorbancy at a fixed wavelength, the total absorbancy equals the sum of the individual absorbancies. Thus, if two components x and y contribute to the absorbancy at wavelength λ_1,

$$A_{total_1} = A_x + A_y \quad \text{(all at } \lambda_1\text{)}$$

Applying the Lambert-Beer Law to each of the two components and letting the breadth of the sample cell b equal unity for both,

$$A_{total_1} = a_{x_1}c_x + a_{y_1}c_y \quad \text{(all at } \lambda_1\text{)}$$

A similar equation may be written for the total absorbancy at another wavelength λ_2:

$$A_{total_2} = a_{x_2}c_x + a_{y_2}c_y \quad \text{(all at } \lambda_2\text{)}$$

The numerical values of the absorbancy coefficient a_{x_1} and a_{x_2} may be determined at λ_1 and at λ_2, respectively, by measurements upon a standard solution of x, that is, upon a solution of which c_x is known and c_y is zero. The numerical values of a_{y_1} and a_{y_2} at the two wavelengths may be determined similarly upon a standard solution of y. (Note that no error arises

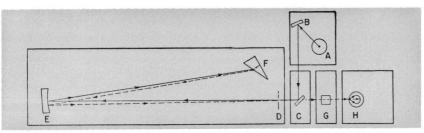

FIGURE 58. Optical diagram of Beckman model DU spectrophotometer. Light from source (*A*) passes to the mirrors (*B*) (*C*), through entrance slit (*D*) and mirror (*E*) to the quartz prism (*F*), then back to mirror (*E*) and through exit slit (*D*) (the entrance and exit slits are mounted one above the other) to the test solution (*G*) and photocell (*H*).

from the assumption that the breadth b equals unity so long as the same sample cell is used throughout.)

Then when we measure the absorbancies at the two wavelengths upon an unknown mixture of the two components, we have two equations containing only c_x and c_y as unknowns, so the equations may be solved for the composition of the unknown sample. It is preferable for one of the wavelengths to be one at which x absorbs much more intensely than y and one for which y absorbs to a greater extent than x. This entire procedure is another application of the principle of indirect analysis described in Chapter 6. Two (or *n*) components can be determined without separation by making two (or *n*) measurements upon the mixture, by writing the results of each measurement as a mathematical equation, and by solving the equations for the desired information. The principle is applicable whether the measurements are gravimetric, volumetric, colorimetric or of some other type; it is not even necessary that the two (or *n*) measurements be of the same type.

Infrared Spectrophotometry. The design of an infrared spectrophotometer is similar to that of a visible or ultraviolet instrument, but again the light source, the optical components including the sample holder, and the detector must be selected for use in this portion of the electromagnetic spectrum. The light source is of the incandescent type, but the ordinary tungsten light bulb is not satisfactory in the infrared region except in that part immediately adjacent to the visible region because the glass bulb of the lamp absorbs light of the longer wavelengths. Two good infrared sources are the Nernst glower and the globar. The former is an electrically heated hollow rod of oxides of zirconium, yttrium and thorium, while the latter is an electrically heated rod of silicon carbide. Common materials for construction of optical components include sodium chloride and potassium bromide. Unfortunately, these materials are water soluble so aqueous test solutions cannot be employed, and the atmosphere within and around the instrument must be kept dry. Water vapor is inadmissible also because it absorbs much infrared illumination. Common types of photoelectric cells do not respond adequately to infrared illumination, but three other suitable types of detector have been developed: the thermocouple; the bolometer; the thermistor. In all three of these types of detectors, light energy is first transformed into heat energy and from thence into electrical energy for final indication.

The infrared absorption characteristics of substances are of extreme analytical usefulness, particularly in qualitative analysis. As with visible and ultraviolet light, the absorption spectrum of a substance is characteristic of what the substance is, and the amount of absorbancy at a fixed wavelength is characteristic of the amount of that substance present. The special usefulness of infrared data lies in the fact that each type of atomic grouping within a molecule causes that molecule to absorb infrared light of certain wavelengths, largely independently of what other types of atomic groupings may be present in the absorbing molecules. This is especially useful in dealing with organic molecules. For example, every type of molecule containing carbon to carbon double bonds will absorb at or near a certain wavelength, every type of molecule containing —O—H groups will absorb at or near another wavelength, and so forth. This fact makes infrared spectrophotometry very valuable in ascertaining or in checking the structure of a newly synthesized or discovered compound. This type of analysis has been employed more in organic than in inorganic work. However, as methods of handling inorganic substances without the use of aqueous solutions are being devised, more and more inorganic applications are being developed.

TURBIDIMETRY AND NEPHELOMETRY

Turbidimetric and nephelometric methods differ from colorimetric methods chiefly in two ways: the unknown substance is not in solution but rather is in colloidal suspension; some of the light photons incident upon the sample are removed from the straightforward beam by scattering rather than by absorption. If the light transmitted through the suspension is measured, as in colorimetric procedures, the method is called a turbidimetric one. In a nephelometric method the measurement is of the intensity of scattered light. In either case the measurement may be of direct intensity, or it may be of comparison by either standard series or variable depth technique.

Many standard colorimetric instruments may be used for nephelometric or turbidimetric methods. A Duboscq colorimeter with provision for illumination at right angles to the direction of viewing makes a good nephelometer. Most standard photoelectric filter photometers make usable turbidimeters. Several manufacturers make instruments with provision for choice of detection at right angles to the incident beam or in direct line with the incident beam, and these may be used at will for colorimetric, turbidimetric and nephelometric determinations.

A special type of variable depth technique which has been used for many years employs a tube for the test solution so arranged that light enters from the base and is viewed from above. The liquid level is adjusted until the light source just appears or disappears from sight.

The results obtained in turbidimetric and nephelometric determinations are generally not so accurate as are those of color absorption methods. In colorimetric work, the accuracy of the results is often limited only by the instrument. In turbidimetric and nephelometric procedures, however, a larger error arises from the difficulty of preparing and maintaining all standards and unknown suspensions in a uniform and reproducible degree of dispersion. The suspended particles must be uniform in size and shape in order to be reproducible. They must be very small, for example, one-hundred-thousandth of a centimeter in average dimension, in order to remain in a stable state of dispersion long enough for the measurements to be made. The colloidally dispersed particles must be of uniform size because the amount of light scattered per unit weight of scattering substance is a function of particle size; this requirement is difficult to fulfill in practice and is the chief limitation upon the general applicability and accuracy of turbidimetric and nephelometric methods of analysis.

The determination of small amounts of sulfur after its precipitation as barium sulfate is one of the classical applications of turbidimetry. In order to provide results that are even reasonably accurate, the precipitation must be conducted by rigorous adherence to a predetermined rate of mixing reagents, temperature, digestion time, and so forth. The determination of trace amounts of hydrogen cyanide after conversion of the cyanide to insoluble silver cyanide and the determination of carbon dioxide after bubbling it through a solution of a barium salt to precipitate barium carbonate may be mentioned as other examples of the useful turbidimetric and nephelometric procedures which have been developed.

Turbidimetric measurements may be made periodically during a titration in which an insoluble precipitate is formed. At the start of the titration, no precipitate is present to scatter light. As the titration proceeds to the equivalence point, the precipitate forms. Beyond the equivalence point, no further precipitate is formed. The measurements may be made of $\log \dfrac{I_0}{I}$ as in colorimetric and spectrophotometric procedures, but it is better to call this quantity by the more general term optical density, rather than absorbancy, because light photons are removed by scattering and not by absorbing. Ideally, the titration curve of optical density vs. volume of titrant should consist of two straight lines, one increasing toward the equivalence point and one horizontal after that point. In practice this ideal is seldom reached for several reasons. If conditions which have been established empirically are maintained, however, titration end points can be determined with an accuracy within a few percent. This is inferior to most gravimetric and volumetric procedures but is adequate for some purposes. The laboratory procedure which follows is designed for the determination of the fluoride content of a solution by titration with a calcium solution to precipitate calcium fluoride. At fluoride concentrations initially greater than about 0.1 molar and less than about 0.01 molar, it is difficult to obtain constant readings at a given point in the titration due to slow formation and recrystallization of the precipitate and to its coagulation. Other ions which react with either calcium or fluoride ion, either to form another precipitate or to form a complex which would prevent precipitation of calcium fluoride, must be absent.

Laboratory Experiment 38

TURBIDIMETRIC TITRATION OF FLUORIDE IN A
SOLUTION

Reagents

Calcium chloride, 0.2 M standard solution, prepared by weighing (to the nearest 0.01 gram) 2 grams $CaCO_3$, dissolving in about 25 ml. 1:5 dilution of stock hydrochloric acid, heating just to boiling to remove carbon dioxide, and diluting to the mark in a 100 ml. volumetric flask

A nonionic detergent (Tergitol or Triton)

Special Apparatus

Bausch and Lomb Spectronic Colorimeter. (See operating directions in Experiment 35; the instructor will provide operating directions if some other measuring device is used.)

Procedure

Pipet 5 ml. of the unknown fluoride solution (which should contain from 2 to 6 mg. F in this aliquot) into a test tube of the size which can be used directly in the colorimeter. Add one drop of the detergent (to provide some stability to the suspension which will be formed and to enhance nucleation at the expense of crystal growth). Use this solution to set the zero optical density reading of the colorimeter. Titrate with 0.10 ml. increments (measuring pipet) of the standard solution of calcium chloride. After each addition, shake the suspension by hand for ten seconds, let settle until the detergent-froth rises to the surface, and measure the optical density. Continue until the optical density readings have ceased to increase for at least three readings. Plot optical density vs. volume of titrant, and read the end point volume from this graph. If the end point does not come between 0.5 and 1.5 ml., increase or decrease the volume of the unknown solution used in replicate titrations. If the optical density readings are too high or too low for accurate readings to be made, consult your instructor. In any case, run at least three titrations. If time permits, also run three titrations without using the detergent. Calculate the mg. F per ml. of the unknown solution.

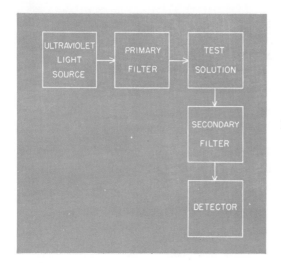

FIGURE 59. Block diagram for fluorescent measurements.

FLUORIMETRY

Fluorimetric analysis is similar to colorimetry in that the test solution absorbs some of the incident light photons, and it is similar to nephelometry in that observation is made of light emerging from the test solution at right angles to the beam of incident light. However, the mechanism of interaction between incident light photons and the test solution is distinctively different in fluorimetry than in other forms of optical analysis. In fluorimetry some of the energy of the incident light photons which are absorbed by the test solution is re-emitted as light photons of a longer wavelength. A substance capable of performing this function is called a fluorescent substance and may be determined quantitatively by the fluorimetric method.

A fluorimeter for analytical use consists basically of an ultraviolet light source, a cell into which the fluorescent test solution is placed, and a detector situated so as to measure the intensity of visible fluorescent light emitted in a direction perpendicular to the incident ultraviolet beam (Fig. 59). The primary filter, between the light source and the test solution, passes ultraviolet light but absorbs any visible components which may be emitted by the source. The secondary filter, between the test solution and the detector, passes the visible fluorescent light but absorbs any ultraviolet light which may have been scattered or reflected from the sample cell. The fluorescent light emerges from the test solution in all directions, but of course, only that emerging in the direction of the detector is actually measured. The light source may be a mercury arc lamp and the detector a photoelectric cell. In some instruments, either one or both of the filters is replaced by a more refined monochromator.

For any specific quantitative determination, one or more standard solutions of the fluorescent substance must be prepared and measured with the fluorimeter to provide calibration data. Since a number of factors other than concentration may affect the intensity of fluorescent light, the standard and unknown solutions must be prepared, maintained and measured under the same conditions. Among the variables which frequently must be controlled are pH, temperature, foreign ion concentration and intensity of incident light.

Fluorimetric methods have been employed successfully for the determinations of certain organic and inorganic substances. Thiamine (vitamin B) may be determined quantitatively after oxidation to fluorescent thiochrome. Riboflavin may be determined directly, after removal of any fluorescent impurities which may accompany it. Both these determinations are useful even when the unknown concentration is as low as 0.1 microgram per milliliter of solution. Aluminum yields a fluorescent compound when treated with the dye, morin, and solutions containing from 0.1 to 1 microgram of aluminum in each milliliter of solution may be analyzed fluorimetrically.

EMISSION SPECTROGRAPHY

When an element is ignited in a flame, an arc or a spark, a spectrum of light is emitted that is characteristic of that element. The spectrum, as recorded on photographic film, consists of a series of lines at positions corresponding to various wavelengths, and the intensity of any specific line is proportional to the concentration of the element. Therefore, emission spectra are useful for both qualitative and quantitative analysis.

A block diagram of an emission spectrograph is shown in Figure 60. This diagram differs from that of the absorption spectrophotometer, shown earlier in Figure 48, simply in that here the test specimen is included as part of the light source rather than being external to it. There are three major types of source, the flame, the d-c electrical arc, and the a-c electrical spark. The flame must be quite hot, so usually an oxygen-air or acetylene-air flame is used. The test specimen, in the form of a solution, is introduced into the flame at a uniform rate while measurements are made. The arc or spark, when used, is caused to pass between two solid electrodes. When convenient, the sample is used in the form of a solid rod or wire, in which case the sample itself serves as one of the electrodes. A powdered solid specimen may be

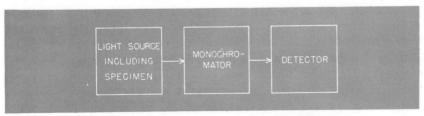

FIGURE 60.   Block diagram for emission spectrograph.

inserted right onto one of the electrodes. Liquid and gas specimens are also occasionally used with arc or spark sources.

The monochromator may be identical with that of an absorption spectrophotometer as already discussed, including an entrance slit, a prism or grating as the monochromator proper, and an exit slit. The light emerging through the exit slit then falls upon a photoelectric detector. More commonly, however, the exit slit is omitted and the entire spectrum emerging from the prism or grating is allowed to fall upon a photographic film which serves as the detector. The former system is usually used with the flame source and the latter with arc and spark sources, although either type of detector could be adapted for use with any of the three types of source.

The emission spectrographic method of analysis is predominantly a method of metal and metal ion analysis. Flame sources are usually used in determinations of such elements as the alkalies and alkaline earths, although this type of source is not limited to these elements. Arc and spark sources are widely used in determinations of nearly all of the metals and metal ions. It makes little or no difference whether the element involved is present in the sample as free metal, in an alloy or as a chemical compound. Spectrographic methods are very sensitive. Minute traces, parts per million and even less in some cases, may be detected and determined. The over-all accuracy is generally of the order of about 5% of the measured quantity; this is really very good in dealing with trace amounts of substances.

Since quantitative determinations are based upon intensity measurements, all conditions of exciting the sample and detecting the illumination should ideally be held perfectly constant in obtaining the spectra of standards for calibration and of the unknown. It is difficult to achieve even approximate constancy in some of the conditions involved, so quantitative spectrographic procedures frequently utilize the *internal standard technique*. In this method a standard substance in fixed concentration is inserted in each standard and unknown sample. Then the intensity of the desired line of the unknown substance is measured, not absolutely, but relative to that of a nearby line of the standard substance. The influence of a slight shift in conditions of excitation or detection is thus effectively cancelled out, since it affects both standard and unknown lines similarly. Whether the internal standard technique is employed or not, calibration data must be obtained with standard samples before unknown samples can be determined quantitatively.

A single determination by emission spectrographic methods would be rather complex, due to the necessary preparation of standards and of calibration data. The method is very practical, however, for the routine analysis of large numbers of similar samples. Frequently, a determination that takes hours by the more classical chemical methods may be completed in a few minutes by this method once the necessary calibration experiments are done. Many specimens require no preliminary treatment or separation prior to analysis. Up to ten or twelve constituents may be determined successfully from one spectrum of an unknown preparation.

X-RAY METHODS

Electromagnetic radiation which is of wavelengths of the order of tenths of angstroms to several angstroms (1 angstrom equals 1×10^{-8} centimeters) is very useful in analysis. This radiation is within the x-ray region of the electromagnetic spectrum. There are three major types of analytical applications of x-rays: absorption; emission; diffraction. X-ray absorption and emission methods are similar in principle to simple colorimetry and to emission spectroscopy, respectively, except for differences which arise because of the considerably different wavelengths of radiation employed. X-ray diffraction methods are quite distinct in analysis; they provide very useful measurements of characteristic distances between planes of atoms in crystalline substances.

X-Ray Absorption. The chief components of an instrument for use in analytical x-ray absorption methods are a source of x-radiation, a filter or other monochromator, if any, a test sample container, and a detector. It may be noted that these components are strictly analogous to those of a visible light colorimeter (Fig. 48). The source consists of a specially designed two-electrode tube, and associated power supplies, which generates a beam of x-rays. The monochromator may consist of a thin metal or metal oxide film, or of a single crystal of quartz, calcite or other suitable material. The thin film serves to pass some wavelengths of x-rays more readily than others, so it is the same in function as is a colored glass filter in visible light colorimetry. The quartz or calcite crystal functions with x-rays as does a ruled glass or plastic grating with visible and ultraviolet light. The detector may consist of a photographic film, a Geiger tube with electronic power supplies and associated amplifying and counting circuits, or of a fluorescent screen which absorbs x-ray photons and re-emits a portion of this energy as visible light for subsequent detection by the human eye or by conventional photoelectric means.

X-rays of the wavelengths commonly employed are very penetrating in comparison to electromagnetic radiation of the infrared, visible and ultraviolet regions. Absorption of x-rays is largely an atomic phenomenon; that is to say, the x-ray absorption characteristics of any substance are determined by the elements of which that substance is composed, rather than by the ionic or molecular groupings of those elements. In general, elements of greater atomic number absorb more readily than do those of lower atomic number. Each element does absorb certain wavelengths of x-rays more readily than others. However, most practical applications of x-ray absorption use "white," or polychromatic, x-radiation and do not require an elaborate monochromator. Accordingly, most of the applications are in quantitative rather than in qualitative analysis.

The usefulness of the x-ray absorption method of analysis may be illustrated by a few examples. In commercial automotive gasoline, the lead in the tetraethyl lead is about the only component of high atomic number. Even though all elements of which the gasoline is composed do contribute to its x-ray absorption characteristics, the over-all absorption of any sample of gasoline is determined principally by the concentration of lead present. Therefore, tetraethyl lead in gasoline may be determined readily by x-ray absorption methods. Another example is encountered in the determination of sulfur in crude oils. Whenever sulfur is the heaviest element present in appreciable concentration, as it frequently is, a simple measurement of x-ray absorption suffices for the determination. It is also possible to determine the concentration of a single inorganic solute, such as silver nitrate in water, by x-ray absorption methods, but this type of determination can be performed much more accurately and satisfactorily by other methods. The emphasis in assessing the importance of any method of analysis should be placed upon what it can do that other methods cannot do or cannot do as satisfactorily.

X-Ray Emission (Fluorescent) Methods. X-rays may be generated by bombardment of a metal or salt either by high velocity electrons or by other x-rays. Under proper conditions, the wavelengths of the generated rays are determined by the elemental composition of the metal or the salt. It is possible to make use of these x-ray emission spectra for analytical purposes, just as it is possible to use visible and ultraviolet emission spectra. In practice, the test specimen is usually bombarded with x-rays so the process is one of fluorescence. The bombarding x-rays must be of shorter wavelength than the characteristic rays emitted by the sample.

The basic components of an instrument for x-ray fluorescent work include an intense source of x-rays, a container for the specimen, a monochromator and a detector. The monochromator and detector together serve to analyze spectrally, and to measure intensities of, the fluorescent rays emerging from the specimen at right angles to the incident beam of x-rays. The sample may be in liquid form or in solid form. Once again, a quartz, calcite or other suitable crystal is used as the x-ray monochromator, functioning analogously to a ruled grating with visible or ultraviolet light.

The determination of tetraethyl lead in gasoline is one of the practical applications of x-ray emission, or fluorescent, work. This determination may also be performed by the x-ray absorption method, so it is of interest to compare the methods on the basis of this determination. X-ray absorption methods yield data on the over-all absorption characteristics of the test specimen, and all of the elements comprising that specimen contribute to the measured quantity. However, x-ray fluorescent methods yield separate spectral information for each of the elements present in the sample. Thus, absorption methods in the tetraethyl lead determination yield accurate results only when the absorption due to lead atoms is far greater than that due to all other compounds combined or when the relative concentrations of other components are kept adequately uniform in all samples, both standard and unknown. Yet the fluorescent method yields proper tetraethyl lead data, largely independently of what the remainder of the test sample may contain.

Thus, one method involves measurement of an over-all or cumulative property of the sample while the other yields individual data for individual elements present in the sample.

X-ray fluorescent methods have been found to be useful for determinations of the composition of some metal alloys. It is not necessary to dissolve or otherwise destroy the specimen in any way. In recent years numerous other useful applications have been developed for this method of analysis.

X-Ray Diffraction Methods. When a monochromatic beam of x-rays is passed through a powdered crystalline specimen, a spectrum of diffracted rays is obtained. Every crystalline compound exhibits a characteristic x-ray diffraction spectrum, so the placement of lines or rings in the spectrum may be used as the basis of qualitative determinations. The diffraction spectrum of a mixture is a simple combination of the various component spectra, and the relative intensities of the two or more component spectra are determined by their relative concentrations in the mixture. Therefore, intensity measurements permit quantitative determinations.

The necessary apparatus consists of a source of x-rays, a filter to render the rays essentially monochromatic, a specimen holder and a detector. In analytical work the specimen is usually, but not necessarily, a powdered solid. The detector may be either a photographic film or of the Geiger tube type. A typical photographically recorded pattern is shown in Figure 61. The diameters of these rings are characteristic of what the crystalline specimen is.

It must be emphasized that the x-ray diffraction method provides analyses on the basis of crystalline compounds, not on the basis of elements or ions or atomic groupings as is the case with most other methods of analysis. For example, this method makes possible the determination of whether a certain mixture contains sodium chloride and potassium bromide or sodium bromide and potassium chloride. It is also possible to distinguish between different crystalline forms of the same substance. For example, titanium dioxide occurs in three distinct crystalline forms, one of which is far superior to the others as a white pigment. X-ray diffraction methods can reveal which one or ones are present in any sample of titanium dioxide.

X-ray diffraction analyses are nondestructive of the sample. Quantitative determinations are generally accurate only within 5 to 10%, and any crystalline component present in amount less than about 5% of the sample is usually not detected except by special techniques. This method of analysis

FIGURE 61. A typical x-ray powder diffraction pattern which has been recorded on photographic film; this is a pattern of a sample of calcium hydroxy phosphate.

is used primarily for the many analyses of crystalline substances which are not possible by other methods.

X-ray diffraction methods are very useful for many purposes other than for straightforward qualitative and quantitative analysis. Since the diffraction characteristics of a crystalline specimen are determined by the geometrical arrangements of the atoms or ions within the crystals, it is possible with special x-ray techniques to arrive at ultimate structural information on crystalline substances. Other fields of application include measurement of particle size of powdered materials and the detection of physical stress and strain in metals and plastics.

MASS SPECTROMETRY

The mass spectrometer is an instrument in which the molecules of a gaseous specimen are ionized and in which those ions are sorted out according to their mass (actually mass to charge ratio, but in most cases each ion is singly charged). The main parts of a mass spectrometer are the following: a sampling system, in which a suitable quantity of gas is prepared for analysis; an ionizing region, in which gas molecules are ionized, usually by bombardment with a stream of electrons; an electrostatic accelerating region, in which the ions are caused to move in a fixed direction at suitable velocities, thus forming a beam of ions; a magnetic field, in which the incoming ion beam is, in effect, sorted into separate beams for each mass of ion present; a photographic or electrical detector, by which the oncoming ion beams are located and measured.

Nearly every specimen which is a gas or which may be converted to a gas may be analyzed both qualitatively and quantitatively by means of mass spectrometry, and countless practical examples have been found. For example, traces of oxygen present as an impurity in tank nitrogen may be determined by measurement of the mass 32 intensity (due to singly charged oxygen molecules) relative to that of mass 28 (singly charged nitrogen molecules). As another example, the isotopic composition of hydrogen gas may be determined by measurement of the mass 2, 3 and 4 intensities, which correspond to singly ionized molecules of H_2, HD and D_2, respectively (letting H represent the mass one isotope of hydrogen and D the mass two isotope commonly called "heavy hydrogen").

Perhaps the largest field of application of mass spectrometry is in hydrocarbon analysis. This importance is based, in part, upon the fact that even molecules of the same molecular weight may be determined in the presence of each other because they may be caused to split apart into smaller fragments in the process of being ionized. For example,

both butane, $CH_3—CH_2—CH_2—CH_3$, and isobutane,
$$CH_3$$
$$|$$
$$CH_3—CH_2—CH_3,$$

have the same molecular weight. But each will give its own characteristic fractions of ions of mass 15 (CH_3^+), mass 29 $(CH_3\!-\!CH_2^+)$,

$$\text{mass 43} \left(\begin{array}{c} CH_3 \\ | \\ CH_3\!-\!CH^+ \end{array} \text{ or } CH_3\!-\!CH_2\!-\!CH_2^+ \right) \text{ and}$$

$$\text{mass 58} \left(CH_3\!-\!CH_2\!-\!CH_2\!-\!CH_3^+ \text{ or } \begin{array}{c} CH_3 \\ | \\ CH_3\!-\!CH\!-\!CH_3^+ \end{array} \right).$$

Although the mass spectrometer is basically an instrument for gas
analysis, it is often used for analyzing liquid specimens merely by testing a
portion of the liquid vapor. Some successful attempts have also been made
to devise methods for ionizing solid specimens, so the method may possibly
be extended further in the future to the analysis of solids.

It is interesting to note that the mass spectrometer has also been employed
for purposes other than straightforward analyses. For example, instruments
built on the principle of the mass spectrometer were used successfully during
World War II to separate uranium, U^{235}, from its normal mixture with
larger amounts of other isotopes of uranium. This application was possible
because the mass spectrometer actually separates molecules, after ionization,
in accordance with their mass numbers.

REVIEW QUESTIONS

1. Compare a spectrophotometer with a simple colorimeter on the bases of construction, usefulness in qualitative work, and usefulness in quantitative work.
2. Of what particular usefulness is ultraviolet light in spectrophotometry?
3. Of what particular usefulness is infrared light in spectrophotometry?
4. Draw block diagrams to illustrate colorimetry, spectrophotometry, emission
   spectrography, turbidimetry, nephelometry, and fluorimetry methods of analysis.
5. Compare x-ray absorption methods with visible light absorption methods on the
   bases of apparatus and applicability.
6. Describe the unique role of x-ray diffraction methods in analysis.

SUGGESTIONS FOR ADDITIONAL READING

Items 3, 4, 18, 19 and 29, Appendix 7.

Part Five

ELECTRICAL METHODS

Chapter 19

Electrodeposition Methods

THERE ARE several distinct groups of electrical methods of analysis, with several varied types of procedure within each of the groups. In one of these groups, called electrodeposition methods, an electrical current is used as a precipitating agent, reducing or oxidizing ions in solution to some insoluble substance which may subsequently be weighed. It should be noted that electrodeposition methods form, in effect, one branch of gravimetric analysis, with the chief measurements in each determination being of weight.

PRINCIPLES

When two electrodes are placed in a solution and connected to an external, unidirectional voltage source, positive ions migrate toward the cathode and negative ions toward the anode. Since these ions cannot accumulate indefinitely in the vicinity of the electrodes, electrical current flows continuously only when electrochemical reactions take place at both electrodes to consume the ions arriving at the electrode surfaces. For example, a solution of copper sulfate may be electrolyzed between platinum electrodes with the following reactions taking place at the electrodes:

$$Cu^{++} + 2\,e \longrightarrow Cu \quad \text{at the cathode;}$$
$$2\,H_2O - 4\,e \longrightarrow O_2 + 4\,H^+ \quad \text{at the anode.}$$

Thus the cupric ion is deposited as metallic copper at the cathode. If essentially all of the cupric ion is plated out from the solution in this manner, the copper content of the initial solution may be determined merely by weighing the cathode both before and after receiving the deposit of metallic copper. It may be noted further from this example that the main anode process involves molecules of the water rather than nitrate ions from the solute. The anodic liberation of oxygen is frequently encountered in the electrolysis of aqueous solutions. The selectivity of electrolysis reactions will be discussed subsequently.

Most of the practical examples of quantitative electrodeposition work involve the reduction at the cathode of the cations of a metal salt to the corresponding free metal. Typical examples include the electrodepositions

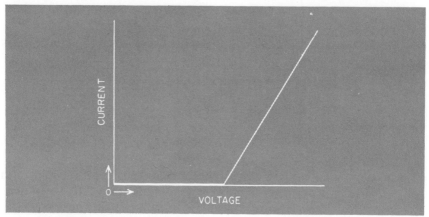

FIGURE 62.   Current-voltage plot showing decomposition potential.

of silver and of copper. There are, however, a few substances which may be oxidized at the anode to an insoluble substance suitable for weighing. An example of the latter type is the oxidation of lead ion from the +2 to the +4 state, in which it deposits on the anode as insoluble lead dioxide.

Decomposition Potential.   When two platinum gauze electrodes are immersed in a solution and connected to an external d.c. voltage source, that voltage must exceed a certain value called the *decomposition potential* in order for a current to flow continuously through that solution. A typical plot of current flow versus applied voltage is shown in Figure 62. Practically no current flows until the decomposition potential of the solution is reached, and the current flow increases linearly with further increases in applied voltage.

The theoretical decomposition potential is equal to the potential of the electrochemical cell consisting of the materials involved. The latter potential is simply the difference between the two electrode potentials, which may be calculated with the appropriate Nernst equations as described in Chapter 14. It is necessary, of course, to know what electrode reactions occur before one can calculate the theoretical decomposition potential, and the nature of these electrode reactions must be established ultimately by experiment.

Example I.   Electrolysis of a solution of zinc iodide between platinum electrodes occurs with deposition of free zinc at the cathode and free iodine at the anode. Calculate the theoretical decomposition potential of a 1.0 molar solution of zinc iodide.

The cathode reaction is $Zn^{++} + 2\,e \longrightarrow Zn$

Let E_c = cathode potential

$$E_c = E° + \frac{.059}{n} \log [Zn^{++}]$$

$$E_c = -0.76 + \frac{.059}{2} \log 1.0$$

$$E_c = -0.76$$

The anode reaction is $I_2 + 2\,e \longleftarrow 2\,I^-$

Let E_a = anode potential

$$E_a = E^\circ + \frac{.059}{n} \log \frac{1}{[I^-]^2}$$

$$E_a = 0.54 + \frac{.059}{2} \log \frac{1}{(2)^2}$$

$$E_a = 0.52$$

The theoretical decomposition potential is the difference between E_c and E_a, that is, between -0.76 and $+0.52$, or 1.28 volts. (It is quite arbitrary whether this over-all potential be stated as $+1.28$ or -1.28; for our purposes it will suffice to say that the theoretical decomposition potential is 1.28 volts with zinc liberated at the cathode and iodine at the anode.)

Example 2.   Electrolysis of a sulfuric acid solution occurs with the liberation of oxygen and hydrogen at the anode and cathode, respectively. Calculate the theoretical decomposition potential of a solution of 1.0 N H_2SO_4.

The cathode reaction is $2\,H^+ + 2\,e \longrightarrow H_2$

$$E_c = E^\circ + \frac{.059}{n} \log [H^+]^2$$

$$E_c = 0.00 + \frac{.059}{2} \log (1)^2$$

$$E_c = 0.00$$

The anode reaction is $O_2 + 4\,H^+ + 4\,e \longleftarrow 2\,H_2O$

$$E_a = E^\circ + \frac{.059}{n} \log [H^+]^4$$

$$E_a = 1.23 + \frac{.059}{4} \log (1)^4$$

$$E_a = 1.23$$

The theoretical decomposition potential is the difference between 0.00 and 1.23, or 1.23 volts.

During an electrolysis, the concentrations of the materials which react at the electrodes are continuously changing. In Example 1, the zinc ion concentration is one molar at the beginning of the electrolysis, but it becomes less and less as the deposition of zinc metal proceeds. Since the decomposition potential calculations involve the concentrations of the reacting components, the contribution of each electrode to the decomposition potential changes during the deposition. Accordingly, the answers derived in the two examples are valid only at the beginning of the depositions, at which times the electrolyte concentrations are as indicated.

In practice the theoretical decomposition potential must not only be equaled in order for current to flow, but it must be exceeded by an amount known as the *overvoltage.* Each of the two electrode reactions contributes something to the overvoltage. The magnitude of the overvoltage for any particular electrode process is influenced quite empirically by a number of factors, including electrode materials and physical form thereof, current density (amount of current flow per unit area of electrode surface), nature of electrode surface and temperature. The overvoltage is usually much greater for electrode reactions in which a gas is liberated than for one in which a metal is deposited, typically being several tenths of a volt for the former and less than one-tenth of a volt for the latter. Mathematically, the practical decomposition potential may be expressed in the equation

$$E_{dec.} = (E_c - E_a) + \omega,$$

in which ω is the total overvoltage, including that at both electrodes. The signs of the $(E_c - E_a)$ term and the ω term must both be the same. When the applied potential is less than this value, essentially no current flows through the solution. Any increase in applied potential above this value causes increasing current to flow through the solution. The over-all applied potential, then, is related to the decomposition potential and the current flow in accordance with the equation

$$E_{applied} = E_{dec.} + IR$$

or $$E_{applied} = (E_c - E_a) + \omega + IR$$

in which I is the current flow and R is the electrical resistance of the solution between the electrodes. Again, the signs of three terms, $(E_c - E_a)$, ω and IR, must all be the same; each of the three "uses up" a part of the over-all applied potential. As already noted, the decomposition potential varies as ion concentrations are diminished during an electrolysis. It should be noted further that the resistance quantity, R, increases as ions are removed from the solution. Therefore, the right-hand quantities in the immediately preceding equation vary during the electrodeposition process, so application of a constant potential between the two electrodes does not result in a constant current flow through the solution.

Selective Electrode Reactions. Consider now a solution containing more than one type of ion which may be reduced at the cathode. Actually, every aqueous ionic solution falls into this category, since every such solution contains hydrogen ions from the solvent in addition to cations of the solute. Unless it be by pure coincidence, the decomposition potentials involving each type of cation differ one from the other. Therefore, it should be possible to separate one type of cation from the other by application of an external voltage source of magnitude sufficient to deposit one but insufficient to deposit the other. The completeness of such a separation depends upon a number of factors, chief among which is the difference in the decomposition potentials involving the two types of cation.

In the case of a solution containing, for example, cupric and hydrogen ions, separation may be accomplished even if both are reduced at the cathode, since the reduction products are solid and gaseous, respectively. However, the potentials involved are much more critical when the test solution contains two types of cation, both of which are reducible to free metal.

Now let us consider a solution which is one molar in each of the solutes, zinc sulfate, sulfuric acid and cupric sulfate, and let us try to predict the possibility of a quantitative separation of the copper from the zinc by electrodeposition. First, calculate the decomposition potentials for each of the three possible decompositions as done in Examples 1 and 2. It must be recognized in this instance that the anode process is one of liberating oxygen no matter what the cathode process may be.

For 1.0 M zinc sulfate:

at the cathode, $Zn^{++} + 2 e \longrightarrow Zn$, and E_c is -0.76

at the anode, $O_2 + 4 H^+ + 4 e \longleftarrow 2 H_2O$, and E_a is $+1.25$

(note that the H^+ ion concentration is 2 molar in this solution)

so the decomposition potential is 2.01 volts.

For 1.0 M sulfuric acid:

at the cathode, $2 H^+ + 2 e \longrightarrow H_2$, and E_c is $+0.02$

at the anode, $O_2 + 4 H^+ + 4 e \longleftarrow 2 H_2O$, and E_a is $+1.25$

so the decomposition potential is 1.23 volts

For 1.0 M cupric sulfate:

at the cathode, $Cu^{++} + 2 e \longrightarrow Cu$, and E_c is $+0.34$

at the anode, $O_2 + 4 H^+ + 4 e \longleftarrow 2 H_2O$, and E_a is $+1.25$

so the decomposition potential is 0.91 volts.

Next, consider the overvoltage factor. No meaningful calculations may be made because of the several empirical factors involved. Therefore, the true experimental decomposition potentials can be determined only by experiment. However, the total overvoltage would probably be about 0.4 volt for each of the three since at least one gas deposition is involved in each of the three. Thus, the experimental decomposition potentials would be approximately as follows:

for zinc sulfate, 2.4

for sulfuric acid, 1.6

for cupric sulfate, 1.3

Therefore, it should be possible to deposit copper selectively from zinc by application of a voltage greater than 1.3 and less than 2.4. No particular harm is done if the applied voltage exceeds the 1.6 value, since any hydrogen gas codeposited with copper would bubble off and escape into the atmosphere. In practice an applied potential of two volts would seem reasonable.

Next, let us consider the degree of completeness with which copper may be separated from zinc by this procedure. To do this we must remember that the decomposition potential involving the copper deposition increases as the deposition proceeds. So we are interested in determining whether or not the copper ion concentration remaining in solution may be reduced to a negligible quantity by application of a potential less than 2.4 and not merely in whether we can start the deposition of copper. There are several methods of carrying out this calculation, but one of the simplest and most satisfactory is as follows: Ascertain how low the cupric ion concentration must be in order for it to be negligible by considering the accuracy required and the experimental method to be used for weighing the deposit. For example, an ordinary analytical balance provides weighings to within 0.1 milligram, so a cupric ion concentration of less than 0.1 milligram would be negligible. Assuming a solution volume of 100 ml., this limiting concentration value would be about 1.6×10^{-5} molar. Thus, the separation of copper from zinc can readily be effected quantitatively if the decomposition potential of copper sulfate is still below that of one molar zinc sulfate when the cupric ion concentration is 1.6×10^{-5} molar. This decomposition potential may be found as before, and it turns out to be 1.06 volts. (Note in this calculation that the E_a is approximately constant during the deposition of copper.) Considering again an overvoltage of about 0.4 volt, it is evident that the decomposition potential of 1.6×10^{-5} molar cupric sulfate is far below that of one molar zinc sulfate. *Therefore, electrodeposition provides a valid means for the quantitative separation of copper from zinc.*

Several more points of significance may be noted from this example. Even though the estimates of overvoltage may have been decidedly in error, the conclusion would have been the same because the decomposition potential of 10^{-5} molar cupric sulfate is still far below that of 1 molar zinc sulfate. Furthermore, if a microbalance were to be used and the cupric ion concentration would need to be reduced still further, say by an additional factor of ten, before it were to be negligible, the separation could still be accomplished satisfactorily. Finally, and perhaps of most significance, although the extent of separation possible is determined by the difference in decomposition potentials of the deposited substance when a negligible amount is left in solution and of the substance remaining in solution, a comparison of the two initial theoretical decomposition potentials provides a good guide in predicting the possibility of quantitative separation. The initial difference between 0.91 volt for 1 molar cupric sulfate and 2.01 volt for 1 molar zinc sulfate was found in the above calculations to be far more than needed to permit separation. As a general rule, a difference of 0.20 volts suffices for separation of one bivalent cation from another, while a difference of 0.35 volt is adequate if one or both are univalent. It must be recognized, however, that the other factors such as overvoltage become increasingly significant as the difference in decomposition potentials becomes smaller.

The analyst must also give heed to the physical form of the deposit. Some deposits are very brittle and others do not adhere tightly to the electrode surface but tend rather to crumble and fall off. It is obviously impossible to weigh the latter type readily. The physical form of a deposit is influenced by many factors, including rate of deposition, whether or not a gas such as hydrogen is liberated simultaneously, and the foreign ion content of the solution. Some of these factors are not fully understood and so are not predictable even though their influences are very real. Therefore, in quantitative work, either proven or provable procedures must be employed to insure a suitable deposit.

EXPERIMENTAL APPARATUS AND METHODS

There are many experimental methods by which electrodeposition reactions may be brought about. The two which are the most basic and also the most widely used are the limited cathode potential method and the constant applied potential method.

Limited Cathode Potential Method. It has already been seen that an ion will deposit at an electrode only if the potential of that electrode exceeds the decomposition potential of that ion. When two or more types of reactable ion are present in a solution, each will deposit only when its characteristic deposition potential is exceeded by the potential at the electrode. It has also been seen that the decomposition potential of any species of ion is influenced by its concentration, so the required potential changes as ions are continuously removed from the solution by the electrode reaction. Therefore, if it is desired to deposit selectively one type of ion at the cathode, the cathode potential must be adequate to overcome the decomposition potential of that ion, until a quantitatively negligible amount of that ion is left in solution, without exceeding the starting decomposition potential of the other type of ion. This value of the cathode potential is designated the limiting cathode potential.

In Figure 63 is diagramed the apparatus necessary for limited cathode potential depositions. The auxiliary reference electrode, RE, may be any standard reference electrode (as discussed in Chapter 20). Resistor R serves to select that portion of the voltage from battery B which is applied between the two electrodes, A and C. The vacuum-tube voltmeter serves to provide direct indication of the cathode potential with respect to the reference electrode. The cathode potential is adjusted by adjustment of R, and the cathode potential must be kept from exceeding the limiting value throughout the electrolysis. It is usually necessary to determine the limiting cathode potential by empirical experiment, although approximations may be obtained by calculation of the appropriate deposition potentials with the aid of the Nernst equation.

It must be remembered that the over-all applied potential is related to the cathode potential by the equation

$$E_{applied} = (E_c - E_a) + \omega + IR$$

The cathode potential would vary during the electrolysis unless the applied

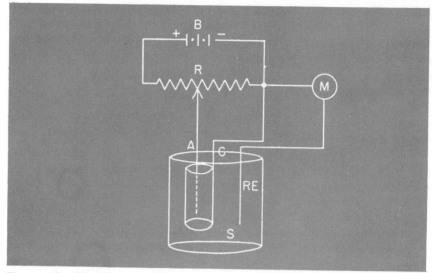

FIGURE 63.   Electrical circuit for electrodeposition by limited cathode potential method. *B*, battery; *R*, adjustable resistor; *M*, vacuum tube voltmeter; *S*, sample solution; *A*, anode; *C*, cathode; *RE*, reference electrode.

potential were frequently, or even continually, readjusted during the process. In practice, continual readjustment is essential if the cathode potential is to be kept even reasonably constant. Several devices have been developed whereby the continual readjustment of $E_{applied}$ needed to keep E_c from exceeding its limiting value is accomplished automatically. Nevertheless, simple manually operated apparatus as diagramed can serve very well even in refined analytical work.

The limited cathode potential method permits separations by electrodeposition processes right up to the theoretically limiting closeness factors listed on page 430. When deposition potentials of two substances differ to much larger extents, and particularly when a gas such as hydrogen is deposited between the two types of metal ion which are to be separated, the limited cathode potential method is not required. Instead, the simpler method of constant applied potential may be used satisfactorily.

Constant Applied Potential Method. The apparatus for the constant applied potential method is identical to that of Figure 63, except for the omission of the components needed to measure the cathode potential, M and RE, and addition of a simple voltmeter between A and C to measure the voltage applied between the anode and the cathode. In this method, the applied potential is initially raised to a value definitely great enough to overcome the decomposition potential of the desired component until the amount left in solution is negligible. When that component is completely deposited, the I term in the preceding equation either tends to drop near to zero, or else it is maintained by the deposition of a gas such as hydrogen at the cathode. In the former case, the actual cathode potential increases markedly, but it must be assumed that it will still not exceed the potential required to start deposition of an unwanted component. In the latter case, the evolution of hydrogen from water serves, in effect, as a buffer to prevent the cathode potential from rising too high.

The name "constant applied potential method" may be a bit misleading. Actually, the applied potential is merely set at some value and left there, with no special precautions being taken to insure absolute constancy.

This simple method is adequate when the decomposition potentials of the substances to be separated are far removed from each other and, especially, when hydrogen deposits from water at intermediate potentials. In the latter situation, the applied potential may be adjusted initially until a moderate amount of hydrogen gas is evolved at the cathode along with the desired metal. Then, as the deposition of metal proceeds at a decreasing rate, the rate of hydrogen evolution may increase, but the second type of metal ion remains safely in solution. The actual applied potential is not very critical in experiments of this type.

The constant applied potential method is probably the most widely used in analytical electrodeposition experiments. However, the somewhat more complex limited cathode potential method permits closer and sharper separations.

DETERMINATION OF COPPER

In this determination copper is plated out from an acid solution in the absence of any other metals which can be plated out ahead of hydrogen. Thus, the constant applied potential method may be used. Separate procedures will now be given for determinations of copper starting with a cupric solution and starting with a brass sample.

Laboratory Experiment 39

DETERMINATION OF COPPER IN A SOLUTION BY ELECTRODEPOSITION

Reagents

Acetone
Ammonium hydroxide, stock solution
Nitric acid, stock solution
Nitric acid, 1 volume stock solution diluted with 1 volume water

Sulfuric acid, stock solution
(One or more pairs of platinum gauze electrodes and an electro-deposition apparatus are also needed.)

Procedure

Prepare platinum gauze electrodes by rinsing in nitric acid (stock solution) for one minute, in nitric acid (1:1 dilution) for fifteen minutes, in tap water several times and finally in acetone. Dry the cathode for five minutes at 110° C., cool and weigh accurately. Place the electrodes in the electrodeposition apparatus, but do not connect the voltage source yet. By means of a pipet, transfer an aliquot of the unknown solution into a tall-form 200 ml. beaker. Add about 1.5 ml. nitric acid (stock solution) and 2 or 3 ml. sulfuric acid (stock solution), and dilute to 100 ml. Mount the beaker in the electrodeposition apparatus, cover with the two halves of a broken watch glass, and start the stirring motor. Connect the voltage source and electrolyze at 1.5 to 2.0 amperes for thirty to forty minutes or until the solution becomes colorless. Reduce the current flow to 0.5 ampere, and test for Cu^{++} ion by withdrawing 1 ml. of the solution and adding 1 ml. ammonium hydroxide (stock solution)—a blue color due to $Cu(NH_3)_4^{++}$ ion indicates the presence of copper. Electrolyze until a negative test for copper is obtained. Without stopping the flow of current, lower the beaker gradually while a stream of water from the wash bottle is directed upon the electrodes. When the beaker is completely below the electrodes, rinse them further, catching the rinsings in the beaker, and then turn off the voltage source. Remove the cathode, rinse in water, then in acetone, and dry in an oven at 110° C. for five minutes. Cool and weigh. Calculate the weight of Cu in the entire sample solution.

Laboratory Experiment 40

DETERMINATION OF COPPER IN BRASS BY ELECTRODEPOSITION

(This experiment is a combination of parts of Experiment 8 and Experiment 39.)

Reagents

As listed for tin and lead precipitations in Experiment 8 and for copper deposition in Experiment 39.

Procedure

Follow the procedure for the tin and lead precipitation in Experiment 8. Evaporate the filtrate and washings from the lead precipitation to about 100 ml., if the volume is greater than that, in a tall-form beaker. Add 1.5 ml. nitric acid (stock solution). Prepare platinum gauze electrodes, mount the electrodes and the beaker in the electrodeposition apparatus, and proceed through the remainder of the experiment, all as in Experiment 39. Calculate the percentage Cu in the sample.

REVIEW QUESTIONS

1. Define or characterize the terms decomposition potential and overvoltage.
2. Compare the limited cathode potential method of electrodeposition with the constant applied potential method on the bases of apparatus and sharpness of separations.

SUGGESTIONS FOR ADDITIONAL READING

Items 3, 4, 16, 18, 19 and 29, Appendix 7.

Chapter 20

Electrometric Titrations, Polarography and Coulometry

IN ADDITION to the electrodeposition methods described in the preceding chapter, there are four distinct groups of electrical methods of analysis, with several varied types of procedure within each of the groups. First, the concentration of any one of a number of substances in solution may be measured by measurement of the potential existing between two properly chosen electrodes inserted in the solution. These methods are designated *potentiometric methods* and are most widely used in measuring concentration changes during titrations. Second, *conductometric methods* are those in which the over-all ionic content of a test solution is determined by measurement of the electrical conductance (or resistance) between two electrodes inserted in the test solution. Conductometric methods are also most useful analytically in measuring changes in ionic content during titrations. Third, *polarographic methods* are those in which information useful in analysis is obtained by measurement of the magnitude of current passing through a solution as a function of the potential applied between two properly chosen electrodes immersed in the solution. Fourth, passage of an electric current through a solution may cause an oxidation-reduction reaction to proceed, either directly or by generating a needed reagent, and the quantity of reactable substance present in the original solution may be determined by measurement of the quantity of electricity required to cause it to react completely. These methods are designated *coulometric methods*, since the coulomb is the fundamental unit of quantity of electricity. It may be noted that all four of these groups of methods are based in large part upon the measurement of one or more of the fundamental electrical units.

POTENTIOMETRIC METHODS

The general principles of the potentiometric measurement of ion concentrations and concentration ratios were discussed in Chapter 14, to which the student is referred for review. It remains, therefore, to discuss in the present chapter the practical apparatus and the useful applicability of these methods. Each potentiometric determination involves the measurement of the potential difference between two electrodes, one designated the indicating electrode and the other the reference electrode, both of which are in contact with the test solution. Thus, the potentiometric apparatus need consist merely of three things: a reference electrode, an indicating electrode, a potential measuring meter.

Reference Electrode. The reference electrode is an electrode whose potential is independent of the concentration of the substance to be determined. For example, in a pH measurement or in a neutralization titration, the reference electrode potential must be independent of hydrogen ion concentration. Similarly, in an oxidation-reduction titration of ferrous iron with dichromate, the reference electrode potential must be independent of the ratio of ferric ion concentration to ferrous ion concentration.

The most commonly used reference electrode is the calomel electrode. This electrode is composed of metallic mercury and solid mercurous chloride in contact with, and in equilibrium with, a solution of potassium chloride. Some form of electrical contact must be provided between the solution in the electrode and the test solution. The chemical and electrochemical equilibria within the electrode may be represented by two chemical equations:

$$Hg_2^{++} + 2\,e \rightleftharpoons 2\,Hg$$
$$Hg_2^{++} + 2\,Cl^- \rightleftharpoons Hg_2Cl_2$$

These chemical equations may be represented mathematically as follows:

$$E = E° + \frac{.059}{2} \log [Hg_2^{++}]$$

$$K_{sp} = [Hg_2^{++}][Cl^-]^2$$

The two mathematical equations may be combined into one by solving the second for the $[Hg_2^{++}]$ value and substituting into the first.

$$[Hg_2^{++}] = \frac{K_{sp}}{[Cl^-]^2}$$

$$E = E° + \frac{.059}{2} \log \frac{K_{sp}}{[Cl^-]^2}$$

This latter equation may be simplified somewhat:

$$E = E° + \frac{.059}{2} \log K_{sp} + \frac{.059}{2} \log \frac{1}{[Cl^-]^2}$$

$$E = E^1 - .059 \log [Cl^-]$$

$$\text{(in which} \quad E^1 = E° + \frac{.059}{2} \log K_{sp})$$

This is an equation for the potential of the calomel electrode. This potential is thus shown to be dependent upon chloride ion concentration within the electrode but to be independent of all other ionic concentrations. The chloride ion concentration is determined almost entirely by the amount of potassium chloride inserted in the electrode, and calomel electrodes are designated saturated, normal and tenth-normal, depending upon this concentration. The corresponding potentials are:

saturated calomel, 0.246
normal calomel, 0.280
tenth-normal calomel, 0.338

This type of reference electrode should be suitable in all measurements and titrations except those in which the chloride ion is a variable quantity, and even then it is useful if the solution within the electrode is kept from mixing with the test solution. Thus, the calomel reference electrode may be used in pH measurement, in neutralization titrations, in oxidation-reduction titrations, in complex formation reactions and in precipitation titrations.

The second most popular type of reference electrode is the silver-silver chloride electrode. This type is analogous to the calomel, with silver and silver chloride replacing the mercury and mercurous chloride, respectively.

Indicating Electrode. The indicating electrode must be an electrode whose potential is dependent upon the concentration of the substance being determined. In all pH measurements and neutralization titrations, the potential of the indicating electrode must be a function of the hydrogen ion concentration. There are several distinctly different types of pH indicating electrodes, but the glass electrode is most widely used. The glass electrode consists of a thin glass bulb, inside of which is a buffer solution or a tenth-normal solution of hydrochloric acid and a silver wire coated with a thin layer of silver chloride. An electrical contact is made to the silver wire for connection to the potential measuring meter, and the bulb is immersed in the test solution. The glass membrane serves to establish a potential, the magnitude of which is determined by the relative pH values on the two sides of the membrane. The pH inside is fixed. The potential may be designated by the Nernst equation,

$$E = E° + 0.059 \log [H^+]$$

The $E°$ value is approximately $+0.07$. However, it may vary somewhat from this value from one glass electrode to another. Therefore, each glass electrode should be calibrated empirically by measurement of the pH of a standard buffer solution.

Another pH indicating electrode is the quinhydrone electrode. Quinhydrone consists of an equimolar mixed crystal formation of quinone, $C_6H_4O_2$, and hydroquinone, $C_6H_4O_2H_2$. The two substances are related to each other by means of a half-reaction equation

$$C_6H_4O_2 + 2 H^+ + 2 e \rightleftharpoons C_6H_4O_2H_2$$

for which the $E°$ value was listed in Table 14 (p. 314) as $+0.70$ volts. The Nernst equation for this system is

$$E = 0.70 + \frac{.059}{2} \log \frac{[C_6H_4O_2][H^+]^2}{[C_6H_4O_2H_2]}$$

The oxidized and reduced forms are present in equal concentrations in a solution of quinhydrone, so

$$E = 0.70 + \frac{.059}{2} \log [H^+]^2$$

or
$$E = 0.70 - .059 \times pH$$

Quinhydrone is only slightly soluble in water, so the electrode system is established experimentally by placing a pinch of solid quinhydrone into the solution of which the pH is to be measured and by inserting a platinum wire to make contact with the solution. The quinhydrone electrode takes up to thirty seconds to establish a state of equilibrium when inserted into a solution or when the pH is changed and, unlike the glass electrode system, the test solution is contaminated in the process of measurement.

The indicating electrode for oxidation-reduction titrations is almost always a platinum wire dipping into the solution. Both oxidized and reduced forms of reacting substances in nearly all oxidation-reduction titrations are in solution, so electrical contact may be made with all forms by the platinum wire dipping into the solution. Thus, as described in Chapter 14, the oxidized and reduced forms will come to equilibrium with each other at the electrode. Taking the iron by dichromate titration as an example, the electrode reaction, and thus the electrode potential, may be expressed by either one of two equivalent equations,

$$Fe^{+++} + e \rightleftharpoons Fe^{++}$$

for which

$$E = 0.77 + .059 \log \frac{[Fe^{+++}]}{[Fe^{++}]}$$

and
$$Cr_2O_7^= + 14\,H^+ + 6\,e \rightleftharpoons 2\,Cr^{+++} + 7\,H_2O,$$

for which

$$E = 1.30 + \frac{.059}{6} \log \frac{[Cr_2O_7^=][H^+]^{14}}{[Cr^{+++}]^2}$$

Thus, the ratio of $[Fe^{+++}]/[Fe^{++}]$ and/or the ratio of $\frac{[Cr_2O_7^=][H^+]^{14}}{[Cr^{+++}]^2}$ is indicated by the potential of this electrode.

The indicating electrode in a volumetric precipitation titration must be selected specially for each pair of reactants. Since titrations with a standard solution of silver nitrate are very common in volumetric precipitation work, an indicating electrode for these titrations is of special significance. This electrode may consist simply of a silver wire dipping into the test solution. The chemical equation for the electrode reaction is

$$Ag^+ + e \rightleftharpoons Ag$$

for which the corresponding Nernst equation is

$$E = 0.81 + .059 \log [Ag^+]$$

The silver electrode may also serve as an indicating electrode for titrations of chloride, or of any other anion which reacts quantitatively with silver nitrate.

It has been shown, therefore, that different indicating electrodes are available so that almost any titration may be carried out potentiometrically. General indicating electrodes are available for neutralization and for oxidation-reduction titrations, and more specific indicators are available for many volumetric precipitation titrations. In essence, the potentiometric method provides a nearly universal type of indicator action, and many titrations for which conventional color indicators are unavailable or are inapplicable may be carried out potentiometrically.

Potential Measuring Meter.   Every one of the indicating electrode reactions causes the liberation or using up of some of the ions whose concentration is to be measured if the electrode reaction is permitted to proceed very far in either direction. To illustrate this point, consider the titration of ferrous ion with dichromate with a platinum wire indicating electrode. This electrode reaction may be expressed as

$$Fe^{+++} + e \rightleftharpoons Fe^{++}$$

If, for example, the process of measurement caused this reaction to proceed appreciably to the left, ferrous ions would be changed to ferric ions by the measuring process. Presumably, reaction with dichromate ions should be the only way ferrous ions could be changed to ferric ions in this titration. Furthermore, local concentration changes near the surface of the indicator electrode would lead to erroneous potential readings. To prevent these errors, the measurement must be made without drawing or passing an appreciable amount of current through the system. This precludes the use of simple magnetic coil dial-face voltmeters (the most familiar type being the so-called d'Arsonval meter). Several laboratory type instruments are available, however, for such measurements. The most common type for general use is the vacuum tube voltmeter. The operation of this type of voltmeter need not be discussed here; suffice it to say that it is an instrument for measuring voltages without causing or permitting a significant amount of current to flow through the system being measured. The instrument used must be capable of measuring voltages of the range of magnitude up to about 1.5 volts.

This potential measuring meter may be calibrated directly in voltage units, as it frequently is. Since many potential measurements are made for pH determinations, it is common practice to calibrate some of the meters directly in terms of pH rather than in terms of voltages from which pH numbers must be calculated.

Some devices for potentiometric titrations employ an electron-ray indicator tube ("magic-eye" tube) in place of the final indicating meter. The instrument is designed so that the "eye" will be open (or closed) above a certain potential and closed (or open) below that potential. The critical potential is adjustable. In use, the operator sets the adjustment to the potential which will exist between his indicating and reference electrodes at the equivalence point; this value must be known in advance, or measured roughly in a trial titration. The operator merely titrates, then, until the eye goes from open to closed, or vice versa, at which point he stops the titration and reads his buret. There are also instruments commercially available whereby the buret is automatically turned off when the potential developed between the two electrodes immersed in the solution arrives at its equivalence point value.

Applications. Single measurements of ion concentration or of ratio of ion concentrations in solutions may be made. Other than in pH measurement, however, most practical applications of the potentiometric method involve taking measurements at intervals during a titration. A plot of the data in terms of potential vs. ml. added reagent yields directly a titration curve on which the end point may be located. It is not necessary in the titrations to standardize the electrodes or even to know, for example, what the potential of the electrode may be, because it is the change in measured potential during the titration that is of significance in locating the end point. It is likewise unnecessary to take readings throughout the titration, as the potential changes abruptly around the end point so that only the point of maximum rate of change of potential is needed. As already emphasized, the potentiometric method may be used in titrations of any of the three classes, neutralization, oxidation-reduction and volumetric precipitation.

The potentiometric method is particularly useful in measurements of colored solutions for which color indicators are not suitable. It is also useful for many titrations for which no suitable color indicators have been developed. It may also be used in titrations in nonaqueous solvents. The accuracy which may be achieved in potentiometric titrations is fully as good as with conventional color indicators and, under certain conditions, may be even better.

Any titration for which a procedure has been given in preceding chapters may be carried out potentiometrically merely by inserting reference and indicating electrodes of the types just described and measuring the potential difference between them at successive points throughout the titration with a commercial vacuum tube voltmeter with range up to about 1.5 volts. The titration data may be plotted and the end point observed on the graph.

The two laboratory procedures which follow are designed to provide direct experimental measurement of acid-base and of oxidation-reduction titration curves for comparison to the curves calculated in Chapters 11 and 14. In each case the reference electrode consists of the same type of electrode used as the indicating electrode but in a separate solution of constant composition. The procedures are written specifically for use with the Heathkit vacuum tube voltmeter, which is commercially available in kit form for less than thirty dollars. Any other vacuum tube voltmeter with a full scale deflection of 0 to 1.5 volts or less may be used. If a "pH meter" is used as the voltmeter, readings should be taken directly in volts, not in pH units, for the maximum instructional value. The same experimental procedures may be used for titrations of unknown samples if desired.

Laboratory Experiment 41

POTENTIOMETRIC MEASUREMENT OF ACID-BASE TITRATION CURVES

Reagents

Hydrochloric acid, the solution prepared and standardized in Experiment 10. (If none remains, prepare 250 ml. of an approximately comparable solution.)

Sodium hydroxide, the solution prepared and standardized in Experiment 10. (If none remains, prepare 250 ml. of an approximately comparable solution.)

Acetic acid, approximately 0.2 N solution, prepared by diluting 5.6 ml. stock solution to 1/2 liter with water

Ammonium hydroxide, approximately 0.2 N solution, prepared by diluting 6.8 ml. stock solution to 1/2 liter with water

Buffer solution, pH 7

Quinhydrone

Special Apparatus

Vacuum tube voltmeter, such as Heathkit model V-7A, set to read 0 to 1.5 volts D.C.

Salt bridge, prepared in a U-shaped glass tube, consisting of KCl in agar (always keep immersed in water or in KCl solution when not in use)

Platinum wire, two pieces each about 4 inches long

Procedure

Pipet 25 ml. of the hydrochloric acid solution into a 150 ml. flask or beaker, add about 25 ml. of water and a small pinch of quinhydrone. Turn on the vacuum tube voltmeter, let warm up for a few minutes, and adjust the zero control so the meter reads zero. Put about 10 ml. of the pH 7 buffer solution in a 50 ml. beaker, add a small pinch of quinhydrone, insert a platinum wire into this solution, and connect to the negative ("common") lead to the voltmeter. Place the salt bridge so that one arm dips into each beaker. Insert another platinum wire into the test solution and connect to the positive ("D.C.") lead to the voltmeter. Set the left meter switch to read "d.c.+" or "d.c.−", whichever causes the meter to read on-scale (the sign of this switch position is then that of the platinum wire in the test solution relative to that in the buffer solution). Read the voltage. Titrate with sodium hydroxide solution in increments of 2 or 3 ml. each except when within about 2 ml. of the equivalence point, during which range the increments should be much smaller. After each increment of titrant, swirl the titration vessel gently, wait about 30 seconds and read the voltage. Include several readings far beyond the equivalence point. Plot the data in terms of voltage of test electrode vs. volume of added titrant. Every 0.059 volts theoretically corresponds to one pH unit difference between the two electrodes, one of which is in the pH 7 buffer, so relabel the y-axis in pH units. Repeat as necessary to get a smooth titration curve.

Repeat the experiment with titrations of hydrochloric acid by ammonium hydroxide, acetic acid by sodium hydroxide and acetic acid by ammonium hydroxide. The same buffer solution may be used in all titrations. Prepare graphs of the data from all titrations. Briefly explain the significance of the results in relation to the discussion of Chapter 11.

Laboratory Experiment 42

POTENTIOMETRIC MEASUREMENT OF OXIDATION-REDUCTION TITRATION CURVES

Reagents

Potassium dichromate, standard solution prepared in Experiment 22
Ferrous ammonium sulfate, solution prepared by dissolving 10 grams
   of $Fe(NH_4)_2(SO_4)_2 \cdot 2 H_2O$ in about 250 ml. of water
Hydrochloric acid, stock solution
Phosphoric acid, stock solution

Special Apparatus

Vacuum tube voltmeter, such as Heathkit model V-7A, set to read
   0. to 1.5 volts D.C.

Salt bridge, prepared in a U-shaped glass tube, consisting of KCl in agar (always keep immersed in water or in KCl solution when not in use)

Platinum wire, two pieces each about 4 inches long

Procedure

Pipet 25 ml. of the ferrous iron solution into a 150 ml. flask or beaker. Add about 25 ml. water, 5 ml. hydrochloric acid and 5 ml. phosphoric acid. Turn on the vacuum tube voltmeter, let warm up for a few minutes, and adjust the zero control on the meter so the meter reads zero. Put about 10 ml. of a solution consisting of 2 parts of the ferrous iron solution, 1 part of the dichromate solution and a few drops of hydrochloric acid in a 50 ml. beaker; insert a platinum wire into this reference solution and connect to the negative ("common") lead to the voltmeter. Place the salt bridge so that one arm dips into each beaker. Insert the other platinum wire into the test solution and connect to the positive ("D.C.") lead to the voltmeter. Set the left meter switch to read "d.c.+" or "d.c.−", whichever causes the meter to read on-scale (the sign of this switch position is then the sign of the platinum wire in the test solution relative to that in the reference solution). Read the voltage. Titrate with potassium dichromate in increments of 2 or 3 ml. each except when within about 2 ml. of the equivalence point, during which range the increments should be much smaller. After each increment of titrant, swirl the vessel gently and record the voltage. Include several readings far beyond the equivalence point. Plot the data in terms of voltage of outside electrode vs. volume of added titrant. Repeat the titration as necessary to get a smooth titration curve.

Repeat the experiment, leaving out in turn, the hydrochloric acid, the phosphoric acid, and both the hydrochloric and phosphoric acids. Prepare graphs of the data from all titrations, and briefly explain the significance of the results.

CONDUCTOMETRIC METHODS

The electrical resistance between two electrodes immersed in a solution is dependent upon several factors: size of electrodes, distance between electrodes, temperature, types of ion present, concentration of each type of ion present. If the first three factors are held constant, a measurement of the electrical resistance provides a measure of the ionic content of the solution. The electrical conductance is defined as the reciprocal of the electrical resistance, and analytical methods based upon measurement of this quantity are designated conductometric methods.

Conductometric methods differ in a very significant respect from all of the other indicator types described thus far. All of the other indicators considered in prior sections of this book, except the turbidimetric type, have provided a measurement based upon the concentration of some particular ion or of the concentration ratio of specific types of ion. In other words, the indicator has been selective for a certain ion or ions. In conductometric methods, however, the measured quantity is influenced by any and all types of ion present. Thus, an over-all property of the test solution is measured. The significance of this factor will become apparent when types of application are considered.

Apparatus. The special apparatus required for conductometric methods of analysis usually consists merely of a titration beaker or flask, in which are inserted two platinum electrodes, and some type of A.C. ohmmeter. It will be remembered that electrode reactions were caused to take place in electrodeposition experiments; a unidirectional (D.C.) potential source is required so that the electrode reactions may proceed. In conductance work, however, the conductance is to be measured, and no electrode reactions are to be permitted. So the electrodes should be of noble metal that will not react in any way with the test solution, and the ohmmeter must be of an A.C. type rather than of a D.C. type. The platinum electrodes are often "platinized," that is, coated with a thin layer of porous, spongy, black platinum before use, although bright platinum is adequate for most analytical purposes.

An apparatus which is simple and yet directly suitable for many purposes is shown in the complete circuit diagram of Figure 64. The A.C. ohmmeter consists merely of a small step-down voltage transformer, a resistance in series with the test solution cell and an A.C. vacuum tube voltmeter to read the voltage drop across the series resistance. The entire apparatus is made of readily available items and may be constructed for about five dollars, including the platinum wires but excluding the meter. The suggested meter is the same one used in Laboratory Experiments 41 and 42. Ohm's law may be applied to this circuit as follows:

$$(1) \qquad\qquad E_t = I(R_{1,2} + R_x)$$

in which E_t is the total applied voltage (6.3 volts), $R_{1,2}$ is the sum of R_1 and R_2, R_x is the cell resistance and I is the current flowing through the series circuit consisting of $R_{1,2}$ and R_x. Assuming that R_x is much greater than $R_{1,2}$, equation (1) may be simplified and rearranged

$$E_t = IR_x$$

$$(2) \qquad\qquad I = \frac{E_t}{R_x}$$

The voltage read on the meter, E_m, equals the voltage drop across $R_{1,2}$

$$(3) \qquad\qquad E_m = IR_{1,2}$$

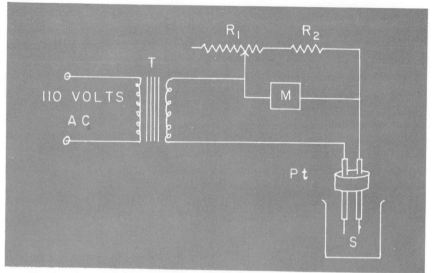

FIGURE 64. Simple, complete apparatus for conductance measurements. *T*, 110 to 6.3 volt "filament" transformer; *M*, 0 to 1.5 volt A.C. vacuum tube voltmeter (such as Heathkit); R_1, 0 to 1000 ohm potentiometer; R_2, 10 ohm 5 watt resistor; *Pt*, two platinum wire electrodes mounted and sealed in the ends of glass tubes; *S*, solution to be measured.

Substituting equation (2) into (3), and maintaining E_t and $R_{1,2}$ as constants

(4) $$E_m = \frac{E_t}{R_x} \times R_{1,2}$$

or

$$E_m = \frac{k}{R_x}$$

The conductance of the cell is the reciprocal of R_x, so

(5) $$E_m = k \times (\text{conductance})$$

Thus, the meter reading is directly proportional to the conductance of the cell, as long as R_x is much greater than $R_{1,2}$ and E_t, R_1 and R_2 are constant. If exact conductance values rather than relative ones are desired, or if any of these provisions are not fulfilled, calculation may be made from experimental data by means of equations (1) and (4) rather than (5). This simple, inexpensive apparatus is entirely adequate with equation (5) for conductometric titrations.

Conductance bridges are often used for refined measurements of electrical conductance, particularly if absolute rather than relative conductance values are desired. The basic diagram of a conductance bridge is shown in Figure 65. The voltage source, S, must be A.C. as already discussed; it may be a simple 60-cycle source of a few volts obtained from the 110-volt 60-cycle line receptacle with a transformer as used in Figure 64, or it may be a higher frequency A.C. source operating either mechanically or electrically. The detector, D, may be an A.C. current meter for visual indication, a headphone for audio indication, or an electronic device ending up, for example, with a "magic-eye" tube as the final indication. An analysis of this circuit reveals that the detector will exhibit zero response only when the following condition exists:

$$\frac{R_x}{R_1} = \frac{R_3}{R_2}, \quad \text{or} \quad R_x = \frac{R_1 R_3}{R_2}$$

or $\qquad$ conductance of test solution $= \dfrac{1}{R_x} = \dfrac{R_2}{R_1 R_3}$

In practice the apparatus is turned on with the test solution in place, and R_3 is adjusted until the detector indicates zero (or minimum) response. From known, fixed values of R_1 and R_2 and the observed value of R_3, the desired conductance value is calculated. Frequently, the resistance values of R_1 and R_2 are made equal, so the resistance of R_3 when properly adjusted is equal to that of R_x. It is possible, of course, to make any one or more of the resistors R_1, R_2 and R_3 variable, rather than just R_3 as described. Several refinements may be made in this bridge circuit for refined work, but even the simplest apparatus suffices for much work.

It must be emphasized that the conductance of any solution is a function of its temperature. In absolute conductance measurements it is necessary to regulate and control the temperature of the test solution very closely. As will be seen, however, titrations require measurements of changes in conductance during the titration. In titration, then, it is not necessary that the temperature be adjusted to any particular value nor even that the temperature

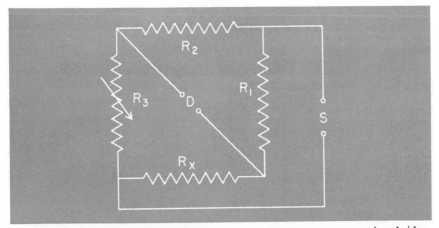

FIGURE 65. Basic electrical circuit for a conductance measuring bridge. R_x, resistance of test solution between electrodes in that solution; R_1, R_2, and R_3 standard resistances, R_3 being variable; S, A.C. voltage source; D, detector.

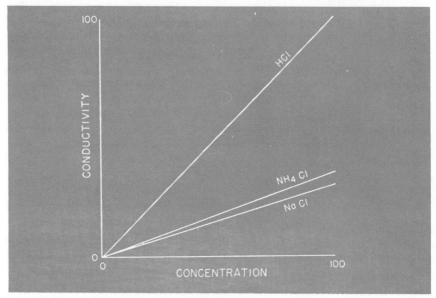

Figure 66.   Relationship between conductivity and concentration for three typical
electrolytes (both axes in arbitrary units).

be known, but merely that the temperature remain constant throughout the
titration. Thus, conductance titrations are often performed with no special
temperature precaution on the assumption that the room temperature will
not change appreciably during any one titration. Many titration reactions do
generate or consume some heat, and the measuring process liberates some
heat in the test solution, so in refined titration experiments some adequate
type of temperature control is advisable.

   Types of Application.   Conductance measurements are of analytical
usefulness primarily in neutralization titrations and secondarily in certain

Table 17. Relative Mobilities of Some Ions

H^+	350
Li^+	42
Na^+	51
NH_4^+	75
Ag^+	63
OH^-	193
Cl^-	76
NO_3^-	71
$C_2H_3O_2^-$	41

volumetric precipitation titrations. The reasons will become apparent from
consideration of a few examples with the aid of the data of Table 17. These

data represent a simplified portion of much more complete listings which are available in reference books of chemistry, but this table will suffice for present purposes. The ions with higher mobilities are more highly conducting than those with lower mobilities. For example, a given amount of hydrogen ion would contribute about seven times as much to the conductivity of a solution as would the same concentration of sodium ion. Similarly, chloride ions are slightly more conducting than are nitrate ions. Then, for a given type of ion, the conductance is directly proportional to its concentration, at least for a reasonable concentration range. The influences of types of ion and of concentration of ion are illustrated by the graphs of Figure 66. The over-all conductance of each solution is actually the sum of the conductance contributions of each type of ion present. Thus, the HCl solution conductivity represents a sum of the contribution of both hydrogen and chloride ions, and so forth. A solution containing two or more solutes will exhibit a conductance made up of the parts contributed by each and every type of ion present.

Consider a titration of hydrochloric acid by sodium hydroxide. Initially the conductance is determined by the highly mobile hydrogen ion and the chloride ions. At the end point the solution contains essentially sodium ions and the same chloride ions. In other words, the initial hydrogen ions have been replaced by sodium ions in going to the end point, so the conductance has decreased. Beyond the end point, excess sodium and hydroxide ions are being added, so the conductance rises again. The titration curve is as shown in Figure 67.

The intersection of the two straight line portions is the equivalence point. In practice it is not necessary to take data at or near the equivalence point as

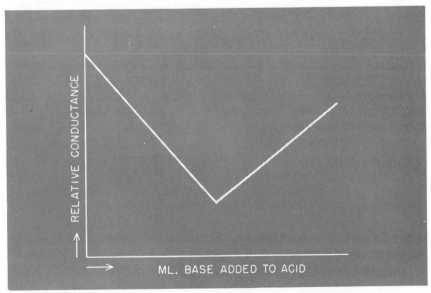

FIGURE 67. A typical conductometric titration graph.

this point may be determined graphically from the results of a few measurements before and a few after the equivalence point.

A titration of a weak acid would yield a rising titration curve before the equivalence point since the salt formed would be expected to be more highly conducting than the undissociated initial weak acid molecules. Unless the slopes of the rising portions of the curve before and after the equivalence point are the same, or nearly so, the end point can still be ascertained from the titration curve. Titration of an acid with a weak base results in a curve that is flat after the equivalence point, since this part of the titration consists merely of adding undissociated weak base molecules, which contribute little or nothing to the measured conductances. In fact, it is even possible to titrate a weak acid by a weak base conductometrically since the conductance rises up to the equivalence point due to the salt being formed and remains flat after the equivalence point. In brief, nearly any type of neutralization titration may be performed conductometrically.

Consider next a titration of silver nitrate by lithium chloride. The initial solution consists of silver nitrate, the end point solution consists of lithium nitrate (plus solid silver chloride), while the solution after the equivalence point contains lithium nitrate plus the excess lithium chloride added. Since lithium ion is slightly less mobile than silver ion, the conductance decreases slightly from the start to the equivalence point; then the conductance rises after the equivalence point. The end point is thus found by noting graphically the intersection of two straight lines. None of these ions is so highly mobile as are hydrogen and hydroxyl ions, so the conductance changes encountered in volumetric precipitation titrations are generally less than those encountered in many acid-base titrations. The accuracy of the results is correspondingly reduced.

As already noted, all ions present in a solution contribute to the conductivity of a solution. The effect of foreign ions is one of increasing the over-all conductance uniformly throughout the entire titration. If the foreign ion contribution is large, the analyst is confronted with the problem of measuring small changes in conductance in the presence of high conductances, an experimentally difficult thing to accomplish. Most otherwise feasible oxidation-reduction titrations necessitate the use of a strongly acid medium throughout. Since the hydrogen ions are so highly conducting, oxidation-reduction titrations are seldom performed by conductometric methods.

The accuracy of results obtained in conductance titrations is of the order of 1 % or so in typical instances. This is inferior to typical titrations by other methods, but the method is useful for many purposes, particularly in titrations for which other indicating methods are for one reason or another not available. Also, conductance titrations are very useful with small amounts of material. Even microgram quantities can often be titrated successfully.

Laboratory Experiment 43

CONDUCTOMETRIC TITRATIONS

Reagents

Acetic acid, approx. 0.1 N solution, prepared by diluting 3 ml. stock
solution to 500 ml.

Ammonium hydroxide, approx. 0.1 N solution, prepared by diluting
3.5 ml. stock solution to 500 ml.

Hydrochloric acid, approx. 0.1 N solution, prepared by diluting 4 ml.
stock solution to 500 ml.

Silver nitrate, approx. 0.1 N solution, prepared by dissolving 8.5
grams $AgNO_3$ in 500 ml. water

Sodium chloride, approx. 0.1 N solution, prepared by dissolving 2.9
grams NaCl in 500 ml. water

Sodium hydroxide, approx. 0.1 N solution, prepared by dissolving 2
grams NaOH in 500 ml. water

Special Apparatus

The conductance apparatus shown in Figure 64.

Procedure

Pipet 5 ml. of the hydrochloric acid solution into a 150 ml.
beaker. Add about 100 ml. water. Insert a pair of platinum wire
electrodes (short pieces of Pt wire protruding from the sealed ends
of glass tubes with the two tubes taped together and with connections
made from within the tubes). Turn on the apparatus and adjust
R_1 so the meter reads about one volt. Do not change R_1 again
during the titration. Titrate with 1 ml. portions (pipet or buret) of
the sodium hydroxide solution. After each increment of titrant,
swirl the beaker by hand and then read the meter. Continue until
four or five readings are taken beyond the end point. Plot the data
as meter reading (which is proportional to conductance) vs. volume
of titrant.

Repeat with titrations of hydrochloric acid by ammonium
hydroxide, hydrochloric acid plus acetic acid (2.5 ml. each) by
sodium hydroxide, acetic acid by sodium hydroxide, acetic acid by

ammonium hydroxide, sodium chloride by silver nitrate, and sodium chloride plus a few drops of nitric acid (stock solution) by silver nitrate. For each titration, make the initial adjustment of R_1 so the maximum reading during the titration will not exceed about one volt (use trial and error if necessary). Plot all titration curves and explain the significance and the usefulness of each.

POLAROGRAPHY

Principles.   Let us return to the subject of what happens when ions react at an electrode. Consider two electrodes immersed in a solution of cadmium sulfate, with a D.C. potential applied between the two electrodes. If the potential is not sufficiently.large to reduce cadmium ions, that portion of solution immediately surrounding the cathode contains the several cations and anions, each in the same concentration as the rest of the solution, Figure 68, *A*. If, however, the applied potential is suddenly made large enough to reduce cadmium ions, the cadmium ions immediately surrounding the cathode will have been deposited on the cathode, leaving a deficiency of such ions in the immediate vicinity, Figure 68, *B*. Now assume that ions from the bulk of the solution were unable to move in to replace those ions which have reacted at the electrode surface. The flow of current would cease, not because the cathode potential is insufficiently negative, but because there would be no more cadmium ions available for reduction. This phenomenon is one of *polarization*, which term may be defined as any change produced at an electrode (by electrolysis) which causes the redox potential to differ from the normal or reversible value in that particular solution. This type of polarization is designated *concentration polarization* since it results from a depletion of ions, that is, a lowering of ionic concentration around the electrode.

In practice, of course, some ions will move in from the bulk of the solution as the electrode begins to become polarized. A complete state of concentration polarization never exists. However, a partial state frequently does exist. Let r_1 represent the rate at which cadmium ions could react at the cathode if no concentration polarization existed, and let r_2 represent the rate at which cadmium ions from the bulk of the solution can move into the immediate vicinity of the cathode. If r_2 exceeds r_1, no concentration polarization occurs, whereas it does occur if r_1 exceeds r_2. In the latter case, ions cannot move in so readily as they could otherwise react at the electrode surface; so the over-all current flow is limited, not by r_1, but rather by r_2, and the electrode is partially polarized.

Now, let us generalize as to what conditions govern the rates r_1 and r_2. One of the significant factors is the area of cathode exposed to the solution. With a large exposed area, as in the case of a platinum gauze electrode, there is relatively more solution in the immediate vicinity of the cathode surface than is the case when the cathode has very small surface area. Thus, concentration polarization is relatively insignificant with cathodes of large surface area and much more significant with electrodes with only minute surface area exposed to the test solution. Other significant factors are those which govern how readily ions from the bulk of the solution can move into the vicinity of the cathode. There are two distinct mechanisms whereby this can occur: random diffusion of ions throughout the solution; electrostatic attraction of the negative cathode for the positive cadmium ions. The contributions of the two factors are designated *diffusion current* and *migration current,* respectively.

The mechanism of the diffusion current has been studied both theoretically and experimentally, and it has been found to be of tremendous practical value for the analyst. For a given type of electrode reaction (for example, the reduction of cadmium ions) and for a given experimental apparatus, the diffusion current, i_d, has been found proportional to the concentration, C,

$$i_d = kC$$

Thus, an experimental measurement of diffusion current is useful as the basis of a method of quantitative analysis.

The mechanism of the migration current has also been studied, both theoretically and experimentally. The migration current tends to maintain the electroneutrality of the solution. In Figure 68, *B,* the electroneutrality of the solution is upset by an excess of anions over cations near the electrode surface. This condition may be relieved both by anions moving away from this region and by cations moving into it. The effect, in the present example, is to cause an apparent increase in the diffusion current. If the metal ion were to be in the form of a complex anion, such as $MX_4^=$, the effect would be

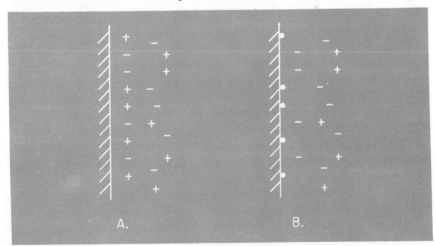

FIGURE 68. Diagram to illustrate the phenomenon of polarization. $+$. Cadmium ion; $-$. anion; $\cdot$. deposited cadmium atom; *A,* just prior to turning on source of potential on electrode; *B,* just after turning on source of potential on electrode.

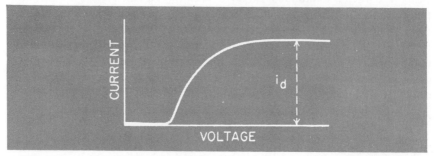

FIGURE 69.   An idealized plot of polarographic data; i_d is diffusion current.

an apparent decrease in the diffusion current. The whole effect of the migration current can be eliminated simply by adding an excess of some nonreducible salt. A hundredfold excess is frequently used. This "inert" salt, present in considerable excess, handles a proportionately large part of the migration current so the latter does not influence the desired diffusion of the ion being reduced at the electrode.

In summary, then, (1) concentration polarization develops most readily with a microelectrode, that is, an electode with small area of contact with the test solution, (2) the observed current flow is governed by the rate at which ions arrive at the electrode from the bulk of the solution when concentration polarization exists to an appreciable extent, and (3) the rate of arrival of ions in the electrode vicinity is governed by the concentration of substance in the bulk of the solution whenever an excess of foreign electrolyte is present to minimize the effect of the migration current. Therefore, the concentration in the solution may be determined by measurement of the observed current flow.

In the foregoing discussion, the cathode potential was assumed to be adequate to permit reduction of cadmium ions to free metal. If, however, the cathode potential is inadequate to accomplish this reaction, no current can flow through the solution. An idealized plot of current flow vs. applied potential, for a given solution of cadmium sulfate and with a microcathode, would be of the shape shown in Figure 69. The current i_d is the diffusion current which is useful for quantitative analysis. *Polarography* is that branch of electrochemistry which deals with current-voltage curves obtained with two electrodes, one of which is a microelectrode and one of which has a large area of contact with the test solution.

Apparatus.   The basic apparatus for polarography is really very simple (Fig. 70). It consists of a variable D.C. voltage source, a cell to hold the test solution and the two electrodes, and some means of measuring the current and the voltage. The potentials required are generally not greater than about two volts. The current flows are quite small, usually the order of a few microamperes (millionths of an ampere). The microelectrode often consists of a tiny tip of platinum wire extending through the end of a sealed glass tubing; this electrode may be rotated during use or it may be left stationary. The most widely used type of microelectrode, however, is the dropping mercury electrode, (Fig. 71), in which mercury is exposed at the electrode surface. The exposed surface is continuously fresh as each drop grows and falls off and a new drop forms. A polarogram obtained with this type of microelectrode differs from the idealized curve of Figure 69 in several ways. Perhaps the most significant is the fact that a slight but measurable current flows even at cathode potentials less than that at which the desired cathode reaction can occur. This is called the *residual current*. It presumably arises principally from two causes: (1) electrode reactions of impurities; (2) each drop of mercury takes on electrons from the source of applied potential as the drop forms and grows, and this "charge" is carried away when the drop falls off the cathode. There is also a very slight residual current with a platinum microelectrode, which must arise from impurities alone. A correction for the residual current must be applied, either mathematically or graphically, in the experimental determination of the diffusion current. Another feature of polarograms obtained with the dropping mercury electrode is the fact that the potential at which the current flow equals half the diffusion current, assuming correction has been made for residual current, is useful for qualitative analysis. The latter potential is designated the *half-wave potential*, and it is characteristic of the electroactive substance. The reference electrode may very conveniently consist of the pool of mercury at the bottom of the cell (Fig. 71), or it may consist of a specially designed calomel or other electrode.

Some polarographic work is performed manually. That is, the applied potential is set in turn at each of several values, and the corresponding current flows are noted to provide data for plotting as the polarogram. There are, however, several commercial instruments available with which the current-voltage curves are plotted automatically once the test liquid and electrodes are prepared.

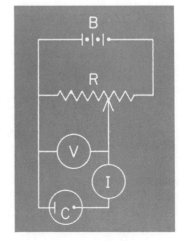

FIGURE 70. Basic electrical circuit for polarographic measurements. *B*, battery; *R*, adjustable resistor; *V*, voltmeter; *I*, current meter; *C*, cell with test solution and electrodes.

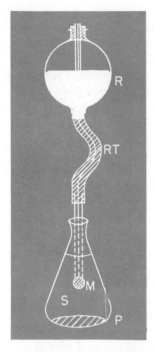

FIGURE 71. Polarographic cell with test solution and dropping mercury electrode. *R*, mercury reservoir; *RT*, rubber tubing, *M*, drop of mercury forming at end of capillary tubing; *S*, test solution; *P*, pool of mercury.

Types of Applications. As noted in the preceding discussion of the principles, polarography is useful in both qualitative and quantitative work, but especially in the latter. The half-wave potentials of many common ions do not differ very much from each other, so polarography is used for qualitative analysis only in special situations rather than in general qualitative schemes of analysis. Very small quantities of material may, in many instances, be detected and determined by polarographic means. The limit of sensitivity is in many, perhaps in most, cases of the order of parts per million. Many useful applications have been developed in both organic and inorganic analysis. In addition to what might be called straightforward analytical applications, the polarographic methods may be extended to provide much useful fundamental chemical and physico-chemical information concerning substances. The polarograph is truly one of the most useful tools of modern instrumental analysis.

Amperometric Titrations. Because the diffusion current may be measured readily, and because it is a function of concentration, the end points in titrations may be determined from a plot of the diffusion current vs. volume of added reagent. Such a titration is designated an *amperometric titration*. Consider, for example, the titration of substance A, which yields a diffusion current at −1.0 volt, being titrated by substance B, which yields no diffusion current at −1.0 volt. The titration curve would look like Figure 72. Until the equivalence point, the concentration of A is being decreased, so the diffusion current decreases. The B concentration increases beyond the equivalence point, but the current remains essentially at zero. If the reagents are reversed, the curve is merely reversed with zero diffusion current until the equivalence point and a linearly increasing current flow thereafter. If both A and B are able to react at the microelectrode at the potential employed, a V-shaped titration curve is obtained. As is the case with conductometric titrations, the end point is determined graphically. No data need be taken at or even near the end point; a few points before and a few after the equivalence point suffice.

The apparatus may consist simply of that shown in Figure 70, simplified by the fact that no accurate means of voltage measurement is required. It should be emphasized that, in each amperometric titration, all measurements are made at the same applied potential and the test solution is altered by each addition of titrating agent. In regular polarography, all measurements for each polarogram are made on one solution but at various potentials.

The amperometric titration method is not used as generally as, for example, the potentiometric method. However, there are numerous useful applications and more are being developed. One type of useful application is in volumetric precipitation titrations, for many of which color indicators and even potentiometric indicating electrodes are lacking. This is particularly true in titrations involving metallo-organic precipitates. The amperometric method also makes possible the titration of very small amounts of substances.

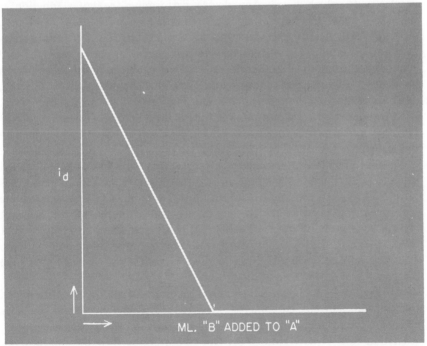

FIGURE 72. A typical amperometric titration graph (assuming that "A" yields a diffusion current and "B" does not under the conditions of measurement).

Good results are usually obtainable in titrating solutions as dilute as 0.001 N and, in some cases, even much more dilute.

COULOMETRIC METHODS

Coulometric methods are, in many respects, similar to electrodeposition methods. The chief difference lies in the choice of what to measure. In the deposition methods, the unknown substance is deposited on the electrode and its weight found by weighing the electrode both before and after receiving the deposit. In coulometric methods, the amount of material reacting at the electrode is determined not by weighing it, but rather by measuring the quantity of electricity which has flowed in the process. Several distinguishing features of coulometric analysis immediately become apparent, including the following: useful applications are not limited to those electrode reactions in which a solid is deposited upon one electrode, but include others in which both oxidized and reduced forms of the substance involved are in solution; the substance being determined must be the sole substance reacting at one electrode, so the limited cathode potential method is especially useful.

The experimental apparatus may be that used in electrodeposition processes with the addition of some means of measuring the total quantity of electricity which flows. Any device performing the latter function is called a *coulometer*. Several types of coulometers have been developed, including both electronic devices and gas coulometers. In the latter, a separate cell containing, for example, water is placed in series with the cell containing the unknown so that the same electrical current must pass through both cells. The hydrogen and/or oxygen gas from the water cell is collected, its volume measured, and the quantity of current flow calculated therefrom.

Another very useful means of measuring the quantity of electrical current flow has recently come into prominence. An electrical circuit is designed so that, when it is connected to the electrodes in the test solution, current flows at a constant rate. The total quantity of electricity may then be calculated simply by multiplying the duration of time during which the apparatus is turned on by the fixed rate of current flow. There must, of course, be some sort of indicating device to tell the operator when to shut off the constant current generator (or else to shut it off directly and simultaneously to shut off the timer, all automatically). In a sense, this is a titration method with the electrical current serving as the "added reagent" and with this "added reagent" being introduced at a constant rate.

In Figure 73 is shown the electrical diagram for an apparatus designed for constant current coulometric measurements. The apparatus includes provision for keeping the current flowing at a constant rate and for measuring what that rate is. The battery B_a, causes current to flow through a series circuit consisting of R_1, R_2 and R_s (R_s is the resistance between the two platinum electrodes, Pt, immersed in the test solution, S). The meter, M, is a voltmeter, such as a vacuum tube voltmeter, the internal resistance of which is large compared to R_2. Applying Ohm's law to this series circuit, and letting E_{B_a} and I represent the battery voltage and the current flow, respectively,

(1) $$E_{B_a} = I(R_1 + R_2 + R_s) \quad \text{or} \quad I = \frac{E_{B_a}}{R_1 + R_2 + R_s}$$

The numerical values of E_{B_a}, R_1 and R_2 are constants, but R_s is not because the composition of the solution changes as electrolysis proceeds. However, if the sum, $R_1 + R_2$, is made very large relative to R_s, equation (1) becomes

(2) $$I = \frac{E_{B_a}}{R_1 + R_2} = \text{constant}$$

so the rate of current flow is constant. The magnitude of I is determined from the voltage drop across the known resistor, R_2, as read on meter, M,

(3) $$I = \frac{E_M}{R_2}$$

The quantity of current in coulombs is, thus, the product of I, equation (3), and the time during which it flows, expressed respectively in amperes and seconds. The magnitude of B_a must be such that the current flows through the system at an appropriate rate, that is, so that the entire "coulometric titration" is neither too fast for accurate time measurement nor too slow for convenience. No precise provision is made in the apparatus of Figure 73 for limiting the electrode potentials within the test solution, so more refined apparatus must be used if the particular test solution makes this necessary.

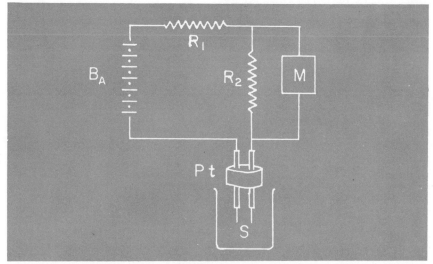

FIGURE 73.   Simple, complete apparatus for constant-current type of coulometric measurements (see text).

Coulometric methods are very versatile and have been developed quite extensively in the last few years. Undoubtedly, this method of analysis will become one of the more widely used methods in years to come.

REVIEW QUESTIONS

1. Describe the construction and the electrochemical basis of the calomel electrode.
2. Suggest a suitable indicating electrode for each of the following titrations:
   a. Strong acid vs. strong base.
   b. Weak acid vs. strong base.
   c. Dichromate vs. ferrous ion.
   d. Cerate vs. ferrous ion.
   e. Chloride vs. silver ion.
3. Why are potentiometric electrode systems so useful for automatic titration devices?
4. Compare potentiometric and conductometric methods on the bases of selectivity and general applicability.
5. Define or characterize the terms residual current, diffusion current and polarization.
6. State the principles upon which polarographic methods are useful in qualitative analysis and in quantitative analysis.
7. Describe the principles of coulometric analysis.
8. Compare "coulometric titrations" to potentiometric titrations and to electro-deposition methods on as many significant points as you can.

SUGGESTIONS FOR ADDITIONAL READING

Items 3, 4, 16, 18, 19 and 29, Appendix 7.

Part Six

APPENDICES

Solubility Product Constants

Substance	Formula	Constant
Aluminum hydroxide	$Al(OH)_3$	3.7×10^{-15}
Barium carbonate	$BaCO_3$	8.1×10^{-9}
Barium chromate	$BaCrO_4$	2.4×10^{-10}
Barium fluoride	BaF_2	1.73×10^{-6}
Barium iodate	$Ba(IO_3)_2 \cdot 2\ H_2O$	6.5×10^{-10}
Barium oxalate	$BaC_2O_4 \cdot 2\ H_2O$	1.2×10^{-7}
Barium sulfate	$BaSO_4$	1.08×10^{-10}
Cadmium oxalate	$CdC_2O_4 \cdot 3\ H_2O$	1.53×10^{-8}
Cadmium sulfide	CdS	7.8×10^{-27}
Calcium carbonate	$CaCO_3$	8.7×10^{-9}
Calcium fluoride	CaF_2	3.95×10^{-11}
Calcium iodate	$Ca(IO_3)_2 \cdot 6\ H_2O$	6.44×10^{-7}
Calcium oxalate	$CaC_2O_4 \cdot H_2O$	2.57×10^{-9}
Calcium sulfate	$CaSO_4$	1.95×10^{-4}
Cupric iodate	$Cu(IO_3)_2$	1.4×10^{-7}
Cupric sulfide	CuS	8.7×10^{-36}
Cuprous iodide	CuI	5.06×10^{-12}
Cuprous sulfide	Cu_2S	2×10^{-47}
Cuprous thiocyanate	$CuSCN$	1.6×10^{-11}
Ferric hydroxide	$Fe(OH)_3$	1.1×10^{-36}
Ferrous hydroxide	$Fe(OH)_2$	1.64×10^{-14}
Lead carbonate	$PbCO_3$	3.3×10^{-14}
Lead chromate	$PbCrO_4$	1.77×10^{-14}
Lead fluoride	PbF_2	3.7×10^{-8}
Lead iodate	$Pb(IO_3)_2$	2.6×10^{-13}
Lead sulfate	$PbSO_4$	1.06×10^{-8}
Lead sulfide	PbS	8.4×10^{-28}
Magnesium ammonium phosphate	$MgNH_4PO_4 \cdot 6\ H_2O$	2.5×10^{-13}
Magnesium hydroxide	$Mg(OH)_2$	1.2×10^{-11}
Magnesium oxalate	MgC_2O_4	8.57×10^{-5}
Nickel sulfide	NiS	1.8×10^{-21}
Silver bromate	$AgBrO_3$	5.77×10^{-5}
Silver bromide	$AgBr$	7.7×10^{-13}
Silver chloride	$AgCl$	1.56×10^{-10}
Silver chromate	Ag_2CrO_4	9×10^{-12}
Silver cyanide	$Ag[Ag(CN)_2]$	2.2×10^{-12}
Silver dichromate	$Ag_2Cr_2O_7$	2×10^{-7}
Silver hydroxide	$AgOH$	1.52×10^{-8}
Silver iodate	$AgIO_3$	1.0×10^{-8}

Substance	Formula	Constant
Silver iodide	AgI	1.5×10^{-16}
Silver sulfide	Ag_2S	1.6×10^{-49}
Silver thiocyanate	AgSCN	1.16×10^{-12}
Strontium carbonate	$SrCO_3$	1.6×10^{-9}
Strontium fluoride	SrF_2	2.8×10^{-9}
Strontium sulfate	$SrSO_4$	3.81×10^{-7}
Zinc hydroxide	$Zn(OH)_2$	1.8×10^{-14}
Zinc sulfide	ZnS	1.1×10^{-21}

All listed values are valid at or near room temperature.

Ionization Constants for
Weak Acids and Weak Bases

ACIDS

Acid	Formula	K
Acetic	$HC_2H_3O_2$	1.75×10^{-5}
Benzoic	$HC_7H_5O_2$	6.3×10^{-5}
Boric	H_3BO_3	$6.4 \times 10^{-10}(K_1)$
Bromoacetic	$HC_2H_2O_2Br$	1.38×10^{-3}
Butyric	$HC_4H_7O_2$	1.48×10^{-5}
Carbonic	H_2CO_3	$3.8 \times 10^{-7}(K_1)$
Carbonic	H_2CO_3	$4.4 \times 10^{-11}(K_2)$
Chloroacetic	$HC_2H_2O_2Cl$	1.54×10^{-3}
Formic	$HCHO_2$	1.76×10^{-4}
Hydrocyanic	HCN	7.2×10^{-10}
Hydrosulfuric	H_2S	$9.1 \times 10^{-8}(K_1)$
Hydrosulfuric	H_2S	$1.2 \times 10^{-15}(K_2)$
Hypochlorous	$HClO$	3.7×10^{-8}
Iodic	HIO_3	1.9×10^{-1}
Lactic	$HC_3H_5O_3$	1.38×10^{-4}
Nitrous	HNO_2	4×10^{-4}
Oxalic	$H_2C_2O_4$	$6.5 \times 10^{-2}(K_1)$
Oxalic	$H_2C_2O_4$	$6.1 \times 10^{-5}(K_2)$
Phosphoric	H_3PO_4	$1.1 \times 10^{-2}(K_1)$
Phosphoric	H_3PO_4	$7.5 \times 10^{-8}(K_2)$
Phosphoric	H_3PO_4	$4.8 \times 10^{-13}(K_3)$
Salicylic	$HC_7H_5O_3$	$1.06 \times 10^{-3}(K_1)$
Salicylic	$HC_7H_5O_3$	$1 \times 10^{-13}(K_2)$
Sulfuric	H_2SO_4	$2 \times 10^{-2}(K_2)$
Sulfurous	H_2SO_3	$1.7 \times 10^{-2}(K_1)$
Sulfurous	H_2SO_3	$6.24 \times 10^{-6}(K_2)$
Tartaric	$H_2C_4H_4O_6$	$1.1 \times 10^{-3}(K_1)$
Tartaric	$H_2C_4H_4O_6$	$6.9 \times 10^{-5}(K_2)$

BASES

Base	Formula	K
Acetamide	CH_3CONH_2	3.1×10^{-15}
Ammonium hydroxide	NH_4OH	1.8×10^{-5}
Aniline	$C_6H_5NH_2$	4.6×10^{-10}
Ethylamine	$C_2H_5NH_2$	5.6×10^{-4}
Methylamine	CH_3NH_2	5×10^{-4}
Silver hydroxide	$AgOH$	1.1×10^{-4}
Thiourea	$CS(NH_2)_2$	1.1×10^{-15}
Triethylamine	$(C_2H_5)_3N$	6.4×10^{-4}
Trimethylamine	$(CH_3)_3N$	7.4×10^{-5}
Tripropylamine	$(C_3H_7)_3N$	5.5×10^{-4}
Urea	$CO(NH_2)_2$	1.5×10^{-14}

All listed values are valid at or near room temperature.

Dissociation

Constants for Complex Ions[*]

Complex	K	Complex	K
$Ag(NH_3)_2{}^+$	6.8×10^{-8}	$CoY^=$	4.9×10^{-17}
$Ag(S_2O_3)_2{}^=$	1×10^{-13}	$CuY^=$	1.6×10^{-19}
$Ag(CN)_2{}^-$	1×10^{-21}	$FeY^=$	4.7×10^{-15}
$Cu(CN)_4{}^=$	5×10^{-28}	FeY^-	7.9×10^{-26}
$Fe(SCN)^{++}$	8.0×10^{-3}	$HgY^=$	1.6×10^{-22}
$AgY^{\equiv}$	5.0×10^{-8}	$MgY^=$	2.0×10^{-9}
AlY^-	7.4×10^{-17}	$NiY^=$	2.4×10^{-19}
$BaY^=$	1.7×10^{-8}	$SrY^=$	2.3×10^{-9}
$CaY^=$	2.5×10^{-11}	$ZnY^=$	3.2×10^{-17}
$CdY^=$	3.4×10^{-17}		

[*] In a dissociation constant of a complex, the concentrations of the dissociated forms are in the numerator and of the undissociated form in the denominator (see page 20).

($Y^=$ is the ethylene diamine tetraacetate ion).

Formula Weights

AgBr	187.80	HBr	80.92
AgCl	143.34	HCl	36.47
Ag$_2$CrO$_4$	331.77	HClO$_4$	100.46
Ag$_2$Cr$_2$O$_7$	431.78	HCHO$_2$	46.03
AgI	234.80	HC$_2$H$_3$O$_2$	60.05
AgIO$_3$	282.79	H$_4$C$_{10}$H$_{12}$O$_8$N$_2$ (E.D.T.A.)	292.25
AgNO$_3$	169.89	H$_2$C$_2$O$_4$·2 H$_2$O	126.07
Ag$_2$S	247.83	HNH$_2$SO$_3$	97.10
Ag$_2$SO$_4$	311.83	HNO$_3$	63.02
AlCl$_3$	133.35	H$_2$O	18.02
Al$_2$O$_3$	101.94	H$_2$O$_2$	34.02
As$_2$O$_3$	197.82	H$_2$S	34.08
		H$_2$SO$_4$	98.08
BaBr$_2$	297.19		
BaCl$_2$	208.27	KBr	119.02
BaCl$_2$·2 H$_2$O	244.30	KBrO$_3$	167.01
BaCO$_3$	197.37	KCl	74.55
BaCrO$_4$	237.37	KClO$_3$	122.56
BaF$_2$	175.36	KClO$_4$	138.55
BaO	153.36	KCN	65.12
Ba(OH)$_2$	171.38	K$_2$CO$_3$	138.21
BaSO$_4$	233.43	K$_2$CrO$_4$	194.20
		K$_2$Cr$_2$O$_7$	294.21
CaCO$_3$	100.09	KHC$_4$H$_4$O$_6$	188.18
CaC$_2$O$_4$	128.10	KHC$_8$H$_4$O$_4$	204.22
CaO	56.08	KHCO$_3$	100.12
CaSO$_4$	136.15	KI	166.02
CdS	144.48	KIO$_3$	214.02
Ce(SO$_4$)$_2$	332.26	KMnO$_4$	158.04
CO$_2$	44.01	KNO$_3$	101.11
Cu(IO$_3$)$_2$	413.36	K$_2$O	94.19
CuS	95.61	KOH	56.11
CuSCN	121.62	K$_2$PtCl$_6$	486.16
CuSO$_3$	159.61	KSCN	97.18
FeO	71.85	LiCl	42.40
Fe$_2$O$_3$	159.70		
Fe$_3$O$_4$	231.55	MgCl$_2$	95.23
Fe$_2$(SO$_4$)$_3$	399.90	MgCO$_3$	84.33
FeSO$_4$·(NH$_4$)$_3$SO$_4$·6 H$_2$O	392.15	MgNH$_4$PO$_4$	137.34

$MgNH_4PO_4 \cdot 6 \, H_2O$ 245.44
MgO 40.32
$Mg(OH)_2$ 58.34
$Mg_2P_2O_7$ 222.59
$MgSO_4 \cdot 2 \, H_2O$ 156.42
MnO_2 .... 86.94
Mn_3O_4 ....228.82

$NaBr$ 102.91
$NaC_2H_3O_2$ 82.04
$NaCl$ 58.45
$Na_2H_2C_{10}H_{12}O_8N_2 \cdot 2 \, H_2O$ 372.25
$NaCN$ 49.02
Na_2CO_3 ....106.00
$Na_2C_2O_4$ 134.01
$NaHCO_3$ 84.02
NaI 149.90
$NaNO_3$ 85.00
Na_2O 61.99
$NaOH$ 40.00
Na_2SO_4 ....142.05
$Na_2S_2O_3$ 158.11
$Na_2S_2O_3 \cdot 5 \, H_2O$ 248.19

NH_3 .... 17.03
NH_4Cl 53.50
$(NH_4)_2C_2O_4$ 124.10
NH_4OH 35.05
$(NH_4)_2P(Mo_3O_{10})_4$ 1876.50

$PbCl_2$ 278.12
$PbCrO_4$ 323.22
$Pb(IO_3)_2$ 557.03
$PbSO_4$ 303.28
PdI_2 ....360.22

Sb_2S_3 ....339.72
SiO_2 .... 60.09
SnO_2 ....150.70
SO_2 .... 64.07
SO_3 .... 80.07
$SrCO_3$ 147.64

$TlCl$ 239.85

$Zn_2P_2O_7$ 304.72

Five-Place Logarithms

The five-place logarithm tables are on pages 470 to 487.

FIVE-PLACE LOGARITHMS

N.	0	1	2	3	4	5	6	7	8	9	Proportional parts
100	00 000	043	087	130	173	217	260	303	346	389	**44 43 42**
101	432	475	518	561	604	647	689	732	775	817	1| 4,4 4,3 4,2
102	860	903	945	988	*030	*072	*115	*157	*199	*242	2| 8,8 8,6 8,4
103	01 284	326	368	410	452	494	536	578	620	662	3| 13,2 12,9 12,6
104	703	745	787	828	870	912	953	995	*036	*078	4| 17,6 17,2 16,8
105	02 119	160	202	243	284	325	366	407	449	490	5| 22,0 21,5 21,0
106	531	572	612	653	694	735	776	816	857	898	6| 26,4 25,8 25,2
107	938	979	*019	*060	*100	*141	*181	*222	*262	*302	7| 30,8 30,1 29,4
108	03 342	383	423	463	503	543	583	623	663	703	8| 35,2 34,4 33,6
109	743	782	822	862	902	941	981	*021	*060	*100	9| 39,6 38,7 37,8
110	04 139	179	218	258	297	336	376	415	454	493	**41 40 39**
111	532	571	610	650	689	727	766	805	844	883	1| 4,1 4,0 3,9
112	922	961	999	*038	*077	*115	*154	*192	*231	*269	2| 8,2 8,0 7,8
113	05 308	346	385	423	461	500	538	576	614	652	3| 12,3 12,0 11,7
114	690	729	767	805	843	881	918	956	994	*032	4| 16,4 16,0 15,6
115	06 070	108	145	183	221	258	296	333	371	408	5| 20,5 20,0 19,5
116	446	483	521	558	595	633	670	707	744	781	6| 24,6 24,0 23,4
117	819	856	893	930	967	*004	*041	*078	*115	*151	7| 28,7 28,0 27,3
118	07 188	225	262	298	335	372	408	445	482	518	8| 32,8 32,0 31,2
119	555	591	628	664	700	737	773	809	846	882	9| 36,9 36,0 35,1
120	918	954	990	*027	*063	*099	*135	*171	*207	*243	**38 37 36**
121	08 279	314	350	386	422	458	493	529	565	600	1| 3,8 3,7 3,6
122	636	672	707	743	778	814	849	884	920	955	2| 7,6 7,4 7,2
123	991	*026	*061	*096	*132	*167	*202	*237	*272	*307	3| 11,4 11,1 10,8
124	09 342	377	412	447	482	517	552	587	621	656	4| 15,2 14,8 14,4
125	691	726	760	795	830	864	899	934	968	*003	5| 19,0 18,5 18,0
126	10 037	072	106	140	175	209	243	278	312	346	6| 22,8 22,2 21,6
127	380	415	449	483	517	551	585	619	653	687	7| 26,6 25,9 25,2
128	721	755	789	823	857	890	924	958	992	*025	8| 30,4 29,6 28,8
129	11 059	093	126	160	193	227	261	294	327	361	9| 34,2 33,3 32,4
130	394	428	461	494	528	561	594	628	661	694	**35 34 33**
131	727	760	793	826	860	893	926	959	992	*024	1| 3,5 3,4 3,3
132	12 057	090	123	156	189	222	254	287	320	352	2| 7,0 6,8 6,6
133	385	418	450	483	516	548	581	613	646	678	3| 10,5 10,2 9,9
134	710	743	775	808	840	872	905	937	969	*001	4| 14,0 13,6 13,2
135	13 033	066	098	130	162	194	226	258	290	322	5| 17,5 17,0 16,5
136	354	386	418	450	481	513	545	577	609	640	6| 21,0 20,4 19,8
137	672	704	735	767	799	830	862	893	925	956	7| 24,5 23,8 23,1
138	988	*019	*051	*082	*114	*145	*176	*208	*239	*270	8| 28,0 27,2 26,4
139	14 301	333	364	395	426	457	489	520	551	582	9| 31,5 30,6 29,7
140	613	644	675	706	737	768	799	829	860	891	**32 31 30**
141	922	953	983	*014	*045	*076	*106	*137	*168	*198	1| 3,2 3,1 3,0
142	15 229	259	290	320	351	381	412	442	473	503	2| 6,4 6,2 6,0
143	534	564	594	625	655	685	715	746	776	806	3| 9,6 9,3 9,0
144	836	866	897	927	957	987	*017	*047	*077	*107	4| 12,8 12,4 12,0
145	16 137	167	197	227	256	286	316	346	376	406	5| 16,0 15,5 15,0
146	435	465	495	524	554	584	613	643	673	702	6| 19,2 18,6 18,0
147	732	761	791	820	850	879	909	938	967	997	7| 22,4 21,7 21,0
148	17 026	056	085	114	143	173	202	231	260	289	8| 25,6 24,8 24,0
149	319	348	377	406	435	464	493	522	551	580	9| 28,8 27,9 27,0
150	609	638	667	696	725	754	782	811	840	869	
N.	0	1	2	3	4	5	6	7	8	9	Proportional parts

FIVE-PLACE LOGARITHMS (Continued)

N.	0	1	2	3	4	5	6	7	8	9	Proportional parts	
150	17 609	638	667	696	725	754	782	811	840	869	**29**	**28**
151	898	926	955	984	*013	*041	*070	*099	*127	*156	1 2,9	2,8
152	18 184	213	241	270	298	327	355	384	412	441	2 5,8	5,6
153	469	498	526	554	583	611	639	667	696	724	3 8,7	8,4
154	752	780	808	837	865	893	921	949	977	*005	4 11,6	11,2
155	19 033	061	089	117	145	173	201	229	257	285	5 14,5	14,0
156	312	340	368	396	424	451	479	507	535	562	6 17,4	16,8
157	590	618	645	673	700	728	756	783	811	838	7 20,3	19,6
158	866	893	921	948	976	*003	*030	*058	*085	*112	8 23,2	22,4
159	20 140	167	194	222	249	276	303	330	358	385	9 26,1	25,2
160	412	439	466	493	520	548	575	602	629	656	**27**	**26**
161	683	710	737	763	790	817	844	871	898	925	1 2,7	2,6
162	952	978	*005	*032	*059	*085	*112	*139	*165	*192	2 5,4	5,2
163	21 219	245	272	299	325	352	378	405	431	458	3 8,1	7,8
164	484	511	537	564	590	617	643	669	696	722	4 10,8	10,4
165	748	775	801	827	854	880	906	932	958	985	5 13,5	13,0
166	22 011	037	063	089	115	141	167	194	220	246	6 16,2	15,6
167	272	298	324	350	376	401	427	453	479	505	7 18,9	18,2
168	531	557	583	608	634	660	686	712	737	763	8 21,6	20,8
169	789	814	840	866	891	917	943	968	994	*019	9 24,3	23,4
170	23 045	070	096	121	147	172	198	223	249	274	**25**	
171	300	325	350	376	401	426	452	477	502	528	1 2,5	
172	553	578	603	629	654	679	704	729	754	779	2 5,0	
173	805	830	855	880	905	930	955	980	*005	*030	3 7,5	
174	24 055	080	105	130	155	180	204	229	254	279	4 10,0	
175	304	329	353	378	403	428	452	477	502	527	5 12,5	
176	551	576	601	625	650	674	699	724	748	773	6 15,0	
177	797	822	846	871	895	920	944	969	993	*018	7 17,5	
178	25 042	066	091	115	139	164	188	212	237	261	8 20,0	
179	285	310	334	358	382	406	431	455	479	503	9 22,5	
180	527	551	575	600	624	648	672	696	720	744	**24**	**23**
181	768	792	816	840	864	888	912	935	959	983	1 2,4	2,3
182	26 007	031	055	079	102	126	150	174	198	221	2 4,8	4,6
183	245	269	293	316	340	364	387	411	435	458	3 7,2	6,9
184	482	505	529	553	576	600	623	647	670	694	4 9,6	9,2
185	717	741	764	788	811	834	858	881	905	928	5 12,0	11,5
186	951	975	998	*021	*045	*068	*091	*114	*138	*161	6 14,4	13,8
187	27 184	207	231	254	277	300	323	346	370	393	7 16,8	16,1
188	416	439	462	485	508	531	554	577	600	623	8 19,2	18,4
189	646	669	692	715	738	761	784	807	830	852	9 21,6	20,7
190	875	898	921	944	967	989	*012	*035	*058	*081	**22**	**21**
191	28 103	126	149	171	194	217	240	262	285	307	1 2,2	2,1
192	330	353	375	398	421	443	466	488	511	533	2 4,4	4,2
193	556	578	601	623	646	668	691	713	735	758	3 6,6	6,3
194	780	803	825	847	870	892	914	937	959	981	4 8,8	8,4
195	29 003	026	048	070	092	115	137	159	181	203	5 11,0	10,5
196	226	248	270	292	314	336	358	380	403	425	6 13,2	12,6
197	447	469	491	513	535	557	579	601	623	645	7 15,4	14,7
198	667	688	710	732	754	776	798	820	842	863	8 17,6	16,8
199	885	907	929	951	973	994	*016	*038	*060	*081	9 19,8	18,9
200	30 103	125	146	168	190	211	233	255	276	298		
N.	0	1	2	3	4	5	6	7	8	9	Proportional parts	

FIVE-PLACE LOGARITHMS (Continued)

N.	0	1	2	3	4	5	6	7	8	9
200	30 103	125	146	168	190	211	233	255	276	298
201	320	341	363	384	406	428	449	471	492	514
202	535	557	578	600	621	643	664	685	707	728
203	750	771	792	814	835	856	878	899	920	942
204	963	984	*006	*027	*048	*069	*091	*112	*133	*154
205	31 175	197	218	239	260	281	302	323	345	366
206	387	408	429	450	471	492	513	534	555	576
207	597	618	639	660	681	702	723	744	765	785
208	806	827	848	869	890	911	931	952	973	994
209	32 015	035	056	077·	098	118	139	160	181	201
210	222	243	263	284	305	325	346	366	387	408
211	428	449	469	490	510	531	552	572	593	613
212	634	654	675	695	715	736	756	777	797	818
213	838	858	879	899	919	940	960	980	*001	*021
214	33 041	062	082	102	122	143	163	183	203	224
215	244	264	284	304	325	345	365	385	405	425
216	445	465	486	506	526	546	566	586	606	626
217	646	666	686	706	726	746	766	786	806	826
218	846	866	885	905	925	945	965	985	*005	*025
219	34 044	064	084	104	124	143	163	183	203	223
220	242	262	282	301	321	341	361	380	400	420
221	439	459	479	498	518	537	557	577	596	616
222	635	655	674	694	713	733	753	772	792	811
223	830	850	869	889	908	928	947	967	986	*005
224	35 025	044	064	083	102	122	141	160	180	199
225	218	238	257	276	295	315	334	353	372	392
226	411	430	449	468	488	507	526	545	564	583
227	603	622	641	660	679	698	717	736	755	774
228	793	813	832	851	870	889	908	927	946	965
229	984	*003	*021	*040	*059	*078	*097	*116	*135	*154
230	36 173	192	211	229	248	267	286	305	324	342
231	361	380	399	418	436	455	474	493	511	530
232	549	568	586	605	624	642	661	680	698	717
233	736	754	773	791	810	829	847	866	884	903
234	922	940	959	977	996	*014	*033	*051	*070	*088
235	37 107	125	144	162	181	199	218	236	254	273
236	291	310	328	346	365	383	401	420	438	457
237	475	493	511	530	548	566	585	603	621	639
238	658	676	694	712	731	749	767	785	803	822
239	840	858	876	894	912	931	949	967	985	*003
240	38 021	039	057	075	093	112	130	148	166	184
241	202	220	238	256	274	292	310	328	346	364
242	382	399	417	435	453	471	489	507	525	543
243	561	578	596	614	632	650	668	686	703	721
244	739	757	775	792	810	828	846	863	881	899
245	917	934	952	970	987	*005	*023	*041	*058	*076
246	39 094	111	129	146	164	182	199	217	235	252
247	270	287	305	322	340	358	375	393	410	428
248	445	463	480	498	515	533	550	568	585	602
249	620	637	655	672	690	707	724	742	759	777
250	794	811	829	846	863	881	898	915	933	950

Proportional parts

	22	21
1	2,2	2,1
2	4,4	4,2
3	6,6	6,3
4	8,8	8,4
5	11,0	10,5
6	13,2	12,6
7	15,4	14,7
8	17,6	16,8
9	19,8	18,9

	20
1	2,0
2	4,0
3	6,0
4	8,0
5	10,0
6	12,0
7	14,0
8	16,0
9	18,0

	19
1	1,9
2	3,8
3	5,7
4	7,6
5	9,5
6	11,4
7	13,3
8	15,2
9	17,1

	18
1	1,8
2	3,6
3	5,4
4	7,2
5	9,0
6	10,8
7	12,6
8	14,4
9	16,2

	17
1	1,7
2	3,4
3	5,1
4	6,8
5	8,5
6	10,2
7	11,9
8	13,6
9	15,3

FIVE-PLACE LOGARITHMS (Continued)

N.	0	1	2	3	4	5	6	7	8	9	Proportional parts
250	39 794	811	829	846	863	881	898	915	933	950	**18**
251	967	985	*002	*019	*037	*054	*071	*088	*106	*123	1| 1,8
252	40 140	157	175	192	209	226	243	261	278	295	2| 3,6
253	312	329	346	364	381	398	415	432	449	466	3| 5,4
254	483	500	518	535	552	569	586	603	620	637	4| 7,2
255	654	671	688	705	722	739	756	773	790	807	5| 9,0
256	824	841	858	875	892	909	926	943	960	976	6| 10,8
257	993	*010	*027	*044	*061	*078	*095	*111	*128	*145	7| 12,6
258	41 162	179	196	212	229	246	263	280	296	313	8| 14,4
259	330	347	363	380	397	414	430	447	464	481	9| 16,2
260	497	514	531	547	564	581	597	614	631	647	**17**
261	664	681	697	714	731	747	764	780	797	814	1| 1,7
262	830	847	863	880	896	913	929	946	963	979	2| 3,4
263	996	*012	*029	*045	*062	*078	*095	*111	*127	*144	3| 5,1
264	42 160	177	193	210	226	243	259	275	292	308	4| 6,8
265	325	341	357	374	390	406	423	439	455	472	5| 8,5
266	488	504	521	537	553	570	586	602	619	635	6| 10,2
267	651	667	684	700	716	732	749	765	781	797	7| 11,9
268	813	830	846	862	878	894	911	927	943	959	8| 13,6
269	975	991	*008	*024	*040	*056	*072	*088	*104	*120	9| 15,3
270	43 136	152	169	185	201	217	233	249	265	281	**16**
271	297	313	329	345	361	377	393	409	425	441	1| 1,6
272	457	473	489	505	521	537	553	569	584	600	2| 3,2
273	616	632	648	664	680	696	712	727	743	759	3| 4,8
274	775	791	807	823	838	854	870	886	902	917	4| 6,4
275	933	949	965	981	996	*012	*028	*044	*059	*075	5| 8,0
276	44 091	107	122	138	154	170	185	201	217	232	6| 9,6
277	248	264	279	295	311	326	342	358	373	389	7| 11,2
278	404	420	436	451	467	483	498	514	529	545	8| 12,8
279	560	576	592	607	623	638	654	669	685	700	9| 14,4
280	716	731	747	762	778	793	809	824	840	855	**15**
281	871	886	902	917	932	948	963	979	994	*010	1| 1,5
282	45 025	040	056	071	086	102	117	133	148	163	2| 3,0
283	179	194	209	225	240	255	271	286	301	317	3| 4,5
284	332	347	362	378	393	408	423	439	454	469	4| 6,0
285	484	500	515	530	545	561	576	591	606	621	5| 7,5
286	637	652	667	682	697	712	728	743	758	773	6| 9,0
287	788	803	818	834	849	864	879	894	909	924	7| 10,5
288	939	954	969	984	*000	*015	*030	*045	*060	*075	8| 12,0
289	46 090	105	120	135	150	165	180	195	210	225	9| 13,5
290	240	255	270	285	300	315	330	345	359	374	**14**
291	389	404	419	434	449	464	479	494	509	523	1| 1,4
292	538	553	568	583	598	613	627	642	657	672	2| 2,8
293	687	702	716	731	746	761	776	790	805	820	3| 4,2
294	835	850	864	879	894	909	923	938	953	967	4| 5,6
295	982	997	*012	*026	*041	*056	*070	*085	*100	*114	5| 7,0
296	47 129	144	159	173	188	202	217	232	246	261	6| 8,4
297	276	290	305	319	334	349	363	378	392	407	7| 9,8
298	422	436	451	465	480	494	509	524	538	553	8| 11,2
299	567	582	596	611	625	640	654	669	683	698	9| 12,6
300	712	727	741	756	770	784	799	813	828	842	
N.	0	1	2	3	4	5	6	7	8	9	Proportional parts

FIVE-PLACE LOGARITHMS (Continued)

N.	0	1	2	3	4	5	6	7	8	9	Proportional parts	
300	47 712	727	741	756	770	784	799	813	828	842		
301	857	871	885	900	914	929	943	958	972	986		
302	48 001	015	029	044	058	073	087	101	116	130		
303	144	159	173	187	202	216	230	244	259	273		**15**
304	287	302	316	330	344	359	373	387	401	416	1	1,5
305	430	444	458	473	487	501	515	530	544	558	2	3,0
306	572	586	601	615	629	643	657	671	686	700	3	4,5
307	714	728	742	756	770	785	799	813	827	841	4	6,0
308	855	869	883	897	911	926	940	954	968	982	5	7,5
309	996	*010	*024	*038	*052	*066	*080	*094	*108	*122	6	9,0
											7	10,5
310	49 136	150	164	178	192	206	220	234	248	262	8	12,0
311	276	290	304	318	332	346	360	374	388	402	9	13,5
312	415	429	443	457	471	485	499	513	527	541		
313	554	568	582	596	610	624	638	651	665	679		
314	693	707	721	734	748	762	776	790	803	817		
315	831	845	859	872	886	900	914	927	941	955		**14**
316	969	982	996	*010	*024	*037	*051	*065	*079	*092	1	1,4
317	50 106	120	133	147	161	174	188	202	215	229	2	2,8
318	243	256	270	284	297	311	325	338	352	365	3	4,2
319	379	393	406	420	433	447	461	474	488	501	4	5,6
											5	7,0
320	515	529	542	556	569	583	596	610	623	637	6	8,4
321	651	664	678	691	705	718	732	745	759	772	7	9,8
322	786	799	813	826	840	853	866	880	893	907	8	11,2
323	920	934	947	961	974	987	*001	*014	*028	*041	9	12,6
324	51 055	068	081	095	108	121	135	148	162	175		
325	188	202	215	228	242	255	268	282	295	308		
326	322	335	348	362	375	388	402	415	428	441		
327	455	468	481	495	508	521	534	548	561	574		**13**
328	587	601	614	627	640	654	667	680	693	706	1	1,3
329	720	733	746	759	772	786	799	812	825	838	2	2,6
											3	3,9
330	851	865	878	891	904	917	930	943	957	970	4	5,2
331	983	996	*009	*022	*035	*048	*061	*075	*088	*101	5	6,5
332	52 114	127	140	153	166	179	192	205	218	231	6	7,8
333	244	257	270	284	297	310	323	336	349	362	7	9,1
334	375	388	401	414	427	440	453	466	479	492	8	10,4
335	504	517	530	543	556	569	582	595	608	621	9	11,7
336	634	647	660	673	686	699	711	724	737	750		
337	763	776	789	802	815	827	840	853	866	879		
338	892	905	917	930	943	956	969	982	994	*007		
339	53 020	033	046	058	071	084	097	110	122	135		**12**
											1	1,2
340	148	161	173	186	199	212	224	237	250	263	2	2,4
341	275	288	301	314	326	339	352	364	377	390	3	3,6
342	403	415	428	441	453	466	479	491	504	517	4	4,8
343	529	542	555	567	580	593	605	618	631	643	5	6,0
344	656	668	681	694	706	719	732	744	757	769	6	7,2
345	782	794	807	820	832	845	857	870	882	895	7	8,4
346	908	920	933	945	958	970	983	995	*008	*020	8	9,6
347	54 033	045	058	070	083	095	108	120	133	145	9	10,8
348	158	170	183	195	208	220	233	245	258	270		
349	283	295	307	320	332	345	357	370	382	394		
350	407	419	432	444	456	469	481	494	506	518		
N.	0	1	2	3	4	5	6	7	8	9	Proportional parts	

FIVE-PLACE LOGARITHMS (Continued)

N.	0	1	2	3	4	5	6	7	8	9	Proportional parts
350	54 407	419	432	444	456	469	481	494	506	518	
351	531	543	555	568	580	593	605	617	630	642	
352	654	667	679	691	704	716	728	741	753	765	
353	777	790	802	814	827	839	851	864	876	888	**13**
354	900	913	925	937	949	962	974	986	998	*011	1 1,3
355	55 023	035	047	060	072	084	096	108	121	133	2 2,6
356	145	157	169	182	194	206	218	230	242	255	3 3,9
357	267	279	291	303	315	328	340	352	364	376	4 5,2
358	388	400	413	425	437	449	461	473	485	497	5 6,5
359	509	522	534	546	558	570	582	594	606	618	6 7,8
											7 9,1
360	630	642	654	666	678	691	703	715	727	739	8 10,4
361	751	763	775	787	799	811	823	835	847	859	9 11,7
362	871	883	895	907	919	931	943	955	967	979	
363	991	*003	*015	*027	*038	*050	*062	*074	*086	*098	
364	56 110	122	134	146	158	170	182	194	205	217	**12**
365	229	241	253	265	277	289	301	312	324	336	1 1,2
366	348	360	372	384	396	407	419	431	443	455	2 2,4
367	467	478	490	502	514	526	538	549	561	573	3 3,6
368	585	597	608	620	632	644	656	667	679	691	4 4,8
369	703	714	726	738	750	761	773	785	797	808	5 6,0
											6 7,2
370	820	832	844	855	867	879	891	902	914	926	7 8,4
371	937	949	961	972	984	996	*008	*019	*031	*043	8 9,6
372	57 054	066	078	089	101	113	124	136	148	159	9 10,8
373	171	183	194	206	217	229	241	252	264	276	
374	287	299	310	322	334	345	357	368	380	392	
375	403	415	426	438	449	461	473	484	496	507	
376	519	530	542	553	565	576	588	600	611	623	
377	634	646	657	669	680	692	703	715	726	738	**11**
378	749	761	772	784	795	807	818	830	841	852	1 1,1
379	864	875	887	898	910	921	933	944	955	967	2 2,2
											3 3,3
380	978	990	*001	*013	*024	*035	*047	*058	*070	*081	4 4,4
381	58 092	104	115	127	138	149	161	172	184	195	5 5 5
382	206	218	229	240	252	263	274	286	297	309	6 6,6
383	320	331	343	354	365	377	388	399	410	422	7 7,7
384	433	444	456	467	478	490	501	512	524	535	8 8,8
385	546	557	569	580	591	602	614	625	636	647	9 9,9
386	659	670	681	692	704	715	726	737	749	760	
387	771	782	794	805	816	827	838	850	861	872	
388	883	894	906	917	928	939	950	961	973	984	
389	995	*006	*017	*028	*040	*051	*062	*073	*084	*095	**10**
											1 1,0
390	59 106	118	129	140	151	162	173	184	195	207	2 2,0
391	218	229	240	251	262	273	284	295	306	318	3 3,0
392	329	340	351	362	373	384	395	406	417	428	4 4,0
393	439	450	461	472	483	494	506	517	528	539	5 5,0
394	550	561	572	583	594	605	616	627	638	649	6 6,0
395	660	671	682	693	704	715	726	737	748	759	7 7,0
396	770	780	791	802	813	824	835	846	857	868	8 8,0
397	879	890	901	912	923	934	945	956	966	977	9 9,0
398	988	999	*010	*021	*032	*043	*054	*065	*076	*086	
399	60 097	108	119	130	141	152	163	173	184	195	
400	206	217	228	239	249	260	271	282	293	304	
N.	0	1	2	3	4	5	6	7	8	9	Proportional parts

FIVE-PLACE LOGARITHMS (Continued)

N.	0	1	2	3	4	5	6	7	8	9
400	60 206	217	228	239	249	260	271	282	293	304
401	314	325	336	347	358	369	379	390	401	412
402	423	433	444	455	466	477	487	498	509	520
403	531	541	552	563	574	584	595	606	617	627
404	638	649	660	670	681	692	703	713	724	735
405	746	756	767	778	788	799	810	821	831	842
406	853	863	874	885	895	906	917	927	938	949
407	959	970	981	991	*002	*013	*023	*034	*045	*055
408	61 066	077	087	098	109	119	130	140	151	162
409	172	183	194	204	215	225	236	247	257	268
410	278	289	300	310	321	331	342	352	363	374
411	384	395	405	416	426	437	448	458	469	479
412	490	500	511	521	532	542	553	563	574	584
413	595	606	616	627	637	648	658	669	679	690
414	700	711	721	731	742	752	763	773	784	794
415	805	815	826	836	847	857	868	878	888	899
416	909	920	930	941	951	962	972	982	993	*003
417	62 014	024	034	045	055	066	076	086	097	107
418	118	128	138	149	159	170	180	190	201	211
419	221	232	242	252	263	273	284	294	304	315
420	325	335	346	356	366	377	387	397	408	418
421	428	439	449	459	469	480	490	500	511	521
422	531	542	552	562	572	583	593	603	613	624
423	634	644	655	665	675	685	696	706	716	726
424	737	747	757	767	778	788	798	808	818	829
425	839	849	859	870	880	890	900	910	921	931
426	941	951	961	972	982	992	*002	*012	*022	*033
427	63 043	053	063	073	083	094	104	114	124	134
428	144	155	165	175	185	195	205	215	225	236
429	246	256	266	276	286	296	306	317	327	337
430	347	357	367	377	387	397	407	417	428	438
431	448	458	468	478	488	498	508	518	528	538
432	548	558	568	579	589	599	609	619	629	639
433	649	659	669	679	689	699	709	719	729	739
434	749	759	769	779	789	799	809	819	829	839
435	849	859	869	879	889	899	909	919	929	939
436	949	959	969	979	988	998	*008	*018	*028	*038
437	64 048	058	068	078	088	098	108	118	128	137
438	147	157	167	177	187	197	207	217	227	237
439	246	256	266	276	286	296	306	316	326	335
440	345	355	365	375	385	395	404	414	424	434
441	444	454	464	473	483	493	503	513	523	532
442	542	552	562	572	582	591	601	611	621	631
443	640	650	660	670	680	689	699	709	719	729
444	738	748	758	768	777	787	797	807	816	826
445	836	846	856	865	875	885	895	904	914	924
446	933	943	953	963	972	982	992	*002	*011	*021
447	65 031	040	050	060	070	079	089	099	108	118
448	128	137	147	157	167	176	186	196	205	215
449	225	234	244	254	263	273	283	292	302	312
450	321	331	341	350	360	369	379	389	398	408

Proportional parts

11
1	1.1
2	2.2
3	3.3
4	4.4
5	5.5
6	6.6
7	7.7
8	8.8
9	9.9

10
1	1.0
2	2.0
3	3.0
4	4.0
5	5.0
6	6.0
7	7.0
8	8.0
9	9.0

9
1	0.9
2	1.8
3	2.7
4	3.6
5	4.5
6	5.4
7	6.3
8	7.2
9	8.1

FIVE-PLACE LOGARITHMS (Continued)

N.	0	1	2	3	4	5	6	7	8	9
450	65 321	331	341	350	360	369	379	389	398	408
451	418	427	437	447	456	466	475	485	495	504
452	514	523	533	543	552	562	571	581	591	600
453	610	619	629	639	648	658	667	677	686	696
454	706	715	725	734	744	753	763	772	782	792
455	801	811	820	830	839	849	858	868	877	887
456	896	906	916	925	935	944	954	963	973	982
457	992	*001	*011	*020	*030	*039	*049	*058	*068	*077
458	66 087	096	106	115	124	134	143	153	162	172
459	181	191	200	210	219	229	238	247	257	266
460	276	285	295	304	314	323	332	342	351	361
461	370	380	389	398	408	417	427	436	445	455
462	464	474	483	492	502	511	521	530	539	549
463	558	567	577	586	596	605	614	624	633	642
464	652	661	671	680	689	699	708	717	727	736
465	745	755	764	773	783	792	801	811	820	829
466	839	848	857	867	876	885	894	904	913	922
467	932	941	950	960	969	978	987	997	*006	*015
468	67 025	034	043	052	062	071	080	089	099	108
469	117	127	136	145	154	164	173	182	191	201
470	210	219	228	237	247	256	265	274	284	293
471	302	311	321	330	339	348	357	367	376	385
472	394	403	413	422	431	440	449	459	468	477
473	486	495	504	514	523	532	541	550	560	569
474	578	587	596	605	614	624	633	642	651	660
475	669	679	688	697	706	715	724	733	742	752
476	761	770	779	788	797	806	815	825	834	843
477	852	861	870	879	888	897	906	916	925	934
478	943	952	961	970	979	988	997	*006	*015	*024
479	68 034	043	052	061	070	079	088	097	106	115
480	124	133	142	151	160	169	178	187	196	205
481	215	224	233	242	251	260	269	278	287	296
482	305	314	323	332	341	350	359	368	377	386
483	395	404	413	422	431	440	449	458	467	476
484	485	494	502	511	520	529	538	547	556	565
485	574	583	592	601	610	619	628	637	646	655
486	664	673	681	690	699	708	717	726	735	744
487	753	762	771	780	789	797	806	815	824	833
488	842	851	860	869	878	886	895	904	913	922
489	931	940	949	958	966	975	984	993	*002	*011
490	69 020	028	037	046	055	064	073	082	090	099
491	108	117	126	135	144	152	161	170	179	188
492	197	205	214	223	232	241	249	258	267	276
493	285	294	302	311	320	329	338	346	355	364
494	373	381	390	399	408	417	425	434	443	452
495	461	469	478	487	496	504	513	522	531	539
496	548	557	566	574	583	592	601	609	618	627
497	636	644	653	662	671	679	688	697	705	714
498	723	732	740	749	758	767	775	784	793	801
499	810	819	827	836	845	854	862	871	880	888
500	897	906	914	923	932	940	949	958	966	975

Proportional parts

	10		**9**		**8**
1	1,0	1	0,9	1	0,8
2	2,0	2	1,8	2	1,6
3	3,0	3	2,7	3	2,4
4	4,0	4	3,6	4	3,2
5	5,0	5	4,5	5	4,0
6	6,0	6	5,4	6	4,8
7	7,0	7	6,3	7	5,6
8	8,0	8	7,2	8	6,4
9	9,0	9	8,1	9	7,2

FIVE-PLACE LOGARITHMS (Continued)

N.	0	1	2	3	4	5	6	7	8	9	Proportional parts
500	69 897	906	914	923	932	940	949	958	966	975	
501	984	992	*001	*010	*018	*027	*036	*044	*053	*062	
502	70 070	079	088	096	105	114	122	131	140	148	
503	157	165	174	183	191	200	209	217	226	234	
504	243	252	260	269	278	286	295	303	312	321	
505	329	338	346	355	364	372	381	389	398	406	
506	415	424	432	441	449	458	467	475	484	492	
507	501	509	518	526	535	544	552	561	569	578	**9**
508	586	595	603	612	621	629	638	646	655	663	1 | 0,9
509	672	680	689	697	706	714	723	731	740	749	2 | 1,8
											3 | 2,7
510	757	766	774	783	791	800	808	817	825	834	4 | 3,6
511	842	851	859	868	876	885	893	902	910	919	5 | 4,5
512	927	935	944	952	961	969	978	986	995	*003	6 | 5,4
513	71 012	020	029	037	046	054	063	071	079	088	7 | 6,3
514	096	105	113	122	130	139	147	155	164	172	8 | 7,2
515	181	189	198	206	214	223	231	240	248	257	9 | 8,1
516	265	273	282	290	299	307	315	324	332	341	
517	349	357	366	374	383	391	399	408	416	425	
518	433	441	450	458	466	475	483	492	500	508	
519	517	525	533	542	550	559	567	575	584	592	
520	600	609	617	625	634	642	650	659	667	675	**8**
521	684	692	700	709	717	725	734	742	750	759	1 | 0,8
522	767	775	784	792	800	809	817	825	834	842	2 | 1,6
523	850	858	867	875	883	892	900	908	917	925	3 | 2,4
524	933	941	950	958	966	975	983	991	999	*008	4 | 3,2
525	72 016	024	032	041	049	057	066	074	082	090	5 | 4,0
526	099	107	115	123	132	140	148	156	165	173	6 | 4,8
527	181	189	198	206	214	222	230	239	247	255	7 | 5,6
528	263	272	280	288	296	304	313	321	329	337	8 | 6,4
529	346	354	362	370	378	387	395	403	411	419	9 | 7,2
530	428	436	444	452	460	469	477	485	493	501	
531	509	518	526	534	542	550	558	567	575	583	
532	591	599	607	616	624	632	640	648	656	665	
533	673	681	689	697	705	713	722	730	738	746	
534	754	762	770	779	787	795	803	811	819	827	
535	835	843	852	860	868	876	884	892	900	908	**7**
536	916	925	933	941	949	957	965	973	981	989	1 | 0,7
537	997	*006	*014	*022	*030	*038	*046	*054	*062	*070	2 | 1,4
538	73 078	086	094	102	111	119	127	135	143	151	3 | 2,1
539	159	167	175	183	191	199	207	215	223	231	4 | 2,8
											5 | 3,5
540	239	247	255	263	272	280	288	296	304	312	6 | 4,2
541	320	328	336	344	352	360	368	376	384	392	7 | 4,9
542	400	408	416	424	432	440	448	456	464	472	8 | 5,6
543	480	488	496	504	512	520	528	536	544	552	9 | 6,3
544	560	568	576	584	592	600	608	616	624	632	
545	640	648	656	664	672	679	687	695	703	711	
546	719	727	735	743	751	759	767	775	783	791	
547	799	807	815	823	830	838	846	854	862	870	
548	878	886	894	902	910	918	926	933	941	949	
549	957	965	973	981	989	997	*005	*013	*020	*028	
550	74 036	044	052	060	068	076	084	092	099	107	

N.	0	1	2	3	4	5	6	7	8	9	Proportional parts

FIVE-PLACE LOGARITHMS (Continued)

N.	0	1	2	3	4	5	6	7	8	9	Proportional parts	
550	74 036	044	052	060	068	076	084	092	099	107		
551	115	123	131	139	147	155	162	170	178	186		
552	194	202	210	218	225	233	241	249	257	265		
553	273	280	288	296	304	312	320	327	335	343		
554	351	359	367	374	382	390	398	406	414	421		
555	429	437	445	453	461	468	476	484	492	500		
556	507	515	523	531	539	547	554	562	570	578		
557	586	593	601	609	617	624	632	640	648	656		
558	663	671	679	687	695	702	710	718	726	733		
559	741	749	757	764	772	780	788	796	803	811		
560	819	827	834	842	850	858	865	873	881	889		**8**
561	896	904	912	920	927	935	943	950	958	966	1	0,8
562	974	981	989	997	*005	*012	*020	*028*	035	*043	2	1,6
563	75 051	059	066	074	082	089	097	105	113	120	3	2,4
564	128	136	143	151	159	166	174	182	189	197	4	3,2
565	205	213	220	228	236	243	251	259	266	274	5	4,0
566	282	289	297	305	312	320	328	335	343	351	6	4,8
567	358	366	374	381	389	397	404	412	420	427	7	5,6
568	435	442	450	458	465	473	481	488	496	504	8	6,4
569	511	519	526	534	542	549	557	565	572	580	9	7,2
570	587	595	603	610	618	626	633	641	648	656		
571	664	671	679	686	694	702	709	717	724	732		
572	740	747	755	762	770	778	785	793	800	808		
573	815	823	831	838	846	853	861	868	876	884		
574	891	899	906	914	921	929	937	944	952	959		
575	967	974	982	989	997	*005	*012	*020	*027	*035		
576	76 042	050	057	065	072	080	087	095	103	110		
577	118	125	133	140	148	155	163	170	178	185		
578	193	200	208	215	223	230	238	245	253	260		
579	268	275	283	290	298	305	313	320	328	335		
580	343	350	358	365	373	380	388	395	403	410		**7**
581	418	425	433	440	448	455	462	470	477	485	1	0,7
582	492	500	507	515	522	530	537	545	552	559	2	1,4
583	567	574	582	589	597	604	612	619	626	634	3	2,1
584	641	649	656	664	671	678	686	693	701	708	4	2,8
585	716	723	730	738	745	753	760	768	775	782	5	3,5
586	790	797	805	812	819	827	834	842	849	856	6	4,2
587	864	871	879	886	893	901	908	916	923	930	7	4,9
588	938	945	953	960	967	975	982	989	997	*004	8	5,6
589	77 012	019	026	034	041	048	056	063	070	078	9	6,3
590	085	093	100	107	115	122	129	137	144	151		
591	159	166	173	181	188	195	203	210	217	225		
592	232	240	247	254	262	269	276	283	291	298		
593	305	313	320	327	335	342	349	357	364	371		
594	379	386	393	401	408	415	422	430	437	444		
595	452	459	466	474	481	488	495	503	510	517		
596	525	532	539	546	554	561	568	576	583	590		
597	597	605	612	619	627	634	641	648	656	663		
598	670	677	685	692	699	706	714	721	728	735		
599	743	750	757	764	772	779	786	793	801	808		
600	815	822	830	837	844	851	859	866	873	880		
N.	0	1	2	3	4	5	6	7	8	9	Proportional parts	

FIVE-PLACE LOGARITHMS (Continued)

N.	0	1	2	3	4	5	6	7	8	9
600	77 815	822	830	837	844	851	859	366	873	880
601	887	895	902	909	916	924	931	938	945	952
602	960	967	974	981	988	996	*003	*010	*017	*025
603	78 032	039	046	053	061	068	075	082	089	097
604	104	111	118	125	132	140	147	154	161	168
605	176	183	190	197	204	211	219	226	233	240
606	247	254	262	269	276	283	290	297	305	312
607	319	326	333	340	347	355	362	369	376	383
608	390	398	405	412	419	426	433	440	447	455
609	462	469	476	483	490	497	504	512	519	526
610	533	540	547	554	561	569	576	583	590	597
611	604	611	618	625	633	640	647	654	661	668
612	675	682	689	696	704	711	718	725	732	739
613	746	753	760	767	774	781	789	796	803	810
614	817	824	831	838	845	852	859	866	873	880
615	888	895	902	909	916	923	930	937	944	951
616	958	965	972	979	986	993	*000	*007	*014	*021
617	79 029	036	043	050	057	064	071	078	085	092
618	099	106	113	120	127	134	141	148	155	162
619	169	176	183	190	197	204	211	218	225	232
620	239	246	253	260	267	274	281	288	295	302
621	309	316	323	330	337	344	351	358	365	372
622	379	386	393	400	407	414	421	428	435	442
623	449	456	463	470	477	484	491	498	505	511
624	518	525	532	539	546	553	560	567	574	581
625	588	595	602	609	616	623	630	637	644	650
626	657	664	671	678	685	692	699	706	713	720
627	727	734	741	748	754	761	768	775	782	789
628	796	803	810	817	824	831	837	844	851	858
629	865	872	879	886	893	900	906	913	920	927
630	934	941	948	955	962	969	975	982	989	996
631	80 003	010	017	024	030	037	044	051	058	065
332	072	079	085	092	099	106	113	120	127	134
633	140	147	154	161	168	175	182	188	195	202
634	209	216	223	229	236	243	250	257	264	271
635	277	284	291	298	305	312	318	325	332	339
636	346	353	359	366	373	380	387	393	400	407
637	414	421	428	434	441	448	455	462	468	475
638	482	489	496	502	509	516	523	530	536	543
639	550	557	564	570	577	584	591	598	604	611
640	618	625	632	638	645	652	659	665	672	679
641	686	693	699	706	713	720	726	733	740	747
642	754	760	767	774	781	787	794	801	808	814
643	821	828	835	841	848	855	862	868	875	882
644	889	895	902	909	916	922	929	936	943	949
645	956	963	969	976	983	990	996	*003	*010	*017
646	81 023	030	037	043	050	057	064	070	077	084
647	090	097	104	111	117	124	131	137	144	151
648	158	164	171	178	184	191	198	204	211	218
649	224	231	238	245	251	258	265	271	278	285
650	291	298	305	311	318	325	331	338	345	351

Proportional parts

8		**7**		**6**	
1	0,8	1	0,7	1	0,6
2	1,6	2	1,4	2	1,2
3	2,4	3	2,1	3	1,8
4	3,2	4	2,8	4	2,4
5	4,0	5	3,5	5	3,0
6	4,8	6	4,2	6	3,6
7	5,6	7	4,9	7	4,2
8	6,4	8	5,6	8	4,8
9	7,2	9	6,3	9	5,4

FIVE-PLACE LOGARITHMS (Continued)

N.	0	1	2	3	4	5	6	7	8	9	Proportional parts
650	81 291	298	305	311	318	325	331	338	345	351	
651	358	365	371	378	385	391	398	405	411	418	
652	425	431	438	445	451	458	465	471	478	485	
653	491	498	505	511	518	525	531	538	544	551	
654	558	564	571	578	584	591	598	604	611	617	
655	624	631	637	644	651	657	664	671	677	684	
656	690	697	704	710	717	723	730	737	743	750	
657	757	763	770	776	783	790	796	803	809	816	
658	823	829	836	842	849	856	862	869	875	882	
659	889	895	902	908	915	921	928	935	941	948	
660	954	961	968	974	981	987	994	*000	*007	*014	**7**
661	82 020	027	033	040	046	053	060	066	073	079	1 | 0·7
662	086	092	099	105	112	119	125	132	138	145	2 | 1·4
663	151	158	164	171	178	184	191	197	204	210	3 | 2·1
664	217	223	230	236	243	249	256	263	269	276	4 | 2·8
665	282	289	295	302	308	315	321	328	334	341	5 | 3·5
666	347	354	360	367	373	380	387	393	400	406	6 | 4·2
667	413	419	426	432	439	445	452	458	465	471	7 | 4·9
668	478	484	491	497	504	510	517	523	530	536	8 | 5·6
669	543	549	556	562	569	575	582	588	595	601	9 | 6·3
670	607	614	620	627	633	640	646	653	659	666	
671	672	679	685	692	698	705	711	718	724	730	
672	737	743	750	756	763	769	776	782	789	795	
673	802	808	814	821	827	834	840	847	853	860	
674	866	872	879	885	892	898	905	911	918	924	
675	930	937	943	950	956	963	969	975	982	988	
676	995	*001	*008	*014	*020	*027	*033	*040	*046	*052	
677	83 059	065	072	078	085	091	097	104	110	117	
678	123	129	136	142	149	155	161	168	174	181	
679	187	193	200	206	213	219	225	232	238	245	
680	251	257	264	270	276	283	289	296	302	308	**6**
681	315	321	327	334	340	347	353	359	366	372	1 | 0·6
682	378	385	391	398	404	410	417	423	429	436	2 | 1·2
683	442	448	455	461	467	474	480	487	493	499	3 | 1·8
684	506	512	518	525	531	537	544	550	556	563	4 | 2·4
685	569	575	582	588	594	601	607	613	620	626	5 | 3·0
686	632	639	645	651	658	664	670	677	683	689	6 | 3·6
687	696	702	708	715	721	727	734	740	746	753	7 | 4·2
688	759	765	771	778	784	790	797	803	809	816	8 | 4·8
689	822	828	835	841	847	853	860	866	872	879	9 | 5·4
690	885	891	897	904	910	916	923	929	935	942	
691	948	954	960	967	973	979	985	992	998	*004	
692	84 011	017	023	029	036	042	048	055	061	067	
693	073	080	086	092	098	105	111	117	123	130	
694	136	142	148	155	161	167	173	180	186	192	
695	198	205	211	217	223	230	236	242	248	255	
696	261	267	273	280	286	292	298	305	311	317	
697	323	330	336	342	348	354	361	367	373	379	
698	386	392	398	404	410	417	423	429	435	442	
699	448	454	460	466	473	479	485	491	497	504	
700	510	516	522	528	535	541	547	553	559	566	
N.	0	1	2	3	4	5	6	7	8	9	Proportional parts

FIVE-PLACE LOGARITHMS (Continued)

N.	0	1	2	3	4	5	6	7	8	9	Proportional parts
700	84 510	516	522	528	535	541	547	553	559	566	
701	572	578	584	590	597	603	609	615	621	628	
702	634	640	646	652	658	665	671	677	683	689	
703	696	702	708	714	720	726	733	739	745	751	
704	757	763	770	776	782	788	794	800	807	813	
705	819	825	831	837	844	850	856	862	868	874	
706	880	887	893	899	905	911	917	924	930	936	
707	942	948	954	960	967	973	979	985	991	997	**7**
708	85 003	009	016	022	028	034	040	046	052	058	1 0.7
709	065	071	077	083	089	095	101	107	114	120	2 1.4 / 3 2.1
710	126	132	138	144	150	156	163	169	175	181	4 2.8
711	187	193	199	205	211	217	224	230	236	242	5 3.5
712	248	254	260	266	272	278	285	291	297	303	6 4.2
713	309	315	321	327	333	339	345	352	358	364	7 4.9
714	370	376	382	388	394	400	406	412	418	425	8 5.6
715	431	437	443	449	455	461	467	473	479	485	9 6.3
716	491	497	503	509	516	522	528	534	540	546	
717	552	558	564	570	576	582	588	594	600	606	
718	612	618	625	631	637	643	649	655	661	667	
719	673	679	685	691	697	703	709	715	721	727	
720	733	739	745	751	757	763	769	775	781	788	
721	794	800	806	812	818	824	830	836	842	848	**6**
722	854	860	866	872	878	884	890	896	902	908	1 0.6
723	914	920	926	932	938	944	950	956	962	968	2 1.2
724	974	980	986	992	998	*004	*010	*016	*022	*028	3 1.8
725	86 034	040	046	052	058	064	070	076	082	088	4 2.4
726	094	100	106	112	118	124	130	136	141	147	5 3.0
727	153	159	165	171	177	183	189	195	201	207	6 3.6
728	213	219	225	231	237	243	249	255	261	267	7 4.2
729	273	279	285	291	297	303	308	314	320	326	8 4.8 / 9 5.4
730	332	338	344	350	356	362	368	374	380	386	
731	392	398	404	410	415	421	427	433	439	445	
732	451	457	463	469	475	481	487	493	499	504	
733	510	516	522	528	534	540	546	552	558	564	
734	570	576	581	587	593	599	605	611	617	623	
735	629	635	641	646	652	658	664	670	676	682	**5**
736	688	694	700	705	711	717	723	729	735	741	1 0.5
737	747	753	759	764	770	776	782	788	794	800	2 1.0
738	806	812	817	823	829	835	841	847	853	859	3 1.5
739	864	870	876	882	888	894	900	906	911	917	4 2.0 / 5 2.5
740	923	929	935	941	947	953	958	964	970	976	6 3.0
741	982	988	994	999	*005	*011	*017	*023	*029	*035	7 3.5
742	87 040	046	052	058	064	070	075	081	087	093	8 4.0
743	099	105	111	116	122	128	134	140	146	151	9 4.5
744	157	163	169	175	181	186	192	198	204	210	
745	216	221	227	233	239	245	251	256	262	268	
746	274	280	286	291	297	303	309	315	320	326	
747	332	338	344	349	355	361	367	373	379	384	
748	390	396	402	408	413	419	425	431	437	442	
749	448	454	460	466	471	477	483	489	495	500	
750	506	512	518	523	529	535	541	547	552	558	
N.	0	1	2	3	4	5	6	7	8	9	Proportional parts

FIVE-PLACE LOGARITHMS (Continued)

N.	0	1	2	3	4	5	6	7	8	9	Proportional parts
750	87 506	512	518	523	529	535	541	547	552	558	
751	564	570	576	581	587	593	599	604	610	616	
752	622	628	633	639	645	651	656	662	668	674	
753	679	685	691	697	703	708	714	720	726	731	
754	737	743	749	754	760	766	772	777	783	789	
755	795	800	806	812	818	823	829	835	841	846	
756	852	858	864	869	875	881	887	892	898	904	
757	910	915	921	927	933	938	944	950	955	961	
758	967	973	978	984	990	996	*001	*007	*013	*018	
759	88 024	030	036	041	047	053	058	064	070	076	
760	081	087	093	098	104	110	116	121	127	133	**6**
761	138	144	150	156	161	167	173	178	184	190	1 | 0,6
762	195	201	207	213	218	224	230	235	241	247	2 | 1,2
763	252	258	264	270	275	281	287	292	298	304	3 | 1,8
764	309	315	321	326	332	338	343	349	355	360	4 | 2,4
765	366	372	377	383	389	395	400	406	412	417	5 | 3,0
766	423	429	434	440	446	451	457	463	468	474	6 | 3,6
767	480	485	491	497	502	508	513	519	525	530	7 | 4,2
768	536	542	547	553	559	564	570	576	581	587	8 | 4,8
769	593	598	604	610	615	621	627	632	638	643	9 | 5,4
770	649	655	660	666	672	677	683	689	694	700	
771	705	711	717	722	728	734	739	745	750	756	
772	762	767	773	779	784	790	795	801	807	812	
773	818	824	829	835	840	846	852	857	863	868	
774	874	880	885	891	897	902	908	913	919	925	
775	930	936	941	947	953	958	964	969	975	981	
776	986	992	997	*003	*009	*014	*020	*025	*031	*037	
777	89 042	048	053	059	064	070	076	081	087	092	
778	098	104	109	115	120	126	131	137	143	148	
779	154	159	165	170	176	182	187	193	198	204	
780	209	215	221	226	232	237	243	248	254	260	**5**
781	265	271	276	282	287	293	298	304	310	315	1 | 0,5
782	321	326	332	337	343	348	354	360	365	371	2 | 1,0
783	376	382	387	393	398	404	409	415	421	426	3 | 1,5
784	432	437	443	448	454	459	465	470	476	481	4 | 2,0
785	487	492	498	504	509	515	520	526	531	537	5 | 2,5
786	542	548	553	559	564	570	575	581	586	592	6 | 3,0
787	597	603	609	614	620	625	631	636	642	647	7 | 3,5
788	653	658	664	669	675	680	686	691	697	702	8 | 4,0
789	708	713	719	724	730	735	741	746	752	757	9 | 4,5
790	763	768	774	779	785	790	796	801	807	812	
791	818	823	829	834	840	845	851	856	862	867	
792	873	878	883	889	894	900	905	911	916	922	
793	927	933	938	944	949	955	960	966	971	977	
794	982	988	993	998	*004	*009	*015	*020	*026	*031	
795	90 037	042	048	053	059	064	069	075	080	086	
796	091	097	102	108	113	119	124	129	135	140	
797	146	151	157	162	168	173	179	184	189	195	
798	200	206	211	217	222	227	233	238	244	249	
799	255	260	266	271	276	282	287	293	298	304	
800	309	314	320	325	331	336	342	347	352	358	
N.	0	1	2	3	4	5	6	7	8	9	Proportional parts

FIVE-PLACE LOGARITHMS (Continued)

N.	0	1	2	3	4	5	6	7	8	9	Proportional parts
800	90 309	314	320	325	331	336	342	347	352	358	
801	363	369	374	380	385	390	396	401	407	412	
802	417	423	428	434	439	445	450	455	461	466	
803	472	477	482	488	493	499	504	509	515	520	
804	526	531	536	542	547	553	558	563	569	574	
805	580	585	590	596	601	607	612	617	623	628	
806	634	639	644	650	655	660	666	671	677	682	
807	687	693	698	703	709	714	720	725	730	736	
808	741	747	752	757	763	768	773	779	784	789	
809	795	800	806	811	816	822	827	832	838	843	
810	849	854	859	865	870	875	881	886	891	897	**6**
811	902	907	913	918	924	929	934	940	945	950	1 | 0 6
812	956	961	966	972	977	982	988	993	998	*004	2 | 1,2
813	91 009	014	020	025	030	036	041	046	052	057	3 | 1,8
814	062	068	073	078	084	089	094	100	105	110	4 | 2,4
815	116	121	126	132	137	142	148	153	158	164	5 | 3,0
816	169	174	180	185	190	196	201	206	212	217	6 | 3,6
817	222	228	233	238	243	249	254	259	265	270	7 | 4,2
818	275	281	286	291	297	302	307	312	318	323	8 | 4,8
819	328	334	339	344	350	355	360	365	371	376	9 | 5,4
820	381	387	392	397	403	408	413	418	424	429	
821	434	440	445	450	455	461	466	471	477	482	
822	487	492	498	503	508	514	519	524	529	535	
823	540	545	551	556	561	566	572	577	582	587	
824	593	598	603	609	614	619	624	630	635	640	
825	645	651	656	661	666	672	677	682	687	693	
826	698	703	709	714	719	724	730	735	740	745	
827	751	756	761	766	772	777	782	787	793	798	
828	803	808	814	819	824	829	834	840	845	850	
829	855	861	866	871	876	882	887	892	897	903	
830	908	913	918	924	929	934	939	944	950	955	**5**
831	960	965	971	976	981	986	991	997	*002	*007	1 | 0,5
832	92 012	018	023	028	033	038	044	049	054	059	2 | 1,0
833	065	070	075	080	085	091	096	101	106	111	3 | 1,5
834	117	122	127	132	137	143	148	153	158	163	4 | 2,0
835	169	174	179	184	189	195	200	205	210	215	5 | 2,5
836	221	226	231	236	241	247	252	257	262	267	6 | 3,0
837	273	278	283	288	293	298	304	309	314	319	7 | 3,5
838	324	330	335	340	345	350	355	361	366	371	8 | 4,0
839	376	381	387	392	397	402	407	412	418	423	9 | 4,5
840	428	433	438	443	449	454	459	464	469	474	
841	480	485	490	495	500	505	511	516	521	526	
842	531	536	542	547	552	557	562	567	572	578	
843	583	588	593	598	603	609	614	619	624	629	
844	634	639	645	650	655	660	665	670	675	681	
845	686	691	696	701	706	711	716	722	727	732	
846	737	742	747	752	758	763	768	773	778	783	
847	788	793	799	804	809	814	819	824	829	834	
848	840	845	850	855	860	865	870	875	881	886	
849	891	896	901	906	911	916	921	927	932	937	
850	942	947	952	957	962	967	973	978	983	988	
N.	0	1	2	3	4	5	6	7	8	9	Proportional parts

FIVE-PLACE LOGARITHMS (Continued)

N.	0	1	2	3	4	5	6	7	8	9
850	92 942	947	952	957	962	967	973	978	983	988
851	993	998	*003	*008	*013	*018	*024	*029	*034	*039
852	93 044	049	054	059	064	069	075	080	085	090
853	095	100	105	110	115	120	125	131	136	141
854	146	151	156	161	166	171	176	181	186	192
855	197	202	207	212	217	222	227	232	237	242
856	247	252	258	263	268	273	278	283	288	293
857	298	303	308	313	318	323	328	334	339	344
858	349	354	359	364	369	374	379	384	389	394
859	399	404	409	414	420	425	430	435	440	445
860	450	455	460	465	470	475	480	485	490	495
861	500	505	510	515	520	526	531	536	541	546
862	551	556	561	566	571	576	581	586	591	596
863	601	606	611	616	621	626	631	636	641	646
864	651	656	661	666	671	676	682	687	692	697
865	702	707	712	717	722	727	732	737	742	747
866	752	757	762	767	772	777	782	787	792	797
867	802	807	812	817	822	827	832	837	842	847
868	852	857	862	867	872	877	882	887	892	897
869	902	907	912	917	922	927	932	937	942	947
870	952	957	962	967	972	977	982	987	992	997
871	94 002	007	012	017	022	027	032	037	042	047
872	052	057	062	067	072	077	082	086	091	096
873	101	106	111	116	121	126	131	136	141	146
874	151	156	161	166	171	176	181	186	191	196
875	201	206	211	216	221	226	231	236	240	245
876	250	255	260	265	270	275	280	285	290	295
877	300	305	310	315	320	325	330	335	340	345
878	349	354	359	364	369	374	379	384	389	394
879	399	404	409	414	419	424	429	433	438	443
880	448	453	458	463	468	473	478	483	488	493
881	498	503	507	512	517	522	527	532	537	542
882	547	552	557	562	567	571	576	581	586	591
883	596	601	606	611	616	621	626	630	635	640
884	645	650	655	660	665	670	675	680	685	689
885	694	699	704	709	714	719	724	729	734	738
886	743	748	753	758	763	768	773	778	783	787
887	792	797	802	807	812	817	822	827	832	836
888	841	846	851	856	861	866	871	876	880	885
889	890	895	900	905	910	915	919	924	929	934
890	939	944	949	954	959	963	968	973	978	983
891	988	993	998	*002	*007	*012	*017	*022	*027	*082
892	95 036	041	046	051	056	061	066	071	075	080
893	085	090	095	100	105	109	114	119	124	129
894	134	139	143	148	153	158	163	168	173	177
895	182	187	192	197	202	207	211	216	221	226
896	231	236	240	245	250	255	260	265	270	274
897	279	284	289	294	299	303	308	313	318	323
898	328	332	337	342	347	352	357	361	366	371
899	376	381	386	390	395	400	405	410	415	419
900	424	429	434	439	444	448	453	458	463	468
N.	0	1	2	3	4	5	6	7	8	9

Proportional parts

6
1 | 0,6
2 | 1,2
3 | 1,8
4 | 2,4
5 | 3,0
6 | 3,6
7 | 4,2
8 | 4,8
9 | 5,4

5
1 | 0,5
2 | 1,0
3 | 1,5
4 | 2,0
5 | 2,5
6 | 3,0
7 | 3,5
8 | 4,0
9 | 4,5

4
1 | 0,4
2 | 0,8
3 | 1,2
4 | 1,6
5 | 2,0
6 | 2,4
7 | 2,8
8 | 3,2
9 | 3,6

FIVE-PLACE LOGARITHMS (Continued)

N.	0	1	2	3	4	5	6	7	8	9	Proportional parts
900	95 424	429	434	439	444	448	453	458	463	468	
901	472	477	482	487	492	497	501	506	511	516	
902	521	525	530	535	540	545	550	554	559	564	
903	569	574	578	583	588	593	598	602	607	612	
904	617	622	626	631	636	641	646	650	655	660	
905	665	670	674	679	684	689	694	698	703	708	
906	713	718	722	727	732	737	742	746	751	756	
907	761	766	770	775	780	785	789	794	799	804	
908	809	813	818	823	828	832	837	842	847	852	
909	856	861	866	871	875	880	885	890	895	899	
910	904	909	914	918	923	928	933	938	942	947	**5**
911	952	957	961	966	971	976	980	985	990	995	1 | 0.5
912	999	*004	*009	*014	*019	*023	*028	*033	*038	*042	2 | 1.0
913	96 047	052	057	061	066	071	076	080	085	090	3 | 1.5
914	095	099	104	109	114	118	123	128	133	137	4 | 2.0
915	142	147	152	156	161	166	171	175	180	185	5 | 2.5
916	190	194	199	204	209	213	218	223	227	232	6 | 3.0
917	237	242	246	251	256	261	265	270	275	280	7 | 3.5
918	284	289	294	298	303	308	313	317	322	327	8 | 4.0
919	332	336	341	346	350	355	360	365	369	374	9 | 4.5
920	379	384	388	393	398	402	407	412	417	421	
921	426	431	435	440	445	450	454	459	464	468	
922	473	478	483	487	492	497	501	506	511	515	
923	520	525	530	534	539	544	548	553	558	562	
924	567	572	577	581	586	591	595	600	605	609	
925	614	619	624	628	633	638	642	647	652	656	
926	661	666	670	675	680	685	689	694	699	703	
927	708	713	717	722	727	731	736	741	745	750	
928	755	759	764	769	774	778	783	788	792	797	
929	802	806	811	816	820	825	830	834	839	844	
930	848	853	858	862	867	872	876	881	886	890	**4**
931	895	900	904	909	914	918	923	928	932	937	1 | 0.4
932	942	946	951	956	960	965	970	974	979	984	2 | 0.8
933	988	993	997	*002	*007	*011	*016	*021	*025	*030	3 | 1.2
934	97 035	039	044	049	053	058	063	067	072	077	4 | 1.6
935	081	086	090	095	100	104	109	114	118	123	5 | 2.0
936	128	132	137	142	146	151	155	160	165	169	6 | 2.4
937	174	179	183	188	192	197	202	206	211	216	7 | 2.8
938	220	225	230	234	239	243	248	253	257	262	8 | 3.2
939	267	271	276	280	285	290	294	299	304	308	9 | 3.6
940	313	317	322	327	331	336	340	345	350	354	
941	359	364	368	373	377	382	387	391	396	400	
942	405	410	414	419	424	428	433	437	442	447	
943	451	456	460	465	470	474	479	483	488	493	
944	497	502	506	511	516	520	525	529	534	539	
945	543	548	552	557	562	566	571	575	580	585	
946	589	594	598	603	607	612	617	621	626	630	
947	635	640	644	649	653	658	663	667	672	676	
948	681	685	690	695	699	704	708	713	717	722	
949	727	731	736	740	745	749	754	759	763	768	
950	772	777	782	786	791	795	800	804	809	813	
N.	0	1	2	3	4	5	6	7	8	9	Proportional parts

FIVE-PLACE LOGARITHMS (Continued)

N.	0	1	2	3	4	5	6	7	8	9	Proportional parts
950	97 772	777	782	786	791	795	800	804	809	813	
951	818	823	827	832	836	841	845	850	855	859	
952	864	868	873	877	882	886	891	896	900	905	
953	909	914	918	923	928	932	937	941	946	950	
954	955	959	964	968	973	978	982	987	991	996	
955	98 000	005	009	014	019	023	028	032	037	041	
956	046	050	055	059	064	068	073	078	082	087	
957	091	096	100	105	109	114	118	123	127	132	
958	137	141	146	150	155	159	164	168	173	177	
959	182	186	191	195	200	204	209	214	218	223	
960	227	232	236	241	245	250	254	259	263	268	**5**
961	272	277	281	286	290	295	299	304	308	313	1 ǀ 0,5
962	318	322	327	331	336	340	345	349	354	358	2 ǀ 1,0
963	363	367	372	376	381	385	390	394	399	403	3 ǀ 1,5
964	408	412	417	421	426	430	435	439	444	448	4 ǀ 2,0
965	453	457	462	466	471	475	480	484	489	493	5 ǀ 2,5
966	498	502	507	511	516	520	525	529	534	538	6 ǀ 3,0
967	543	547	552	556	561	565	570	574	579	583	7 ǀ 3,5
968	588	592	597	601	605	610	614	619	623	628	8 ǀ 4,0
969	632	637	641	646	650	655	659	664	668	673	9 ǀ 4,5
970	677	682	686	691	695	700	704	709	713	717	
971	722	726	731	735	740	744	749	753	758	762	
972	767	771	776	780	784	789	793	798	802	807	
973	811	816	820	825	829	834	838	843	847	851	
974	856	860	865	869	874	878	883	887	892	896	
975	900	905	909	914	918	923	927	932	936	941	
976	945	949	954	958	963	967	972	976	981	985	
977	989	994	998	*003	*007	*012	*016	*021	*025	*029	
978	99 034	038	043	047	052	056	061	065	069	074	
979	078	083	087	092	096	100	105	109	114	118	
980	123	127	131	136	140	145	149	154	158	162	**4**
981	167	171	176	180	185	189	193	198	202	207	1 ǀ 0,4
982	211	216	220	224	229	233	238	242	247	251	2 ǀ 0,8
983	255	260	264	269	273	277	282	286	291	295	3 ǀ 1,2
984	300	304	308	313	317	322	326	330	335	339	4 ǀ 1,6
985	344	348	352	357	361	366	370	373	379	383	5 ǀ 2,0
986	388	392	396	401	405	410	414	419	423	427	6 ǀ 2,4
987	432	436	441	445	449	454	458	463	467	471	7 ǀ 2,8
988	476	480	484	489	493	498	502	506	511	515	8 ǀ 3,2
989	520	524	528	533	537	542	546	550	555	559	9 ǀ 3,6
990	564	568	572	577	581	585	590	594	599	603	
991	607	612	616	621	625	629	634	638	642	647	
992	651	656	660	664	669	673	677	682	686	691	
993	695	699	704	708	712	717	721	726	730	734	
994	739	743	747	752	756	760	765	769	774	778	
995	782	787	791	795	800	804	808	813	817	822	
996	826	830	835	839	843	848	852	856	861	865	
997	870	874	878	883	887	891	896	900	904	909	
998	913	917	922	926	930	935	939	944	948	952	
999	957	961	965	970	974	978	983	987	991	996	
1000	00 000	004	009	013	017	022	026	030	035	039	
N.	0	1	2	3	4	5	6	7	8	9	Proportional parts

Answers to the Problems

Only the numerical portions of the answers are listed here. The complete answer to each problem must include an indication of the units, such as "24.29% chloride" or "0.2169 gram sample."

Chapter 3
1. +0.52
2. 0.26
3. 10.1259
4. 16.4119
5. 12.0447
6. 11.3280
7. 0.999906; 19.2642
8. 16.1545
9. 16.1473
10. 0.9983
11. 13.547
12. 0.9990

Chapter 5
1. 23.
2. 60.054
3. 342.9
4. 2.3×10^2
5. 16.8
6. 60.10; 0.26; 0.43
7. 0.56; 0.0092
8. 12.0104; 0.0012; 12.0104 ± 0.0012
9. No; 39.02 ± 0.31; 0.36; 7.9
10. No; 0.0975 ± 0.0003; 0.0975 ± 0.0011
11. Yes
12. Inconclusive

Chapter 6
1. ——

2. 0.2474; 0.3430; 0.1374; 0.6994; 0.5603; 0.3623; 0.5293
3. 0.3897
4. 1.383
5. 48.64
6. 4.121
7. 2.582
8. 396.0
9. 4.134
10. 1.371
11. 0.8924
12. +4.2
13. 145.3
14. 51.82
15. 86.04
16. 49.95
17. 53.52
18. 20.07; 6.596; 3.663; 18.65; 47.59
19. 2.504
20. 30.06
21. 0.09675; 2.622
22. 83.23
23. 90.02; 0.5898
24. 89.95
25. 0.3634
26. 36.52
27. 91.98; 3.95
28. 6.966; 85.21
29. 0.9214
30. $C_3H_6Cl_2$; 62.79
31. 0.36
32. 0.65 to 0.26

33. 0.4947
34. 0.3416
35. 1.0000; 0.4119
36. 0.4116
37. 0.9277
38. 1.441

Chapter 7

1. 11.98
2. 16.18
3. 31.65
4. 46.79
5. 25.75
6. 31.44; 18.50; 4.20; 30.16; 15.66
7. 5.02; 2.98; 70.11; 2.06; 19.84
8. 0.327; 0.673
9. 31.3
10. 0.394; 0.228
11. 31.2
12. 1.38; 2.67
13. 77.8; 0.0197
14. 44.2
15. 55.1; 44.9
16. 34.6 to 65.4
17. 32.6; 50.8; 16.7
18. 43.9
19. 0.340; 0.238; 0.300

Chapter 8

1. 1.78×10^{-4}
2. 2.52×10^{-13}
3. 1.42×10^{-16}
4. 1.24×10^{-11}
5. 4.2×10^{-11}
6. 8.9×10^{-4}
7. 1.08×10^{-4}
8. 6.4×10^{-12}
9. 0.662
10. 0.707
11. 4.39×10^{-12}
12. 2.4×10^{-6}; 2.4×10^{-8}
13. 2.6×10^{-5}; 2.6×10^{-9}
14. 159
15. 3.2×10^{-4}
16. 1.00×10^{-4}

17. 3.5×10^{-5}
18. 6.1×10^{-20}
19. Yes
20. $AgCl$
21. $Ag_2Cr_2O_7$
22. 2.78×10^{-4}
23. 3.0×10^{-24}
24. 7.8×10^{-26}
25. 3.9
26. 4.7×10^{-7}

Chapter 9

1. 25.01
2. +0.05
3. 3.647; 4.904; 5.300; 6.005; 20.42; 5.611; 8.569; 3.505
4. 18.24
5. 24.52
6. 1.810
7. 6.464
8. 8.809
9. 14.61
10. 8.062
11. 7.096
12. 5.520
13. 138.7
14. 120.0
15. 80.00
16. 0.1590
17. 0.3425
18. 116
19. 0.08946
20. 0.04045
21. 0.3
22. 0.09920; 0.08590

Chapter 10

1. 1.158; 1.242
2. 180.0
3. 0.4049
4. 0.1132
5. 1750.
6. 0.3449
7. 118.7
8. 4.804

9. 4.216
10. 91.00
11. 35.52
12. 46.89; 27.42; 20.34
13. 1.011
14. 6.351
15. 90.69
16. 0.2932
17. 2.213
18. 0.1887
19. 2.303
20. 6.005
21. 0.2284
22. 2.650
23. 0.1835; 0.0680
24. 0.1148
25. 8.040

Chapter 11

1. 6.31×10^{-7}; 5.01×10^{-12}; 2.00×10^{-5}
2. 6.31×10^{-11}; 1.58×10^{-5}; 3.98×10^{-12}
3. 1.82; -0.18; 4.70
4. 1.00
5. 0.40
6. 11.73
7. 12.40
8. -0.14
9. 7.00
10. 3.38
11. 2.72
12. 4.92
13. 9.21
14. 5.13
15. 8.88
16. 2.70
17. 2.00
18. 4.76
19. 7.00
20. 7.00
21. 9.56
22. 4.46
23. 1.30
24. 4.76

25. 27.6 to 1.00
26. 7.17 to 1.00
27. 1.00; 1.48; 7.00
28. 3.00; 3.48; 7.00
29. 2.60; 4.20; 8.45
30. 11.13; 9.26; 5.28
31. 0.0600; 0.0530
32. 61.77; 30.16; 8.07
33. 63.60; 23.11
34. 25.00; 11.90
35. 27.09; 72.91

Chapter 12

1. 0.70
2. 1.00
3. 6.06
4. 10.64
5. 35.07
6. 13.61
7. 25.80
8. 0.08594
9. 0.5000
10. 0.1817
11. 69.55
12. 26.98
13. 0.1269; 0.0302
14. 2.00; 5.31; 92.69
15. 0.09823; 0.1965
16. 66.01; 30.23; 3.76
17. 10.83; 89.17
18. 22.70
19. 63.00
20. 169.7

Chapter 13

1. ——; 2.00
2. 18.9; 2.40
3. 8.82; 7.51
4. 2.37; 13.96
5. 4.8×10^{-5}; 4.8×10^{-3}; 9.5×10^{-2}; 6.0×10^{-4}; 3.0×10^{-8}
6. 1.48
7. 16.3
8. 30.64

9. 0.01922
10. 0.884
11. 572.
12. 1.861
13. 7.904
14. 0.0855

Chapter 14

1. 0.70
2. −0.30
3. −0.14
4. 0.11
5. 0.79
6. 0.18
7. 0.39
8. 0.21
9. 3.2×10^{18}
10. 3.1×10^{9}
11. 5.0×10^{62}
12. 6.7×10^{-11}
13. 3.73
14. 2.17
15. 0.71
16. 0.78
17. 0.77
18. 10^{-60} (concentrations of this order of magnitude are quite meaningless)
19. 2.5×10^{-3}
20. 4.9×10^{-9}
21. 0.35
22. 3.33×10^{-2}
23. 2×10^{-16}
24. $8.3 \times$ about 10^{-31}
25. 1.03
26. 3.33×10^{-2}
27. 3.33×10^{-2}
28. ——

Chapter 15

1. 0.1345
2. 0.08953
3. 0.1093
4. 142
5. 8.780
6. 2.5
7. 24.50
8. 83.35
9. 0.2188
10. 85.20
11. 28.87
12. 41.66
13. 1.0
14. 0.08043
15. 29.82
16. 17.32; 8.220; 15.63
17. 0.1283
18. 61.89
19. 3.473
20. 0.4044
21. 98.82
22. 0.5585
23. 3.296
24. 6.806; 6.580
25. 0.7308
26. 8.780
27. 298.5
28. 3
29. 0.1792
30. 0.7511

Chapter 16

1. 0.2705
2. 0.2079
3. 0.09608
4. 0.08139
5. 5.009
6. 6.052; 8.442
7. 46.62
8. 4.656
9. 0.3238
10. 7.032
11. 70.32
12. 0.9531
13. 0.08412
14. 35.30
15. 2
16. 31.07
17. 58.19
18. 13.02

Suggestions for
Additional Reading

Reference is made to each of these items by number at the end of one or more of the chapters in this book. Many of these items are of interest in other areas of quantitative chemical analysis as well. In most instances the title provides a sufficient clue as to the content. This list is intended solely to provide some suggestions for additional reading and is not intended to be a complete survey of the literature of quantitative chemical analysis.

1. R. Belcher and C. L. Wilson: "New Methods in Analytical Chemistry," Reinhold Publishing Corp., New York, 1955.
2. W. J. Blaedel and V. W. Meloche: "Elementary Quantitative Analysis: Theory and Practice," Row, Peterson & Co., Evanston, Illinois, 1957. (The "Supplement" contains much information of a semi-advanced level.)
3. P. Delahay: "Instrumental Analysis," The Macmillan Co., New York, 1957.
4. G. Ewing: "Instrumental Methods of Chemical Analysis," Second Edition, McGraw-Hill Book Co., Inc., New York, 1960.
5. J. S. Fritz: "Acid-Base Titrations in Nonaqueous Solvents," G. Frederick Smith Chemical Co., Columbus, Ohio, 1952. (This company has issued several booklets on selected topics in quantitative chemical analysis.)
6. J. S. Fritz and G. S. Hammond: "Quantitative Organic Analysis," John Wiley & Sons, Inc., New York, 1957.
7. L. Gordon, M. L. Salutsky and H. H. Willard: "Precipitation from Homogeneous Solution," John Wiley & Sons, Inc., New York, 1959.
8. L. F. Hamilton and S. G. Simpson: "Calculations of Analytical Chemistry," Sixth Edition, McGraw-Hill Book Co., Inc., New York, 1960.
9. I. M. Kolthoff and R. Belcher: "Volumetric Analysis, Volume III, Titration Methods: Oxidation-Reduction Reactions," Interscience Publishers, Inc., New York, 1957. (See also 12 and 13.)
10. I. M. Kolthoff and P. J. Elving, Editors: "Treatise on Analytical Chemistry," Interscience Publishers, Inc., New York (Volume 1 of Part I, 1959). (This is to be a thorough, comprehensive series of books on virtually all phases of analytical chemistry.)
11. I. M. Kolthoff and E. B. Sandell: "Textbook of Quantitative Inorganic Analysis," Third Edition, The Macmillan Co., New York, 1952.
12. I. M. Kolthoff and V. J. Stenger: "Volumetric Analysis, Volume I: Theoretical Fundamentals," Interscience Publishers, Inc., New York, 1942. (See also 9 and 13.)

13. I. M. Kolthoff and V. J. Stenger: "Volumetric Analysis, Volume II: Acid-Base, Precipitation and Complex-Formation Reactions," Interscience Publishers, Inc., New York, 1947. (See also 9 and 12.)

14. H. A. Laitinen: "Chemical Analysis: An Advanced Text and Reference," McGraw-Hill Book Co., Inc., New York, 1960.

15. T. W. Lashof and L. B. Macurdy: "Precision Laboratory Standards of Mass and Laboratory Weights," National Bureau of Standards Circular 547, Section I, 1954. (Available from U.S. Government Printing Office, Washington, D.C., for 25 cents.)

16. J. J. Lingane: "Electroanalytical Chemistry," Second Edition, Interscience Publishers, Inc., New York, 1958.

17. G. E. F. Lundell, H. A. Bright and J. I. Hoffman: "Applied Inorganic Analysis," John Wiley & Sons, Inc., New York, 1953.

18. L. Meites, editor: "Handbook of Analytical Chemistry," McGraw-Hill Book Co., Inc., New York, 1961.

19. L. Meites and H. C. Thomas: "Advanced Analytical Chemistry," McGraw-Hill Book Co., Inc., New York, 1958. (Deals primarily with optical and electrical methods.)

20. G. H. Morrison and H. Freiser: "Solvent Extraction in Analytical Chemistry," John Wiley & Sons, Inc., New York, 1957.

21. O. Samuelson: "Ion Exchangers in Analytical Chemistry," John Wiley & Sons, Inc., New York, 1953.

22. E. B. Sandell: "Colorimetric Determination of Traces of Metals," Interscience Publishers, Inc., New York, 1959.

23. G. Schwarzenbach (revised and translated into English by H. Irving): "Complexometric Titrations," Methuen & Co., Ltd., London, 1957.

24. S. Siggia and H. J. Stolten: "An Introduction to Modern Organic Analysis," Interscience Publishers, Inc., New York, 1956.

25. T. B. Smith: "Analytical Processes: A Physico-Chemical Interpretation," Edward Arnold, Ltd., London, 1940.

26. C. R. N. Stouts, J. H. Gilfillan and H. N. Wilson: "Analytical Chemistry; The Working Tools," in two volumes, Oxford University Press, London, 1955.

27. H. F. Walton: "Principles and Methods of Chemical Analysis," Prentice-Hall, Inc., New York, 1952.

28. H. H. Willard and H. Diehl: "Advanced Quantitative Analysis," D. Van Nostrand Co., Inc., Princeton, N.J., 1943.

29. H. H. Willard, L. L. Merritt and J. A. Dean: "Instrumental Methods of Analysis," Third Edition, D. Van Nostrand Co., Inc., Princeton, N.J., 1958.

30. C. L. Wilson, editor: "Comprehensive Analytical Chemistry," D. Van Nostrand Co., Inc., Princeton, N.J., Volume 1-A in 1959. (This is to be a thorough, comprehensive series of books on virtually all phases of analytical chemistry.)

31. W. J. Youden: "Statistical Methods for Chemists," John Wiley & Sons, Inc., New York, 1951.

Every student of chemistry should become familiar with some of the periodicals in which new information is reported and summarized. The following three publications, in particular, should be consulted by every student of quantitative chemical analysis:

1. The journal "Analytical Chemistry" is published monthly by the American Chemical Society. Each issue contains reports of new research on the principles and the practice of analytical chemistry. A series of review articles is issued every April.

2. The "Journal of Chemical Education," published monthly by the Division of Chemical Education of the American Chemical Society, frequently contains articles related to the subject matter of this book. One of the monthly features is a section, "Chemical Instrumentation," written by S. Z. Lewin, which discusses from time to time topics of interest in gravimetric and volumetric procedures as well as those of interest for optical and electrical methods.

3. "Chemical Abstracts," a semi-monthly publication of the American Chemical Society, consists of short abstracts of virtually all chemical articles, patents and books published anywhere in the world. Subject and author indexes are issued annually.

Index